Student Solutions Manual for Revathi Nara...

Precalculus: Building Concepts and Connections
Second Edition

Prepared by

Ross Rueger

Department of Mathematics

College of the Sequoias

Visalia, California

Student Solutions Manual for
Revathi Narasimhan's Precalculus: Building
Concepts and Connections, Second Edition

Ross Rueger

Publisher: XYZ Textbooks

Sales: Amy Jacobs, Richard Jones, Bruce Spears,
Rachael Hillman

Cover Design: Kyle Schoenberger

ISBN-13: 978-1-63098-041-2 / ISBN-10: 1-63098-041-2

For product information and technology assistance, contact us at
XYZ Textbooks, 1-877-745-3499

For permission to use material from this text or product,
e-mail: **info@mathtv.com**

XYZ Textbooks
1339 Marsh Street
San Luis Obispo, CA 93401
USA

Printed in the United States of America

For your course and learning solutions, visit **www.xyztextbooks.com**

Student Solutions Manual to Accompany

Precalculus: Building Concepts and Connections
By
Revathi Narasimhan

Prepared by

Ross Rueger

Department of Mathematics
College of the Sequoias
Visalia, California

XYZ Textbooks

Contents

Chapter 8   **Systems of Equations and Inequalities**   **393**

8.1	Systems of Linear Equations and Inequalities in Two Variables	393
8.2	Systems of Linear Equations in Three Variables	402
8.3	Solving Systems of Equations Using Matrices	412
8.4	Operations with Matrices	421
8.5	Matrices and Inverses	425
8.6	Determinants and Cramer's Rule	438
8.7	Partial Fractions	442
8.8	Systems of Nonlinear Equations	449
	Chapter 8 Review Exercises	459
	Chapter 8 Test	474

Chapter 9   **Conic Sections**   **481**

9.1	The Parabola	481
9.2	The Ellipse	488
9.3	The Hyperbola	496
9.4	Rotation of Axes; General Form of Conic Sections	504
9.5	Polar Equations of Conic Sections	510
9.6	Parametric Equations	512
	Chapter 9 Review Exercises	517
	Chapter 9 Test	539

Chapter 10   **More Topics in Algebra**   **547**

10.1	Sequences	547
10.2	Sums of Terms of Sequences	552
10.3	General Sequences and Series	557
10.4	Counting Methods	560
10.5	Probability	562
10.6	The Binomial Theorem	564
10.7	Mathematical Induction	566
	Chapter 10 Review Exercises	569
	Chapter 10 Test	576

Preface

This *Student Solutions Manual* contains complete solutions to all odd-numbered exercises, and complete solutions to all chapter tests, of *Precalculus: Building Concepts and Connections* by Revathi Narasimhan. I have attempted to format solutions for readability and accuracy, and apologize to you for any errors that you may encounter. If you have any comments, suggestions, error corrections, or alternative solutions please feel free to send me an email (address below).

Please use this manual with some degree of caution. Be sure that you have attempted a solution, and re-attempted it, before you look it up in this manual. Mathematics can only be learned by *doing*, and not by observing! As you use this manual, do not just read the solution but work it along with the manual, using my solution to check your work. If you use this manual in that fashion then it should be helpful to you in your studying.

I would like to thank Katherine Heistand Shields, Jennifer Thomas and Amy Jacobs at XYZ Textbooks for their help with this project and for getting back to me with corrections so quickly. Producing a manual such as this is a team effort, and this is an excellent team to work with.

I wish to express my deep appreciation to Pat McKeague for asking me to be involved with this textbook. I find this to be an excellent Precalculus textbook which should be easy for you to read and understand. I especially appreciate Pat's efforts through XYZ Textbooks to make textbooks affordable for students to purchase.

Good luck!

Ross Rueger
College of the Sequoias
rossrueger@gmail.com

August, 2016

Chapter 1
Algebra Review

1.1 The Real Number System

1. The integers are $-1, 0 \ 10$, and 40.

3. The rational numbers are $-1.67, -1, 0, 0.5, \dfrac{4}{5}, 10$, and 40 .

5. The whole numbers are 0, 10, and 40.

7. The integers that are not positive are -1 and 0.

9. Associative property of multiplication

11. Distributive property of multiplication over addition

13. Commutative property of multiplication

15. Sketching the graph:

17. Sketching the graph:

19. Sketching the graph:

21. Sketching the graph:

23. Sketching the graph:

25. Writing in interval notation: $[-3, 4]$

27. Writing in interval notation: $[0, \infty)$

29. Writing in interval notation: $(-2, 4)$

31. Writing in interval notation: $(1, \infty)$

33. The interval notation is $[4, 10]$. Sketching the graph:

35. The interval notation is $[-3, 0)$. Sketching the graph:

37. The inequality is $2 \le x \le 12$ and the interval notation is $[2, 12]$.

39. Evaluating the expression: $|-3.2| = 3.2$

41. Evaluating the expression: $|253| = 253$

43. Evaluating the expression: $\left|\dfrac{5}{4}\right| = \dfrac{5}{4}$

45. Evaluating the expression: $\left|-\dfrac{4}{3}\right| = \dfrac{4}{3}$

47. Evaluating the expression: $|-2| + 4 = 2 + 4 = 6$

49. Evaluating the expression: $-|-4.5| = -4.5$

51. Evaluating the expression: $|5 - 2| + 4 = |3| + 4 = 3 + 4 = 7$

53. Evaluating the expression: $5 - |12 - 4| = 5 - |8| = 5 - 8 = -3$

55. Finding the distance: $|-2 - 4| = |-6| = 6$

57. Finding the distance: $|0 - 9| = |-9| = 9$

59. Finding the distance: $|-7.5 - (-12)| = |-7.5 + 12| = |4.5| = 4.5$

61. Finding the distance: $|-4.3 - 7.9| = |-12.2| = 12.2$

63. Finding the distance: $\left|-\dfrac{1}{2} - \dfrac{5}{2}\right| = |-3| = 3$

65. Finding the distance: $\left|\dfrac{1}{3} - \dfrac{4}{5}\right| = \left|\dfrac{5}{15} - \dfrac{12}{15}\right| = \left|-\dfrac{7}{15}\right| = \dfrac{7}{15}$

67. Evaluating the expression: $9 - 3(2) - 8 = 9 - 6 - 8 = -5$

69. Evaluating the expression: $(3-5)^2 = (-2)^2 = 4$

71. Evaluating the expression: $3^2 + 3(5) - 10 = 9 + 3(5) - 10 = 9 + 15 - 10 = 14$

73. Evaluating the expression: $(-3)^5 + 3 = -243 + 3 = -240$

75. Evaluating the expression: $\dfrac{10 - 4^2}{2 + 3^2} = \dfrac{10 - 16}{2 + 9} = -\dfrac{6}{11}$

77. Evaluating the expression: $-3^2 = -1 \cdot 3^2 = -1 \cdot 3 \cdot 3 = -9$

79. Evaluating the expression: $1 + \dfrac{2}{3} - 4^2 = 1 + \dfrac{2}{3} - 16 = \dfrac{3}{3} + \dfrac{2}{3} - \dfrac{48}{3} = -\dfrac{43}{3}$

81. Evaluating the expression: $\dfrac{2}{3+5} = \dfrac{2}{8} = \dfrac{1}{4}$

83. Evaluating the expression: $\dfrac{4^2 + 3}{5} = \dfrac{16 + 3}{5} = \dfrac{19}{5}$

85. The possible shoe sizes are 5, 6, 7, 8 and 9.

87. In interval notation, the temperature range is $[25°, 36°]$.

89. Finding the distance between the two elevations: $|20,320 - (-282)| = |20,320 + 282| = |20,602| = 20,602$ ft

91. No. It can be zero, which is neither negative nor positive.

93. Moving 4 units to the left of –3 you land on –7. Moving 4 units to the right of –3 you land on 1. Therefore the two points are –7 and 1.

1.2 Exponents, Roots, and Radicals

1. Evaluating the expression: $-3^2 = -1 \cdot 3^2 = -9$

3. Evaluating the expression: $4^{-3} = \dfrac{1}{4^3} = \dfrac{1}{64}$

5. Evaluating the expression: $-2^0 = -1 \cdot 2^0 = -1 \cdot 1 = -1$

7. Evaluating the expression: $\left(\dfrac{3}{4}\right)^{-2} = \left(\dfrac{4}{3}\right)^2 = \left(\dfrac{4}{3}\right)\left(\dfrac{4}{3}\right) = \dfrac{16}{9}$

9. Simplifying the expression: $-\left(4x^2y^4\right)^2 = -\left(4^2 x^{2\cdot2} y^{4\cdot2}\right) = -\left(16x^4y^8\right) = -16x^4y^8$

11. Simplifying the expression: $\left(2x^5\right)^{-2} = 2^{-2} x^{-10} = \dfrac{1}{2^2 x^{10}} = \dfrac{1}{4x^{10}}$

13. Simplifying the expression: $-2\left(a^2b^5\right)^2 = -2\left(a^4b^{10}\right) = -2a^4b^{10}$

15. Simplifying the expression: $\left(-4xy^2\right)^{-2} = (-4)^{-2} x^{-2} y^{-4} = \dfrac{1}{(-4)^2 x^2 y^4} = \dfrac{1}{16x^2y^4}$

17. Simplifying the expression: $\dfrac{7x^6y^2}{21x^3} = \dfrac{x^{6-3}y^2}{3} = \dfrac{x^3y^2}{3}$

19. Simplifying the expression: $\dfrac{\left(2y^{-3}\right)^2}{y^{-5}} = \dfrac{2^2 y^{-6}}{y^{-5}} = 4y^{-6-(-5)} = 4y^{-1} = \dfrac{4}{y}$

21. Simplifying the expression: $\left(\dfrac{2x^{-2}y^3}{xy^4}\right)^2 = \left(\dfrac{2}{x^3y}\right)^2 = \dfrac{2^2}{x^6y^2} = \dfrac{4}{x^6y^2}$

23. Simplifying the expression: $\left(\dfrac{-4s^5t^{-2}}{12s^3t}\right)^{-2} = \left(\dfrac{-1s^2}{3t^3}\right)^{-2} = \dfrac{(-1)^2 s^{-4}}{3^{-2}t^{-6}} = \dfrac{3^2t^6}{s^4} = \dfrac{9t^6}{s^4}$

25. Writing in scientific notation: $0.0051 = 5.1 \times 10^{-3}$ 27. Writing in scientific notation: $5,600 = 5.6 \times 10^3$

29. Writing in scientific notation: $0.0000567 = 5.67 \times 10^{-5}$ 31. Writing in scientific notation: $1,760,000 = 1.76 \times 10^{6}$

33. Writing in decimal form: $3.71 \times 10^{2} = 371$ 35. Writing in decimal form: $2.8 \times 10^{-2} = 0.028$

37. Writing in decimal form: $5.96 \times 10^{5} = 596,000$ 39. Writing in decimal form: $4.367 \times 10^{7} = 43,670,000$

41. Computing in scientific notation: $\left(2.1 \times 10^{3}\right)\left(4.3 \times 10^{4}\right) = \left(2.1 \times 4.3\right) \times \left(10^{3} \cdot 10^{4}\right) = 9.03 \times 10^{7}$

43. Computing in scientific notation: $\dfrac{9.4 \times 10^{2}}{4.7 \times 10^{3}} = \dfrac{9.4}{4.7} \times \dfrac{10^{2}}{10^{3}} = 2.0 \times 10^{-1}$

45. Evaluating the expression: $\sqrt{49} = 7$

47. Evaluating the expression: $\sqrt[3]{\dfrac{1}{8}} = \dfrac{1}{2}$

49. Evaluating the expression: $\left(49\right)^{3/2} = \left(\sqrt{49}\right)^{3} = \left(7\right)^{3} = 343$

51. Evaluating the expression: $\left(\dfrac{16}{625}\right)^{1/4} = \sqrt[4]{\dfrac{16}{625}} = \dfrac{2}{5}$

53. Simplifying the radical: $\sqrt{32} = \sqrt{16 \cdot 2} = \sqrt{16}\sqrt{2} = 4\sqrt{2}$

55. Simplifying the radical: $\sqrt[3]{250} = \sqrt[3]{125 \cdot 2} = \sqrt[3]{125} \cdot \sqrt[3]{2} = 5\sqrt[3]{2}$

57. Simplifying the radical: $\sqrt{32} \cdot \sqrt{8} = \sqrt{16 \cdot 2} \cdot \sqrt{4 \cdot 2} = 4\sqrt{2} \cdot 2\sqrt{2} = 8\sqrt{4} = 8 \cdot 2 = 16$

59. Simplifying the radical: $\sqrt[3]{\dfrac{-16}{125}} = \dfrac{\sqrt[3]{-16}}{\sqrt[3]{125}} = \dfrac{\sqrt[3]{-8 \cdot 2}}{5} = \dfrac{\sqrt[3]{-8}\sqrt[3]{2}}{5} = \dfrac{-2\sqrt[3]{2}}{5}$

61. Simplifying the radical: $\sqrt{\dfrac{3}{5}} = \dfrac{\sqrt{3}}{\sqrt{5}} = \dfrac{\sqrt{3}}{\sqrt{5}} \cdot \dfrac{\sqrt{5}}{\sqrt{5}} = \dfrac{\sqrt{15}}{5}$

63. Simplifying the radical: $\sqrt[3]{\dfrac{7}{9}} = \dfrac{\sqrt[3]{7}}{\sqrt[3]{9}} = \dfrac{\sqrt[3]{7}}{\sqrt[3]{9}} \cdot \dfrac{\sqrt[3]{3}}{\sqrt[3]{3}} = \dfrac{\sqrt[3]{21}}{\sqrt[3]{27}} = \dfrac{\sqrt[3]{21}}{3}$

65. Simplifying the radical: $\sqrt{\dfrac{50}{147}} = \dfrac{\sqrt{50}}{\sqrt{147}} = \dfrac{\sqrt{25 \cdot 2}}{\sqrt{49 \cdot 3}} = \dfrac{5\sqrt{2}}{7\sqrt{3}} = \dfrac{5\sqrt{2}}{7\sqrt{3}} \cdot \dfrac{\sqrt{3}}{\sqrt{3}} = \dfrac{5\sqrt{6}}{7 \cdot 3} = \dfrac{5\sqrt{6}}{21}$

67. Simplifying the radical: $\sqrt[3]{\dfrac{-48}{81}} = \dfrac{\sqrt[3]{-8 \cdot 6}}{\sqrt[3]{27 \cdot 3}} = \dfrac{-2\sqrt[3]{2}}{\sqrt[3]{27}} = -\dfrac{2\sqrt[3]{2}}{3}$

69. Simplifying the radical: $\sqrt{x^{3}y^{4}} = \sqrt{x \cdot x^{2}\left(y^{2}\right)^{2}} = xy^{2}\sqrt{x}$

71. Simplifying the radical: $\sqrt[3]{x^{8}y^{4}} = \sqrt[3]{x^{6}x^{2}y^{3}y} = \sqrt[3]{\left(x^{2}\right)^{3}x^{2}y^{3}y} = x^{2}y\sqrt[3]{x^{2}y}$

73. Simplifying the radical: $\sqrt{3x^{2}y} \cdot \sqrt{15xy^{3}} = \sqrt{45x^{3}y^{4}} = \sqrt{9 \cdot 5x^{2}x\left(y^{2}\right)^{2}} = 3xy^{2}\sqrt{5x}$

75. Simplifying the radical: $\sqrt[3]{6x^{3}y^{2}} \cdot \sqrt[3]{4x^{2}y} = x\sqrt[3]{6y^{2}} \cdot \sqrt[3]{4x^{2}y} = x\sqrt[3]{24x^{2}y^{3}} = x\sqrt[3]{8 \cdot 3x^{2}y^{3}} = 2xy\sqrt[3]{3x^{2}}$

77. Simplifying the radical: $\sqrt{98} + 3\sqrt{32} = \sqrt{49 \cdot 2} + 3\sqrt{16 \cdot 2} = 7\sqrt{2} + 3 \cdot 4\sqrt{2} = 7\sqrt{2} + 12\sqrt{2} = 19\sqrt{2}$

79. Simplifying the radical:
$\sqrt{216} - 4\sqrt{24} + \sqrt{3} = \sqrt{36 \cdot 6} - 4\sqrt{4 \cdot 6} + \sqrt{3} = 6\sqrt{6} - 4 \cdot 2\sqrt{6} + \sqrt{3} = 6\sqrt{6} - 8\sqrt{6} + \sqrt{3} = -2\sqrt{6} + \sqrt{3}$

81. Simplifying the radical: $\left(1 + \sqrt{5}\right)\left(1 - \sqrt{5}\right) = 1 - \sqrt{5} + \sqrt{5} - \sqrt{5}\sqrt{5} = 1 - 5 = -4$

83. Simplifying the radical: $\dfrac{4}{1 - \sqrt{5}} = \dfrac{4}{1 - \sqrt{5}} \cdot \dfrac{1 + \sqrt{5}}{1 + \sqrt{5}} = \dfrac{4\left(1 + \sqrt{5}\right)}{1^{2} - \left(\sqrt{5}\right)^{2}} = \dfrac{4\left(1 + \sqrt{5}\right)}{-4} = -1 - \sqrt{5}$

85. Simplifying the radical: $\dfrac{1}{\sqrt{3} - \sqrt{2}} = \dfrac{1}{\sqrt{3} - \sqrt{2}} \cdot \dfrac{\sqrt{3} + \sqrt{2}}{\sqrt{3} + \sqrt{2}} = \dfrac{\sqrt{3} + \sqrt{2}}{\left(\sqrt{3}\right)^{2} - \left(\sqrt{2}\right)^{2}} = \dfrac{\sqrt{3} + \sqrt{2}}{3 - 2} = \sqrt{3} + \sqrt{2}$

87. Simplifying the expression: $3^{2/3} \cdot 3^{-4/3} = 3^{2/3-4/3} = 3^{-2/3} = \dfrac{1}{3^{2/3}}$

89. Simplifying the expression: $5^{-1/2} \cdot 5^{3/2} = 5^{-1/2+3/2} = 5^1 = 5$

91. Simplifying the expression: $\dfrac{7^{-1/4}}{7^{1/2}} = 7^{-1/4-1/2} = 7^{-1/4-2/4} = 7^{-3/4} = \dfrac{1}{7^{3/4}}$

93. Simplifying the expression: $\dfrac{4^{-1/3}}{4^{1/4}} = 4^{-1/3-1/4} = 4^{-4/12-3/12} = 4^{-7/12} = \dfrac{1}{4^{7/12}}$

95. Simplifying the expression: $\left(x^2 y^3\right)^{-1/2} = x^{-1} y^{-3/2} = \dfrac{1}{xy^{3/2}}$

97. Simplifying the expression: $\dfrac{x^{1/3} \cdot x^{1/2}}{x^2} = x^{1/3+1/2-2} = x^{2/6+3/6-12/6} = x^{-7/6} = \dfrac{1}{x^{7/6}}$

99. Writing in scientific notation: $36{,}800 = 3.68 \times 10^4$ km per hour

101. Writing in scientific notation: $3{,}540{,}000 = 3.54 \times 10^6$ square miles

103. Finding the sum when $s = 5$: $s\sqrt{2} + s\sqrt{2} = 5\sqrt{2} + 5\sqrt{2} = 10\sqrt{2}$ inches

105. Substituting $a = 20$: $386a^{1/4} = 386(20)^{1/4} \approx 816$ species

107. Since $\dfrac{3x^2 y^{-3}}{y} = \dfrac{3x^2}{y^4}$, the expression is defined for $-\infty < x < \infty$ and $y \neq 0$.

109. Let $x = 3$ and $y = 4$. Then $\sqrt{x^2 + y^2} = \sqrt{3^2 + 4^2} = \sqrt{9+16} = \sqrt{25} = 5$ but $x + y = 3 + 4 = 7$. Other answers are possible.

1.3 Polynomials and Factoring

1. The degree is 1: $3y + 16 + 2y + 10 = (3y + 2y) + (16 + 10) = 5y + 26$

3. The degree is 2: $2t^2 - 2t + 5 + t^2 = (2t^2 + t^2) - 2t + 5 = 3t^2 - 2t + 5$

5. The degree is 2: $-7s^2 - 6s + 3 + 3s^2 + 4 = (-7s^2 + 3s^2) - 6s + (3 + 4) = -4s^2 - 6s + 7$

7. Simplifying the polynomial: $(z + 6) + (5z + 8) = (z + 5z) + (6 + 8) = 6z + 14$

9. Simplifying the polynomial: $\left(-9x^2 - 32x + 14\right) + \left(-2x^2 + 15x - 6\right) = -11x^2 - 17x + 8$

11. Simplifying the polynomial: $\left(z^5 - 4z^4 + 7\right) - \left(-z^3 + 15z^2 - 8z\right) = z^5 - 4z^4 + z^3 - 15z^2 + 8z + 7$

13. Simplifying the polynomial: $\left(3v^4 - 6v + 5\right) + \left(25v^5 - 16v^3 + 3v^2\right) = 25v^5 + 3v^4 - 16v^3 + 3v^2 - 6v + 5$

15. Simplifying the polynomial: $\left(-21t^2 + 21t + 21\right) + \left(9t^3 + 2\right) = 9t^3 - 21t^2 + 21t + 23$

17. Simplifying the polynomial: $s(2s + 1) = s(2s) + s(1) = 2s^2 + s$

19. Simplifying the polynomial: $3z\left(-6z^2 - 5\right) = 3z\left(-6z^2\right) + 3z(-5) = -18z^2 - 15z$

21. Simplifying the polynomial: $-t\left(-7t^2 + 3t + 9\right) = -t\left(-7t^2\right) - t(3t) - t(9) = 7t^3 - 3t^2 - 9t$

23. Simplifying the polynomial: $7z^2\left(z^2 + 9z - 8\right) = 7z^2\left(z^2\right) + 7z^2(9z) + 7z^2(-8) = 7z^4 + 63x^3 - 56z^2$

25. Simplifying the polynomial: $(y + 6)(y + 5) = y^2 + 5y + 6y + 30 = y^2 + 11y + 30$

27. Simplifying the polynomial: $(-v - 12)(v - 3) = -v^2 + 3v - 12v + 36 = -v^2 - 9v + 36$

29. Simplifying the polynomial: $(5 + 4v)(-7v - 6) = -35v - 30 - 28v^2 - 24v = -28v^2 - 59v - 30$

31. Simplifying the polynomial: $\left(u^2 - 9\right)(u + 3) = u^3 + 3u^2 - 9u - 27$

33. Simplifying the polynomial: $(x + 4)^2 = x^2 + 2(x)(4) + 4^2 = x^2 + 8x + 16$

35. Simplifying the polynomial: $(s + 6)^2 = s^2 + 2(s)(6) + 6^2 = s^2 + 12s + 36$

37. Simplifying the polynomial: $(5t+4)^2 = (5t)^2 + 2(5t)(4) + 4^2 = 25t^2 + 40t + 16$

39. Simplifying the polynomial: $(v+9)(v-9) = v^2 - 9^2 = v^2 - 81$

41. Simplifying the polynomial: $(9s+7)(7-9s) = 63s - 81s^2 + 49 - 63s = -81s^2 + 49$

43. Simplifying the polynomial: $(v^2+3)(v^2-3) = (v^2)^2 - 3^2 = v^4 - 9$

45. Simplifying the polynomial: $(5y^2-4)(5y^2+4) = (5y^2)^2 - 4^2 = 25y^4 - 16$

47. Simplifying the polynomial: $(4z^2+5)(4z^2-5) = (4z^2)^2 - 5^2 = 16z^4 - 25$

49. Simplifying the polynomial: $(x+2z)(x-2z) = x^2 - (2z)^2 = x^2 - 4z^2$

51. Simplifying the polynomial:
$$(-t^2-5t+1)(t+6) = (-t^2-5t+1)(t) + (-t^2-5t+1)(6) = -t^3 - 5t^2 + t - 6t^2 - 30t + 6 = -t^3 - 11t^2 - 29t + 6$$

53. Simplifying the polynomial:
$$(x-2)(x^2+3x-7) = x(x^2+3x-7) - 2(x^2+3x-7) = x^3 + 3x^2 - 7x - 2x^2 - 6x + 14 = x^3 + x^2 - 13x + 14$$

55. Simplifying the polynomial:
$$(5u^3-6u^2-7u+9)(-4u+7) = (5u^3-6u^2-7u+9)(-4u) + (5u^3-6u^2-7u+9)(7)$$
$$= -20u^4 + 24u^3 + 28u^2 - 36u + 35u^3 - 42u^2 - 49u + 63$$
$$= -20u^4 + 59u^3 - 14u^2 - 85u + 63$$

57. Factoring the greatest common factor: $2x^3 + 6x^2 - 8x = 2x(x^2 + 3x - 4)$

59. Factoring the greatest common factor: $-2t^6 - 4t^5 + 10t^2 = -2t^2(t^4 + 2t^3 - 5)$

61. Factoring the greatest common factor: $-5x^7 + 10x^5 - 15x^3 = -5x^3(x^4 - 2x^2 + 3)$

63. Factoring by grouping: $3(x+1) + x(x+1) = (x+1)(3+x)$

65. Factoring by grouping:
$$s^3 - 5s^2 - 9s + 45 = (s^3 - 5s^2) + (-9s + 45) = s^2(s-5) - 9(s-5) = (s-5)(s^2-9) = (s-5)(s+3)(s-3)$$

67. Factoring by grouping:
$$12u^3 + 4u^2 - 3u - 1 = (12u^3 + 4u^2) + (-3u - 1) = 4u^2(3u+1) - 1(3u+1) = (3u+1)(4u^2-1) = (3u+1)(2u+1)(2u-1)$$

69. Factoring the trinomial: $x^2 + 4x + 3 = (x+1)(x+3)$

71. Factoring the trinomial: $x^2 - 6x - 16 = (x+2)(x-8)$

73. Factoring the trinomial: $3s^2 + 15s + 12 = 3(s^2 + 5s + 4) = 3(s+4)(s+1)$

75. Factoring the trinomial: $-6t^2 + 24t + 72 = -6(t^2 - 4t - 12) = -6(t+2)(t-6)$

77. Factoring the trinomial: $9u^2 - 27u + 18 = 9(u^2 - 3u + 2) = 9(u-2)(u-1)$

79. Factoring the special product: $x^2 - 16 = x^2 - 4^2 = (x+4)(x-4)$

81. Factoring the special product: $4x^2 + 4x + 1 = (2x+1)^2$

83. Factoring the special product: $y^3 + 64 = y^3 + 4^3 = (y+4)(y^2 - y(4) + 4^2) = (y+4)(y^2 - 4y + 16)$

85. Factoring the special product: $8y^3 + 1 = (2y)^3 + 1^3 = (2y+1)((2y)^2 - (2y)(1) + 1^2) = (2y+1)(4y^2 - 2y + 1)$

87. Factoring the polynomial: $z^2 + 13z + 42 = (z+7)(z+6)$

89. Factoring the polynomial: $x^2 + 12x + 36 = (x+6)^2$

91. Factoring the polynomial: $-y^2 + 4y - 4 = -(y^2 - 4y + 4) = -(y-2)^2$

93. Factoring the polynomial: $z^2 - 16z + 64 = (z-8)^2$

95. Factoring the polynomial: $-2y^2 + 7y - 3 = -(2y^2 - 7y + 3) = -(2y-1)(y-3)$

97. Factoring the polynomial: $9y^2 + 12y + 4 = (3y+2)^2$

99. Factoring the polynomial: $6z^2 - 3z - 18 = 3(2z^2 - z - 6) = 3(2z+3)(z-2)$

101. Factoring the polynomial: $15t^2 - 70t - 25 = 5(3t^2 - 14t - 5) = 5(3t+1)(t-5)$

103. Factoring the polynomial: $-10u^2 - 45u - 20 = -5(2u^2 + 9u + 4) = -5(2u+1)(u+4)$

105. Factoring the polynomial: $v^2 - 4 = v^2 - 2^2 = (v+2)(v-2)$

107. Factoring the polynomial: $-s^2 + 49 = 49 - s^2 = 7^2 - s^2 = (7+s)(7-s)$

109. Factoring the polynomial: $-25t^2 + 4 = 4 - 25t^2 = 2^2 - (5t)^2 = (2+5t)(2-5t)$

111. Factoring the polynomial: $t^3 - 16t^2 = t^2(t-16)$

113. Factoring the polynomial: $12u^3 + 4u^2 - 40u = 4u(3u^2 + u - 10) = 4u(3u-5)(u+2)$

115. Factoring the polynomial: $-10t^3 + 5t^2 + 15t = -5t(2t^2 - t - 3) = -5t(2t-3)(t+1)$

117. Factoring the polynomial: $-15z^3 - 5z^2 + 20z = -5z(3z^2 + z - 4) = -5z(3z+4)(z-1)$

119. Factoring the polynomial:
$$2y^3 + 3y^2 - 8y - 12 = (2y^3 + 3y^2) + (-8y - 12) = y^2(2y+3) - 4(2y+3) = (2y+3)(y^2-4) = (2y+3)(y+2)(y-2)$$

121. Factoring the polynomial:
$$-18z^3 + 27z^2 + 32z - 48 = (-18z^3 + 27z^2) + (32z - 48)$$
$$= -9z^2(2z-3) + 16(2z-3)$$
$$= (2z-3)(-9z^2+16)$$
$$= (2z-3)(4+3z)(4-3z)$$

123. Factoring the polynomial: $3y^4 + 18y^3 + 24y^2 = 3y^2(y^2 + 6y + 8) = 3y^2(y+4)(y+2)$

125. Factoring the polynomial: $7x^5 - 63x^3 = 7x^3(x^2 - 9) = 7x^3(x+3)(x-3)$

127. Factoring the polynomial: $-6s^5 - 30s^3 = -6s^3(s^2+5)$

129. Factoring the polynomial: $8x^3 + 64 = 8(x^3 + 8) = 8(x^3 + 2^3) = 8(x+2)(x^2 - 2x + 4)$

131. Factoring the polynomial: $-8y^3 + 1 = 1 - 8y^3 = 1^3 - (2y)^3 = (1-2y)(1+2y+4y^2)$

133. Finding the difference: $132x - 108x = 24x$
There is $24x$ more paint needed for the bedroom than for the den.

135. a. Finding the perimeter with side s: $P = 4(s) = 4s$

  b. Finding the perimeter with side $2s$: $P = 4(2s) = 8s$

137. a. Simplifying the polynomial: $1000(1+r)^2 = 1000(1+2r+r^2) = 1000 + 2000r + 1000r^2 = 1000r^2 + 2000r + 1000$

  b. Substituting $r = 0.05$: $1000(1+.05)^2 = \$1,102.50$
The investment will be worth $\$1,102.50$ in two years.

139. Not necessarily. If the leading terms are opposites (such as $2x^3$ and $-2x^3$), then when they are added the resulting polynomial will be degree 2, not degree 3.

141. The constant term is $(2)(0) = 0$.

143. We must have $a = 0$ so that the third term does not appear.

145. One example is $x^2 + 4x + 4 = (x+2)^2$. Other answers are possible.

1.4 Rational Expressions

1. Simplifying: $\dfrac{57}{24} = \dfrac{3 \cdot 19}{3 \cdot 8} = \dfrac{19}{8}$

3. Simplifying: $\dfrac{x^2 - 4}{6(x+2)} = \dfrac{(x+2)(x-2)}{6(x+2)} = \dfrac{x-2}{6}$. The expression is defined as long as $x \neq -2$.

5. Simplifying: $\dfrac{x^2 - 2x - 3}{x^2 - 9} = \dfrac{(x-3)(x+1)}{(x+3)(x-3)} = \dfrac{x+1}{x+3}$. The expression is defined as long as $x \neq -3, 3$.

7. Simplifying: $\dfrac{x^4 - x^2}{x+1} = \dfrac{x^2(x^2 - 1)}{x+1} = \dfrac{x^2(x+1)(x-1)}{x+1} = x^2(x-1)$

   The expression is defined as long as $x \neq -1$.

9. Simplifying: $\dfrac{x^3 - 1}{x^2 - 1} = \dfrac{(x-1)(x^2 + x + 1)}{(x+1)(x-1)} = \dfrac{x^2 + x + 1}{x+1}$. The expression is defined as long as $x \neq -1, 1$.

11. Multiplying: $\dfrac{3x}{6y^2} \cdot \dfrac{2xy}{x^3} = \dfrac{6x^2 y}{6x^3 y^2} = \dfrac{1}{xy}$

13. Multiplying: $\dfrac{x+2}{x^2 - 9} \cdot \dfrac{x+3}{x^2 + 4x + 4} = \dfrac{(x+2)(x+3)}{(x+3)(x-3) \cdot (x+2)^2} = \dfrac{1}{(x-3)(x+2)}$

15. Multiplying: $\dfrac{3x+9}{x^2 + x - 6} \cdot \dfrac{2x-4}{x+6} = \dfrac{(3x+9)(2x-4)}{(x^2 + x - 6)(x+6)} = \dfrac{3(x+3) \cdot 2(x-2)}{(x+3)(x-2)(x+6)} = \dfrac{6}{x+6}$

17. Multiplying: $\dfrac{6x-12}{3x^3 - 12x} \cdot \dfrac{x^2 - 4x + 4}{x^2 + 3x - 10} = \dfrac{6(x-2)}{3x(x^2 - 4)} \cdot \dfrac{(x-2)^2}{(x+5)(x-2)} = \dfrac{2(x-2)}{x(x+2)(x-2)} \cdot \dfrac{x-2}{x+5} = \dfrac{2(x-2)}{x(x+2)(x+5)}$

19. Multiplying: $\dfrac{x^3 + 1}{x^2 - 1} \cdot \dfrac{2x^2 - x - 1}{x+2} = \dfrac{(x+1)(x^2 - x + 1)}{(x+1)(x-1)} \cdot \dfrac{(2x+1)(x-1)}{x+2} = \dfrac{(x^2 - x + 1)(2x+1)}{x+2}$

21. Dividing: $\dfrac{5x-20}{x^2 - 4x - 5} \div \dfrac{x^2 - 8x + 16}{x-5} = \dfrac{5x-20}{x^2 - 4x - 5} \cdot \dfrac{x-5}{x^2 - 8x + 16} = \dfrac{5(x-4)}{(x-5)(x+1)} \cdot \dfrac{x-5}{(x-4)^2} = \dfrac{5}{(x+1)(x-4)}$

23. Dividing:

$$\dfrac{6x^3 - 24x}{3x^2 - 3} \div \dfrac{2x^2 + 4x}{x^2 - 2x + 1} = \dfrac{6x^3 - 24x}{3x^2 - 3} \cdot \dfrac{x^2 - 2x + 1}{2x^2 + 4x} = \dfrac{6x(x^2 - 4)}{3(x^2 - 1)} \cdot \dfrac{(x-1)^2}{2x(x+2)} = \dfrac{(x+2)(x-2)}{(x+1)(x-1)} \cdot \dfrac{(x-1)^2}{(x+2)} = \dfrac{(x-2)(x-1)}{x+1}$$

25. Dividing: $\dfrac{x^3 - 8}{2x^2 - 3x - 2} \div \dfrac{x^2 - 4}{2x+1} = \dfrac{x^3 - 8}{2x^2 - 3x - 2} \cdot \dfrac{2x+1}{x^2 - 4} = \dfrac{(x-2)(x^2 + 2x + 4)}{(2x+1)(x-2)} \cdot \dfrac{2x+1}{(x+2)(x-2)} = \dfrac{x^2 + 2x + 4}{(x+2)(x-2)}$

27. Adding: $\dfrac{2}{x} + \dfrac{3}{x^2} = \dfrac{2}{x} \cdot \dfrac{x}{x} + \dfrac{3}{x^2} = \dfrac{2x}{x^2} + \dfrac{3}{x^2} = \dfrac{2x+3}{x^2}$

29. Adding: $\dfrac{1}{x+1} + \dfrac{4}{x-1} = \dfrac{1}{x+1} \cdot \dfrac{x-1}{x-1} + \dfrac{4}{x-1} \cdot \dfrac{x+1}{x+1} = \dfrac{x-1}{(x+1)(x-1)} + \dfrac{4x+4}{(x+1)(x-1)} = \dfrac{5x+3}{(x+1)(x-1)}$

31. Adding:

$$\frac{4x}{x^2-9}+\frac{2x^2}{3x+9}=\frac{4x}{(x+3)(x-3)}+\frac{2x^2}{3(x+3)}$$

$$=\frac{4x}{(x+3)(x-3)}\cdot\frac{3}{3}+\frac{2x^2}{3(x+3)}\cdot\frac{x-3}{x+3}$$

$$=\frac{12x}{3(x+3)(x-3)}+\frac{2x^3-6x^2}{3(x+3)(x-3)}$$

$$=\frac{2x^3-6x^2+12x}{3(x+3)(x-3)}$$

$$=\frac{2x\left(x^2-3x+6\right)}{3(x+3)(x-3)}$$

33. Subtracting:

$$\frac{x}{x+1}-\frac{x-4}{x-1}=\frac{x}{x+1}\cdot\frac{x-1}{x-1}-\frac{x-4}{x-1}\cdot\frac{x+1}{x+1}$$

$$=\frac{x^2-x}{(x+1)(x-1)}-\frac{x^2-3x-4}{(x+1)(x-1)}$$

$$=\frac{\left(x^2-x\right)-\left(x^2-3x-4\right)}{(x+1)(x-1)}$$

$$=\frac{2x+4}{(x+1)(x-1)}$$

$$=\frac{2\left(x+2\right)}{(x+1)(x-1)}$$

35. Subtracting:

$$\frac{-3x}{x^2-16}-\frac{3x^2}{3x+12}=\frac{-3x}{(x+4)(x-4)}-\frac{3x^2}{3(x+4)}$$

$$=\frac{-3x}{(x+4)(x-4)}\cdot\frac{3}{3}-\frac{3x^2}{3(x+4)}\cdot\frac{x-4}{x-4}$$

$$=\frac{-9x}{3(x+4)(x-4)}-\frac{3x^3-12x^2}{3(x+4)(x-4)}$$

$$=\frac{-3x^3+12x^2-9x}{3(x+4)(x-4)}$$

$$=\frac{-3x(x^2-4x+3)}{3(x+4)(x-4)}$$

$$=\frac{-x(x-3)(x-1)}{(x+4)(x-4)}$$

37. Adding: $\dfrac{3}{x-1}+\dfrac{4}{1-x}=\dfrac{3}{x-1}+\dfrac{4}{-(x-1)}=\dfrac{3}{x-1}-\dfrac{4}{x-1}=\dfrac{-1}{x-1}=\dfrac{1}{1-x}$

39. Simplifying:

$$\frac{4}{x+2} - \frac{2}{x-2} + \frac{1}{x^2-4} = \frac{4}{x+2} - \frac{2}{x-2} + \frac{1}{(x+2)(x-2)}$$

$$= \frac{4}{x+2}\cdot\frac{x-2}{x-2} - \frac{2}{x-2}\cdot\frac{x+2}{x+2} + \frac{1}{(x+2)(x-2)}$$

$$= \frac{4x-8}{(x+2)(x-2)} - \frac{2x+4}{(x+2)(x-2)} + \frac{1}{(x+2)(x-2)}$$

$$= \frac{(4x-8)-(2x+4)+1}{(x+2)(x-2)}$$

$$= \frac{2x-11}{(x+2)(x-2)}$$

41. Simplifying:

$$\frac{7}{3-x} - \frac{1}{x+2} + \frac{4}{x^2-x-6} = \frac{7}{-(x-3)} - \frac{1}{x+2} + \frac{4}{(x+2)(x-3)}$$

$$= \frac{-7(x+2)}{(x-3)(x+2)} - \frac{x-3}{(x+2)(x-3)} + \frac{4}{(x+2)(x-3)}$$

$$= \frac{(-7x-14)-(x-3)+4}{(x+2)(x-3)}$$

$$= \frac{-8x-7}{(x+2)(x-3)}$$

43. Simplifying: $\dfrac{\dfrac{x+1}{x}}{\dfrac{x^2-1}{x^2}} = \dfrac{x+1}{x} \div \dfrac{x^2-1}{x^2} = \dfrac{x+1}{x} \cdot \dfrac{x^2}{x^2-1} = \dfrac{x+1}{x} \cdot \dfrac{x^2}{(x+1)(x-1)} = \dfrac{x}{x-1}$

45. Simplifying: $\dfrac{\dfrac{1}{x}+\dfrac{1}{y}}{\dfrac{1}{y^2}-\dfrac{2}{x}} = \dfrac{\left(\dfrac{1}{x}+\dfrac{1}{y}\right)xy^2}{\left(\dfrac{1}{y^2}-\dfrac{2}{x}\right)xy^2} = \dfrac{\dfrac{1}{x}(xy^2)+\dfrac{1}{y}(xy^2)}{\dfrac{1}{y^2}(xy^2)-\dfrac{2}{x}(xy^2)} = \dfrac{y^2+xy}{x-2y^2} = \dfrac{y(y+x)}{x-2y^2}$

47. Simplifying: $\dfrac{1}{\dfrac{1}{r}+\dfrac{1}{s}+\dfrac{1}{t}} = \dfrac{1(rst)}{\left(\dfrac{1}{r}+\dfrac{1}{s}+\dfrac{1}{t}\right)rst} = \dfrac{rst}{\dfrac{1}{r}(rst)+\dfrac{1}{s}(rst)+\dfrac{1}{t}(rst)} = \dfrac{rst}{st+rt+rs}$

49. Simplifying: $\dfrac{1+x^{-1}}{x^{-2}-1} = \dfrac{1+\dfrac{1}{x}}{\dfrac{1}{x^2}-1} = \dfrac{\left(1+\dfrac{1}{x}\right)x^2}{\left(\dfrac{1}{x^2}-1\right)x^2} = \dfrac{x^2+\left(\dfrac{1}{x}\right)x^2}{\left(\dfrac{1}{x^2}\right)x^2-x^2} = \dfrac{x^2+x}{1-x^2} = \dfrac{x(x+1)}{(1+x)(1-x)} = \dfrac{x}{1-x}$

51. Simplifying:

$$\frac{\dfrac{1}{x-1}-\dfrac{1}{x-3}}{\dfrac{2}{x-1}+\dfrac{3}{x+1}}=\frac{\left(\dfrac{1}{x-1}-\dfrac{1}{x-3}\right)(x-1)(x+1)(x-3)}{\left(\dfrac{2}{x-1}+\dfrac{3}{x+1}\right)(x-1)(x+1)(x-3)}$$

$$=\frac{(x+1)(x-3)-(x-1)(x+1)}{2(x+1)(x-3)+3(x-1)(x-3)}$$

$$=\frac{\left(x^2-2x-3\right)-\left(x^2-1\right)}{2\left(x^2-2x-3\right)+3\left(x^2-4x+3\right)}$$

$$=\frac{-2x-2}{5x^2-16x+3}$$

$$=\frac{-2(x+1)}{(5x-1)(x-3)}$$

53. Simplifying: $\dfrac{\dfrac{1}{x+h}-\dfrac{1}{x}}{h}=\dfrac{\left(\dfrac{1}{x+h}-\dfrac{1}{x}\right)\cdot x(x+h)}{h\cdot x(x+h)}=\dfrac{x-(x+h)}{hx(x+h)}=\dfrac{-h}{hx(x+h)}=-\dfrac{1}{x(x+h)}$

55. Simplifying: $\dfrac{\dfrac{2}{x^2-4}+\dfrac{1}{x+2}}{\dfrac{4}{x+2}}=\dfrac{\dfrac{2}{(x+2)(x-2)}+\dfrac{1}{x+2}}{\dfrac{4}{x+2}}=\dfrac{\left(\dfrac{2}{(x+2)(x-2)}+\dfrac{1}{x-2}\right)(x+2)(x-2)}{\left(\dfrac{4}{x+2}\right)(x+2)(x-2)}=\dfrac{2+(x+2)}{4(x-2)}=\dfrac{x+4}{4(x-2)}$

57. Simplifying: $\dfrac{\dfrac{a}{a^2-b^2}+\dfrac{b}{a+b}}{\dfrac{1}{a-b}}=\dfrac{\dfrac{a}{(a+b)(a-b)}+\dfrac{b}{a+b}}{\dfrac{1}{a-b}}=\dfrac{\left(\dfrac{a}{(a+b)(a-b)}+\dfrac{b}{a+b}\right)(a+b)(a-b)}{\left(\dfrac{1}{a-b}\right)(a+b)(a-b)}=\dfrac{a+b(a-b)}{a+b}=\dfrac{a+ba-b^2}{a+b}$

59. Evaluating when $t=8$: $\dfrac{400}{t}=\dfrac{400}{8}=50$

The average driving speed is 50 mph for driving 400 miles in 8 hours.

61. Simplifying the expression: $R=\dfrac{1}{\dfrac{1}{R_1}+\dfrac{1}{R_2}+\dfrac{1}{R_3}}=\dfrac{1\cdot R_1R_2R_3}{\left(\dfrac{1}{R_1}+\dfrac{1}{R_2}+\dfrac{1}{R_3}\right)\cdot R_1R_2R_3}=\dfrac{R_1R_2R_3}{R_2R_3+R_1R_3+R_1R_2}$

63. We must exclude $x=-1$, which results in a 0 denominator.

65. No. Since x^2+4 does not factor, the expression does not simplify.

1.5 Linear and Quadratic Equations

1. Solving the equation:
$$3x + 5 = 8$$
$$3x = 3$$
$$x = 1$$

3. Solving the equation:
$$-2x - 5 = 3x + 10$$
$$-5x - 5 = 10$$
$$-5x = 15$$
$$x = -3$$

5. Solving the equation:
$$-3(x - 1) = 12$$
$$-3x + 3 = 12$$
$$-3x = 9$$
$$x = -3$$

7. Solving the equation:
$$-2(x + 4) - 3 = 7$$
$$-2x - 8 - 3 = 7$$
$$-2x - 11 = 7$$
$$-2x = 18$$
$$x = -9$$

9. Solving the equation:
$$-3(x - 4) = -(x + 1) - 6$$
$$-3x + 12 = -x - 1 - 6$$
$$-3x + 12 = -x - 7$$
$$-2x + 12 = -7$$
$$-2x = -19$$
$$x = \frac{19}{2}$$

11. Solving the equation:
$$-2(5 + x) - (x - 2) = 10(x + 1)$$
$$-10 - 2x - x + 2 = 10x + 10$$
$$-3x - 8 = 10x + 10$$
$$-13x - 8 = 10$$
$$-13x = 18$$
$$x = -\frac{18}{13}$$

13. Solving the equation:
$$\frac{1}{2} + \frac{x}{3} = \frac{7}{6}$$
$$6\left(\frac{1}{2} + \frac{x}{3}\right) = \frac{7}{6} \cdot 6$$
$$3 + 2x = 7$$
$$2x = 4$$
$$x = 2$$

15. Solving the equation:
$$\frac{x + 3}{4} + \frac{x}{3} = 6$$
$$12\left(\frac{x + 3}{4} + \frac{x}{3}\right) = 6 \cdot 12$$
$$3(x + 3) + 4x = 72$$
$$3x + 9 + 4x = 72$$
$$7x + 9 = 72$$
$$7x = 63$$
$$x = 9$$

17. Solving the equation:
$$\frac{2x - 3}{3} - \frac{x}{2} = -\frac{2}{3}$$
$$6\left(\frac{2x - 3}{3} - \frac{x}{2}\right) = -\frac{2}{3} \cdot 6$$
$$2(2x - 3) - 3x = -4$$
$$4x - 6 - 3x = -4$$
$$x - 6 = -4$$
$$x = 2$$

19. Solving the equation:
$$\frac{3x + 4}{2} + x = 4$$
$$2\left(\frac{3x + 4}{2} + x\right) = 4 \cdot 2$$
$$3x + 4 + 2x = 8$$
$$5x + 4 = 8$$
$$5x = 4$$
$$x = \frac{4}{5}$$

21. Solving the equation:
$$0.4(x-1)+1=0.5x$$
$$10[0.4(x-1)+1]=10(0.5x)$$
$$4(x-1)+10=5x$$
$$4x-4+10=5x$$
$$4x+6=5x$$
$$x=6$$

23. Solving the equation:
$$1.2(x+5)=3.1x$$
$$10[1.2(x+5)]=10(3.1x)$$
$$12(x+5)=31x$$
$$12x+60=31x$$
$$60=19x$$
$$x=\frac{60}{19}$$

25. Solving the equation:
$$0.01(x-3)-0.02=0.05$$
$$100[0.01(x-3)-0.02]=100(0.05)$$
$$x-3-2=5$$
$$x-5=5$$
$$x=10$$

27. Solving the equation:
$$0.5(2x-1)-0.02x=0.3$$
$$100[0.5(2x-1)-0.02x]=100(0.3)$$
$$50(2x-1)-2x=30$$
$$100x-50-2x=30$$
$$98x-50=30$$
$$98x=80$$
$$x=\frac{80}{98}=\frac{40}{49}$$

29. Solving the equation:
$$\pi x+3=4\pi x$$
$$3=4\pi x-\pi x$$
$$3=3\pi x$$
$$x=\frac{3}{3\pi}=\frac{1}{\pi}$$

31. Solving for y:
$$x+y=5$$
$$y=5-x$$

33. Solving for y:
$$-4x+2y=6$$
$$2y=4x+6$$
$$y=\frac{4x+6}{2}=2x+3$$

35. Solving for y:
$$5x+4y=10$$
$$4y=10-5x$$
$$y=\frac{10-5x}{4}=\frac{5}{2}-\frac{5}{4}x$$

37. Solving for y:
$$4x+y-5=0$$
$$y=5-4x$$

39. Solving by factoring:
$$x^2-25=0$$
$$(x+5)(x-5)=0$$
$$x=-5,5$$

41. Solving by factoring:
$$x^2-7x+12=0$$
$$(x-4)(x-3)=0$$
$$x=3,4$$

43. Solving by factoring:
$$-3x^2+12=0$$
$$-3(x^2-4)=0$$
$$-3(x+2)(x-2)=0$$
$$x=-2,2$$

45. Solving by factoring:
$$6x^2-x-2=0$$
$$(2x+1)(3x-2)=0$$
$$x=-\frac{1}{2},\frac{2}{3}$$

47. Solving by factoring:

$$4x^2 + 1 = 4x$$
$$4x^2 - 4x + 1 = 0$$
$$(2x-1)^2 = 0$$
$$2x - 1 = 0$$
$$x = \frac{1}{2}$$

49. Solving by factoring:

$$2t^2 = t + 3$$
$$2t^2 - t - 3 = 0$$
$$(2t-3)(t+1) = 0$$
$$t = -1, \frac{3}{2}$$

51. Solving by completing the square:

$$x^2 + 4x = -3$$
$$x^2 + 4x + 4 = -3 + 4$$
$$(x+2)^2 = 1$$
$$x + 2 = \pm 1$$
$$x + 2 = -1, 1$$
$$x = -3, -1$$

53. Solving by completing the square:

$$x^2 - 2x = 4$$
$$x^2 - 2x + 1 = 4 + 1$$
$$(x-1)^2 = 5$$
$$x - 1 = \pm\sqrt{5}$$
$$x = 1 \pm \sqrt{5}$$

55. Solving by completing the square:

$$x^2 + x = 2$$
$$x^2 + x + \frac{1}{4} = 2 + \frac{1}{4}$$
$$\left(x + \frac{1}{2}\right)^2 = \frac{9}{4}$$
$$x + \frac{1}{2} = \pm\frac{3}{2}$$
$$x + \frac{1}{2} = -\frac{3}{2}, \frac{3}{2}$$
$$x = -2, 1$$

57. Solving by completing the square:

$$2x^2 + 8x - 1 = 0$$
$$2x^2 + 8x = 1$$
$$x^2 + 4x = \frac{1}{2}$$
$$x^2 + 4x + 4 = \frac{1}{2} + 4$$
$$(x+2)^2 = \frac{9}{2}$$
$$x + 2 = \pm\sqrt{\frac{9}{2}} \cdot \frac{\sqrt{2}}{\sqrt{2}} = \pm\frac{3\sqrt{2}}{2}$$
$$x = -2 \pm \frac{3\sqrt{2}}{2}$$

59. Using $a = 1$, $b = 2$, and $c = -1$ in the quadratic formula: $x = \dfrac{-2 \pm \sqrt{(2)^2 - 4(1)(-1)}}{2(1)} = \dfrac{-2 \pm \sqrt{8}}{2} = \dfrac{-2 \pm 2\sqrt{2}}{2} = -1 \pm \sqrt{2}$

61. Using $a = -2$, $b = 2$, and $c = 1$ in the quadratic formula: $x = \dfrac{-2 \pm \sqrt{(2)^2 - 4(-2)(1)}}{2(-2)} = \dfrac{-2 \pm \sqrt{12}}{-4} = \dfrac{-2 \pm 2\sqrt{3}}{-4} = \dfrac{1}{2} \pm \dfrac{\sqrt{3}}{2}$

63. First write the equation as $-x^2 - x + 3 = 0$. Using $a = -1$, $b = -1$, and $c = 3$ in the quadratic formula:

$$x = \dfrac{1 \pm \sqrt{(1)^2 - 4(-1)(3)}}{2(-1)} = \dfrac{1 \pm \sqrt{13}}{-2} = -\dfrac{1}{2} \pm \dfrac{\sqrt{13}}{2}$$

65. Using $a = 2$, $b = 1$, and $c = 2$ in the quadratic formula: $x = \dfrac{-1 \pm \sqrt{(1)^2 - 4(2)(2)}}{2(2)} = \dfrac{-1 \pm \sqrt{-15}}{4}$

There are no real solutions.

67. First write the equation as $-l^2 + 40l - 100 = 0$. Using $a = -1$, $b = 40$, and $c = -100$ in the quadratic formula:

$$l = \dfrac{-40 \pm \sqrt{(40)^2 - 4(-1)(-100)}}{2(-1)} = \dfrac{-40 \pm \sqrt{1200}}{-2} = \dfrac{-40 \pm 20\sqrt{3}}{-2} = 20 \pm 10\sqrt{3}$$

69. First multiply both sides of the equation by 2 to produce the equation $t^2 - 8t - 6 = 0$. Using $a = 1, b = -8$, and $c = -6$ in the quadratic formula: $t = \dfrac{8 \pm \sqrt{(-8)^2 - 4(1)(-6)}}{2(1)} = \dfrac{8 \pm \sqrt{88}}{2} = \dfrac{8 \pm 2\sqrt{22}}{2} = 4 \pm \sqrt{22}$

71. First write the equation as $-0.75x^2 - 2x + 2 = 0$. Using $a = -\dfrac{3}{4}, b = -2$, and $c = 2$ in the quadratic formula:

$$x = \dfrac{2 \pm \sqrt{(-2)^2 - 4\left(-\dfrac{3}{4}\right)(2)}}{2\left(-\dfrac{3}{4}\right)} = \dfrac{2 \pm \sqrt{10}}{-\dfrac{3}{2}} = \dfrac{-4 \pm 2\sqrt{10}}{3} = -\dfrac{4}{3} \pm \dfrac{2\sqrt{10}}{3}$$

73. Solving the equation by factoring:
$$x^2 - 4 = 0$$
$$(x+2)(x-2) = 0$$
$$x = -2, 2$$

75. Solving the equation by factoring:
$$-x^2 + 2x = 1$$
$$-x^2 + 2x - 1 = 0$$
$$-(x^2 - 2x + 1) = 0$$
$$-(x-1)^2 = 0$$
$$x - 1 = 0$$
$$x = 1$$

77. Solving the equation by factoring:
$$-2x^2 - 1 = 3x$$
$$-2x^2 - 3x - 1 = 0$$
$$2x^2 + 3x + 1 = 0$$
$$(2x+1)(x+1) = 0$$
$$x = -1, -\dfrac{1}{2}$$

79. Solving the equation by factoring:
$$x^2 - 2x = 9$$
$$x^2 - 2x + 1 = 9 + 1$$
$$(x-1)^2 = 10$$
$$x - 1 = \pm\sqrt{10}$$
$$x = 1 \pm \sqrt{10}$$

81. Solving the equation:
$$(x-1)(x+2) = 1$$
$$x^2 + x - 2 = 1$$
$$x^2 + x - 3 = 0$$

Using $a = 1, b = 1$, and $c = -3$ in the quadratic formula: $x = \dfrac{-1 \pm \sqrt{(1)^2 - 4(1)(-3)}}{2(1)} = \dfrac{-1 \pm \sqrt{13}}{2} = -\dfrac{1}{2} \pm \dfrac{\sqrt{13}}{2}$

83. Finding the discriminant: $b^2 - 4ac = (-2)^2 - 4(1)(-1) = 8 > 0$
There are two real solutions.

85. First write the equation as $x^2 + 2x + 3 = 0$. Finding the discriminant: $b^2 - 4ac = (2)^2 - 4(1)(3) = -8 < 0$
There are no real solutions.

87. Solving the equation:
$$40x - 200 = 800$$
$$40x = 1000$$
$$x = 25$$
There must be 25 DVD players sold in order to make a profit of $800.

89. Substituting $l = 30$ and $P = 96$ in the perimeter formula:
$$2l + 2w = 96$$
$$2(30) + 2w = 96$$
$$60 + 2w = 96$$
$$2w = 36$$
$$w = 18$$
The width of the frame is 18 inches.

91. Substituting $p = 12$ results in the equation:
$$0.0489t^2 - 0.7815t + 10.31 = 12$$
$$0.0489t^2 - 0.7815t - 1.69 = 0$$
Using the quadratic formula with $a = 0.0489$, $b = -0.7815$, and $c = -1.69$:
$$t = \frac{0.7815 \pm \sqrt{(-0.7815)^2 - 4(0.0489)(-1.69)}}{2(0.0489)} = \frac{0.7815 \pm \sqrt{0.9433}}{0.0978} = \frac{0.7815 \pm 0.9712}{0.0978} \approx 17.9 \ \text{(since } t \geq 0)$$
The year is $1981 + 17.9 = 1998.9$. The revenue reached \$12 million near the end of 1998.

93. First find the area: $A = \text{base} \times \text{height} = (20 - 2x)x = 20x - 2x^2$

Setting the area equal to 30 results in the equation:
$$20x - 2x^2 = 30$$
$$-2x^2 + 20x - 30 = 0$$
$$x^2 - 10x + 15 = 0$$
Using the quadratic formula with $a = 1$, $b = -10$, and $c = 15$:
$$x = \frac{10 \pm \sqrt{(-10)^2 - 4(1)(15)}}{2(1)} = \frac{10 \pm \sqrt{40}}{2} = \frac{10 \pm 2\sqrt{10}}{2} = 5 \pm \sqrt{10} \approx 8.2 \text{ or } 1.8$$
The amount to bend up is either 1.8 inches or 8.2 inches in length.

95. Substituting $l = 2.5$: $w = \frac{1}{2}(15 - 2l) = \frac{1}{2}(15 - 2(2.5)) = 5$ ft

Substituting $l = 10$: $w = \frac{1}{2}(15 - 2(10)) = \frac{1}{2}(-5) = -2.5$ ft

This value is not realistic, since $w > 0$.

97. Solving the equation for x:
$$ax + x = 5$$
$$(a + 1)x = 5$$
$$x = \frac{5}{a + 1}$$
The equation has a solution as long as $a \neq -1$.

99. Solving the equation:
$$x^2 - k = 0$$
$$x^2 = k$$
$$x = \pm\sqrt{k}$$
As long as $k > 0$ there will be two distinct real solutions.

1.6 Linear Inequalities

1. Substituting $x = 1$:

$$x + 1 < 2$$
$$1 + 1 < 2$$
$$2 < 2$$

Since this is false, $x = 1$ does not satisfy the inequality.

3. Substituting $s = 3.2$:

$$2s - 1 \le 10$$
$$2(3.2) + 1 \le 10$$
$$7.4 \le 10$$

Since this is true, $s = 3.2$ does satisfy the inequality.

5. Solving the inequality:

$$-3x + 2 \le 5x + 10$$
$$-8x \le 8$$
$$-\frac{1}{8}(-8x) \ge -\frac{1}{8}(8)$$
$$x \ge -1$$

The solution is $[-1, \infty)$.

7. Solving the inequality:

$$8s - 9 \ge 2s + 15$$
$$6s \ge 24$$
$$s \ge 4$$

The solution is $[4, \infty)$.

9. Solving the inequality:

$$2x < 3x - 10$$
$$-x < -10$$
$$-1(-x) > -1(-10)$$
$$x > 10$$

The solution is $(10, \infty)$.

11. Solving the inequality:

$$2x + 3 \ge 0$$
$$2x \ge -3$$
$$x \ge -\frac{3}{2}$$

The solution is $\left[-\frac{3}{2}, \infty\right)$.

13. Solving the inequality:

$$4x - 5 > 3$$
$$4x > 8$$
$$x > 2$$

The solution is $(2, \infty)$.

15. Solving the inequality:

$$2 - 2x \ge x - 1$$
$$-3x \ge -3$$
$$x \le 1$$

The solution is $(-\infty, 1]$.

17. Solving the inequality:

$$-4(x + 2) \ge x + 5$$
$$-4x - 8 \ge x + 5$$
$$-5x \ge 13$$
$$x \le -\frac{13}{5}$$

The solution is $\left(-\infty, -\frac{13}{5}\right]$.

19. Solving the inequality:

$$\frac{x}{3} \le \frac{2x}{3} - 1$$
$$3\left(\frac{x}{3}\right) \le 3\left(\frac{2x}{3} - 1\right)$$
$$x \le 2x - 3$$
$$-x \le -3$$
$$x \ge 3$$

The solution is $[3, \infty)$.

21. Solving the inequality:

$$\frac{1}{3}(x + 1) < x + 3$$
$$3 \cdot \frac{1}{3}(x + 1) < 3(x + 3)$$
$$x + 1 < 3x + 9$$
$$-2x < 8$$
$$x > -4$$

The solution is $(-4, \infty)$.

23. Solving the inequality:

$$\frac{1}{3}x + 2 \le \frac{3}{2}x - 1$$
$$6\left(\frac{1}{3}x + 2\right) \le 6\left(\frac{3}{2}x - 1\right)$$
$$2x + 12 \le 9x - 6$$
$$-7x \le -18$$
$$x \ge \frac{18}{7}$$

The solution is $\left[\frac{18}{7}, \infty\right)$.

25. Solving the inequality:
$$-2 \le 2x+1 \le 3$$
$$-3 \le 2x \le 2$$
$$-\frac{3}{2} \le x \le 1$$

The solution is $\left[-\frac{3}{2}, 1\right]$.

27. Solving the inequality:
$$0 < -x+5 < 4$$
$$-5 < -x < -1$$
$$5 > x > 1$$
$$1 < x < 5$$

The solution is $(1,5)$.

29. Solving the inequality:
$$0 < \frac{x+3}{2} < 3$$
$$2(0) < 2\left(\frac{x+3}{2}\right) < 2(3)$$
$$0 < x+3 < 6$$
$$-3 < x < 3$$

The solution is $(-3,3)$.

31. **a.** Finding the break-even point:
$$C(q) = R(q)$$
$$2q+10 = 4q$$
$$10 = 2q$$
$$q = 5$$

The break-even point is (5, 20).

b. Finding when the revenue exceeds the cost:
$$R(q) > C(q)$$
$$4q > 2q+10$$
$$2q > 10$$
$$q > 5$$

The revenue exceeds cost whenever $q > 5$.

33. **a.** Finding the break-even point:
$$C(q) = R(q)$$
$$10q+200 = 15q$$
$$200 = 5q$$
$$q = 40$$

The break-even point is (40, 600).

b. Finding when the revenue exceeds the cost:
$$R(q) > C(q)$$
$$15q > 10q+200$$
$$5q > 200$$
$$q > 40$$

The revenue exceeds cost whenever $q > 40$.

35. **a.** The cost is given by $C = 750+2q = 2q+750$.

b. The revenue is given by $R = 4q$.

c. Finding when the revenue exceeds the cost:
$$4q > 2q+750$$
$$2q > 750$$
$$q > 375$$

The revenue exceeds cost whenever $q > 375$.

37. Let x represent the number of minutes jogging. Solving the inequality:
$$3.2x \ge 200$$
$$32x \ge 200$$
$$x \ge 62.5$$

The jogger must jog at least 62.5 minutes to burn at least 200 calories.

39. Let x represent the score on the fifth exam. Solving the inequality:

$$\text{Average} \geq 90$$

$$\frac{94 + 86 + 84 + 97 + x}{5} \geq 90$$

$$5\left(\frac{361 + x}{5}\right) \geq 5(90)$$

$$361 + x \geq 450$$

$$x \geq 89$$

The range of scores on the fifth exam is between 89 and 100, which is the interval $[89, 100]$.

41. **a.** Let m represent the number of minutes used. The cost for plan A is: $A(m) = 4.95 + 0.07m$

  b. The cost for plan B is: $B(m) = 0.10m$

  c. Setting the two costs equal:

$$4.95 + 0.07m = 0.10m$$

$$4.95 = 0.03m$$

$$165 = m$$

$$B(165) = 0.10(165) = 16.5$$

At 165 minutes of usage, each plan will cost $16.50.

43. Solving the inequality:

$$RH(x) \geq 50$$

$$-2.58x + 280 \geq 50$$

$$-2.58x \geq -230$$

$$x \leq 89.147$$

The relative humidity is greater than or equal to 50% for the range of temperatures between 70° and 89.1°, which is the interval $[70°, 89.1°]$.

45. The inequality is equivalent to $4 \geq 0$, which is always true. The solution set is $(-\infty, \infty)$.

1.7 Equations and Inequalities Involving Absolute Value

1. Solving the equation:

$$|x + 4| = 6$$

$$x + 4 = -6, 6$$

$$x = -10, 2$$

3. Solving the equation:

$$|2x - 4| = 8$$

$$2x - 4 = -8, 8$$

$$2x = -4, 12$$

$$x = -2, 6$$

5. Solving the equation:

$$\left|2s - \frac{3}{2}\right| = 10$$

$$2s - \frac{3}{2} = -10, 10$$

$$4s - 3 = -20, 20$$

$$4s = -17, 23$$

$$s = -\frac{17}{4}, \frac{23}{4}$$

7. Solving the equation:

$$4|t + 5| = 16$$

$$|t + 5| = 4$$

$$t + 5 = -4, 4$$

$$t = -9, -1$$

9. Solving the equation:
$$2|2x+1| = 10$$
$$|2x+1| = 5$$
$$2x+1 = -5, 5$$
$$2x = -6, 4$$
$$x = -3, 2$$

11. Solving the equation:
$$|x-1| + 5 = 9$$
$$|x-1| = 4$$
$$x-1 = -4, 4$$
$$x = -3, 5$$

13. Solving the equation:
$$1 + |-2x+5| = 3$$
$$|-2x+5| = 2$$
$$-2x+5 = -2, 2$$
$$-2x = -7, -3$$
$$x = \frac{3}{2}, \frac{7}{2}$$

15. Solving the equation:
$$|x^2 - 8| = 1$$
$$x^2 - 8 = -1, 1$$
$$x^2 = 7, 9$$
$$x = \pm\sqrt{7}, \pm 3$$

17. Substituting $x = 3$:
$$|3-2| > 4$$
$$|3| > 4$$
$$3 > 4$$
False
The value does not satisfy the inequality.

19. Substituting $x = \frac{3}{2}$:
$$\left|3\left(\frac{3}{2}\right) - 2\right| \le 4$$
$$\left|\frac{9}{2} - 2\right| \le 4$$
$$\left|\frac{5}{2}\right| \le 4$$
$$\frac{5}{2} \le 4$$
True
The value satisfies the inequality.

21. Graphing the inequality:

23. Graphing the inequality:

The value satisfies the inequality.

25. Graphing the inequality:

27. Graphing the inequality:

29. Solving the inequality:
$$|2x| > 8$$
$$2x < -8 \quad \text{or} \quad 2x > 8$$
$$x < -4 \qquad x > 4$$
The solution is $(-\infty, -4) \cup (4, \infty)$.

Graphing the solution set:

31. Solving the inequality:
$$|x+3| \le 4$$
$$-4 \le x+3 \le 4$$
$$-7 \le x \le 1$$
The solution is $[-7, 1]$.

Graphing the solution set:

33. Solving the inequality:

$$|x-10| > 6$$

$$x-10 < -6 \quad \text{or} \quad x-10 > 6$$

$$x < 4 \qquad\qquad x > 16$$

The solution is $(-\infty, 4) \cup (16, \infty)$.

Graphing the solution set:

35. Solving the inequality:

$$|2s-7| > 3$$

$$2s-7 < -3 \quad \text{or} \quad 2s-7 > 3$$

$$2s < 4 \qquad\qquad 2s > 10$$

$$s < 2 \qquad\qquad s > 5$$

The solution is $(-\infty, 2) \cup (5, \infty)$.

Graphing the solution set:

37. Solving the inequality:

$$|2-3x| \le 10$$

$$-10 \le 2-3x \le 10$$

$$-12 \le -3x \le 8$$

$$4 \ge x \ge -\frac{8}{3}$$

$$-\frac{8}{3} \le x \le 4$$

The solution is $\left[-\frac{8}{3}, 4\right]$.

Graphing the solution set:

39. Solving the inequality:

$$\left|\frac{1}{2}x+6\right| \le 5$$

$$-5 \le \frac{1}{2}x+6 \le 5$$

$$-10 \le x+12 \le 10$$

$$-22 \le x \le -2$$

The solution is $[-22, -2]$.

Graphing the solution set:

41. Solving the inequality:

$$\left|\frac{x+7}{6}\right| < 5$$

$$-5 < \frac{x+7}{6} < 5$$

$$-30 < x+7 < 30$$

$$-37 < x < 23$$

The solution is $(-37, 23)$.

Graphing the solution set:

43. Solving the inequality:

$$|x-4|-2 \ge 6$$

$$|x-4| \ge 8$$

$$x-4 \le -8 \quad \text{or} \quad x-4 \ge 8$$

$$x \le -4 \qquad\qquad x \ge 12$$

The solution is $(-\infty, -4] \cup [12, \infty)$.

Graphing the solution set:

45. Solving the inequality:

$$|3x+7|-2 < 8$$

$$|3x+7| < 10$$

$$-10 < 3x+7 < 10$$

$$-17 < 3x < 3$$

$$-\frac{17}{3} < x < 1$$

The solution is $\left(-\frac{17}{3}, 1\right)$.

Graphing the solution set:

47. Solving the inequality:

$$|t-6| \ge 0$$

Always true

The solution is $(-\infty, \infty)$.

Graphing the solution set:

49. Solving the inequality:

$$|x - 4| < 0.001$$
$$-0.001 < x - 4 < 0.001$$
$$3.999 \le x \le 4.001$$

The solution is $(3.999, 4.001)$.

Graphing the solution set:

3.998 3.999 4.000 4.001 4.002

51. Writing as an absolute value equation: $|x - (-7)| = 3$, or $|x + 7| = 3$

53. Writing as an absolute value inequality: $|x - 8| < 5$

55. Writing as an absolute value inequality: $|x - (-6.5)| > 8$, or $|x + 6.5| > 8$

57. Solving the inequality:

$$|T + 10| < 20$$
$$-20 < T + 10 < 20$$
$$-30 < T < 10$$

This means the temperature is always less than 10°F but greater than –30°F.

59. If Omaha is assumed to be the origin, then all points within 30 miles north or south of the center of Omaha would be given by the inequality $|x| < 30$, where x is the distance directly north of Omaha (points due south are represented by a negative distance).

61. Let T represent the temperature. The inequality is given by: $|T - 68| \le 1.5$

63. These expressions are not the same because $|-3(x + 2)|$ will produce strictly nonnegative values for all real x, whereas $-3|x + 2|$ will produce strictly nonpositive values for all real x.

65. By definition, $|x - k| = x - k$ or $k - x$. Similarly, $|k - x| = k - x$ or $x - k$. Therefore, these are identical values.

67. The smallest value of $|x|$ is 0 when $x = 0$, so there is no value of x for which $|x| < 0$.

1.8 Other Types of Equations

1. Simplifying: $(x - 2)\left(\dfrac{3}{x - 2}\right) = 3$

3. Simplifying: $x(x + 2)\left(\dfrac{2}{x} + \dfrac{x}{x + 2}\right) = (x + 2) \cdot 2 + x \cdot x = 2x + 4 + x^2 = x^2 + 2x + 4$

5. Let $u = x^2$. Solving the equation:

$$x^4 - 49 = 0$$
$$\left(x^2\right)^2 - 49 = 0$$
$$u^2 - 49 = 0$$
$$(u + 7)(u - 7) = 0$$
$$u = 7 \quad (u \ne -7)$$
$$x^2 = 7$$
$$x = \pm\sqrt{7}$$

7. Let $u = x^2$. Solving the equation:

$$x^4 - 10x^2 = -21$$
$$\left(x^2\right)^2 - 10x^2 = -21$$
$$u^2 - 10u = -21$$
$$u^2 - 10u + 21 = 0$$
$$(u - 3)(u - 7) = 0$$
$$u = 3, 7$$
$$x^2 = 3, 7$$
$$x = \pm\sqrt{3}, \pm\sqrt{7}$$

9. Let $u = s^2$. Solving the equation:

$$6s^4 - s^2 - 2 = 0$$
$$6(s^2)^2 - s^2 - 2 = 0$$
$$6u^2 - u - 2 = 0$$
$$(2u+1)(3u-2) = 0$$
$$u = \frac{2}{3} \quad \left(u \neq -\frac{1}{2}\right)$$
$$s^2 = \frac{2}{3}$$
$$s = \pm\sqrt{\frac{2}{3}} = \pm\frac{\sqrt{6}}{3}$$

11. Let $u = x^2$. Solving the equation:

$$4x^4 - 7x^2 = 2$$
$$4(x^2)^2 - 7x^2 = 2$$
$$4u^2 - 7u = 2$$
$$4u^2 - 7u - 2 = 0$$
$$(4u+1)(u-2) = 0$$
$$u = 2 \quad \left(u \neq -\frac{1}{4}\right)$$
$$x^2 = 2$$
$$x = \pm\sqrt{2}$$

13. Let $u = x^3$. Solving the equation:

$$x^6 - 4x^3 = 5$$
$$(x^3)^2 - 4x^3 = 5$$
$$u^2 - 4u = 5$$
$$u^2 - 4u - 5 = 0$$
$$(u+1)(u-5) = 0$$
$$u = -1, 5$$
$$x^3 = -1, 5$$
$$x = -1, \sqrt[3]{5}$$

15. Let $u = t^3$. Solving the equation:

$$3t^6 + 14t^3 = -8$$
$$3(t^3)^2 + 14t^3 = -8$$
$$3u^2 + 14u = -8$$
$$3u^2 + 14u + 8 = 0$$
$$(3u+2)(u+4) = 0$$
$$u = -4, -\frac{2}{3}$$
$$t^3 = -4, -\frac{2}{3}$$
$$t = -\sqrt[3]{4}, -\sqrt[3]{\frac{2}{3}} \cdot \frac{\sqrt[3]{9}}{\sqrt[3]{9}} = -\frac{\sqrt[3]{18}}{3}$$

17. Solving the equation:

$$\frac{2}{3} + \frac{3}{5} = \frac{2}{x}$$
$$15x\left(\frac{2}{3}\right) + 15x\left(\frac{3}{5}\right) = 15x\left(\frac{2}{x}\right)$$
$$10x + 9x = 30$$
$$19x = 30$$
$$x = \frac{30}{19}$$

This value checks in the original equation.

19. Solving the equation:

$$-\frac{2}{3x} + \frac{1}{x} = \frac{1}{4}$$
$$12x\left(-\frac{2}{3x}\right) + 12x\left(\frac{1}{x}\right) = 12x\left(\frac{1}{4}\right)$$
$$-8 + 12 = 3x$$
$$4 = 3x$$
$$x = \frac{4}{3}$$

This value checks in the original equation.

21. Solving the equation:

$$\frac{1}{x^2} - \frac{3}{x} = 10$$
$$x^2\left(\frac{1}{x^2}\right) - x^2\left(\frac{3}{x}\right) = x^2(10)$$
$$1 - 3x = 10x^2$$
$$10x^2 + 3x - 1 = 0$$
$$(2x+1)(5x-1) = 0$$
$$x = -\frac{1}{2}, \frac{1}{5}$$

These values check in the original equation.

23. Solving the equation:

$$\frac{2x}{x-1} - \frac{3}{x} = 2$$
$$x(x-1)\left(\frac{2x}{x-1}\right) - x(x-1)\left(\frac{3}{x}\right) = x(x-1)(2)$$
$$x \cdot 2x - 3(x-1) = 2x(x-1)$$
$$2x^2 - 3x + 3 = 2x^2 - 2x$$
$$-3x + 3 = -2x$$
$$-x = -3$$
$$x = 3$$

This value checks in the original equation.

25. Solving the equation:

$$\frac{3}{x+1}+\frac{2}{x-3}=4$$

$$(x+1)(x-3)\left(\frac{3}{x+1}\right)+(x+1)(x-3)\left(\frac{2}{x-3}\right)=4(x+1)(x-3)$$

$$3(x-3)+2(x+1)=4\left(x^2-2x-3\right)$$

$$3x-9+2x+2=4x^2-8x-12$$

$$5x-7=4x^2-8x-12$$

$$0=4x^2-13x-5$$

$$x=\frac{13\pm\sqrt{(-13)^2-4(4)(-5)}}{2(4)}=\frac{13\pm\sqrt{249}}{8}$$

These values check in the original equation.

27. Solving the equation:

$$\frac{1}{x^2-x-6}+\frac{3}{x+2}=\frac{-4}{x-3}$$

$$\frac{1}{(x+2)(x-3)}+\frac{3}{x+2}=\frac{-4}{x-3}$$

$$(x+2)(x-3)\left(\frac{1}{(x+2)(x-3)}\right)+(x+2)(x-3)\left(\frac{3}{x+2}\right)=(x+2)(x-3)\left(\frac{-4}{x-3}\right)$$

$$1+3(x-3)=-4(x+2)$$

$$1+3x-9=-4x-8$$

$$3x-8=-4x-8$$

$$7x=0$$

$$x=0$$

This value checks in the original equation.

29. Solving the equation:

$$\frac{x}{2x^2+x-3}+\frac{1}{x-1}=\frac{3}{2x+3}$$

$$\frac{x}{(2x+3)(x-1)}+\frac{1}{x-1}=\frac{3}{2x+3}$$

$$(2x+3)(x-1)\left(\frac{x}{(2x+3)(x-1)}\right)+(2x+3)(x-1)\left(\frac{1}{x-1}\right)=(2x+3)(x-1)\left(\frac{3}{2x+3}\right)$$

$$x+(2x+3)=3(x-1)$$

$$x+2x+3=3x-3$$

$$3x+3=3x-3$$

$$3=-3$$

Since this statement is false, there is no solution to the equation.

31. Solving the equation:

$$\frac{x-3}{2x-4} + \frac{1}{x^2-4} = \frac{1}{x+2}$$

$$\frac{x-3}{2(x-2)} + \frac{1}{(x+2)(x-2)} = \frac{1}{x+2}$$

$$2(x+2)(x-2)\left(\frac{x-3}{2(x-2)}\right) + 2(x+2)(x-2)\left(\frac{1}{(x+2)(x-2)}\right) = 2(x+2)(x-2)\left(\frac{1}{x+2}\right)$$

$$(x+2)(x-3) + 2(1) = 2(x-2)(1)$$

$$x^2 - x - 6 + 2 = 2x - 4$$

$$x^2 - x - 4 = 2x - 4$$

$$x^2 - 3x = 0$$

$$x(x-3) = 0$$

$$x = 0, 3$$

These values check in the original equation.

33. Solving the equation:

$$\sqrt{x+3} = 5$$

$$\left(\sqrt{x+3}\right)^2 = (5)^2$$

$$x + 3 = 25$$

$$x = 22$$

This value checks in the original equation.

35. Solving the equation:

$$\sqrt{x^2+1} = \sqrt{17}$$

$$\left(\sqrt{x^2+1}\right)^2 = \left(\sqrt{17}\right)^2$$

$$x^2 + 1 = 17$$

$$x^2 = 16$$

$$x = \pm 4$$

These values check in the original equation.

37. Solving the equation:

$$\sqrt{x^2+6x} - 1 = 3$$

$$\sqrt{x^2+6x} = 4$$

$$\left(\sqrt{x^2+6x}\right)^2 = (4)^2$$

$$x^2 + 6x = 16$$

$$x^2 + 6x - 16 = 0$$

$$(x+8)(x-2) = 0$$

$$x = -8, 2$$

These values check in the original equation.

39. Solving the equation:

$$\sqrt{x+1} + 2 = x$$

$$\sqrt{x+1} = x - 2$$

$$\left(\sqrt{x+1}\right)^2 = (x-2)^2$$

$$x + 1 = x^2 - 4x + 4$$

$$0 = x^2 - 5x + 3$$

$$x = \frac{5 \pm \sqrt{(-5)^2 - 4(1)(3)}}{2(1)} = \frac{5 \pm \sqrt{13}}{2}$$

Only $x = \dfrac{5+\sqrt{13}}{2}$ checks in the original equation.

41. Solving the equation:
$$\sqrt{x-4}+\sqrt{x}=2$$
$$\sqrt{x-4}=2-\sqrt{x}$$
$$\left(\sqrt{x-4}\right)^2=\left(2-\sqrt{x}\right)^2$$
$$x-4=4-4\sqrt{x}+x$$
$$x-4=x+4-4\sqrt{x}$$
$$-8=-4\sqrt{x}$$
$$2=\sqrt{x}$$
$$x=4$$

This value checks in the original equation.

45. Solving the equation:
$$\sqrt[3]{x+3}=5$$
$$\left(\sqrt[3]{x+3}\right)^3=(5)^3$$
$$x+3=125$$
$$x=122$$

This value checks in the original equation.

49. Let $u=x^{1/3}$. Then the equation becomes:
$$3x^{2/3}+2x^{1/3}-1=0$$
$$3\left(x^{1/3}\right)^2+2x^{1/3}-1=0$$
$$3u^2+2u-1=0$$
$$(3u-1)(u+1)=0$$
$$u=-1,\frac{1}{3}$$
$$x^{1/3}=-1,\frac{1}{3}$$
$$x=-1,\frac{1}{27}$$

These values check in the original equation.

43. Solving the equation:
$$\sqrt{2x+3}-\sqrt{x-2}=2$$
$$\sqrt{2x+3}=2+\sqrt{x-2}$$
$$\left(\sqrt{2x+3}\right)^2=\left(2+\sqrt{x-2}\right)^2$$
$$2x+3=4+4\sqrt{x-2}+x-2$$
$$2x+3=x+2+4\sqrt{x-2}$$
$$x+1=4\sqrt{x-2}$$
$$(x+1)^2=\left(4\sqrt{x-2}\right)^2$$
$$x^2+2x+1=16(x-2)$$
$$x^2+2x+1=16x-32$$
$$x^2-14x+33=0$$
$$(x-3)(x-11)=0$$
$$x=3,11$$

These values check in the original equation.

47. Let $u=\sqrt{x}$. Then the equation becomes:
$$x-4\sqrt{x}=-3$$
$$\left(\sqrt{x}\right)^2-4\sqrt{x}=-3$$
$$u^2-4u=-3$$
$$u^2-4u+3=0$$
$$(u-1)(u-3)=0$$
$$u=1,3$$
$$\sqrt{x}=1,3$$
$$x=1,9$$

These values check in the original equation.

51. Let x represent the total rental cost. The original cost per person is $\dfrac{x}{4}$ and the new cost per person is $\dfrac{x}{4} - 10$.

Since there are now 6 people renting the van, the equation is:

$$\left(\text{cost per person}\right)\left(\text{total people}\right) = \text{total cost}$$

$$\left(\frac{x}{4} - 10\right) \cdot 6 = x$$

$$\frac{3}{2}x - 60 = x$$

$$3x - 120 = 2x$$

$$-120 = -x$$

$$x = 120$$

The rental cost of the van is $120.

53. Let t represent the time for the second pump working alone. Solving the equation:

$$\frac{1}{6} + \frac{1}{t} = \frac{1}{4}$$

$$12t \cdot \frac{1}{6} + 12t \cdot \frac{1}{t} = 12t \cdot \frac{1}{4}$$

$$2t + 12 = 3t$$

$$12 = t$$

It would take the second pump 12 hours to fill the storage tank by itself.

55. Let x be the distance along the river she should dock from the figure. Solving the equation:

$$\text{Time on river} + \text{Time in woods} = 3 \text{ hours}$$

$$\frac{\text{distance on river}}{\text{rate on river}} + \frac{\text{distance on river}}{\text{rate on river}} = 3$$

$$\frac{x}{10} + \frac{\sqrt{\left(12 - x\right)^2 + 49}}{4} = 3$$

$$\frac{x}{10} + \frac{\sqrt{144 - 24x + x^2 + 49}}{4} = 3$$

$$\frac{x}{10} + \frac{\sqrt{x^2 - 24x + 193}}{4} = 3$$

$$20\left(\frac{x}{10}\right) + 20\left(\frac{\sqrt{x^2 - 24x + 193}}{4}\right) = 20(3)$$

$$2x + 5\sqrt{x^2 - 24x + 193} = 60$$

$$5\sqrt{x^2 - 24x + 193} = 60 - 2x$$

$$25\left(x^2 - 24x + 193\right) = 3{,}600 - 240x + 4x^2$$

$$25x^2 - 600x + 4{,}825 = 3{,}600 - 240x + 4x^2$$

$$21x^2 - 360x + 1{,}225 = 0$$

$$x = \frac{360 \pm \sqrt{\left(-360\right)^2 - 4\left(21\right)\left(1{,}225\right)}}{2\left(21\right)} = \frac{360 \pm \sqrt{78{,}150}}{42} \approx 4.681, -12.462$$

She should dock 4.681 km east of the starting point.

57. The left-hand side of the equation is squared incorrectly (there should be a middle term). The correct solution is:

$$\sqrt{x+1} = 2$$
$$\left(\sqrt{x+1}\right)^2 = (2)^2$$
$$x+1 = 4$$
$$x = 3$$

This value checks in the equation.

59. A rational expression equals zero only when the numerator is zero. Here the numerator is 1 and not 0, so there are no real solutions.

Chapter 1 Review Exercises

1. The integers are: $-5, 3, 8$

2. The irrational numbers are: $\sqrt{3}$

3. The non-negative integers are: $3, 8$

4. The rational numbers that are not integers are: $1.2, -1.006, \dfrac{3}{2}$

5. Associative property of addition

6. Distributive property of multiplication over addition

7. Graphing the interval:

$\leftarrow\!\!+\!\bullet\!+\!+\!+\!+\!\circ\!+\!\rightarrow$
$-5\,-4\,-3\,-2\,-1\ 0\ 1\ 2$

8. Graphing the interval:

$\leftarrow\!\!+\!+\!+\!+\!+\!+\!\circ\!+\!\rightarrow$
$-5\,-4\,-3\,-2\,-1\ 0\ 1\ 2\ 3$

9. Graphing the interval:

$\leftarrow\!\!+\!\circ\!+\!+\!+\!+\!+\!+\!\rightarrow$
$-2\,-1\ 0\ 1\ 2\ 3\ 4\ 5$

10. Graphing the interval:

$\leftarrow\!\!+\!+\!+\!+\!+\!+\!+\!\rightarrow$
$-8\,-7\,-6\,-5\,-4\,-3\,-2\,-1$

11. The distance is given by: $|-6-4| = |-10| = 10$

12. The distance is given by: $|4.7-(-3.5)| = |8.2| = 8.2$

13. Evaluating the expression: $-|-3.7| = -3.7$

14. Evaluating the expression: $2^3 - 5(4) + 1 = 8 - 5(4) + 1 = 8 - 20 + 1 = -12 + 1 = -11$

15. Evaluating the expression: $\dfrac{6+3^2}{-2^2+1} = \dfrac{6+9}{-4+1} = \dfrac{15}{-3} = -5$

16. Evaluating the expression: $-7 + 4^2 \div 8 = -7 + 16 \div 8 = -7 + 2 = -5$

17. Simplifying the expression: $6x^{-2}y^4 = \dfrac{6y^4}{x^2}$

18. Simplifying the expression: $-\left(7x^3y^2\right)^2 = -49x^6y^4$

19. Simplifying the expression: $\dfrac{4x^3y^{-2}}{x^{-1}y} = \dfrac{4x^3x}{y^2y} = \dfrac{4x^4}{y^3}$

20. Simplifying the expression: $\dfrac{xy^4}{3^{-1}x^3y^{-2}} = \dfrac{3xy^4y^2}{x^3} = \dfrac{3y^6}{x^2}$

21. Simplifying the expression: $\left(\dfrac{16x^4y^{-2}}{4x^{-2}y}\right)^2 = \left(\dfrac{4x^4x^2}{y^2y}\right)^2 = \left(\dfrac{4x^6}{y^3}\right)^2 = \dfrac{16x^{12}}{y^6}$

22. Simplifying the expression: $\left(\dfrac{5x^{-2}y^3}{15x^3y}\right)^{-1} = \left(\dfrac{y^2}{3x^5}\right)^{-1} = \dfrac{y^{-2}}{3^{-1}x^{-5}} = \dfrac{3x^5}{y^2}$

23. Writing in scientific notation: $-4{,}670{,}000 = -4.67 \times 10^6$

24. Writing in scientific notation: $0.000317 = 3.17 \times 10^{-4}$

25. Writing in decimal form: $3.001 \times 10^4 = 30{,}010$

26. Writing in decimal form: $5.617 \times 10^{-3} = .005617$

27. Computing in scientific notation: $3.2 \times 10^5 \times 2.0 \times 10^{-3} = 3.2 \times 2.0 \times 10^{5-3} = 6.4 \times 10^2$

28. Computing in scientific notation: $\dfrac{4.8 \times 10^{-2}}{1.6 \times 10^{-1}} = \dfrac{4.8}{1.6} \times \dfrac{10^{-2}}{10^{-1}} = 3 \times 10^{-1}$

29. Computing in scientific notation: $3.2 \times 5 \times 10^{-3} = 16 \times 10^{-3} = 1.6 \times 10^{-2}$

There are 1.6×10^{-2} grams of arsenic in 3.2 liters of the solution.

30. Simplifying the expression: $\sqrt{5x} \cdot \sqrt{10x^2} = \sqrt{5x} \cdot x\sqrt{10} = x\sqrt{50x} = x\sqrt{25 \cdot 2x} = 5x\sqrt{2x}$

31. Simplifying the expression: $\sqrt{3x^2} \cdot \sqrt{15x} = x\sqrt{3x} \cdot \sqrt{15x} = x\sqrt{45x} = 3x\sqrt{5x}$

32. Simplifying the expression: $\sqrt{\dfrac{50}{36}} = \dfrac{\sqrt{50}}{\sqrt{36}} = \dfrac{\sqrt{25 \cdot 2}}{6} = \dfrac{5\sqrt{2}}{6}$

33. Simplifying the expression: $\sqrt[3]{\dfrac{-96}{125}} = \dfrac{\sqrt[3]{-8 \cdot 12}}{\sqrt[3]{125}} = \dfrac{-2\sqrt[3]{12}}{5}$

34. Simplifying the expression: $\sqrt{25x} - \sqrt{36x} + \sqrt{16} = 5\sqrt{x} - 6\sqrt{x} + 4 = -\sqrt{x} + 4$

35. Simplifying the expression: $\sqrt[3]{24} - \sqrt[3]{81} + \sqrt[3]{-64} = 2\sqrt[3]{3} - 3\sqrt[3]{3} - 4 = -\sqrt[3]{3} - 4$

36. Rationalizing the denominator: $\dfrac{5}{3-\sqrt{2}} = \dfrac{5}{3-\sqrt{2}} \cdot \dfrac{3+\sqrt{2}}{3+\sqrt{2}} = \dfrac{15+5\sqrt{2}}{(3)^2 - \left(\sqrt{2}\right)^2} = \dfrac{15+5\sqrt{2}}{9-2} = \dfrac{15+5\sqrt{2}}{7}$

37. Rationalizing the denominator: $-\dfrac{2}{1+\sqrt{3}} = -\dfrac{2}{1+\sqrt{3}} \cdot \dfrac{1-\sqrt{3}}{1-\sqrt{3}} = -\dfrac{2-2\sqrt{3}}{(1)^2 - \left(\sqrt{3}\right)^2} = -\dfrac{2-2\sqrt{3}}{1-3} = -\dfrac{2-2\sqrt{3}}{-2} = 1-\sqrt{3}$

38. Evaluating the expression: $-16^{1/2} = -\sqrt{16} = -4$

39. Evaluating the expression: $(-125)^{1/3} = \sqrt[3]{-125} = -5$

40. Evaluating the expression: $64^{3/2} = \left(\sqrt{64}\right)^3 = 8^3 = 512$

41. Evaluating the expression: $(-27)^{2/3} = \left(\sqrt[3]{-27}\right)^2 = (-3)^2 = 9$

42. Simplifying the expression: $3x^{1/3} \cdot 12x^{1/4} = 36x^{1/3+1/4} = 36x^{4/12+3/12} = 36x^{7/12}$

43. Simplifying the expression: $5x^{1/2}y^{1/2} \cdot 4x^{2/3}y = 20x^{1/2+2/3}y^{1/2+1} = 20x^{3/6+4/6}y^{1/2+2/2} = 20x^{7/6}y^{3/2}$

44. Simplifying the expression: $\dfrac{12x^{2/3}}{4x^{1/2}} = 3x^{2/3-1/2} = 3x^{4/6-3/6} = 3x^{1/6}$

45. Simplifying the expression: $\dfrac{16x^{1/3}y^{1/2}}{8x^{2/3}y^{3/2}} = 2x^{1/3-2/3}y^{1/2-3/2} = 2x^{-1/3}y^{-1} = \dfrac{2}{x^{1/3}y}$

46. Substituting $h = 50$: $\sqrt{\dfrac{h}{16}} = \sqrt{\dfrac{50}{16}} = \dfrac{\sqrt{25 \cdot 2}}{4} = \dfrac{5\sqrt{2}}{4} \approx 1.768$

It will take approximately 1.768 seconds for the object to hit the ground.

47. Performing the operations: $\left(13y^2 + 19y - 9\right) + \left(6y^3 + 5y - 3\right) = 13y^2 + 19y - 9 + 6y^3 + 5y - 3 = 6y^3 + 13y^2 + 24y - 12$

48. Performing the operations: $\left(-11z^2 - 4z - 8\right) - \left(6z^3 + 25z + 10\right) = -11z^2 - 4z - 8 - 6z^3 - 25z - 10 = -6z^3 - 11z^2 - 29z - 18$

49. Performing the operations: $\left(3t^4 - 8\right) - \left(-9t^5 + 2\right) = 3t^4 - 8 + 9t^5 - 2 = 9t^5 + 3t^4 - 10$

50. Performing the operations: $\left(17u^5 + 8u\right) + \left(-16u^4 - 21u + 6\right) = 17u^5 + 8u - 16u^4 - 21u + 6 = 17u^5 - 16u^4 - 13u + 6$

51. Performing the operations: $\left(4u + 1\right)\left(3u - 10\right) = 12u^2 - 40u + 3u - 10 = 12u^2 - 37u - 10$

52. Performing the operations: $\left(2y + 7\right)\left(2 - y\right) = 4y - 2y^2 + 14 - 7y = -2y^2 - 3y + 14$

53. Performing the operations: $\left(8z - 9\right)\left(-3z + 8\right) = -24z^2 + 64z + 27z - 72 = -24z^2 + 91z - 72$

54. Performing the operations: $\left(-3y + 5\right)\left(9 + y\right) = -27y - 3y^2 + 45 + 5y = -3y^2 - 22y + 45$

55. Performing the operations: $\left(3z + 5\right)\left(2z^2 - z + 8\right) = 6z^3 - 3z^2 + 24z + 10z^2 - 5z + 40 = 6z^3 + 7z^2 + 19z + 40$

56. Performing the operations: $\left(4t + 1\right)\left(7t^2 - 6t - 5\right) = 28t^3 - 24t^2 - 20t + 7t^2 - 6t - 5 = 28t^3 - 17t^2 - 26t - 5$

57. Finding the product: $\left(3x + 2\right)\left(3x - 2\right) = (3x)^2 - 2^2 = 9x^2 - 4$

58. Finding the product: $\left(2x + 5\right)^2 = (2x)^2 + 2(2x)(5) + (5)^2 = 4x^2 + 20x + 25$

59. Finding the product: $\left(5 - x\right)^2 = 5^2 - 2(5)(x) + x^2 = x^2 - 10x + 25$

60. Finding the product: $\left(x + \sqrt{3}\right)\left(x - \sqrt{3}\right) = x^2 - \left(\sqrt{3}\right)^2 = x^2 - 3$

61. Factoring the expression: $8z^3 + 4z^2 = 4z^2(2z+1)$

62. Factoring the expression: $125u^3 - 5u^2 = 5u^2(25u-1)$

63. Factoring the expression: $y^2 + 11y + 28 = (y+7)(y+4)$

64. Factoring the expression: $-y^2 + 2y + 15 = -(y^2 - 2y - 15) = -(y+3)(y-5)$

65. Factoring the expression: $3x^2 - 7x - 20 = (3x+5)(x-4)$

66. Factoring the expression: $2x^2 + 3x - 9 = (2x-3)(x+3)$

67. Factoring the expression: $5x^2 - 8x - 4 = (5x+2)(x-2)$

68. Factoring the expression: $-3x^2 - 10x + 8 = -(3x^2 + 10x - 8) = -(3x-2)(x+4)$

69. Factoring the expression: $9u^2 - 49 = (3u)^2 - 7^2 = (3u+7)(3u-7)$

70. Factoring the expression: $4y^2 - 25 = (2y)^2 - 5^2 = (2y+5)(2y-5)$

71. Factoring the expression: $z^3 + 8z = z(z^2+8)$

72. Factoring the expression: $4z^2 - 16 = 4(z^2-4) = 4(z+2)(z-2)$

73. Factoring the expression: $2x^2 + 4x + 2 = 2(x^2+2x+1) = 2(x+1)^2$

74. Factoring the expression: $3x^3 - 18x^2 + 27x = 3x(x^2-6x+9) = 3x(x-3)^2$

75. Factoring the expression: $4x^3 + 32 = 4(x^3+8) = 4(x^3+2^3) = 4(x+2)(x^2-2x+4)$

76. Factoring the expression: $5y^3 - 40 = 5(y^3-8) = 5(y-2)(y^2+2y+4)$

77. Simplifying the expression: $\dfrac{x^2-9}{x-3} = \dfrac{(x+3)(x-3)}{x-3} = x+3$

The expression is defined if $x \neq 3$.

78. Simplifying the expression: $\dfrac{x^2+2x-15}{x^2-25} = \dfrac{(x+5)(x-3)}{(x+5)(x-5)} = \dfrac{x-3}{x-5}$

The expression is defined if $x \neq -5, 5$.

79. Simplifying the expression: $\dfrac{x^2+2x+1}{x^2-1} \cdot \dfrac{x^2-x-2}{x+1} = \dfrac{(x+1)^2}{(x+1)(x-1)} \cdot \dfrac{(x+1)(x-2)}{x+1} = \dfrac{(x+1)(x-2)}{x-1}$

80. Simplifying the expression: $\dfrac{y^2-y-12}{y^2-9} \cdot \dfrac{y+3}{y^2-4y} = \dfrac{(y+3)(y-4)}{(y+3)(y-3)} \cdot \dfrac{y+3}{y(y-4)} = \dfrac{y+3}{y(y-3)}$

81. Simplifying the expression: $\dfrac{3x+6}{x^2-4} \div \dfrac{3x}{x^2+4x+4} = \dfrac{3x+6}{x^2-4} \cdot \dfrac{x^2+4x+4}{3x} = \dfrac{3(x+2)}{(x+2)(x-2)} \cdot \dfrac{(x+2)^2}{3x} = \dfrac{(x+2)^2}{x(x-2)}$

82. Simplifying the expression: $\dfrac{4x+12}{x^2-9} \div \dfrac{x^2+1}{x+3} = \dfrac{4(x+3)}{(x+3)(x-3)} \cdot \dfrac{x+3}{x^2+1} = \dfrac{4(x+3)}{(x-3)(x^2+1)}$

83. Simplifying the expression: $\dfrac{1}{x+1} + \dfrac{4}{x-3} = \dfrac{1}{x+1} \cdot \dfrac{x-3}{x-3} + \dfrac{4}{x-3} \cdot \dfrac{x+1}{x+1} = \dfrac{x-3}{(x+1)(x-3)} + \dfrac{4x+4}{(x+1)(x-3)} = \dfrac{5x+1}{(x+1)(x-3)}$

84. Simplifying the expression:

$\dfrac{3}{x-4} - \dfrac{2}{x^2-x-12} = \dfrac{3}{x-4} - \dfrac{2}{(x+3)(x-4)} = \dfrac{3}{x-4} \cdot \dfrac{x+3}{x+3} - \dfrac{2}{(x+3)(x-4)} = \dfrac{3x+9-2}{(x+3)(x-4)} = \dfrac{3x+7}{(x+3)(x-4)}$

85. Simplifying the expression:

$$\frac{2x}{x-3}+\frac{1}{x+3}-2x^2-9=\frac{2x}{x-3}\cdot\frac{x+3}{x+3}+\frac{1}{x+3}\cdot\frac{x-3}{x-3}-\left(2x^2+9\right)\cdot\frac{(x+3)(x-3)}{(x+3)(x-3)}$$

$$=\frac{2x^2+6x}{(x+3)(x-3)}+\frac{x-3}{(x+3)(x-3)}-\frac{\left(2x^2+9\right)\left(x^2-9\right)}{(x+3)(x-3)}$$

$$=\frac{2x^2+6x+x-3-\left(2x^4-18x^2+9x^2-81\right)}{(x+3)(x-3)}$$

$$=\frac{2x^2+6x+x-3-2x^4+18x^2-9x^2+81}{(x+3)(x-3)}$$

$$=\frac{-2x^4+11x^2+7x+78}{(x+3)(x-3)}$$

86. Simplifying the expression:

$$\frac{2x+1}{x^2+3x+2}-\frac{3x-1}{2x^2+3x-2}=\frac{2x+1}{(x+2)(x+1)}-\frac{3x-1}{(2x-1)(x+2)}$$

$$=\frac{(2x+1)(2x-1)-(3x-1)(x+1)}{(2x-1)(x+2)(x+1)}$$

$$=\frac{4x^2-1-\left(3x^2+2x-1\right)}{(2x-1)(x+2)(x+1)}$$

$$=\frac{4x^2-1-3x^2-2x+1}{(2x-1)(x+2)(x+1)}$$

$$=\frac{x^2-2x}{(2x-1)(x+2)(x+1)}$$

$$=\frac{x(x-2)}{(2x-1)(x+2)(x+1)}$$

87. Simplifying the expression: $\dfrac{\dfrac{a^2-b^2}{ab}}{\dfrac{a-b}{b}}=\dfrac{a^2-b^2}{ab}\cdot\dfrac{b}{a-b}=\dfrac{(a+b)(a-b)}{ab}\cdot\dfrac{b}{a-b}=\dfrac{a+b}{a}$

88. Simplifying the expression:

$$\frac{\dfrac{3}{x-2}-\dfrac{1}{x+1}}{\dfrac{2}{x-1}+\dfrac{3}{x+1}}=\frac{(x-2)(x+1)(x-1)\left(\dfrac{3}{x-2}-\dfrac{1}{x+1}\right)}{(x-2)(x+1)(x-1)\left(\dfrac{2}{x-1}+\dfrac{3}{x+1}\right)}$$

$$=\frac{3(x+1)(x-1)-(x-2)(x-1)}{2(x-2)(x+1)+3(x-2)(x-1)}$$

$$=\frac{3\left(x^2-1\right)-\left(x^2-3x+2\right)}{2\left(x^2-x-2\right)+3\left(x^2-3x+2\right)}$$

$$=\frac{3x^2-3-x^2+3x-2}{2x^2-2x-4+3x^2-9x+6}$$

$$=\frac{2x^2+3x-5}{5x^2-11x+2}$$

89. Solving the equation:

$$3(x+4) - 2(2x+1) = 13$$
$$3x + 12 - 4x - 2 = 13$$
$$-x + 10 = 13$$
$$-x = 3$$
$$x = -3$$

90. Solving the equation:

$$\frac{3x-1}{5} + 1 = \frac{1}{2}$$
$$10\left(\frac{3x-1}{5} + 1\right) = 10\left(\frac{1}{2}\right)$$
$$2(3x-1) + 10 = 5$$
$$6x - 2 + 10 = 5$$
$$6x + 8 = 5$$
$$6x = -3$$
$$x = -\frac{1}{2}$$

91. Solving the equation:

$$0.02(x+4) - 0.1(x-2) = 0.2$$
$$100\big(0.02(x+4) - 0.1(x-2)\big) = 100(0.2)$$
$$2(x+4) - 10(x-2) = 20$$
$$2x + 8 - 10x + 20 = 20$$
$$-8x + 28 = 20$$
$$-8x = -8$$
$$x = 1$$

92. Solving the equation for y:

$$3x + y = 5$$
$$y = -3x + 5$$

93. Solving the equation for y:

$$2(x-1) = y - 7$$
$$2x - 2 = y - 7$$
$$y = 2x + 5$$

94. Solving by factoring:

$$x^2 - 9 = 0$$
$$(x+3)(x-3) = 0$$
$$x = -3, 3$$

95. Solving by factoring:

$$2x^2 - 8 = 0$$
$$2(x^2 - 4) = 0$$
$$2(x+2)(x-2) = 0$$
$$x = -2, 2$$

96. Solving by factoring:

$$x^2 - 9x + 20 = 0$$
$$(x-4)(x-5) = 0$$
$$x = 4, 5$$

97. Solving by factoring:

$$x^2 + x - 12 = 0$$
$$(x+4)(x-3) = 0$$
$$x = -4, 3$$

98. Solving by factoring:

$$6x^2 - x - 12 = 0$$
$$(2x-3)(3x+4) = 0$$
$$x = -\frac{4}{3}, \frac{3}{2}$$

99. Solving by factoring:

$$-6x^2 - 5x + 4 = 0$$
$$-(6x^2 + 5x - 4) = 0$$
$$-(2x-1)(3x+4) = 0$$
$$x = -\frac{4}{3}, \frac{1}{2}$$

100. Solving by completing the square:
$$x^2 - 4x - 2 = 0$$
$$x^2 - 4x = 2$$
$$x^2 - 4x + 4 = 2 + 4$$
$$(x-2)^2 = 6$$
$$x - 2 = \pm\sqrt{6}$$
$$x = 2 \pm \sqrt{6}$$

101. Solving by completing the square:
$$-x^2 - 2x = -5$$
$$x^2 + 2x = 5$$
$$x^2 + 2x + 1 = 5 + 1$$
$$(x+1)^2 = 6$$
$$x + 1 = \pm\sqrt{6}$$
$$x = -1 \pm \sqrt{6}$$

102. Solving by completing the square:
$$x^2 + 3x - 7 = 0$$
$$x^2 + 3x = 7$$
$$x^2 + 3x + \frac{9}{4} = 7 + \frac{9}{4}$$
$$\left(x + \frac{3}{2}\right)^2 = \frac{37}{4}$$
$$x + \frac{3}{2} = \pm\frac{\sqrt{37}}{2}$$
$$x = -\frac{3}{2} \pm \frac{\sqrt{37}}{2}$$

103. Solving by completing the square:
$$-2x^2 + 8x = 1$$
$$x^2 - 4x = -\frac{1}{2}$$
$$x^2 - 4x + 4 = -\frac{1}{2} + 4$$
$$(x-2)^2 = \frac{7}{2}$$
$$x - 2 = \pm\sqrt{\frac{7}{2} \cdot \frac{\sqrt{2}}{\sqrt{2}}} = \pm\frac{\sqrt{14}}{2}$$
$$x = 2 \pm \frac{\sqrt{14}}{2}$$

104. Let $a = -3, b = -1,$ and $c = 3$ in the quadratic formula: $x = \dfrac{1 \pm \sqrt{(-1)^2 - 4(-3)(3)}}{2(-3)} = \dfrac{1 \pm \sqrt{37}}{-6} = \dfrac{-1 \pm \sqrt{37}}{6}$

105. Let $a = -1, b = 2,$ and $c = 2$ in the quadratic formula: $x = \dfrac{-2 \pm \sqrt{(2)^2 - 4(-1)(2)}}{2(-1)} = \dfrac{-2 \pm \sqrt{12}}{-2} = \dfrac{-2 \pm 2\sqrt{3}}{-2} = 1 \pm \sqrt{3}$

106. Let $a = -3, b = -2,$ and $c = 4$ in the quadratic formula: $t = \dfrac{2 \pm \sqrt{(-2)^2 - 4(-3)(4)}}{2(-3)} = \dfrac{2 \pm \sqrt{52}}{-6} = \dfrac{2 \pm 2\sqrt{13}}{-6} = \dfrac{-1 \pm \sqrt{13}}{3}$

107. First convert the equation to standard form without fractions:
$$\frac{4}{3}x^2 + x = 2$$
$$\frac{4}{3}x^2 + x - 2 = 0$$
$$4x^2 + 3x - 6 = 0$$

Let $a = 4, b = 3,$ and $c = -6$ in the quadratic formula: $x = \dfrac{-3 \pm \sqrt{(3)^2 - 4(4)(-6)}}{2(4)} = \dfrac{-3 \pm \sqrt{105}}{8}$

108. First convert the equation to standard form without fractions:
$$-s^2 - \sqrt{2}\,s = -\frac{1}{2}$$
$$-s^2 - \sqrt{2}\,s + \frac{1}{2} = 0$$
$$2s^2 + 2\sqrt{2}\,s - 1 = 0$$

Let $a = 2, b = 2\sqrt{2}$, and $c = -1$ in the quadratic formula:
$$x = \frac{-2\sqrt{2} \pm \sqrt{(2\sqrt{2})^2 - 4(2)(-1)}}{2(2)} = \frac{-2\sqrt{2} \pm \sqrt{16}}{4} = \frac{-2\sqrt{2} \pm 4}{4} = \frac{-\sqrt{2} \pm 2}{2}$$

109. First convert the equation to standard form:

$$-(x+1)(x-4) = -6$$
$$-x^2 + 3x + 4 = -6$$
$$-x^2 + 3x + 10 = 0$$

Let $a = -1$, $b = 3$, and $c = 10$ in the quadratic formula: $x = \dfrac{-3 \pm \sqrt{(3)^2 - 4(-1)(10)}}{2(-1)} = \dfrac{-3 \pm \sqrt{49}}{-2} = \dfrac{-3 \pm 7}{-2} = -2, 5$

110. Substituting $t = 4$: $s(4) = 0.1525(4)^2 + 0.3055(4) + 18.66 = 22.322$

There will be $22.322 million in sales in the year 2012.

111. **a.** Finding when the function value is equal to 2:

$$-0.0055t^2 + 0.116t + 2.90 = 2$$
$$-0.0055t^2 + 0.116t + 0.90 = 0$$
$$0.0055t^2 - 0.116t - 0.90 = 0$$

Using the quadratic formula with $a = 0.0055$, $b = -0.116$, and $c = -0.90$:

$$t = \frac{0.116 \pm \sqrt{(-0.116)^2 - 4(0.0055)(-0.90)}}{2(0.0055)} = \frac{0.116 \pm \sqrt{0.033256}}{0.011} \approx 27.1, -6.0$$

Using $t \approx 27$ (since t cannot be negative), the year the expenditure was 2% of the total expenses was $1980 + 27 = 2007$.

b. No. Since it is a quadratic function, the graph is a parabola pointing downward, so eventually $f(t)$ will become negative, which is impossible.

112. Solving the inequality:

$$-7x + 3 > 5x - 2$$
$$-12x + 3 > -2$$
$$-12x > -5$$
$$x < \frac{5}{12}$$

The solution is $\left(-\infty, \dfrac{5}{12}\right)$.

113. Solving the inequality:

$$5x - 2 \le 3x + 7$$
$$2x - 2 \le 7$$
$$2x \le 9$$
$$x \le \frac{9}{2}$$

The solution is $\left(-\infty, \dfrac{9}{2}\right]$.

114. Solving the inequality:

$$\frac{1}{3}x - 6 \ge 4x - 1$$
$$x - 18 \ge 12x - 3$$
$$-11x \ge 15$$
$$x \le -\frac{15}{11}$$

The solution is $\left(-\infty, -\dfrac{15}{11}\right]$.

115. Solving the inequality:

$$x - 4 \le \frac{2}{5}x$$
$$5x - 20 \le 2x$$
$$3x \le 20$$
$$x \le \frac{20}{3}$$

The solution is $\left(-\infty, \dfrac{20}{3}\right]$.

116. Solving the inequality:

$$4 \le \frac{2x+2}{3} \le 7$$
$$12 \le 2x + 2 \le 21$$
$$10 \le 2x \le 19$$
$$5 \le x \le \frac{19}{2}$$

The solution is $\left[5, \dfrac{19}{2}\right]$.

117. Solving the inequality:

$$-1 \le \frac{x-4}{3} \le 4$$
$$-3 \le x - 4 \le 12$$
$$1 \le x \le 16$$

The solution is $[1, 16]$.

118. Solving the equation:
$$|x-5| = 6$$
$$x - 5 = -6, 6$$
$$x = -1, 11$$

119. Solving the equation:
$$|x+6| = 7$$
$$x + 6 = -7, 7$$
$$x = -13, 1$$

120. Solving the equation:
$$\left|2s - \frac{1}{2}\right| = 8$$
$$2s - \frac{1}{2} = -8, 8$$
$$4s - 1 = -16, 16$$
$$4s = -15, 17$$
$$s = -\frac{15}{4}, \frac{17}{4}$$

121. Solving the equation:
$$\left|4s + \frac{3}{2}\right| = 10$$
$$4s + \frac{3}{2} = -10, 10$$
$$8s + 3 = -20, 20$$
$$8s = -23, 17$$
$$s = -\frac{23}{8}, \frac{17}{8}$$

122. Solving the equation:
$$1 + 3|2x - 5| = 4$$
$$3|2x - 5| = 3$$
$$|2x - 5| = 1$$
$$2x - 5 = -1, 1$$
$$2x = 4, 6$$
$$x = 2, 3$$

123. Solving the equation:
$$-3 + 2|x - 4| = 7$$
$$2|x - 4| = 10$$
$$|x - 4| = 5$$
$$x - 4 = -5, 5$$
$$x = -1, 9$$

124. Solving the inequality:
$$|3x + 10| > 5$$
$$3x + 10 < -5 \quad \text{or} \quad 3x + 10 > 5$$
$$3x < -15 \qquad\qquad 3x > -5$$
$$x < -5 \qquad\qquad x > -\frac{5}{3}$$

The solution is $\left(-\infty, -5\right) \cup \left(-\frac{5}{3}, \infty\right)$.

Graphing the solution set:

125. Solving the inequality:
$$|x + 6| < 7$$
$$-7 < x + 6 < 7$$
$$-13 < x < 1$$

The solution is $\left(-13, 1\right)$.

Graphing the solution set:

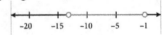

126. Solving the inequality:
$$\left|\frac{1}{2}x + 6\right| \le 5$$
$$-5 \le \frac{1}{2}x + 6 \le 5$$
$$-10 \le x + 12 \le 10$$
$$-22 \le x \le -2$$

The solution is $\left[-22, -2\right]$.

Graphing the solution set:

127. Solving the inequality:
$$\left|\frac{2x + 1}{5}\right| \le 1$$
$$-1 \le \frac{2x + 1}{5} \le 1$$
$$-5 \le 2x + 1 \le 5$$
$$-6 \le 2x \le 4$$
$$-3 \le x \le 2$$

The solution is $\left[-3, 2\right]$.

Graphing the solution set:

128. Solving the inequality:

$$3\left|\frac{3}{2}x+1\right| < 9$$

$$\left|\frac{3}{2}x+1\right| < 3$$

$$-3 < \frac{3}{2}x+1 < 3$$

$$-6 < 3x+2 < 6$$

$$-8 < 3x < 4$$

$$-\frac{8}{3} < x < \frac{4}{3}$$

The solution is $\left(-\frac{8}{3},\frac{4}{3}\right)$.

Graphing the solution set:

129. Solving the inequality:

$$|-2x-7|+4 \le 8$$

$$|-2x-7| \le 4$$

$$-4 \le -2x-7 \le 4$$

$$3 \le -2x \le 11$$

$$-\frac{3}{2} \ge x \ge -\frac{11}{2}$$

$$-\frac{11}{2} \le x \le -\frac{3}{2}$$

The solution is $\left[-\frac{11}{2},-\frac{3}{2}\right]$.

Graphing the solution set:

130. Let $u = x^2$. Solving the equation:

$$x^4 - 11x^2 + 24 = 0$$

$$\left(x^2\right)^2 - 11x^2 + 24 = 0$$

$$u^2 - 11u + 24 = 0$$

$$(u-3)(u-8) = 0$$

$$u = 3, 8$$

$$x^2 = 3, 8$$

$$x = \pm\sqrt{3}, \pm\sqrt{8} = \pm 2\sqrt{2}$$

131. Let $u = x^3$. Solving the equation:

$$x^6 - 4x^3 = 21$$

$$\left(x^3\right)^2 - 4x^3 = 21$$

$$u^2 - 4u = 21$$

$$u^2 - 4u - 21 = 0$$

$$(u+3)(u-7) = 0$$

$$u = -3, 7$$

$$x^3 = -3, 7$$

$$x = -\sqrt[3]{3}, \sqrt[3]{7}$$

132. Let $u = x^2$. Solving the equation:

$$-3x^4 + 11x^2 = -4$$

$$-3\left(x^2\right)^2 + 11x^2 = -4$$

$$-3u^2 + 11u = -4$$

$$-3u^2 + 11u + 4 = 0$$

$$3u^2 - 11u - 4 = 0$$

$$(3u+1)(u-4) = 0$$

$$u = -\frac{1}{3}, 4$$

$$x^2 = 4 \quad \left(x^2 \ne -\frac{1}{3}\right)$$

$$x = \pm 2$$

133. Solving the equation:

$$6x^2 - 7x = 3$$

$$6x^2 - 7x - 3 = 0$$

$$(2x-3)(3x+1) = 0$$

$$x = -\frac{1}{3}, \frac{3}{2}$$

134. Solving the equation:

$$\frac{3x}{x+1}+\frac{1}{x}=\frac{5}{2}$$

$$2x(x+1)\left(\frac{3x}{x+1}\right)+2x(x+1)\left(\frac{1}{x}\right)=2x(x+1)\left(\frac{5}{2}\right)$$

$$2x(3x)+2(x+1)(1)=x(x+1)(5)$$

$$6x^2+2x+2=5x^2+5x$$

$$x^2-3x+2=0$$

$$(x-1)(x-2)=0$$

$$x=1,2$$

Both values check in the original equation.

135. Solving the equation:

$$\frac{5}{x+2}+x=-8$$

$$(x+2)\left(\frac{5}{x+2}\right)+(x+2)(x)=(x+2)(-8)$$

$$5+x^2+2x=-8x-16$$

$$x^2+10x+21=0$$

$$(x+7)(x+3)=0$$

$$x=-7,-3$$

Both values check in the original equation.

136. Solving the equation:

$$\frac{1}{x^2+2x-3}+\frac{4}{x+3}=1$$

$$\frac{1}{(x+3)(x-1)}+\frac{4}{x+3}=1$$

$$(x+3)(x-1)\left(\frac{1}{(x+3)(x-1)}\right)+(x+3)(x-1)\left(\frac{4}{x+3}\right)=(x+3)(x-1)(1)$$

$$1+4(x-1)=(x+3)(x-1)$$

$$4x-3=x^2+2x-3$$

$$0=x^2-2x$$

$$x(x-2)=0$$

$$x=0,2$$

Both values check in the original equation.

137. Solving the equation:

$$\frac{2}{x^2+3x-4}+\frac{1}{x-1}=-\frac{6}{x+4}$$

$$\frac{2}{(x+4)(x-1)}+\frac{1}{x-1}=-\frac{6}{x+4}$$

$$(x+4)(x-1)\left(\frac{2}{(x+4)(x-1)}\right)+(x+4)(x-1)\left(\frac{1}{x-1}\right)=(x+4)(x-1)\left(-\frac{6}{x+4}\right)$$

$$2+(x+4)=-6(x-1)$$

$$x+6=-6x+6$$

$$7x=0$$

$$x=0$$

This value checks in the original equation.

138. Solving the equation:

$$\sqrt{2x+1} - x = -1$$
$$\sqrt{2x+1} = x-1$$
$$\left(\sqrt{2x+1}\right)^2 = (x-1)^2$$
$$2x+1 = x^2 - 2x + 1$$
$$0 = x^2 - 4x$$
$$x(x-4) = 0$$
$$x = 0,4$$

Only $x = 4$ checks in the original equation.

140. Solving the equation:

$$\sqrt{3x-5} - \sqrt{x-3} = 2$$
$$\sqrt{3x-5} = 2 - \sqrt{x-3}$$
$$\left(\sqrt{3x-5}\right)^2 = \left(2 - \sqrt{x-3}\right)^2$$
$$3x-5 = 4 - 4\sqrt{x-3} + (x-3)$$
$$3x-5 = x+1 - 4\sqrt{x-3}$$
$$2x-6 = 4\sqrt{x-3}$$
$$(2x-6)^2 = \left(4\sqrt{x-3}\right)^2$$
$$4x^2 - 24x + 36 = 16(x-3)$$
$$4x^2 - 24x + 36 = 16x - 48$$
$$4x^2 - 40x + 84 = 0$$
$$x^2 - 10x + 21 = 0$$
$$(x-3)(x-7) = 0$$
$$x = 3,7$$

Both values check in the original equation.

139. Solving the equation:

$$\sqrt{3x+4} + 2 = x$$
$$\sqrt{3x+4} = x-2$$
$$\left(\sqrt{3x+4}\right)^2 = (x-2)^2$$
$$3x+4 = x^2 - 4x + 4$$
$$0 = x^2 - 7x$$
$$x(x-7) = 0$$
$$x = 0,7$$

Only $x = 7$ checks in the original equation.

141. Solving the equation:

$$\sqrt{2x+3} + \sqrt{x+6} = 6$$
$$\sqrt{2x+3} = 6 - \sqrt{x+6}$$
$$\left(\sqrt{2x+3}\right)^2 = \left(6 - \sqrt{x+6}\right)^2$$
$$2x+3 = 36 - 12\sqrt{x+6} + (x+6)$$
$$2x+3 = x+42 - 12\sqrt{x+6}$$
$$x-39 = -12\sqrt{x+6}$$
$$(x-39)^2 = \left(-12\sqrt{x+6}\right)^2$$
$$x^2 - 78x + 1521 = 144(x+6)$$
$$x^2 - 78x + 1521 = 144x + 864$$
$$x^2 - 222x + 657 = 0$$
$$(x-219)(x-3) = 0$$
$$x = 3,219$$

Only $x = 3$ checks in the original equation.

Chapter 1 Test

1. The rational numbers are: $-1, 1.55, 41$

2. Distributive property of multiplication over addition.

3. Graphing the interval:

4. Finding the distance: $|4.6 - (-5.7)| = |10.3| = 10.3$

5. Evaluating the expression: $\dfrac{2^3 - 6 \cdot 4 - 2}{-3^2 - 5} = \dfrac{8 - 6 \cdot 4 - 2}{-9 - 5} = \dfrac{8 - 24 - 2}{-14} = \dfrac{-18}{-14} = \dfrac{9}{7}$

6. Substituting $x = -2$: $-3x^2 + 6x - 1 = -3(-2)^2 + 6(-2) - 1 = -3(4) + 6(-2) - 1 = -12 - 12 - 1 = -25$

7. Writing in scientific notation: $8{,}903{,}000 = 8.903 \times 10^6$

8. Simplifying the expression: $-\left(6x^2y^5\right)^2 = -\left(36x^4y^{10}\right) = -36x^4y^{10}$

9. Simplifying the expression: $\left(\dfrac{36x^5y^{-1}}{9x^{-4}y^3}\right)^3 = \left(\dfrac{4x^5x^4}{yy^3}\right)^3 = \left(\dfrac{4x^9}{y^4}\right)^3 = \dfrac{64x^{27}}{y^{12}}$

10. Simplifying the expression: $\sqrt{6x}\sqrt{8x^2} = \sqrt{6x}\sqrt{4 \cdot 2x^2} = \sqrt{6x} \cdot 2x\sqrt{2} = 2x\sqrt{12x} = 2x \cdot 2\sqrt{3x} = 4x\sqrt{3x}$

11. Simplifying the expression: $-5x^{1/3} \cdot 6x^{1/5} = -30x^{1/3+1/5} = -30x^{5/15+3/15} = -30x^{8/15}$

12. Simplifying the expression: $\dfrac{45x^{2/3}y^{-1/2}}{5x^{1/3}y^{5/2}} = 9x^{2/3-1/3}y^{-1/2-5/2} = 9x^{1/3}y^{-3} = \dfrac{9x^{1/3}}{y^3}$

13. Simplifying the expression: $\sqrt[3]{54} - \sqrt[3]{16} = \sqrt[3]{27 \cdot 2} - \sqrt[3]{8 \cdot 2} = 3\sqrt[3]{2} - 2\sqrt[3]{2} = \sqrt[3]{2}$

14. Simplifying the expression: $(-125)^{2/3} = \left(\sqrt[3]{-125}\right)^2 = (-5)^2 = 25$

15. Rationalizing the denominator: $\dfrac{7}{1+\sqrt{5}} = \dfrac{7}{1+\sqrt{5}} \cdot \dfrac{1-\sqrt{5}}{1-\sqrt{5}} = \dfrac{7\left(1-\sqrt{5}\right)}{1-\left(\sqrt{5}\right)^2} = \dfrac{7\left(1-\sqrt{5}\right)}{1-5} = \dfrac{7\left(1-\sqrt{5}\right)}{-4} = \dfrac{-7+7\sqrt{5}}{4}$

16. Factoring the expression: $25 - 49y^2 = (5+7y)(5-7y)$

17. Factoring the expression: $4x^2 + 20x + 25 = (2x+5)^2$

18. Factoring the expression: $6x^2 - 7x - 5 = (3x-5)(2x+1)$

19. Factoring the expression: $4x^3 - 9x = x\left(4x^2 - 9\right) = x(2x+3)(2x-3)$

20. Factoring the expression: $3x^2 + 8x - 35 = (3x-7)(x+5)$

21. Factoring the expression: $2x^3 + 16 = 2\left(x^3 + 8\right) = 2\left(x^3 + 2^3\right) = 2(x+2)\left(x^2 - 2x + 4\right)$

22. Simplifying the expression: $\dfrac{2x+4}{x^2-9} \cdot \dfrac{2x^2-5x-3}{x^2-4} = \dfrac{2(x+2)}{(x+3)(x-3)} \cdot \dfrac{(2x+1)(x-3)}{(x+2)(x-2)} = \dfrac{2(2x+1)}{(x+3)(x-2)}$

23. Simplifying the expression:

$$\dfrac{5x+1}{x^2+4x+4} \div \dfrac{5x^2-9x-2}{x^2+x-2} = \dfrac{5x+1}{x^2+4x+4} \cdot \dfrac{x^2+x-2}{5x^2-9x-2} = \dfrac{5x+1}{(x+2)^2} \cdot \dfrac{(x+2)(x-1)}{(5x+1)(x-2)} = \dfrac{x-1}{(x+2)(x-2)}$$

24. Simplifying the expression:

$$\dfrac{5}{x^2-4} - \dfrac{7}{x+2} = \dfrac{5}{(x+2)(x-2)} - \dfrac{7}{x+2}$$

$$= \dfrac{5}{(x+2)(x-2)} - \dfrac{7(x-2)}{(x+2)(x-2)}$$

$$= \dfrac{5-7(x-2)}{(x+2)(x-2)}$$

$$= \dfrac{5-7x+14}{(x+2)(x-2)}$$

$$= \dfrac{19-7x}{(x+2)(x-2)}$$

25. Simplifying the expression:

$$\dfrac{3x-1}{2x^2-x-1} - \dfrac{1}{x^2+2x-3} = \dfrac{3x-1}{(2x+1)(x-1)} - \dfrac{1}{(x+3)(x-1)}$$

$$= \dfrac{(3x-1)(x+3)}{(2x+1)(x-1)(x+3)} - \dfrac{1(2x+1)}{(2x+1)(x-1)(x+3)}$$

$$= \dfrac{3x^2+9x-x-3-2x-1}{(2x+1)(x-1)(x+3)}$$

$$= \dfrac{3x^2+6x-4}{(2x+1)(x-1)(x+3)}$$

26. Simplifying the expression: $\dfrac{\dfrac{5}{x-2}+\dfrac{3}{x}}{\dfrac{1}{x}-\dfrac{4}{x-2}} = \dfrac{\left(\dfrac{5}{x-2}+\dfrac{3}{x}\right)x(x-2)}{\left(\dfrac{1}{x}-\dfrac{4}{x-2}\right)x(x-2)} = \dfrac{5x+3(x-2)}{(x-2)-4x} = \dfrac{5x+3x-6}{-3x-2} = \dfrac{8x-6}{-3x-2} = \dfrac{6-8x}{3x+2}$

27. Solving the equation:

$$\frac{2x+1}{2}-\frac{3x-2}{5}=2$$

$$10\left(\frac{2x+1}{2}\right)-10\left(\frac{3x-2}{5}\right)=10(2)$$

$$5(2x+1)-2(3x-2)=20$$

$$10x+5-6x+4=20$$

$$4x+9=20$$

$$4x=11$$

$$x=\frac{11}{4}$$

This value checks in the original equation.

28. Solving the inequality:

$$-2\le\frac{5x-1}{2}<4$$

$$-4\le5x-1<8$$

$$-3\le5x<9$$

$$-\frac{3}{5}\le x<\frac{9}{5}$$

The solution is $\left[-\dfrac{3}{5},\dfrac{9}{5}\right)$.

29. Solving the equation:

$$\left|6x+\frac{4}{3}\right|=5$$

$$6x+\frac{4}{3}=-5,5$$

$$18x+4=-15,15$$

$$18x=-19,11$$

$$x=-\frac{19}{18},\frac{11}{18}$$

30. Solving the equation:

$$|4x-7|-3=6$$

$$|4x-7|=9$$

$$4x-7=-9,9$$

$$4x=-2,16$$

$$x=-\frac{1}{2},4$$

31. Solving by factoring:
$$x^2-5x-6=0$$
$$(x+1)(x-6)=0$$
$$x=-1,6$$

32. Solving by completing the square:
$$2x^2-4x-3=0$$
$$2x^2-4x=3$$
$$x^2-2x=\frac{3}{2}$$
$$x^2-2x+1=\frac{3}{2}+1$$
$$(x-1)^2=\frac{5}{2}$$
$$x-1=\pm\sqrt{\frac{5}{2}}\cdot\frac{\sqrt{2}}{\sqrt{2}}=\pm\frac{\sqrt{10}}{2}$$
$$x=1\pm\frac{\sqrt{10}}{2}$$

33. Let $a=3, b=1,$ and $c=-1$ in the quadratic formula: $x=\dfrac{-1\pm\sqrt{(1)^2-4(3)(-1)}}{2(3)}=\dfrac{-1\pm\sqrt{13}}{6}$

34. Let $a=-2, b=2,$ and $c=3$ in the quadratic formula: $x=\dfrac{-2\pm\sqrt{(2)^2-4(-2)(3)}}{2(-2)}=\dfrac{-2\pm\sqrt{28}}{-4}=\dfrac{-2\pm2\sqrt{7}}{-4}=\dfrac{1\pm\sqrt{7}}{2}$

35. Solving by factoring:
$$3x^2 - x - 4 = 0$$
$$(3x - 4)(x + 1) = 0$$
$$x = -1, \frac{4}{3}$$

36. Let $a = 2$, $b = 2$, and $c = -5$ in the quadratic formula: $x = \dfrac{-2 \pm \sqrt{(2)^2 - 4(2)(-5)}}{2(2)} = \dfrac{-2 \pm \sqrt{44}}{4} = \dfrac{-2 \pm 2\sqrt{11}}{4} = \dfrac{-1 \pm \sqrt{11}}{2}$

37. Solving the inequality:
$$2|2x - 5| \geq 6$$
$$|2x - 5| \geq 3$$
$$2x - 5 \leq -3 \quad \text{or} \quad 2x - 5 \geq 3$$
$$2x \leq 2 \qquad\qquad 2x \geq 8$$
$$x \leq 1 \qquad\qquad x \geq 4$$

The solution is $(-\infty, 1] \cup [4, \infty)$.

38. Solving the inequality:
$$|5x + 2| + 6 < 13$$
$$|5x + 2| < 7$$
$$-7 < 5x + 2 < 7$$
$$-9 < 5x < 5$$
$$-\frac{9}{5} < x < 1$$

The solution is $\left(-\dfrac{9}{5}, 1\right)$.

39. Let $u = x^2$. Solving the equation:
$$6x^4 - 5x^2 - 4 = 0$$
$$6(x^2)^2 - 5x^2 - 4 = 0$$
$$6u^2 - 5u - 4 = 0$$
$$(2u + 1)(3u - 4) = 0$$
$$u = -\frac{1}{2}, \frac{4}{3}$$
$$x^2 = \frac{4}{3} \quad \left(x^2 \neq -\frac{1}{2}\right)$$
$$x = \pm\sqrt{\frac{4}{3}} \cdot \frac{\sqrt{3}}{\sqrt{3}} = \pm\frac{2\sqrt{3}}{3}$$

40. Solving the equation:
$$\frac{1}{2x+1} + \frac{3}{x-2} = \frac{5}{2x^2 - 3x - 2}$$
$$\frac{1}{2x+1} + \frac{3}{x-2} = \frac{5}{(2x+1)(x-2)}$$
$$(2x+1)(x-2)\left(\frac{1}{2x+1}\right) + (2x+1)(x-2)\left(\frac{3}{x-2}\right) = (2x+1)(x-2)\left(\frac{5}{(2x+1)(x-2)}\right)$$
$$1(x-2) + 3(2x+1) = 5$$
$$7x + 1 = 5$$
$$7x = 4$$
$$x = \frac{4}{7}$$

This value checks in the original equation.

41. Solving the equation:
$$\sqrt{2x-1}+\sqrt{x+4}=6$$
$$\sqrt{2x-1}=6-\sqrt{x+4}$$
$$2x-1=36-12\sqrt{x+4}+x+4$$
$$2x-1=x+40-12\sqrt{x+4}$$
$$x-41=-12\sqrt{x+4}$$
$$x^2-82x+1681=144(x+4)$$
$$x^2-82x+1681=144x+576$$
$$x^2-226x+1105=0$$
$$(x-221)(x-5)=0$$
$$x=5,221$$
Only $x=5$ checks in the original equation.

42. Computing in scientific notation: $5.7\times\left(5\times10^{-6}\right)=(5.7\times5)\times10^{-6}=28.5\times10^{-6}=2.85\times10^{-5}$

There are 2.85×10^{-5} grams of arsenic in 5.7 liters of the solution.

43. Let x represent the number of minutes used for each plan. Plan A has a cost of $0.18x$ and Plan B has a cost of $8+0.10x$, so solving the inequality:
$$8+0.10x<0.18x$$
$$8<0.08x$$
$$x>100$$
She must use at least 100 minutes in order for the cost of plan B to be less than the cost of plan A.

44. Setting the height equal to 0:
$$-16t^2+256=0$$
$$-16t^2=-256$$
$$t^2=16$$
$$t=\pm4$$
Since $t>0$, $t=4$. The ball will hit the ground in 4 seconds.

Chapter 2
Functions and Graphs

2.1 The Coordinate System; Lines and Their Graphs

1. Solving for y:

$$y - 4 = 2(y+1)$$
$$y - 4 = 2y + 2$$
$$-y - 4 = 2$$
$$-y = 6$$
$$y = -6$$

3. Solving for y:

$$\frac{1}{2}y + 3 = 4$$
$$\frac{1}{2}y = 1$$
$$2\left(\frac{1}{2}y\right) = 2(1)$$
$$y = 2$$

5. Solving for y:

$$4y + 2x - 8 = 0$$
$$4y = -2x + 8$$
$$\frac{4y}{4} = \frac{-2x}{4} + \frac{8}{4}$$
$$y = -\frac{1}{2}x + 2$$

7.
  a. Yes, $y = 1 + 3t$ represents an equation of a line, because it fits the form $y = mx + b$, where $m = 3$ and $b = 1$.
  b. No, it doesn't fit the form $y = mx + b$.
  c. Yes, $y = -5x$ represents an equation of a line, because it fits the form $y = mx + b$ where $m = -5$ and $b = 0$.
  d. No, it doesn't fit the form $y = mx + b$.

9. Finding the slope: $m = \dfrac{y_2 - y_1}{x_2 - x_1} = \dfrac{4 - (-3)}{0 - 1} = \dfrac{7}{-1} = -7$

11. Finding the slope: $m = \dfrac{y_2 - y_1}{x_2 - x_1} = \dfrac{3 - 3}{2 - 1} = \dfrac{0}{1} = 0$

13. Finding the slope: $m = \dfrac{y_2 - y_1}{x_2 - x_1} = \dfrac{0 - 1}{-2 - 0} = \dfrac{-1}{-2} = \dfrac{1}{2}$

15. Finding the slope: $m = \dfrac{y_2 - y_1}{x_2 - x_1} = \dfrac{1 - (-2)}{-5 - (-5)} = \dfrac{3}{0}$, which is undefined.

17. Finding the slope: $m = \dfrac{y_2 - y_1}{x_2 - x_1} = \dfrac{\frac{1}{2} - (-2)}{0 - 0} = \dfrac{5/2}{0}$, which is undefined.

19. Finding the slope: $m = \dfrac{y_2 - y_1}{x_2 - x_1} = \dfrac{-2 - (-1)}{-\dfrac{1}{3} - \dfrac{2}{3}} = \dfrac{-1}{-1} = 1$

21. Finding the slope: $m = \dfrac{y_2 - y_1}{x_2 - x_1} = \dfrac{\dfrac{\pi}{3} - \dfrac{\pi}{2}}{\dfrac{\pi}{4} - \pi} = \dfrac{\left(\dfrac{\pi}{3} - \dfrac{\pi}{2}\right) \cdot 12}{\left(\dfrac{\pi}{4} - \pi\right) \cdot 12} = \dfrac{4\pi - 6\pi}{3\pi - 12\pi} = \dfrac{-2\pi}{-9\pi} = \dfrac{2}{9}$

23. Finding the slope: $m = \dfrac{y_2 - y_1}{x_2 - x_1} = \dfrac{5 - 0}{2 - (-3)} = \dfrac{5}{5} = 1$

25. From $(0, 4)$ to $(1, -3)$, y goes down 7 as x goes right 1.

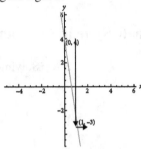

27. Subsituting the point $(2, 1)$: $y = -2(2) + 5 = -4 + 5 = 1$. Yes, $(2, 1)$ is a point on the line.

29. Subsituting the point $(-1, 0)$: $y = -2(-1) + 5 = 2 + 5 = 7 \neq 0$. No, $(-1, 0)$ is not a point on the line.

31. First find the slope: $m = \dfrac{y_2 - y_1}{x_2 - x_1} = \dfrac{4 - (-1)}{1 - 2} = \dfrac{5}{-1} = -5$

   Using the point-slope equation:
   $$y - (-1) = -5(x - 2)$$
   $$y + 1 = -5(x - 2)$$

33. First find the slope: $m = \dfrac{y_2 - y_1}{x_2 - x_1} = \dfrac{-3 - (-4)}{2 - (-1)} = \dfrac{1}{3}$

   Using the point-slope equation:
   $$y - (-4) = \dfrac{1}{3}(x - (-1))$$
   $$y + 4 = \dfrac{1}{3}(x + 1)$$

35. First find the slope: $m = \dfrac{y_2 - y_1}{x_2 - x_1} = \dfrac{5 - 5}{7 - 4} = \dfrac{0}{3} = 0$

   Using the point-slope equation: $y - 5 = 0(x - 4)$

37. First find the slope: $m = \dfrac{y_2 - y_1}{x_2 - x_1} = \dfrac{4.5 - 3.6}{2.5 - 1.5} = \dfrac{0.9}{1} = 0.9$

   Using the point-slope equation: $y - 3.6 = 0.9(x - 1.5)$

39. First find the slope: $m = \dfrac{y_2 - y_1}{x_2 - x_1} = \dfrac{\dfrac{1}{2} - (-1)}{3 - \dfrac{1}{2}} = \dfrac{\left(\dfrac{1}{2} + 1\right) \cdot 2}{\left(3 - \dfrac{1}{2}\right) \cdot 2} = \dfrac{1 + 2}{6 - 1} = \dfrac{3}{5}$

Using the point-slope equation:

$$y - (-1) = \frac{3}{5}\left(x - \frac{1}{2}\right)$$

$$y + 1 = \frac{3}{5}\left(x - \frac{1}{2}\right)$$

41. Solving for y:

$$-3x + 6y - 2 = 0$$

$$6y = 3x + 2$$

$$y = \frac{1}{2}x + \frac{1}{3}$$

The slope is $\dfrac{1}{2}$ and the y-intercept is $\left(0, \dfrac{1}{3}\right)$.

43. Solving for y:

$$3(x - 2) + 4y - 7 = 0$$

$$3x - 6 + 4y - 7 = 0$$

$$3x + 4y - 13 = 0$$

$$4y = -3x + 13$$

$$y = -\frac{3}{4}x + \frac{13}{4}$$

The slope is $-\dfrac{3}{4}$ and the y-intercept is $\left(0, \dfrac{13}{4}\right)$.

45. Solving for x:

$$2(x - 3) = 0$$

$$2x - 6 = 0$$

$$2x = 6$$

$$x = 3$$

The slope is undefined and there is no y-intercept.

47. Solving for y:

$$2x + y = 6$$

$$y = -2x + 6$$

Finding the x-intercept:

$$2x + 0 = 6$$

$$2x = 6$$

$$x = 3$$

The slope is -2, the x-intercept is $(3, 0)$, and the y-intercept is $(0, 6)$. Sketching the graph:

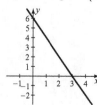

49. Solving for y:

$$4x - 3y = -2$$

$$-3y = -4x - 2$$

$$y = \frac{4}{3}x + \frac{2}{3}$$

Finding the x-intercept:

$$4x - 3(0) = -2$$

$$4x = -2$$

$$x = -\frac{1}{2}$$

The slope is $\frac{4}{3}$, the x-intercept is $\left(-\frac{1}{2}, 0\right)$, and the y-intercept is $\left(0, \frac{2}{3}\right)$. Sketching the graph:

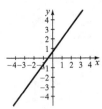

51. Solving for y:

$$y - 3 = -2(x - 6)$$

$$y - 3 = -2x + 12$$

$$y = -2x + 15$$

Finding the x-intercept:

$$0 = -2x + 15$$

$$-2x = -15$$

$$x = \frac{15}{2}$$

The slope is -2, the x-intercept is $\left(\frac{15}{2}, 0\right)$, and the y-intercept is $(0, 15)$. Sketching the graph:

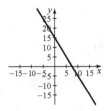

53. Solving for y:

$$-5x + 3y - 9 = 0$$

$$3y = 5x + 9$$

$$y = \frac{5}{3}x + 3$$

Finding the x-intercept:

$$-5x + 3(0) - 9 = 0$$

$$-5x = 9$$

$$x = -\frac{9}{5}$$

The slope is $\dfrac{5}{3}$, the x-intercept is $\left(-\dfrac{9}{5},0\right)$, and the y-intercept is $(0,3)$. Sketching the graph:

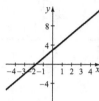

55. Solving for y:

$$2y - 4 = 0$$
$$2y = 4$$
$$y = 2$$

The slope is 0, there is no x-intercept, and the y-intercept is $(0,2)$. Sketching the graph:

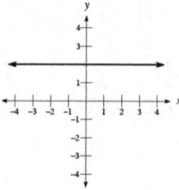

57. The slope is $m = \dfrac{3}{3} = 1$, now using the point-slope formula:

$$y - (-2) = 1(x - (-3))$$
$$y + 2 = x + 3$$
$$y = x + 1$$

59. The slope is $m = \dfrac{2}{5}$, now using the point-slope formula:

$$y - 0 = \dfrac{2}{5}(x - 3)$$
$$y = \dfrac{2}{5}x - \dfrac{6}{5}$$

61. The slope is undefined, and the equation of the line is $x = 2$.

63. Sketching the graph:

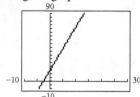

65. Sketching the graph:

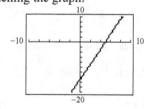

67. Sketching the graph:

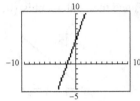

69. Using the slope-intercept formula: $y = -x + 2$

71. Finding the slope: $m = \dfrac{1-0}{0-(-3)} = \dfrac{1}{3}$. Using the slope-intercept formula: $y = \dfrac{1}{3}x + 1$

73. Using the point-slope formula:
$$y - 2 = -\frac{1}{2}(x - 1)$$
$$y - 2 = -\frac{1}{2}x + \frac{1}{2}$$
$$y = -\frac{1}{2}x + \frac{5}{2}$$

75. Using the point-slope formula:
$$y - (-1) = -3(x - 3)$$
$$y + 1 = -3x + 9$$
$$y = -3x + 8$$

77. Using the slope-intercept formula: $y = \dfrac{3}{4}x - \dfrac{3}{2}$

79. Finding the slope: $m = \dfrac{3-0}{0-\dfrac{1}{2}} = -6$. Using the slope-intercept formula: $y = -6x + 3$

81. The vertical line is $x = 4$.

83. The horizontal line is $y = -1$.

85. The horizontal line is $y = 0.5$.

87. The slope of $y = -3x$ is $m = -3$, so the slope of the parallel line is -3. Using the slope-intercept formula: $y = -3x - 1$

89. The slope of $y = -\dfrac{1}{2}x + 2$ is $m = -\dfrac{1}{2}$, so the slope of the parallel line is $-\dfrac{1}{2}$. Using the point-slope formula:
$$y - (-1) = -\frac{1}{2}(x - 4)$$
$$y + 1 = -\frac{1}{2}x + 2$$
$$y = -\frac{1}{2}x + 1$$

91. First find the slope by solving for y:
$$2x + 3y = 6$$
$$3y = -2x + 6$$
$$y = -\frac{2}{3}x + 2;$$
$$m = -\frac{2}{3}$$
Using the point-slope formula:
$$y - 1 = -\frac{2}{3}(x - (-3))$$
$$y - 1 = -\frac{2}{3}(x + 3)$$
$$y - 1 = -\frac{2}{3}x - 2$$
$$y = -\frac{2}{3}x - 1$$

93. The perpendicular slope is $m = -\dfrac{3}{2}$. Using the slope-intercept formula: $y = -\dfrac{3}{2}x - 1$

95. The perpendicular slope is $m = -\dfrac{1}{2}$. Using the point-slope formula:

$$y - 1 = -\frac{1}{2}\left(x - (-2)\right)$$

$$y - 1 = -\frac{1}{2}(x + 2)$$

$$y - 1 = -\frac{1}{2}x - 1$$

$$y = -\frac{1}{2}x$$

97. Solving for y to find the slope:

$$x + 2y = 1$$

$$2y = -x + 1$$

$$y = -\frac{1}{2}x + \frac{1}{2}$$

The perpendicular slope is $m = 2$. Using the point-slope formula:

$$y - 1 = 2(x - 2)$$

$$y - 1 = 2x - 4$$

$$y = 2x - 3$$

99. Since $y = 4$ is a horizontal line, the perpendicular line will be a vertical line, so its equation is $x = 0$.

101. Since $x = 1$ is a vertical line, the parallel line will also be a vertical line, so its equation is $x = -2$.

103. a. Let x represent the number of computers sold, then the earnings is given by $y = 50x + 650$.

    b. The slope is $m = 50$. This represents the amount the salesperson earns for each computer sold. The y-intercept is $b = 650$. This represents the salesperson's base salary if no computers are sold.

105. a. In 2015, $t = 2015 - 2008 = 7$. Substituting into the revenue equation:

$$R = 1.82(7) + 27.46 = 173.4 = 40.2$$

    The revenue will be \$40.2 billion in the year 2015.

    b. The R-intercept of 27.46 represents \$27.46 billion revenue in 2008.

107. a. In 2012, $t = 2012 - 2009 = 3$. Substituting into the sales equation: $h = 160(3) + 500 = 980$

    There were 980 million handbags sold in 2012.

    b. The h-intercept of 500 represents that 500 million handbags were sold in 2009.

    c. Finding when $h = 1,200$:

$$1200 = 160t + 500$$

$$700 = 160t$$

$$t = 4.375$$

    There will be 1,200 million handbags sold in the year $2009 + 4 = 2013$.

109. The equation is $P = 1.50t + 25.50$, where t represents years since 2009.

111. Using the points $(0°, 32°)$ and $(100°, 212°)$ as the (C, F) points, first find the slope: $m = \dfrac{212 - 32}{100 - 0} = \dfrac{9}{5}$

Since they F-intercept is $(0°, 32°)$, the slope intercept form is: $F = \dfrac{9}{5}C + 32$

113. Using the standard [–10,10] x [–10,10] viewing rectangle, the graph does not appear:

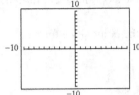

The maximum and minimum values of x and y shown in the viewing window must be manually changed to accommodate the values of this function. Changing the viewing rectangle to [–110,10] x [–10,110] produces an appropriate graph:

115. The slope-intercept form of the equation is $y = -\dfrac{4}{5}x - 1$. Sketching the graph:

117. Using the point-slope formula:

$$y - 6 = \frac{5}{3}\left(x - (-2)\right)$$

$$y - 6 = \frac{5}{3}(x + 2)$$

$$y - 6 = \frac{5}{3}x + \frac{10}{3}$$

$$y = \frac{5}{3}x + \frac{28}{3}$$

Sketching the graph:

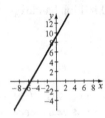

2.2 Coordinate Geometry, Circles and Other Equations

1. This statement is false, since $(x+3)^2 = x^2 + 6x + 9$.

3. Factoring: $x^2 + 8x + 16 = (x+4)(x+4) = (x+4)^2$

5. Finding the distance: $d = \sqrt{(-8-6)^2 + (11-4)^2} = \sqrt{(-14)^2 + 7^2} = \sqrt{196 + 49} = \sqrt{245} = 7\sqrt{5}$

   Finding the midpoint: $\left(\dfrac{6+(-8)}{2}, \dfrac{4+11}{2}\right) = \left(\dfrac{-2}{2}, \dfrac{15}{2}\right) = \left(-1, \dfrac{15}{2}\right)$

7. Finding the distance: $d = \sqrt{(-10-(-4))^2 + (14-20)^2} = \sqrt{(-6)^2 + (-6)^2} = \sqrt{36+36} = \sqrt{72} = 6\sqrt{2}$

   Finding the midpoint: $\left(\dfrac{-4+(-10)}{2}, \dfrac{20+14}{2}\right) = \left(\dfrac{-14}{2}, \dfrac{34}{2}\right) = (-7, 17)$

9. Finding the distance: $d = \sqrt{(5-1)^2 + (5-(-1))^2} = \sqrt{16+36} = \sqrt{52} = 2\sqrt{13}$

   Finding the midpoint: $\left(\dfrac{1+5}{2}, \dfrac{-1+5}{2}\right) = (3, 2)$

11. Finding the distance: $d = \sqrt{(6-6)^2 + (11-(-3))^2} = \sqrt{196} = 14$

    Finding the midpoint: $\left(\dfrac{6+6}{2}, \dfrac{-3+11}{2}\right) = (6, 4)$

13. Finding the distance: $d = \sqrt{\left(-\dfrac{1}{4} - \left(-\dfrac{1}{2}\right)\right)^2 + (0-1)^2} = \sqrt{\left(\dfrac{1}{4}\right)^2 + 1} = \sqrt{\dfrac{1}{16} + 1} = \sqrt{\dfrac{17}{16}} = \dfrac{\sqrt{17}}{4}$

    Finding the midpoint: $\left(\dfrac{-\dfrac{1}{2} + \left(-\dfrac{1}{4}\right)}{2}, \dfrac{1+0}{2}\right) = \left(\dfrac{-3\!/\!4}{2}, \dfrac{1}{2}\right) = \left(-\dfrac{3}{8}, \dfrac{1}{2}\right)$

15. Finding the distance: $d = \sqrt{(b_1 - a_1)^2 + (b_2 - a_2)^2}$

    Finding the midpoint: $\left(\dfrac{a_1 + b_1}{2}, \dfrac{a_2 + b_2}{2}\right)$

17. Writing the equation in standard form:
    $$(x-0)^2 + (y-0)^2 = 5^2$$
    $$x^2 + y^2 = 25$$
    Sketching the graph:

    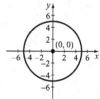

19. Writing the equation in standard form:
    $$(x-(-1))^2 + (y-0)^2 = 3^2$$
    $$(x+1)^2 + y^2 = 9$$
    Sketching the graph:

    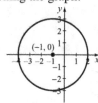

21. Writing the equation in standard form:

$$(x-3)^2 + \left(y-(-1)\right)^2 = 5^2$$
$$(x-3)^2 + (y+1)^2 = 25$$

Sketching the graph:

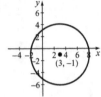

23. Writing the equation in standard form:

$$(x-1)^2 + (y-0)^2 = \left(\frac{3}{2}\right)^2$$
$$(x-1)^2 + y^2 = \frac{9}{4}$$

Sketching the graph:

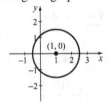

25. Writing the equation in standard form:

$$(x-1)^2 + (y-1)^2 = \left(\sqrt{3}\right)^2$$
$$(x-1)^2 + (y-1)^2 = 3$$

Sketching the graph:

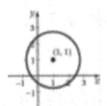

27. The standard form is:

$$(x-0)^2 + (y-1)^2 = r^2$$
$$x^2 + y^2 = r^2$$

Using the point $(1, 3)$:

$$1^2 + 3^2 = r^2$$
$$10 = r^2$$

The equation is $x^2 + y^2 = 10$.

29. The standard form is:

$$(x-2)^2 + (y-0)^2 = r^2$$
$$(x-2)^2 + y^2 = r^2$$

Using the point $(2, 5)$:

$$(2-2)^2 + 5^2 = r^2$$
$$25 = r^2$$

The equation is $(x-2)^2 + y^2 = 25$.

31. The standard form is:

$$(x-1)^2 + \left(y-(-2)\right)^2 = r^2$$
$$(x-1)^2 + (y+2)^2 = r^2$$

Using the point $(5, 1)$:

$$(5-1)^2 + (1+2)^2 = r^2$$
$$4^2 + 3^2 = r^2$$
$$25 = r^2$$

The equation is $(x-1)^2 + (y+2)^2 = 25$.

33. The standard form is:

$$\left(x-\frac{1}{2}\right)^2 + (y-0)^2 = r^2$$
$$\left(x-\frac{1}{2}\right)^2 + y^2 = r^2$$

Using the point $(1, 3)$:

$$\left(1-\frac{1}{2}\right)^2 + (3)^2 = r^2$$
$$\frac{1}{4} + 9 = r^2$$
$$\frac{37}{4} = r^2$$

The equation is $\left(x-\frac{1}{2}\right)^2 + y^2 = \frac{37}{4}$.

35. The number is: $\left(\dfrac{12}{2}\right)^2 = 6^2 = 36$

37. The number is: $\left(\dfrac{-5}{2}\right)^2 = \dfrac{25}{4}$

39. The number is: $\left(\dfrac{-3}{2}\right)^2 = \dfrac{9}{4}$

41. The center is $(0,0)$ and the radius is $\sqrt{36} = 6$.

43. The center is $(1,-2)$ and the radius is $\sqrt{36} = 6$.

45. The center is $(8,0)$ and the radius is $\sqrt{\dfrac{1}{4}} = \dfrac{1}{2}$.

47. First complete the square:
$$x^2 + y^2 - 6x + 4y - 3 = 0$$
$$\left(x^2 - 6x\right) + \left(y^2 + 4y\right) = 3$$
$$\left(x^2 - 6x + 9\right) + \left(y^2 + 4y + 4\right) = 3 + 9 + 4$$
$$(x-3)^2 + (y+2)^2 = 16$$
The center is $(3,-2)$ and the radius is $\sqrt{16} = 4$.

49. First complete the square:
$$x^2 + y^2 - 2x + 2y - 7 = 0$$
$$\left(x^2 - 2x\right) + \left(y^2 + 2y\right) = 7$$
$$\left(x^2 - 2x + 1\right) + \left(y^2 + 2y + 1\right) = 7 + 1 + 1$$
$$(x-1)^2 + (y+1)^2 = 9$$
The center is $(1,-1)$ and the radius is $\sqrt{9} = 3$.

51. First complete the square:
$$x^2 + y^2 - 6x - 4y - 5 = 0$$
$$\left(x^2 - 6x\right) + \left(y^2 - 4y\right) = 5$$
$$\left(x^2 - 6x + 9\right) + \left(y^2 - 4y + 4\right) = 5 + 9 + 4$$
$$(x-3)^2 + (y-2)^2 = 18$$
The center is $(3,2)$ and the radius is $\sqrt{18} = 3\sqrt{2}$.

53. First complete the square:
$$x^2 + y^2 - x = 2$$
$$\left(x^2 - x\right) + y^2 = 2$$
$$\left(x^2 - x + \dfrac{1}{4}\right) + y^2 = 2 + \dfrac{1}{4}$$
$$\left(x - \dfrac{1}{2}\right)^2 + y^2 = \dfrac{9}{4}$$
The center is $\left(\dfrac{1}{2}, 0\right)$ and the radius is $\sqrt{\dfrac{9}{4}} = \dfrac{3}{2}$.

55. The center is $(0,0)$ and the radius is 2, so:
$$(x-0)^2 + (y-0)^2 = 2^2$$
$$x^2 + y^2 = 4$$

57. The center is $(-1,-1)$ and the radius is 2, so:
$$\left(x - (-1)\right)^2 + \left(y - (-1)\right)^2 = 2^2$$
$$(x+1)^2 + (y+1)^2 = 4$$

59. The center is $(0,0)$ and the radius is $\sqrt{6.25} = 2.5$:

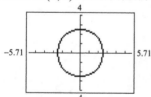

61. The center is $(0,0)$ and the radius is $\sqrt{10}$:

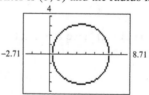

63. Sketching the graph:

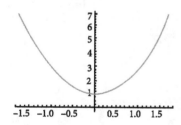

65. Sketching the graph:

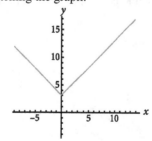

67. Sketching the graph:

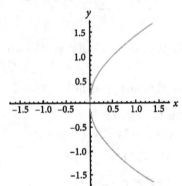

69. Sketching the graph:

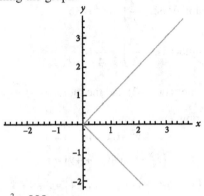

71. **a.** The center is $(0, 0)$ and the radius is 30, so the equation is $x^2 + y^2 = 900$.

   b. The center is $(0, 0)$ and the radius is $30 + 7 = 37$, so the equation is $x^2 + y^2 = 37^2$, or $x^2 + y^2 = 1,369$.

73. **a.** The coordinates of the points are: A(0, 0), B(5, 0), C(10, 0), D(15, 0), E(20, 0), F(15, 12), G(10, 12), and H(5, 12).

   b. The base AE is 20 ft and the top HF is 10 ft for a total of $20 + 10 = 30$ ft. Slanted trusses AH, BG, GD, and FE have the same length of $d(A, H) = \sqrt{5^2 + 12^2} = \sqrt{169} = 13$ ft for a total of $4(13) = 52$ ft. Vertical trusses BH, CG, and DF have the same length of 12 ft for a total of $3(12) = 36$ ft. Thus the total length of all lumber required is $30 + 52 + 36 = 118$ ft.

75. The center is the midpoint: $\left(\dfrac{-3+1}{2}, \dfrac{4+2}{2} \right) = (-1, 3)$

The radius is ½ of the diameter: $r = \dfrac{1}{2}\sqrt{(1-(-3))^2 + (2-4)^2} = \dfrac{1}{2}\sqrt{20} = \dfrac{1}{2} \cdot 2\sqrt{5} = \sqrt{5}$

Therefore the equation is $(x+1)^2 + (y-3)^2 = 5$. Sketching the graph:

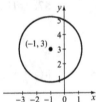

77. Using the formula $A = \pi r^2$, we can find the radius:

$$64\pi = \pi r^2$$
$$64 = r^2$$
$$r = 8$$

Therefore the equation is $\left(x - (-5)\right)^2 + \left(y - (-1)\right)^2 = 8^2$, or $(x+5)^2 + (y+1)^2 = 64$.

79. Label the y-axis points as $(0, y)$. Using the distance formula:

$$\sqrt{(0-1)^2 + (y-(-2))^2} = 8$$
$$\sqrt{1 + (y+2)^2} = 8$$
$$\sqrt{1 + y^2 + 4y + 4} = 8$$
$$\sqrt{y^2 + 4y + 5} = 8$$
$$y^2 + 4y + 5 = 64$$
$$y^2 + 4y - 59 = 0$$

Using the quadratic formula: $y = \dfrac{-4 \pm \sqrt{4^2 - 4(1)(-59)}}{2(1)} = \dfrac{-4 \pm \sqrt{252}}{2} = \dfrac{-4 \pm 6\sqrt{7}}{2} = -2 \pm 3\sqrt{7}$

The points are $\left(0, -2 - 3\sqrt{7}\right), \left(0, -2 + 3\sqrt{7}\right)$.

2.3 Functions

1. This is false, since $\sqrt{-4}$ is not a real number.

3. Solving the inequality:
$$2x + 1 > 0$$
$$2x > -1$$
$$x > -\frac{1}{2}$$

The solution is the interval $\left(-\dfrac{1}{2}, \infty\right)$.

5. Finding the function values:
$$f(3) = 5(3) + 3 = 15 + 3 = 18$$
$$f(-1) = 5(-1) + 3 = -5 + 3 = -2$$
$$f(0) = 5(0) + 3 = 0 + 3 = 3$$

7. Finding the function values:
$$f(3) = -\frac{7}{2}(3) + 2 = -\frac{21}{2} + 2 = -\frac{17}{2}$$
$$f(-1) = -\frac{7}{2}(-1) + 2 = \frac{7}{2} + 1 = \frac{11}{2}$$
$$f(0) = -\frac{7}{2}(0) + 2 = 0 + 2 = 2$$

9. Finding the function values:
$$f(3) = (3)^2 + 2 = 9 + 2 = 11$$
$$f(-1) = (-1)^2 + 2 = 1 + 2 = 3$$
$$f(0) = (0)^2 + 2 = 0 + 2 = 2$$

11. Finding the function values:
$$f(3) = -2(3+1)^2 - 4 = -2(16) - 4 = -36$$
$$f(-1) = -2(-1+1)^2 - 4 = -2(0) - 4 = -4$$
$$f(0) = -2(0+1)^2 - 4 = -2(1) - 4 = -6$$

13. Finding the function values:
$$f(3) = \sqrt{3(3) + 4} = \sqrt{9 + 4} = \sqrt{13}$$
$$f(-1) = \sqrt{3(-1) + 4} = \sqrt{-3 + 4} = \sqrt{1} = 1$$
$$f(0) = \sqrt{3(0) + 4} = \sqrt{0 + 4} = \sqrt{4} = 2$$

15. Finding the function values:
$$f(3) = \frac{(3)^2 - 1}{3 + 3} = \frac{8}{6} = \frac{4}{3}$$
$$f(-1) = \frac{(-1)^2 - 1}{-1 + 3} = \frac{0}{2} = 0$$
$$f(0) = \frac{(0)^2 - 1}{0 + 3} = \frac{-1}{3} = -\frac{1}{3}$$

17. Evaluating the function:

$$f(a) = 4(a) + 3 = 4a + 3$$
$$f(a+1) = 4(a+1) + 3 = 4a + 4 + 3 = 4a + 7$$
$$f\left(\frac{1}{2}\right) = 4\left(\frac{1}{2}\right) + 3 = 2 + 3 = 5$$

19. Evaluating the function:

$$f(a) = -(a)^2 + 4 = -a^2 + 4$$
$$f(a+1) = -(a+1)^2 + 4 = -(a^2 + 2a + 1) + 4 = -a^2 - 2a + 3$$
$$f\left(\frac{1}{2}\right) = -\left(\frac{1}{2}\right)^2 + 4 = -\frac{1}{4} + 4 = \frac{15}{4}$$

21. Evaluating the function:

$$f(a) = \sqrt{3(a) - 1} = \sqrt{3a - 1}$$
$$f(a+1) = \sqrt{3(a+1) - 1} = \sqrt{3a + 2}$$
$$f\left(\frac{1}{2}\right) = \sqrt{3\left(\frac{1}{2}\right) - 1} = \sqrt{\frac{1}{2}} = \frac{1}{\sqrt{2}} = \frac{1}{\sqrt{2}} \cdot \frac{\sqrt{2}}{\sqrt{2}} = \frac{\sqrt{2}}{2}$$

23. Evaluating the function:

$$f(a) = \frac{1}{(a) + 1} = \frac{1}{a + 1}$$
$$f(a+1) = \frac{1}{(a+1) + 1} = \frac{1}{a + 2}$$
$$f\left(\frac{1}{2}\right) = \frac{1}{\left(\frac{1}{2}\right) + 1} = \frac{1}{\frac{3}{2}} = 1 \cdot \frac{2}{3} = \frac{2}{3}$$

25. Evaluating the function:

$$g(-x) = \sqrt{6}$$
$$g(2x) = \sqrt{6}$$
$$g(a+h) = \sqrt{6}$$

27. Evaluating the function:

$$g(-x) = 2(-x) - 3 = -2x - 3$$
$$g(2x) = 2(2x) - 3 = 4x - 3$$
$$g(a+h) = 2(a+h) - 3 = 2a + 2h - 3$$

29. Evaluating the function:

$$g(-x) = 3(-x)^2 = 3x^2$$
$$g(2x) = 3(2x)^2 = 3(4x^2) = 12x^2$$
$$g(a+h) = 3(a+h)^2 = 3(a^2 + 2ah + h^2) = 3a^2 + 6ah + 3h^2$$

31. Evaluating the function:

$$g(-x) = \frac{1}{-x} = -\frac{1}{x}$$
$$g(2x) = \frac{1}{2x}$$
$$g(a+h) = \frac{1}{a+h}$$

33. Evaluating the function:

$$g(-x) = -(-x)^2 - 3(-x) + 5 = -x^2 + 3x + 5$$
$$g(2x) = -(2x)^2 - 3(2x) + 5 = -4x^2 - 6x + 5$$
$$g(a+h) = -(a+h)^2 - 3(a+h) + 5 = -a^2 - 2ah - h^2 - 3a - 3h + 5$$

35. Finding the function values:

$f(-2)$ is undefined

$f(0) = \dfrac{1}{2}$

$f(1) = \dfrac{1}{2}$

37. Finding the function values:

$f(-2) = -2$

$f(0) = 1$

$f(1) = 1$

39. Finding the function values:

$f(-2) = -1$

$f(0) = 2$

$f(1) = 4$

41. Finding the function values:

$f(-2)$ is undefined

$f(0) = \sqrt{0} = 0$

$f(1) = -(1) + 4 = 3$

43. **a.** Evaluating: $g(5) = -1$

b. Evaluating: $g(0) = 2$

c. No. The table does not include an output value $g(t)$ for the input $t = 3$.

45. **a.** Solving the equation:

$2x + 3 = 9$

$2x = 6$

$x = 3$

b. Finding the function value: $f(9) = 2(9) + 3 = 21$

c. Solving the equation:

$f(x) = 11$

$2x + 3 = 11$

$2x = 8$

$x = 4$

47. Yes. The perimeter P of a square is related to its side s by the formula $P = 4s$. For each value of s, only one value of P is output by the formula.

49. No. If a price of \$2.59 is given, the name of more than one item can possibly be found.

51. Yes. For each denomination, the bill can only be one length.

53. Yes. Each input value has only one corresponding output value.

55. The domain is all real numbers, or $(-\infty, \infty)$.

57. The denominator is equal to 0 when $s = -1$. So the domain is all real numbers except -1, or $(-\infty, -1) \cup (-1, \infty)$.

59. The denominator is equal to 0 when $w = 3$. So the domain is all real numbers except 3, or $(-\infty, 3) \cup (3, \infty)$.

61. Setting the denominator equal to 0:

$x^2 - 4 = 0$

$(x + 2)(x - 2) = 0$

$x = \pm 2$

The domain is all real numbers except -2 and 2, or $(-\infty, -2) \cup (-2, 2) \cup (2, \infty)$.

63. The quantity inside the radical must be non-negative. Solving the inequality:

$2 - x \geq 0$

$2 \geq x$

$x \leq 2$

The domain is all real numbers $x \leq 2$, or $(-\infty, 2]$.

65. Since the denominator is always positive, the domain is $(-\infty, \infty)$.

67. The quantity inside the radical must be non-negative. Solving the inequality:
$$x + 7 > 0$$
$$x > -7$$
The domain is all real numbers $x > -7$, or $(-7, \infty)$.

69. Evaluating when $r = 3$: $V(3) = \frac{4}{3}\pi(3)^3 = \frac{4}{3}\pi(27) = 36\pi \approx 113.097$

The volume is $36\pi \approx 113.097$ in^3.

71. Evaluating when $x = 30$: $S(30) = 1{,}000 + 20(30) = 1{,}000 + 600 = 1{,}600$

The salesperson earnings is $1,600 when 30 items are sold.

73. **a.** Let t represent the time (in hours), and d represent the distance. The function is: $d(t) = 45t$

b. Evaluating when $t = 2$: $d(2) = 45(2) = 90$

The car travels 90 miles in 2 hours.

c. The domain is $[0, \infty)$.

75. **a.** $D(\text{The Hunger Games}) = 408$ million dollars.

The dollar amount grossed by *The Hunger Games* is about $408 million.

b. The domain consists of the movies:

The Hobbit : an Unexpected Journey, The Dark Knight Rises, Marvel's The Avenger,

The Amazing Spider – man, The Twilight Saga : Breaking Dawn Part 2, The Hunger Games

77. Substituting $l = 3w$ into the area formula: $A = lw = (3w)w = 3w^2$

The area as a function of width is $A(w) = 3w^2$.

79. **a.** Substituting $t = 0$: $h(0) = -16(0)^2 + 100 = 100$

The height of the ball 0 seconds after it is dropped (its initial position) is 100 feet.

b. Substituting $t = 2$: $h(2) = -16(2)^2 + 100 = 36$

The height of the ball 2 seconds after it is dropped is 36 feet.

81. **a.** This table represents a function because for each year (input), there is only one value for per capita consumption (output).

b. Evaluating: $S(2005) = 59.2$ pounds

c. This is reflected in the table by a steady increase in its use over the three decades 1970-2000.

d. The use of high fructose corn syrup is decreasing.

83. **a.** Because any call lasting 20 minutes or less will cost $1, the cost is not proportional to the length of the call in this case.

b. Writing the function: $C(t) = \begin{cases} 1 & \text{if } 0 < t \le 20 \\ 1 + 0.07(t - 20) & \text{if } t > 20 \end{cases}$

c. Evaluating the function for $t = 5$, $t = 20$, and $t = 30$:
$$C(5) = 1$$
$$C(20) = 1$$
$$C(30) = 1 + 0.07(30 - 20) = 1.7$$

A 5-minute call will cost $1.00, a 20-minute call will cost $1.00, and a 30-minute call will cost $1.70.

85. Using the function value:
$$f(1) = 2$$
$$a(1)^2 + 5 = 2$$
$$a + 5 = 2$$
$$a = -3$$

87. The domain is all real numbers, or $(-\infty, \infty)$.

2.4 Graphs of Functions

1. Evaluating: $-|2| = -2$

3. Evaluating: $|-3| - 1 = 3 - 1 = 2$

5. Evaluating: $\sqrt{-(-9)} = \sqrt{9} = 3$

7. No, for the value $x = 1$ there are two values of y.

9. No, for the value $x = 0$ there are two values of y.

11. No, for the value $x = -5$ there are two values of y.

13. Completing the table:

x	-4	-2	0	2	4
y	-2	-3	-4	-5	-6

Sketching the graph:

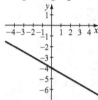

15. Completing the table:

x	0	2	$9/2$	8	18
y	0	2	3	4	6

Sketching the graph:

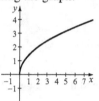

17. The domain is $(-\infty, \infty)$ and the range is $(-\infty, \infty)$.

Sketching the graph:

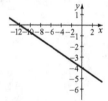

19. The domain is $(-\infty, \infty)$ and the range is $(-\infty, \infty)$.

Sketching the graph:

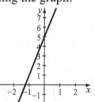

21. The domain is $(-\infty, \infty)$ and the range is $(-\infty, \infty)$.

Sketching the graph:

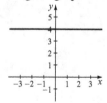

23. The domain is $(-\infty, \infty)$ and the range is $(-\infty, \infty)$.

Sketching the graph:

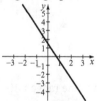

25. The domain is $(-\infty, \infty)$ and the range is $\{4\}$.

Sketching the graph:

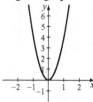

27. The domain is $(-\infty, \infty)$ and the range is $[0, \infty)$.

Sketching the graph:

29. The domain is $(-\infty, \infty)$ and the range is $(-\infty, 4]$.
Sketching the graph:

31. The domain is $[-4, \infty)$ and the range is $[0, \infty)$.
Sketching the graph:

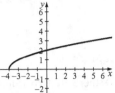

33. The domain is $[0, \infty)$ and the range is $[0, \infty)$.
Sketching the graph:

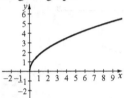

35. The domain is $[0, \infty)$ and the range is $[-2, \infty)$.
Sketching the graph:

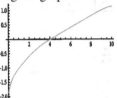

37. The domain is $(-\infty, \infty)$ and the range is $[0, \infty)$.
Sketching the graph:

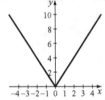

39. The domain is $(-\infty, \infty)$ and the range is $(-\infty, 0]$.
Sketching the graph:

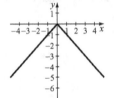

41. The domain is $(-\infty, \infty)$ and the range is $[0, \infty)$.
Sketching the graph:

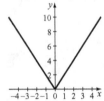

43. The domain is $(-\infty, 0]$ and the range is $[0, \infty)$.
Sketching the graph:

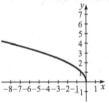

45. The domain is $(-\infty, \infty)$ and the range is $(-\infty, \infty)$. Sketching the graph:

47. Graphing the function:

49. Graphing the function:

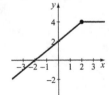

51. Graphing the function:

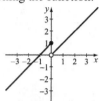

53. Graphing the function:

55. This is not a function. There are some values in the domain for which there is more than one corresponding value in the range (by the vertical line test).

57. This is a function. There is no value in the domain for which there is more than one corresponding value in the range (by the vertical line test).

59. The domain is $(-\infty, \infty)$ and the range is $(-\infty, 1]$.   **61.** The domain is $(-\infty, \infty)$ and the range is $[-1, 2]$.

63. The domain is $(-\infty, \infty)$ and the range is $\{2\} \cup [3, \infty)$.

65. Graphing the function:

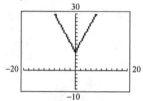

67. Graphing the function:

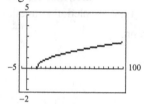

69. Graphing the function:

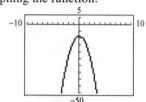

71. Graphing the function:

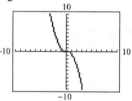

73. **a.** Finding the function values: $f(-1) = 3, f(0) = 3, f(2) = 5$

   b. The domain is $(-\infty, \infty)$.

   c. The x-intercept is $(2, 0)$ and the y-intercept is $(0, 1)$.

75. **a.** Finding the function values: $f(-1) = 1, f(0) = 2, f(2) = 0$

   b. The domain is $(-\infty, \infty)$.

   c. The x-intercepts are $(-2, 0)$ and $(2, 0)$ and the y-intercept is $(0, 2)$.

77. **a.** Finding the function values: $f(-1) = -1.7, f(0) = -2, f(2) = -2.4$

   b. The domain is $[-4, \infty)$.

   c. The x-intercept is $(-4, 0)$ and the y-intercept is $(0, -2)$.

79. Solving for y:
$$3x + y - 1 = 0$$
$$y = -3x + 1$$

Yes, this is a function. For each value of x there is only one value of y.

81. Solving for y:
$$y^2 = x$$
$$y = \pm\sqrt{x}$$

No, this is not a function. For each nonzero value of x in the domain, there are two values of y.

83. Solving for y:
$$y + 2x^2 = 1$$
$$y = -2x^2 + 1$$

Yes, this is a function. For each value of x there is only one value of y.

85. **a.** In 2010, the amount allotted is approximately $18.7 billion.
   b. The amount of increase is approximately $18.75 – $17.75 = $1 billion.

87. Radius is the measure of the distance from the center of a sphere to any point on the sphere. As a distance, it is a positive number. Sketching the graph:

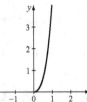

89. If t represents the time traveled, the function is $d(t) = 55t$. The values of t must be greater than or equal to zero. Sketching the graph:

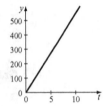

91. **a.** Sketching the graph:

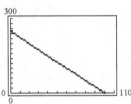

   b. The t-intercept represents the time the when the coastal region has completely eroded.

93. In the graphs, $f(x)$ is independent of x, whereas $g(x)$ increases as x increases:

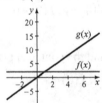

95. In the graphs, $f(x)$ opens downward, whereas $g(x)$ opens upward:

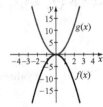

97. This is not a function because each element of the domain greater than zero has two distinct values in the range.

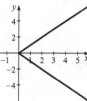

99. The range of $f(x)$ is $[0,\infty)$ and the range of $g(x)$ is $[-3,\infty)$:

101. The range of $f(x)$ is $[0,\infty)$ and the range of $g(x)$ is $[0,\infty)$:

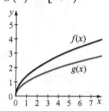

2.5 Analyzing the Graph of a Function

1. This function is even, since the graph is symmetric about the y-axis.
3. This function is neither even nor odd, as the graph doesn't have y-axis or origin symmetry.
5. This function is odd, since the graph is symmetric about the origin.
7. The domain of f is $[-2,2]$.
9. The y-intercept is $(0,4)$.
11. The function is decreasing on the interval $(0,1)$.
13. This function is even, since it is symmetric about the y-axis.
15. The function is decreasing on the intervals $(-3,-2)$ and $(3,4)$.
17. The y-intercept is $(0,1)$.
19. The average rate of change is: $\dfrac{f(2)-f(-2)}{2-(-2)}=\dfrac{2-0}{4}=\dfrac{1}{2}$
21. The average rate of change is: $\dfrac{f(5)-f(4)}{5-4}=\dfrac{0-(-3)}{1}=3$
23. The function is decreasing on the interval $(0,1)$.
25. The average rate of change is: $\dfrac{f(1)-f(0)}{1-0}=\dfrac{0-4}{1}=-4$

27. Finding the values:
$$f(x) = x + 3$$
$$-f(x) = -(x+3) = -x - 3$$
$$f(-x) = -x + 3$$
Since $f(-x) \neq f(x)$ and $f(-x) \neq -f(x)$, the function is neither even nor odd.

29. Finding the values:
$$f(x) = |3x| - 2$$
$$-f(x) = -|3x| + 2$$
$$f(-x) = |3(-x)| - 2 = |3x| - 2$$
Since $f(-x) = f(x)$, the function is even.

31. Finding the values:
$$f(x) = -3x^2 + 1$$
$$-f(x) = -(-3x^2 + 1) = 3x^2 - 1$$
$$f(-x) = -3(-x)^2 + 1 = -3x^2 + 1$$
Since $f(-x) = f(x)$, the function is even.

33. Finding the values:
$$f(x) = -|x| + 1$$
$$-f(x) = -(-|x| + 1) = |x| - 1$$
$$f(-x) = -|-x| + 1 = -|x| + 1$$
Since $f(-x) = f(x)$, the function is even.

35. Finding the values:
$$f(x) = |x - 1|$$
$$-f(x) = -|x - 1|$$
$$f(-x) = |-x - 1| = |x + 1|$$
Since $f(-x) \neq f(x)$ and $f(-x) \neq -f(x)$, the function is neither even nor odd.

37. Finding the values:
$$f(x) = (x^2 + 1)(x - 1)$$
$$-f(x) = -(x^2 + 1)(x - 1)$$
$$f(-x) = ((-x)^2 + 1)(-x - 1) = -(x^2 + 1)(x + 1)$$
Since $f(-x) \neq f(x)$ and $f(-x) \neq -f(x)$, the function is neither even nor odd.

39. Finding the function values:
$$f(-2) = -2(-2)^2 + 5 = -3 \qquad\qquad f(-1) = -2(-1)^2 + 5 = 3$$
The average rate of change is: $\dfrac{f(-1) - f(-2)}{-1 - (-2)} = \dfrac{3 - (-3)}{1} = 6$

41. Finding the function values:
$$f(0) = (0)^3 + 1 = 1 \qquad\qquad f(2) = (2)^3 + 1 = 9$$
The average rate of change is: $\dfrac{f(2) - f(0)}{2 - 0} = \dfrac{9 - 1}{2} = 4$

43. Finding the function values:
$$f(-2) = 2(-2)^2 + 3(-2) - 1 = 1 \qquad\qquad f(-1) = 2(-1)^2 + 3(-1) - 1 = -2$$
The average rate of change is: $\dfrac{f(-1) - f(-2)}{-1 - (-2)} = \dfrac{-2 - 1}{1} = -3$

45. Finding the function values:
$$f(1) = -(1)^4 + 6(1)^2 - 1 = 4 \qquad\qquad f(2) = -(2)^4 + 6(2)^2 - 1 = 7$$
The average rate of change is: $\dfrac{f(2) - f(1)}{2 - 1} = \dfrac{7 - 4}{1} = 3$

47. Finding the function values:
$$f(3) = 2|3| + 4 = 10 \qquad\qquad f(5) = 2|5| + 4 = 14$$
The average rate of change is: $\dfrac{f(5) - f(3)}{5 - 3} = \dfrac{14 - 10}{2} = 2$

49. Finding the function values:
$$f(-4) = \sqrt{-(-4)} = \sqrt{4} = 2 \qquad\qquad f(-3) = \sqrt{-(-3)} = \sqrt{3}$$
The average rate of change is: $\dfrac{f(-3) - f(-4)}{-3 - (-4)} = \dfrac{\sqrt{3} - 2}{1} = \sqrt{3} - 2$

51. Finding the function values:
$$f(a) = 2a - 4 \qquad\qquad f(a+h) = 2(a+h) - 4 = 2a + 2h - 4$$
The average rate of change is: $\dfrac{f(a+h) - f(a)}{(a+h) - a} = \dfrac{(2a+2h-4) - (2a-4)}{h} = \dfrac{2a+2h-4-2a+4}{h} = \dfrac{2h}{h} = 2$

53. Finding the function values:
$$f(a) = a^2 - 1 \qquad\qquad f(a+h) = (a+h)^2 - 1 = a^2 + 2ah + h^2 - 1$$
The average rate of change is:
$$\frac{f(a+h) - f(a)}{(a+h) - a} = \frac{(a^2 + 2ah + h^2 - 1) - (a^2 - 1)}{h} = \frac{a^2 + 2ah + h^2 - 1 - a^2 + 1}{h} = \frac{2ah + h^2}{h} = \frac{h(2a+h)}{h} = 2a + h$$

55. This function is neither even nor odd, as the graph doesn't have y-axis or origin symmetry.

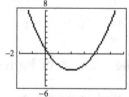

57. This function is odd, since the graph is symmetric about the origin.

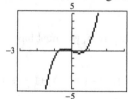

59. This function is even, since the graph is symmetric about the y-axis.

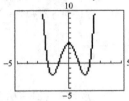

61. This is a decreasing function because as x increases, $d(x)$ decreases. That is, if $x_1 < x_2$, then $d(x_1) > d(x_2)$. This statement holds true only for x positive, and we know that x must be greater than 0 since it represents demand.

63. Finding the function values: $v(0) = 2{,}000 - 300(0) = 2{,}000$; $v(3) = 2{,}000 - 300(3) = 1{,}100$

The average rate of change is: $\dfrac{v(3) - v(0)}{3 - 0} = \dfrac{1{,}100 - 2{,}000}{3} = -300$

The value of the computer decreases at an average rate of \$300 each year over the first 3 years after purchase. The slope is constant, so the average rate of change will be the same on any interval.

65. From 2007 to 2009, the average rate of change is: $\dfrac{30{,}000 - 10{,}000}{2009 - 2007} = \dfrac{20{,}000}{2} = 10{,}000$

From 2009 to 2010, the average rate of change is: $\dfrac{33{,}000 - 30{,}000}{2010 - 2009} = \dfrac{3{,}000}{1} = 3{,}000$

Thus the average rate of change is not the same for both intervals.

67. Completing the table:

Interval	Average Rate of Change
$[1,2]$	-3
$[1.9,2]$	-3.9
$[1.95,2]$	-3.95
$[1.99,2]$	-3.99
$[1.999,2]$	-3.999

As the endpoints of the interval get closer together, the average rate of change over the interval appears to get closer and closer to a single value, in this case, -4.

69. No. It means only that on an interval $[a,b]$, $f(b) - f(a) = 0$, or $f(a) = f(b)$. For example, $f(x) = x^2$ is not constant, but on the interval $[-1,1]$ we have $f(a) = f(b) = 1$ so $\dfrac{f(b) - f(a)}{b - a} = \dfrac{1 - 1}{b - a} = \dfrac{0}{b - a} = 0$.

2.6 The Algebra of Functions

1. A quotient of two polynomial expressions is called a rational expression and is defined whenever the denominator is not equal to 0.

3. The domain is all real numbers, or $(-\infty, \infty)$.

5. For the quantity inside the radical to be non-negative, we must have $x \geq 3$ or $x \leq -3$.
So the domain is $(-\infty, -3] \cup [3, \infty)$.

7. **a.** Finding $(f + g)(x)$: $(f + g)(x) = f(x) + g(x) = (3x - 5) + (-x + 3) = 2x - 2$

The domain is all real numbers, or $(-\infty, \infty)$.

b. Finding $(f - g)(x)$: $(f - g)(x) = f(x) - g(x) = (3x - 5) - (-x + 3) = 3x - 5 + x - 3 = 4x - 8$

The domain is all real numbers, or $(-\infty, \infty)$.

c. Finding $(fg)(x)$: $(fg)(x) = f(x) \cdot g(x) = (3x - 5)(-x + 3) = -3x^2 + 9x + 5x - 15 = -3x^2 + 14x - 15$

The domain is all real numbers, or $(-\infty, \infty)$.

d. Finding $\left(\dfrac{f}{g}\right)(x)$: $\left(\dfrac{f}{g}\right)(x) = \dfrac{f(x)}{g(x)} = \dfrac{3x-5}{-x+3} = \dfrac{3x-5}{3-x}$

The domain is all real numbers $x \neq 3$, or $(-\infty, 3) \cup (3, \infty)$.

9. **a.** Finding $(f+g)(x)$: $(f+g)(x) = f(x) + g(x) = (x-3) + (x^2+1) = x^2 + x - 2$

The domain is all real numbers, or $(-\infty, \infty)$.

b. Finding $(f-g)(x)$: $(f-g)(x) = f(x) - g(x) = (x-3) - (x^2+1) = x - 3 - x^2 - 1 = -x^2 + x - 4$

The domain is all real numbers, or $(-\infty, \infty)$.

c. Finding $(fg)(x)$: $(fg)(x) = f(x) \cdot g(x) = (x-3)(x^2+1) = x^3 + x - 3x^2 - 3 = x^3 - 3x^2 + x - 3$

The domain is all real numbers, or $(-\infty, \infty)$.

d. Finding $\left(\dfrac{f}{g}\right)(x)$: $\left(\dfrac{f}{g}\right)(x) = \dfrac{f(x)}{g(x)} = \dfrac{x-3}{x^2+1}$

The domain is all real numbers, or $(-\infty, \infty)$.

11. **a.** Finding $(f+g)(x)$: $(f+g)(x) = f(x) + g(x) = \dfrac{1}{x} + \dfrac{1}{2x-1} = \dfrac{(2x-1)+x}{x(2x-1)} = \dfrac{3x-1}{x(2x-1)}$

The domain is all real numbers $x \neq 0, \dfrac{1}{2}$, or $(-\infty, 0) \cup \left(0, \dfrac{1}{2}\right) \cup \left(\dfrac{1}{2}, \infty\right)$.

b. Finding $(f-g)(x)$: $(f-g)(x) = f(x) - g(x) = \dfrac{1}{x} - \dfrac{1}{2x-1} = \dfrac{(2x-1)-x}{x(2x-1)} = \dfrac{x-1}{x(2x-1)}$

The domain is all real numbers $x \neq 0, \dfrac{1}{2}$, or $(-\infty, 0) \cup \left(0, \dfrac{1}{2}\right) \cup \left(\dfrac{1}{2}, \infty\right)$.

c. Finding $(fg)(x)$: $(fg)(x) = f(x) \cdot g(x) = \dfrac{1}{x} \cdot \dfrac{1}{2x-1} = \dfrac{1}{x(2x-1)}$

The domain is all real numbers $x \neq 0, \dfrac{1}{2}$, or $(-\infty, 0) \cup \left(0, \dfrac{1}{2}\right) \cup \left(\dfrac{1}{2}, \infty\right)$.

d. Finding $\left(\dfrac{f}{g}\right)(x)$: $\left(\dfrac{f}{g}\right)(x) = \dfrac{f(x)}{g(x)} = \dfrac{\dfrac{1}{x}}{\dfrac{1}{2x-1}} = \dfrac{2x-1}{x}$

The domain is all real numbers $x \neq 0, \dfrac{1}{2}$, or $(-\infty, 0) \cup \left(0, \dfrac{1}{2}\right) \cup \left(\dfrac{1}{2}, \infty\right)$.

13. **a.** Finding $(f+g)(x)$: $(f+g)(x) = f(x) + g(x) = \sqrt{x} + (-x+1) = \sqrt{x} - x + 1$

The domain is all real numbers $x \geq 0$, or $[0, \infty)$.

b. Finding $(f-g)(x)$: $(f-g)(x) = f(x) - g(x) = \sqrt{x} - (-x+1) = \sqrt{x} + x - 1$

The domain is all real numbers $x \geq 0$, or $[0, \infty)$.

c. Finding $(fg)(x)$: $(fg)(x) = f(x) \cdot g(x) = \sqrt{x} \cdot (-x+1) = -x\sqrt{x} + \sqrt{x}$

The domain is all real numbers $x \geq 0$, or $[0, \infty)$.

d. Finding $\left(\dfrac{f}{g}\right)(x)$: $\left(\dfrac{f}{g}\right)(x) = \dfrac{f(x)}{g(x)} = \dfrac{\sqrt{x}}{-x+1}$

The domain is all real numbers $x \geq 0$ and $x \neq 1$, or $[0, 1) \cup (1, \infty)$.

15. **a.** Finding $(f+g)(x)$: $(f+g)(x)=f(x)+g(x)=|x|+\dfrac{1}{2x+5}$

The domain is all real numbers $x\neq-\dfrac{5}{2}$, or $\left(-\infty,-\dfrac{5}{2}\right)\cup\left(-\dfrac{5}{2},\infty\right)$.

b. Finding $(f-g)(x)$: $(f-g)(x)=f(x)-g(x)=|x|-\dfrac{1}{2x+5}$

The domain is all real numbers $x\neq-\dfrac{5}{2}$, or $\left(-\infty,-\dfrac{5}{2}\right)\cup\left(-\dfrac{5}{2},\infty\right)$.

c. Finding $(fg)(x)$: $(fg)(x)=f(x)\cdot g(x)=|x|\cdot\dfrac{1}{2x+5}=\dfrac{|x|}{2x+5}$

The domain is all real numbers $x\neq-\dfrac{5}{2}$, or $\left(-\infty,-\dfrac{5}{2}\right)\cup\left(-\dfrac{5}{2},\infty\right)$.

d. Finding $\left(\dfrac{f}{g}\right)(x)$: $\left(\dfrac{f}{g}\right)(x)=\dfrac{f(x)}{g(x)}=\dfrac{|x|}{\dfrac{1}{2x+5}}=|x|(2x+5)$

The domain is all real numbers $x\neq-\dfrac{5}{2}$, or $\left(-\infty,-\dfrac{5}{2}\right)\cup\left(-\dfrac{5}{2},\infty\right)$.

17. Finding the function and then the value:

$$(f+g)(x)=f(x)+g(x)=-x^2+x+\dfrac{2}{x+1}$$

$$(f+g)(1)=-(1)^2+(1)+\dfrac{2}{(1)+1}=-1+1+1=1$$

19. Finding the function and then the value:

$$(g+h)(x)=g(x)+h(x)=\dfrac{2}{x+1}+(-2x+1)=\dfrac{2}{x+1}-2x+1$$

$$(g+h)(0)=\dfrac{2}{(0)+1}-2(0)+1=2-0+1=3$$

21. Finding the function and then the value:

$$(f-g)(x)=f(x)-g(x)=-x^2+x-\dfrac{2}{x+1}$$

$$(f-g)(2)=-(2)^2+(2)-\dfrac{2}{(2)+1}=-4+2-\dfrac{2}{3}=-\dfrac{8}{3}$$

23. Finding the function and then the value:

$$(g-h)(x)=g(x)-h(x)=\dfrac{2}{x+1}-(-2x+1)=\dfrac{2}{x+1}+2x-1$$

$$(g-h)(-2)=\dfrac{2}{(-2)+1}+2(-2)-1=-2-4-1=-7$$

25. Finding the function and then the value:

$$(fg)(x)=f(x)\cdot g(x)=(-x^2+x)\cdot\dfrac{2}{x+1}=\dfrac{-2x^2+2x}{x+1}$$

$$(fg)(3)=\dfrac{-2(3)^2+2(3)}{(3)+1}=\dfrac{-18+6}{4}=-3$$

27. Finding the function and then the value:

$$(gh)(x) = g(x) \cdot h(x) = \frac{2}{x+1} \cdot (-2x+1) = \frac{-4x+2}{x+1}$$

$$(gh)(-3) = \frac{-4(-3)+2}{(-3)+1} = \frac{14}{-2} = -7$$

29. Finding the function and then the value:

$$\left(\frac{f}{g}\right)(x) = \frac{f(x)}{g(x)} = \frac{-x^2+x}{\frac{2}{x+1}} = \frac{(-x^2+x)(x+1)}{2} = \frac{-x^3+x}{2}$$

$$\left(\frac{f}{g}\right)(-2) = \frac{-(-2)^3+(-2)}{2} = \frac{8-2}{2} = 3$$

31. Finding the function and then the value:

$$\left(\frac{f}{h}\right)(x) = \frac{f(x)}{h(x)} = \frac{-x^2+x}{-2x+1} = \frac{x^2-x}{2x-1}$$

$$\left(\frac{f}{h}\right)(1) = \frac{(1)^2-(1)}{2(1)-1} = \frac{0}{1} = 0$$

33. Evaluating the function: $f(-1) = -2$

35. Evaluating the function: $(f \circ g)(-2) = f(g(-2)) = f(0) = 3$

37. Evaluating the function: $(g \circ f)(-1) = g(f(-1)) = g(-2) = 0$

39. Evaluating the function: $(g \circ f)(0) = g(f(0)) = g(3)$

Since $g(3)$ is undefined, $(g \circ f)(0)$ is undefined.

41. Finding the function and then the value:

$$(f \circ h)(x) = f(h(x)) = f(-3x) = (-3x)^2 + (-3x) = 9x^2 - 3x$$

$$(f \circ h)(5) = 9(5)^2 - 3(5) = 210$$

43. Finding the function and then the value:

$$(h \circ g)(x) = h(g(x)) = h(\sqrt{x}) = -3\sqrt{x}$$

$$(h \circ g)(4) = -3\sqrt{4} = -3(2) = -6$$

45. Finding the function and then the value:

$$(f \circ g)(x) = f(g(x)) = f(\sqrt{x}) = (\sqrt{x})^2 + \sqrt{x} = x + \sqrt{x}$$

$$(f \circ g)(4) = 4 + \sqrt{4} = 4 + 2 = 6$$

47. Finding the function and then the value:

$$(g \circ f)(x) = g(f(x)) = g(x^2+x) = \sqrt{x^2+x}$$

$$(g \circ f)(2) = \sqrt{(2)^2+2} = \sqrt{4+2} = \sqrt{6}$$

49. Finding the function and then the value:

$$(h \circ f)(x) = h(f(x)) = h(x^2+x) = -3(x^2+x) = -3x^2 - 3x$$

$$(h \circ f)(2) = -3(2)^2 - 3(2) = -12 - 6 = -18$$

51. Finding the function and then the value:

$$(h \circ f)(x) = h(f(x)) = h(x^2 + x) = -3(x^2 + x) = -3x^2 - 3x$$

$$(h \circ f)\left(\frac{1}{2}\right) = -3\left(\frac{1}{2}\right)^2 - 3\left(\frac{1}{2}\right) = -\frac{3}{4} - \frac{3}{2} = -\frac{9}{4}$$

53. Finding $(f \circ g)(x)$: $(f \circ g)(x) = f(g(x)) = f(x+1) = -(x+1)^2 + 1 = -(x^2 + 2x + 1) + 1 = -x^2 - 2x$

The domain is all real numbers, or $(-\infty, \infty)$.

Finding $(g \circ f)(x)$: $(g \circ f)(x) = g(f(x)) = g(-x^2 + 1) = (-x^2 + 1) + 1 = -x^2 + 2$

The domain is all real numbers, or $(-\infty, \infty)$.

55. Finding $(f \circ g)(x)$: $(f \circ g)(x) = f(g(x)) = f\left(\frac{x+1}{4}\right) = 4\left(\frac{x+1}{4}\right) - 1 = x + 1 - 1 = x$

The domain is all real numbers, or $(-\infty, \infty)$.

Finding $(g \circ f)(x)$: $(g \circ f)(x) = g(f(x)) = g(4x - 1) = \frac{(4x-1)+1}{4} = \frac{4x}{4} = x$

The domain is all real numbers, or $(-\infty, \infty)$.

57. Finding $(f \circ g)(x)$:

$$\begin{aligned}
(f \circ g)(x) &= f(g(x)) \\
&= f(x+2) \\
&= 3(x+2)^2 + 4(x+2) \\
&= 3(x^2 + 4x + 4) + 4x + 8 \\
&= 3x^2 + 12x + 12 + 4x + 8 \\
&= 3x^2 + 16x + 20
\end{aligned}$$

The domain is all real numbers, or $(-\infty, \infty)$.

Finding $(g \circ f)(x)$: $(g \circ f)(x) = g(f(x)) = g(3x^2 + 4x) = 3x^2 + 4x + 2$

The domain is all real numbers, or $(-\infty, \infty)$.

59. Finding $(f \circ g)(x)$: $(f \circ g)(x) = f(g(x)) = f(2x+5) = \dfrac{1}{2x+5}$

The domain is all real numbers $x \ne -\dfrac{5}{2}$, or $\left(-\infty, -\dfrac{5}{2}\right) \cup \left(-\dfrac{5}{2}, \infty\right)$.

Finding $(g \circ f)(x)$: $(g \circ f)(x) = g(f(x)) = g\left(\dfrac{1}{x}\right) = 2\left(\dfrac{1}{x}\right) + 5 = \dfrac{2}{x} + \dfrac{5x}{x} = \dfrac{5x+2}{x}$

The domain is all real numbers $x \ne 0$, or $(-\infty, 0) \cup (0, \infty)$.

61. Finding $(f \circ g)(x)$: $(f \circ g)(x) = f(g(x)) = f(2x^2) = \dfrac{3}{2(2x^2)+1} = \dfrac{3}{4x^2+1}$

The domain is all real numbers, or $(-\infty, \infty)$.

Finding $(g \circ f)(x)$: $(g \circ f)(x) = g(f(x)) = g\left(\dfrac{3}{2x+1}\right) = 2\left(\dfrac{3}{2x+1}\right)^2 = 2 \cdot \dfrac{9}{(2x+1)^2} = \dfrac{18}{(2x+1)^2}$

The domain is all real numbers $x \ne -\dfrac{1}{2}$, or $\left(-\infty, -\dfrac{1}{2}\right) \cup \left(-\dfrac{1}{2}, \infty\right)$.

63. Finding $(f \circ g)(x)$: $(f \circ g)(x) = f(g(x)) = f(-3x-4) = \sqrt{(-3x-4)+1} = \sqrt{-3x-3}$

To find the domain, we solve the inequality:
$$-3x-3 \geq 0$$
$$-3x \geq 3$$
$$x \leq -1$$

The domain is all real numbers $x \leq -1$, or $(-\infty, -1]$.

Finding $(g \circ f)(x)$: $(g \circ f)(x) = g(f(x)) = g(\sqrt{x+1}) = -3\sqrt{x+1}-4$

The domain is all real numbers $x \geq -1$, or $[-1, \infty)$.

65. Finding $(f \circ g)(x)$: $(f \circ g)(x) = f(g(x)) = f\left(\dfrac{2x}{x-1}\right) = \left|\dfrac{2x}{x-1}\right|$

The domain is all real numbers $x \neq 1$, or $(-\infty, 1) \cup (1, \infty)$.

Finding $(g \circ f)(x)$: $(g \circ f)(x) = g(f(x)) = g(|x|) = \dfrac{2|x|}{|x|-1}$

The domain is all real numbers $x \neq -1, 1$, or $(-\infty, -1) \cup (-1, 1) \cup (1, \infty)$.

67. Finding $(f \circ g)(x)$: $(f \circ g)(x) = f(g(x)) = f(x+1) = (x+1)^2 - 2(x+1)+1 = x^2 + 2x+1-2x-2+1 = x^2$

The domain is all real numbers, or $(-\infty, \infty)$.

Finding $(g \circ f)(x)$: $(g \circ f)(x) = g(f(x)) = g(x^2-2x+1) = (x^2-2x+1)+1 = x^2-2x+2$

The domain is all real numbers, or $(-\infty, \infty)$.

69. Finding $(f \circ g)(x)$: $(f \circ g)(x) = f(g(x)) = f(|x|) = \dfrac{|x|^2+1}{|x|^2-1} = \dfrac{x^2+1}{x^2-1}$

The domain is all real numbers $x \neq -1, 1$, or $(-\infty, -1) \cup (-1, 1) \cup (1, \infty)$.

Finding $(g \circ f)(x)$: $(g \circ f)(x) = g(f(x)) = g\left(\dfrac{x^2+1}{x^2-1}\right) = \left|\dfrac{x^2+1}{x^2-1}\right|$

The domain is all real numbers $x \neq -1, 1$, or $(-\infty, -1) \cup (-1, 1) \cup (1, \infty)$.

71. Finding $(f \circ g)(x)$:

$$(f \circ g)(x) = f(g(x))$$
$$= f\left(\frac{2x+1}{3x-1}\right)$$
$$= \frac{1}{\left(\dfrac{2x+1}{3x-1}\right)^2 + 1}$$
$$= \frac{1}{\dfrac{4x^2+4x+1}{9x^2-6x+1} + 1}$$
$$= \frac{9x^2-6x+1}{4x^2+4x+1 + 1 \cdot (9x^2-6x+1)}$$
$$= \frac{9x^2-6x+1}{13x^2-2x+2}$$

The domain is all real numbers $x \neq \dfrac{1}{3}$, or $\left(-\infty, \dfrac{1}{3}\right) \cup \left(\dfrac{1}{3}, \infty\right)$.

Finding $(g \circ f)(x)$: $(g \circ f)(x) = g(f(x)) = g\left(\dfrac{1}{x^2+1}\right) = \dfrac{2\left(\dfrac{1}{x^2+1}\right)+1}{3\left(\dfrac{1}{x^2+1}\right)-1} = \dfrac{2+(x^2+1)}{3-(x^2+1)} = \dfrac{x^2+3}{2-x^2}$

To find the domain, set the denominator equal to 0:

$2 - x^2 = 0$

$x^2 = 2$

$x = \pm\sqrt{2}$

The domain is all real numbers $x \neq -\sqrt{2}, \sqrt{2}$, or $\left(-\infty, -\sqrt{2}\right) \cup \left(-\sqrt{2}, \sqrt{2}\right) \cup \left(\sqrt{2}, \infty\right)$.

73. The two functions are: $g(x) = 3x-1, f(x) = x^2$

75. The two functions are: $g(x) = 4x^2 - 1, f(x) = \sqrt[3]{x}$

77. The two functions are: $g(x) = 2x+5, f(x) = \dfrac{1}{x}$

79. The two functions are: $g(x) = x^2 + 1, f(x) = \sqrt{x} + 5$

81. The two functions are: $g(x) = 5x+7, f(x) = \sqrt[3]{x} - 2$

83. Evaluating the function: $(f \circ f)(-1) = f(f(-1)) = f\left(-(-1)^2\right) = f(-1) = -(-1)^2 = -1$

85. Finding the composition: $(f \circ f)(t) = f(f(t)) = f\left(-t^2\right) = -\left(-t^2\right)^2 = -t^4$

The domain is all real numbers, or $(-\infty, \infty)$.

87. Evaluating the function: $(f \circ f)(2) = f(f(2)) = f(3(2)+1) = f(7) = 3(7)+1 = 22$

89. Finding the composition: $(f \circ f)(t) = f(f(t)) = f(3t+1) = 3(3t+1)+1 = 9t+3+1 = 9t+4$

The domain is all real numbers, or $(-\infty, \infty)$.

91. First simplify the expression: $f(x+h) = 3(x+h)-1 = 3x+3h-1$

Now finding the difference quotient: $\dfrac{f(x+h)-f(x)}{h} = \dfrac{3x+3h+1-(3x+1)}{h} = \dfrac{3x+3h+1-3x-1}{h} = \dfrac{3h}{h} = 3$

93. First simplify the expression: $f(x+h) = -(x+h)^2 + (x+h) = -\left(x^2+2xh+h^2\right)+x+h = -x^2-2xh-h^2+x+h$

Now finding the difference quotient:

$\dfrac{f(x+h)-f(x)}{h} = \dfrac{-x^2-2xh-h^2+x+h-\left(-x^2+x\right)}{h}$

$= \dfrac{-x^2-2xh-h^2+x+h+x^2-x}{h}$

$= \dfrac{-2xh-h^2+h}{h}$

$= \dfrac{h(-2x-h+1)}{h}$

$= -2x-h+1$

95. First simplify the expression: $f(x+h)-f(x) = \dfrac{1}{x+h-3} - \dfrac{1}{x-3} = \dfrac{(x-3)-(x+h-3)}{(x+h-3)(x-3)} = \dfrac{-h}{(x+h-3)(x-3)}$

Now finding the difference quotient:

$\dfrac{f(x+h)-f(x)}{h} = \dfrac{\dfrac{-h}{(x+h-3)(x-3)}}{h} = \dfrac{-h}{(x+h-3)(x-3)} \cdot \dfrac{1}{h} = \dfrac{-1}{(x+h-3)(x-3)} = \dfrac{-1}{x^2-6x+9+xh-3h}$

97. Finding the profit function: $P(t) = R(t) - C(t) = 327 + 10t - (246 + 20t) = 327 + 10t - 246 - 20t = 81 - 10t$

99. First find the function: $(np)(x) = n(x) \cdot p(x) = (-5x + 100)(-1.5x + 30) = 7.5x^2 - 300x + 3000$

Evaluating the function: $(np)(3) = 7.5(3)^2 - 300(3) + 3{,}000 = \$2{,}167.50$

This is the revenue generated by the sale of the book during the third month after its release.

101. Finding the composition: $(f \circ R)(t) = f(R(t)) = f(40 + 2t) = 0.75(40 + 2t) = 30 + 1.5t$

This function represents the GlobalEx revenue in euros.

103. Finding the composition: $(C \circ A)(r) = C(A(r)) = C(4\pi r^2) = 6.4516(4\pi r^2) = 25.8064\pi r^2$

This function represents the surface area of a sphere in square centimeters based on its radius in inches.

105. In general, it is not true. For example, suppose $f(x) = x + 5$ and $g(x) = 2x$. Then:

$$(fg)(x) = f(x) \cdot g(x) = (x + 5) \cdot 2x = 2x^2 + 10x$$
$$(f \circ g)(x) = f(g(x)) = f(2x) = 2x + 5$$

Thus $(fg)(x) \neq (f \circ g)(x)$.

107. Finding the two functions:

$$(f + g)(x) = f(x) + g(x) = (ax + b) + (cx + d) = ax + cx + b + d = (a + c)x + (b + d)$$
$$(f - g)(x) = f(x) - g(x) = (ax + b) - (cx + d) = ax - cx + b - d = (a - c)x + (b - d)$$

Since $a, b, c,$ and d are constants, so are $a + c$, $a - c$, $b + d$, and $b - d$.
Therefore the resulting functions are linear functions.

2.7 Transformations of the Graph of a Function

1. The graph of $g(t)$ is the graph of $f(t) = t^2$ shifted up by 1 unit. Sketching the graph:

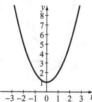

3. The graph of $f(x)$ is the graph of $g(x) = \sqrt{x}$ shifted down by 2 units. Sketching the graph:

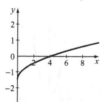

5. The graph of $h(x)$ is the graph of $f(x) = |x|$ shifted right by 2 units. Sketching the graph:

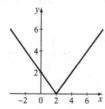

7. The graph of $F(s)$ is the graph of $f(s) = s^2$ shifted left by 5 units. Sketching the graph:

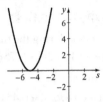

9. The graph of $f(x)$ is the graph of $g(x) = \sqrt{x}$ shifted right by 4 units. Sketching the graph:

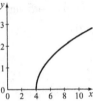

11. The graph of $H(x)$ is the graph of $g(x) = |x|$ shifted right by 2 units and up by 1 unit. Sketching the graph:

13. The graph of $S(x)$ is the graph of $g(x) = x^2$ shifted left by 3 units and down by 1 unit. Sketching the graph:

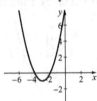

15. The graph of $H(t)$ is the graph of $g(t) = t^2$ stretched vertically away from the x-axis by a factor of 3. Sketching the graph:

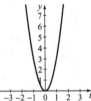

17. The graph of $S(x)$ is the graph of $f(x) = |x|$ reflected across the x-axis and vertically stretched away from the x-axis by a factor of 4. Sketching the graph:

19. The graph of $H(s)$ is the graph of $f(s) = |s|$ reflected across the x-axis and shifted down by 3 units. Sketching the graph:

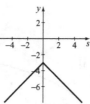

21. The graph of $h(x)$ is the graph of $f(x) = |x|$ reflected across the x-axis, compressed vertically toward the x-axis by a factor of $\frac{1}{2}$, shifted left by 1 unit, and shifted down by 3 units. Sketching the graph:

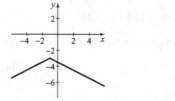

23. The graph of $g(x)$ is the graph of $f(x) = x^2$ reflected across the x-axis, vertically stretched away from the x-axis by a factor of 3, shifted left by 2 units, and shifted down by 4 units. Sketching the graph:

25. The graph of $f(x)$ is the graph of $g(x) = |x|$ compressed horizontally toward the y-axis, scaled by a factor of $\frac{1}{2}$. Sketching the graph:

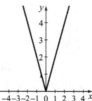

27. The graph of $f(x)$ is the graph of $g(x) = x^2$ compressed horizontally toward the y-axis, scaled by a factor of $\frac{1}{2}$. Sketching the graph:

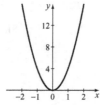

29. The graph of $g(x)$ is the graph of $f(x) = \sqrt{x}$ compressed horizontally toward the y-axis and scaled by a factor of $\frac{1}{3}$. Sketching the graph:

31. The graph is shifted left by 1 unit: $g(x) = |x+1|$

33. The graph is reflected across the x-axis and shifted up by 1 unit: $g(x) = -|x|+1$

35. The graph is shifted right by 2 units: $g(x) = (x-2)^2$

37. The graph is shifted right by 1 unit and down by 2 units: $g(x) = (x-1)^2 - 2$

39. The function is: $g(t) = |t+4| - 3$

41. The function is: $g(t) = -3(t-1)^2$

43. The function is: $h(x) = (2x)^2 - 4$

45. Sketching the graph:

47. Sketching the graph:

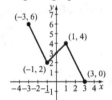

49. Sketching the graph:

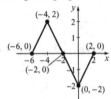

51. Sketching the graph:

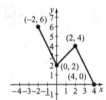

53. Sketching the graph:

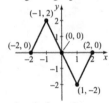

55. Sketching the graph:

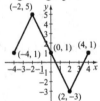

57. Sketching the graph:

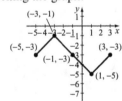

59. Sketching the graph:

61. The value is $k = -2$.

63. The value is $k = 1$.

65. Completing the table:

x	$f(x)$	$g(x) = f(x) - 3$
-2	36	33
-1	25	22
0	16	13
1	9	6
2	4	1

67. The graph of $f(x)$ is a translation of $h(x)$ to the left by 3.5 units, whereas $g(x)$ is a translation of $h(x)$ up by 3.5 units. Sketching the graphs:

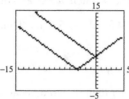

69. The graph of $f(x - 4.5)$ is a translation of $f(x)$ to the right by 4.5 units. Sketching the graphs:

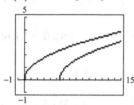

71. The graphs are different. The graph of $-2f(x)$ is a vertical scaling of $f(x)$ by a factor of 2 away from the x-axis, and then reflected across the x-axis. The graph of $f(-2x)$ is a horizontal scaling of $f(x)$ by a factor of $\dfrac{1}{2}$ toward the y-axis, and then reflected across the y-axis. Sketching the graphs:

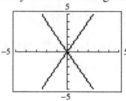

73. The graph of g is the graph of f shifted to the right by 7 units. Sketching the graphs:

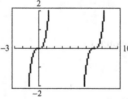

75. Let T represent the sales tax. The function is: $T(x) = 6\%$ of $P(x) = 0.06P(x)$

77. **a.** The cost function is given by: $C(x) = 450 + 3x$

  b. The graph of the decreased cost function has a lower y-intercept but the same slope as the graph of the original cost function. Sketching the graphs:

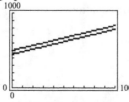

79. **a.** Substituting $h = 0$ and $t = 1$:
$$s(t) = -16t^2 + 30t$$
$$s(1) = -16(1)^2 + 30(1) = 14$$

b. Substituting $h = 20$ and $t = 1$:
$$s(t) = -16t^2 + 30t + 20$$
$$s(1) = -16(1)^2 + 30(1) + 20 = 34$$

c. The value of $s(t)$ is increased by h meters when $h > 0$ and decreased by $|h|$ meters when $h < 0$.

81. From the x-coordinates, the shift is $2 - (-3) = 5$ left by 5 units. Thus, the function is $g(x) = (x + 5)^2$.

83. **a.** The function is: $g(x) = 2|x| + 3$

b. The function is: $g(x) = 2(|x| + 3) = 2|x| + 6$

c. In part **b**, the y-intercept is 3 units higher than in part a because scaling by 2 after adding 3 units effectively scales the original equation by 2 and then moves it up 6 units. In part **a**, the function is moved up by 3 units after it is scaled by 2.

2.8 Linear Functions and Models; Variation

1. Using the points $(x_1, y_1) = (3, 5)$ and $(x_2, y_2) = (4, 9)$ in the slope formula: $m = \dfrac{9 - 5}{4 - 3} = \dfrac{4}{1} = 4$

Using the point-slope form of a function: $f(x) = 4(x - 3) + 5 = 4x - 12 + 5 = 4x - 7$

3. Using the points $(x_1, y_1) = (3.1, -2.5)$ and $(x_2, y_2) = (5.6, 3.5)$ in the slope formula: $m = \dfrac{3.5 - (-2.5)}{5.6 - 3.1} = \dfrac{6}{2.5} = 2.4$

Using the point-slope form of a function: $f(x) = 2.4(x - 3.1) - 2.5 = 2.4x - 7.44 - 2.5 = 2.4x - 9.94$

5. Using the points $(x_1, y_1) = (30, 600)$ and $(x_2, y_2) = (50, 900)$ in the slope formula: $m = \dfrac{900 - 600}{50 - 30} = \dfrac{300}{20} = 15$

Using the point-slope form of a function: $f(x) = 15(x - 30) + 600 = 15x - 450 + 600 = 15x + 150$

7. Substituting $x = 10$ and $y = 40$ in the variation equation:
$$y = kx$$
$$40 = k(10)$$
$$k = 4$$
The variation equation is $y = 4x$.

9. Substituting $x = 2$ and $y = 5$ in the variation equation:
$$y = \frac{k}{x}$$
$$5 = \frac{k}{2}$$
$$k = 10$$
The variation equation is $y = \dfrac{10}{x}$.

11. Substituting $x = 10$ and $y = 35$ in the variation equation:
$$y = kx$$
$$35 = k(10)$$
$$k = 3.5$$
The variation equation is $y = 3.5x$.

13. Substituting $x = 6$ and $y = 2.5$ in the variation equation:

$$y = \frac{k}{x}$$
$$2.5 = \frac{k}{6}$$
$$k = 15$$

The variation equation is $y = \frac{15}{x}$.

15. Substituting $x = 2$ and $y = \frac{1}{3}$ in the variation equation:

$$y = kx$$
$$\frac{1}{3} = k(2)$$
$$k = \frac{1}{6}$$

The variation equation is $y = \frac{1}{6}x$.

17. Substituting $x = 8$ and $y = \frac{3}{4}$ in the variation equation:

$$y = \frac{k}{x}$$
$$\frac{3}{4} = \frac{k}{8}$$
$$k = 6$$

The variation equation is $y = \frac{6}{x}$.

19. Substituting $x = 7$ and $y = 35$ in the variation equation:

$$y = kx$$
$$35 = k(7)$$
$$k = 5$$

The variation equation is $y = 5x$.

21. Substituting $x = 7$ and $y = 14$ in the variation equation:

$$y = \frac{k}{x}$$
$$14 = \frac{k}{7}$$
$$k = 98$$

The variation equation is $y = \frac{98}{x}$.

23. Let n represent the number of minutes and C represent the cost of the call. The function is: $C(n) = 4.50 + 0.07n$

25. Using the points $(32°F, 0°C)$ and $(212°F, 100°C)$, first find the slope: $m = \frac{100 - 0}{212 - 32} = \frac{100}{180} = \frac{5}{9}$

Using the point-slope form of the function: $C(F) = \frac{5}{9}(F - 32) + 0 = \frac{5}{9}F - \frac{160}{9}$

27. Let T represent the temperature and V the volume. Substituting $T = 40$ and $V = 50$ in the variation equation:

$$V = kT$$

$$50 = k(40)$$

$$k = \frac{50}{40} = \frac{5}{4}$$

The variation equation is $V = \frac{5}{4}T$. Substituting $T = 60$: $V = \frac{5}{4}(60) = 75$

The volume at 60°C is 75 cc.

29. Substituting $x = 8$ and $y = 5$ in the variation equation:

$$y = kx$$

$$5 = k(8)$$

$$k = \frac{5}{8}$$

The variation equation is $y = \frac{5}{8}x$. Substituting $x = 20$: $y = \frac{5}{8}(20) = 12.5$

The rise is 12.5 feet when the run is 20 feet.

31. Substituting $t = 5$ and $p = 10$ in the variation equation:

$$t = \frac{k}{p}$$

$$5 = \frac{k}{10}$$

$$k = 50$$

The variation equation is $t = \frac{50}{p}$. Substituting $p = 15$: $t = \frac{50}{15} = \frac{10}{3} = 3\frac{1}{3}$

It will take them $3\frac{1}{3}$ days.

33. **a.** Let m represent the miles driven and C represent the total cost. The function is: $C(m) = 19.95 + 0.99m$

  b. The slope is 0.99. This represents the increase in the total cost for each additional mile driven.
The y-intercept is $(0, 19.95)$. This represents the cost for renting the truck for one day when 0 miles are driven.

  c. Evaluating the function: $C(56) = 19.95 + 0.99(56) = 19.95 + 55.44 = 75.39$

It will cost $75.39 to rent the truck and drive 56 miles.

35. **a.** Sketching the graph:

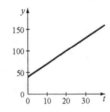

  b. The slope is given by: $m = \frac{18}{6} = 3$

  c. The slope represents the number of additional visitors each month, in millions.

  d. Writing the function: $v(t) = 3t + 40$

  e. July, 2012 corresponds to $t = 10$: Evaluating the function: $v(10) = 3(10) + 40 = 70$

There are 70 million visitors expected in July 2012.

37. **a.** Finding the slope: $m = \dfrac{29.2-18.2}{2011-2001} = \dfrac{11}{10} = 1.1$

When $t = 0, y = 18.2$, so the function is: $f(t) = 1.1t + 18.2$

b. The slope is 1.1. The consumption increases by 1.1 gallons per year.

c. The y-intercept is $(0, 18.2)$. This signifies the gallons of bottled water consumed per person in 2001.

39. **a.** Let P represent the percentage of people buying designer frames and t represent the years since 2008. Using the points $(0, 20\%)$ and $(3, 29\%)$ to find the slope: $m = \dfrac{P_2 - P_1}{t_2 - t_1} = \dfrac{29-20}{3-0} = \dfrac{9}{3} = 3$

The function is: $P(t) = 3t + 20$

b. In 2014, $t = 2014 - 2008 = 6$. Evaluating the function: $P(6) = 3(6) + 20 = 38$

The predicted percentage of people buying designer frames in 2014 is 38%.

c. Finding when $P = 50\%$:

$50 = 3t + 20$

$30 = 3t$

$t = 10$

It is predicted that the percentage of people buying designer frames will reach 50% in 2018 + 10 = 2018.

d. In 2038, $t = 2038 - 2008 = 30$. Evaluating the function: $P(22) = 3(30) + 20 = 110$

No, because the model predicts a percentage of consumers over 100% in 2038.

e. This model cannot accurately predict the buying habits over a long period of time.

41. **a.** Finding the rate of change: $\dfrac{\text{change in volume}}{\text{change in year}} = \dfrac{200{,}000 - 175{,}000}{2011 - 2007} = \dfrac{25{,}000}{4} = 6{,}250$

Traffic increased by 6,250 vehicles per year. This is the slope of a linear model of the traffic volume.

b. Let t represent the number of years since 2007 and T the traffic volume. The function is: $T(t) = 6{,}250t + 175{,}000$

In 2013, $t = 2013 - 2007 = 6$. Evaluating the function: $T(6) = 6{,}250(6) + 175{,}000 = 212{,}500$

The average weekday traffic flow for 2013 was 212,500 vehicles.

43. **a.** The percentage is decreasing over time.

b. Let m represent the mobility rate. The best-fit line is given by: $m(t) = -0.114t + 20.34$

45. No, because direct variation refers to an equation of the form $y = kx$, not $y = kx + b, b \neq 0$.

Chapter 2 Review Exercises

1. Finding the slope: $m = \dfrac{5-0}{0-(-2)} = \dfrac{5}{2}$

2. Finding the slope: $m = \dfrac{5-(-6)}{-4-1} = -\dfrac{11}{5}$

3. Finding the slope: $m = \dfrac{3-1}{-\dfrac{1}{2} - \dfrac{2}{3}} = \dfrac{2}{-7/6} = -\dfrac{12}{7}$

4. Finding the slope: $m = \dfrac{-3.5 - 5.5}{2.1 - 4.1} = \dfrac{-9}{-2} = 4.5$

5. Using the point-slope formula:

$y - (-1) = -2(x - 4)$

$y + 1 = -2x + 8$

$y = -2x + 7$

Graphing the line:

6. The vertical line has equation $x = 5$. Graphing the line:

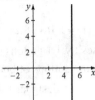

7. Finding the slope: $m = \dfrac{3-0}{0-(-2)} = \dfrac{3}{2}$

Since the y-intercept is $(0, 3)$, the slope-intercept equation is: $y = \dfrac{3}{2}x + 3$

Graphing the line:

8. Finding the slope: $m = \dfrac{-2-0}{0-1} = \dfrac{-2}{-1} = 2$

Since the y-intercept is $(0, -2)$, the slope-intercept equation is: $y = 2x - 2$

Graphing the line:

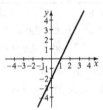

9. Finding the slope: $m = \dfrac{-7-(-3)}{12-(-8)} = \dfrac{-4}{20} = -\dfrac{1}{5}$

Using the point-slope formula:

$$y - (-3) = -\frac{1}{5}\left(x - (-8)\right)$$

$$y + 3 = -\frac{1}{5}(x + 8)$$

$$y + 3 = -\frac{1}{5}x - \frac{8}{5}$$

$$y = -\frac{1}{5}x - \frac{23}{5}$$

Graphing the line:

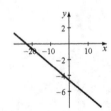

10. Finding the slope: $m = \dfrac{5-(-5)}{0-(-3)} = \dfrac{10}{3}$

Since the y-intercept is $(0, 5)$, the slope-intercept equation is: $y = \dfrac{10}{3}x + 5$

Graphing the line:

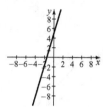

11. Solving for y to find the slope:
$$x - y = 1$$
$$-y = -x + 1$$
$$y = x - 1$$

Since the slope is 1, the perpendicular slope is -1. Using the point-slope formula:
$$y - 2 = -1(x + 1)$$
$$y - 2 = -x - 1$$
$$y = -x + 1$$

Graphing the line:

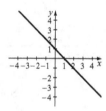

12. Solving for y to find the slope:
$$-3x + y = 4$$
$$y = 3x + 4$$

Since the slope is 3, the perpendicular slope is $-\dfrac{1}{3}$. Using the point-slope formula:

$$y = -\dfrac{1}{3}(x - 2)$$
$$y = -\dfrac{1}{3}x + \dfrac{2}{3}$$

Graphing the line:

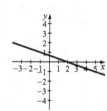

13. Solving for y to find the slope:
$$x + y = 3$$
$$y = -x + 3$$
Since the slope is -1, the parallel slope is -1. Using the point-slope formula:
$$y - (-1) = -1(x - 3)$$
$$y + 1 = -x + 3$$
$$y = -x + 2$$
Graphing the line:

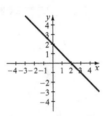

14. Solving for y to find the slope:
$$-2x + y = -1$$
$$y = 2x - 1$$

Since the slope is 2, the parallel slope is 2. Since the y-intercept is $(0, 3)$, the slope-intercept equation is: $y = 2x + 3$
Graphing the line:

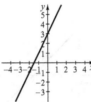

15. Solving for x:
$$3x + 6 = 0$$
$$3x = -6$$
$$x = -2$$

Graphing the line:

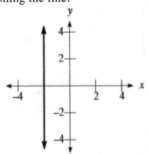

16. Solving for y:
$$3x + 4y + 8 = 0$$
$$4y = -3x - 8$$
$$y = -\frac{3}{4}x - 2$$

Graphing the line:

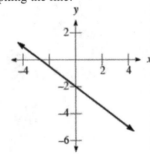

17. Finding when $S = 1500$:
$$S = 800 + 0.1x$$
$$1500 = 800 + 0.1x$$
$$700 = 0.1x$$
$$7000 = x$$
Sales must be $7000 in order to generate a salary of $1500.

18. **a.** In 2011, $t = 2011 - 2008 = 3$. Evaluating the function: $h(3) = 400 + 80(3) = 640$

There were 640 gift-boxed pens sold in 2011.

b. The y-intercept is $(0, 400)$. This represents that 400 pens were sold in 2008.

c. Finding when $h(t) = 1{,}120$:

$$1{,}120 = 400 + 80t$$

$$720 = 80t$$

$$t = 9$$

They will sell 1,120 gift-boxed pens in $2008 + 9 = 2017$.

19. Using the distance formula: $d = \sqrt{(-3-0)^2 + (3-(-2))^2} = \sqrt{9+25} = \sqrt{34}$

Using the midpoint formula: $\left(\dfrac{0+(-3)}{2}, \dfrac{-2+3}{2}\right) = \left(-\dfrac{3}{2}, \dfrac{1}{2}\right)$

20. Using the distance formula: $d = \sqrt{(8-(-4))^2 + (-10-6)^2} = \sqrt{144+256} = \sqrt{400} = 20$

Using the midpoint formula: $\left(\dfrac{-4+8}{2}, \dfrac{6+(-10)}{2}\right) = (2, -2)$

21. Using the distance formula: $d = \sqrt{(11-6)^2 + (13-9)^2} = \sqrt{25+16} = \sqrt{41}$

Using the midpoint formula: $\left(\dfrac{6+11}{2}, \dfrac{9+13}{2}\right) = \left(\dfrac{17}{2}, \dfrac{22}{2}\right) = \left(\dfrac{17}{2}, 11\right)$

22. Using the distance formula: $d = \sqrt{(13-(-7))^2 + (9-(-6))^2} = \sqrt{400+225} = \sqrt{625} = 25$

Using the midpoint formula: $\left(\dfrac{-7+13}{2}, \dfrac{-6+9}{2}\right) = \left(3, \dfrac{3}{2}\right)$

23. Writing the equation in standard form:

$$(x-(-1))^2 + (y-2)^2 = 6^2$$

$$(x+1)^2 + (y-2)^2 = 36$$

Sketching the graph:

24. Writing the equation in standard form:

$$(x-4)^2 + (y-1)^2 = 9$$

Sketching the graph:

25. Writing the equation in standard form:

$$(x-0)^2 + (y-(-1))^2 = \left(\dfrac{1}{2}\right)^2$$

$$x^2 + (y+1)^2 = \dfrac{1}{4}$$

Sketching the graph:

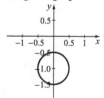

26. Writing the equation in standard form:

$$(x-(-2))^2 + (y-1)^2 = \left(\sqrt{3}\right)^2$$

$$(x+2)^2 + (y-1)^2 = 3$$

Sketching the graph:

27. The center is $(3,2)$ and the radius is $\sqrt{\dfrac{1}{4}} = \dfrac{1}{2}$. Sketching the graph:

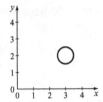

28. The center is $(0,12)$ and the radius is $\sqrt{\dfrac{1}{9}} = \dfrac{1}{3}$. Sketching the graph:

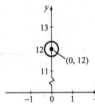

29. Completing the square:
$$x^2 + y^2 - 2x + 2y - 7 = 0$$
$$\left(x^2 - 2x\right) + \left(y^2 + 2y\right) = 7$$
$$\left(x^2 - 2x + 1\right) + \left(y^2 + 2y + 1\right) = 7 + 1 + 1$$
$$\left(x - 1\right)^2 + \left(y + 1\right)^2 = 9$$

The center is $(1,-1)$ and the radius is $\sqrt{9} = 3$. Sketching the graph:

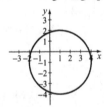

30. Completing the square:
$$x^2 + y^2 - 2x + 6y + 1 = 0$$
$$\left(x^2 - 2x\right) + \left(y^2 + 6y\right) = -1$$
$$\left(x^2 - 2x + 1\right) + \left(y^2 + 6y + 9\right) = -1 + 1 + 9$$
$$\left(x - 1\right)^2 + \left(y + 3\right)^2 = 9$$

The center is $(1,-3)$ and the radius is $\sqrt{9} = 3$. Sketching the graph:

31.　Sketching the graph:

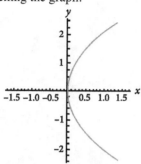

32.　Sketching the graph:

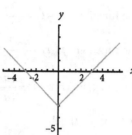

33.　With the statue at the center $(0,0)$, the radius is the distance from the statue to the inner boundary plus the width of the flower border. Thus, $r = 22$ and $r^2 = (22)^2 = 484$ so the equation is $x^2 + y^2 = 484$.

34.　Let d represent the distance between the boats. The boat going west travels $1.5 \text{ hr} \times 30 \dfrac{\text{mi}}{\text{hr}} = 45 \text{ mi}$ in $1\dfrac{1}{2}$ hours, and the boat going north travels $1.5 \text{ hr} \times 44 \dfrac{\text{mi}}{\text{hr}} = 66 \text{ mi}$ in $1\dfrac{1}{2}$ hours. Sketching the graph:

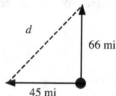

Using the distance formula: $d = \sqrt{45^2 + 66^2} = \sqrt{6381} \approx 80 \text{ mi}$

The boats will be about 80 miles apart in $1\dfrac{1}{2}$ hours.

35.　a.　Evaluating the function: $f(4) = 2(4)^2 - 1 = 31$

　　b.　Evaluating the function: $f(-2) = 2(-2)^2 - 1 = 7$

　　c.　Evaluating the function: $f(a) = 2a^2 - 1$

　　d.　Evaluating the function: $f(a+1) = 2(a+1)^2 - 1 = 2(a^2 + 2a + 1) - 1 = 2a^2 + 4a + 1$

36.　a.　Evaluating the function: $f(4) = \dfrac{1}{(4)^2 + 1} = \dfrac{1}{17}$

　　b.　Evaluating the function: $f(-2) = \dfrac{1}{(-2)^2 + 1} = \dfrac{1}{5}$

　　c.　Evaluating the function: $f(a) = \dfrac{1}{a^2 + 1}$

　　d.　Evaluating the function: $f(a+1) = \dfrac{1}{(a+1)^2 + 1} = \dfrac{1}{(a^2 + 2a + 1) + 1} = \dfrac{1}{a^2 + 2a + 2}$

37.　a.　Evaluating the function: $f(4) = \sqrt{(4)^2 - 4} = \sqrt{12} = 2\sqrt{3}$

　　b.　Evaluating the function: $f(-2) = \sqrt{(-2)^2 - 4} = 0$

　　c.　Evaluating the function: $f(a) = \sqrt{a^2 - 4}$

　　d.　Evaluating the function: $f(a+1) = \sqrt{(a+1)^2 - 4} = \sqrt{a^2 + 2a - 3}$

38. **a.** Evaluating the function: $f(4) = \dfrac{4+1}{4-1} = \dfrac{5}{3}$

      b. Evaluating the function: $f(-2) = \dfrac{-2+1}{-2-1} = \dfrac{1}{3}$

      c. Evaluating the function: $f(a) = \dfrac{a+1}{a-1}$

      d. Evaluating the function: $f(a+1) = \dfrac{(a+1)+1}{(a+1)-1} = \dfrac{a+2}{a}$

39. Evaluating the function: $f(0) = 0$

40. Evaluating the function: $f(-1) = -2(-1)+1 = 2+1 = 3$

41. Evaluating the function: $f(3) = 3$

42. Evaluating the function: $f\left(\dfrac{1}{2}\right) = \dfrac{1}{2}$

43. The domain is all real numbers, or $(-\infty, \infty)$.

44. The quantity inside the radical must be non-negative. Solving the inequality:

$$6 - x \geq 0$$
$$-x \geq -6$$
$$x \leq 6$$

    The domain is all real numbers $x \leq 6$, or $(-\infty, 6]$.

45. The denominator is equal to 0 when $x = 2$. So the domain is all real numbers except 2, or $(-\infty, 2) \cup (2, \infty)$.

46. Setting the denominator equal to 0:

$$x^2 - 4 = 0$$
$$(x+2)(x-2) = 0$$
$$x = \pm 2$$

    The domain is all real numbers except -2 and 2, or $(-\infty, -2) \cup (-2, 2) \cup (2, \infty)$.

47. Since the denominator is never equal to 0, the domain is all real numbers, or $(-\infty, \infty)$.

48. The denominator is equal to 0 when $x = -5$. So the domain is all real numbers except 2, or $(-\infty, -5) \cup (-5, \infty)$.

49. The domain is all real numbers, or $(-\infty, \infty)$.

50. Setting the denominator equal to 0:

$$(x+2)(x-3) = 0$$
$$x = -2, 3$$

    The domain is all real numbers except -2 and 3, or $(-\infty, -2) \cup (-2, 3) \cup (3, \infty)$.

51. Evaluating the function: $S(3) = 4\pi(3)^2 = 36\pi \approx 113.097$

    The surface area of a sphere of radius 3 is 36π, or about 113.097. Values of r must be greater than zero for the function to make sense, since the radius of a sphere must have a positive value.

52. **a.** The slope is 1.5. This represents the infant's average increase in length (in inches) per month.

      b. Evaluating the function: $h(6) = 21 + 1.5(6) = 30$

        At 6 months the infant is 30 in. in length.

53. The domain is $(-\infty, \infty)$ and the range is $(-\infty, \infty)$.
Sketching the graph:

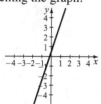

54. The domain is $(-\infty, 5]$ and the range is $[0, \infty)$.
Sketching the graph:

55. The domain is $(-\infty, \infty)$ and the range is $(-\infty, 3]$.
Sketching the graph:

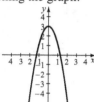

56. The domain is $(-\infty, \infty)$ and the range is $[-4, \infty)$.
Sketching the graph:

57. The domain is $(-\infty, \infty)$ and the range is $(-\infty, 0]$.
Sketching the graph:

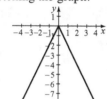

58. The domain is $(-\infty, \infty)$ and the range is $[-2, \infty)$.
Sketching the graph:

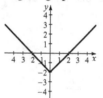

59. Sketching the graph:

60. Sketching the graph:

61. **a.** This is not a function since it does not pass the vertical line test.
  b. This is a function since it does pass the vertical line test.
  c. This is not a function since it does not pass the vertical line test.
  d. This is a function since it does pass the vertical line test.

62. The function values are: $f(-2) = 2, f(1) = 2$

The x-intercept is $(2, 0)$ and the y-intercept is $(0, 2)$.

63. Solving for y:
$$2x + 3y = 6$$
$$3y = -2x + 6$$
$$y = -\frac{2}{3}x + 2$$

This is a function, since there is only one value for y for each value of x.

64. Solving for y:
$$y^2 + 9x = 0$$
$$y^2 = -9x$$
$$y = \pm\sqrt{-9x}$$

This is not a function, since some values of x result in two values for y ($x = -1$, for example).

65. Finding the values:
$$f(x) = -x$$
$$-f(x) = -(-x) = x$$
$$f(-x) = -(-x) = x$$

Since $f(-x) = -f(x)$, the function is odd.

66. Finding the values:
$$f(x) = 3x + 4$$
$$-f(x) = -(3x + 4) = -3x - 4$$
$$f(-x) = 3(-x) + 4 = -3x + 4$$

Since $f(-x) \neq f(x)$ and $f(-x) \neq -f(x)$, the function is neither even nor odd.

67. Finding the values:
$$f(x) = -x^2 + 5$$
$$-f(x) = -(-x^2 + 5) = x^2 - 5$$
$$f(-x) = -(-x)^2 + 5 = -x^2 + 5$$

Since $f(-x) = f(x)$, the function is even.

68. Finding the values:
$$f(x) = x^5 + x^2$$
$$-f(x) = -(x^5 + x^2) = -x^5 - x^2$$
$$f(-x) = (-x)^5 + (-x)^2 = -x^5 + x^2$$

Since $f(-x) \neq f(x)$ and $f(-x) \neq -f(x)$, the function is neither even nor odd.

69. Finding the values:
$$f(x) = -3x^5 - x$$
$$-f(x) = -(-3x^5 - x) = 3x^5 + x$$
$$f(-x) = -3(-x)^5 - (-x) = 3x^5 + x$$

Since $f(-x) = -f(x)$, the function is odd.

70. Finding the values:
$$f(x) = 2x^4 + x^2 + 1$$
$$-f(x) = -(2x^4 + x^2 + 1) = -2x^4 - x^2 - 1$$
$$f(-x) = 2(-x)^4 + (-x)^2 + 1 = 2x^4 + x^2 + 1$$

Since $f(-x) = f(x)$, the function is even.

71. This function is neither even nor odd, as the graph doesn't have y-axis or origin symmetry:

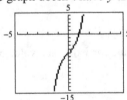

Finding the values:

$$f(x) = 2x^3 + 3x - 5$$
$$-f(x) = -\left(2x^3 + 3x - 5\right) = -2x^3 - 3x + 5$$
$$f(-x) = 2(x)^3 + 3(-x) - 5 = 2x^3 - 3x - 5$$

Since $f(-x) \neq f(x)$ and $f(-x) \neq -f(x)$, the function is neither even nor odd.

72. This function is even, since the graph is symmetric about the y-axis:

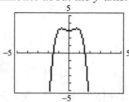

Finding the values:

$$f(x) = -x^4 + x^2 + 3$$
$$-f(x) = -\left(-x^4 + x^2 + 3\right) = x^4 - x^2 - 3$$
$$f(-x) = -(-x)^4 + (-x)^2 + 3 = -x^4 + x^2 + 3$$

Since $f(-x) = f(x)$, the function is even.

73. The function is increasing on the intervals $(-2, 2)$ and $(3, 4)$.

74. The function is decreasing on the intervals $(-4, -2)$ and $(2, 3)$.

75. The function is constant on the interval $(4, 5)$.

76. The average rate of change is: $\dfrac{f(x_2) - f(x_1)}{x_2 - x_1} = \dfrac{f(2) - f(-2)}{2 - (-2)} = \dfrac{1 - (-1)}{4} = \dfrac{2}{4} = \dfrac{1}{2}$

77. The average rate of change is: $\dfrac{f(x_2) - f(x_1)}{x_2 - x_1} = \dfrac{f(4) - f(3)}{4 - 3} = \dfrac{1 - 0}{1} = 1$

78. The y-intercept is $(0, 0)$.

79. Finding the function values:

$$f(2) = -2(2) + 4 = 0 \qquad\qquad f(3) = -2(3) + 4 = -2$$

The average rate of change is: $\dfrac{f(3) - f(2)}{3 - 2} = \dfrac{-2 - 0}{1} = -2$

80. Finding the function values:

$$f(-3) = -2(-3)^3 + 3(-3) = 45 \qquad f(-1) = -2(-1)^3 + 3(-1) = -1$$

The average rate of change is: $\dfrac{f(-1) - f(-3)}{-1 - (-3)} = \dfrac{-1 - 45}{2} = \dfrac{-46}{2} = -23$

81. Finding the function values:

$$f(a) = 2a - 3 \qquad\qquad f(a+h) = 2(a+h) - 3 = 2a + 2h - 3$$

The average rate of change is: $\dfrac{f(a+h) - f(a)}{(a+h) - a} = \dfrac{2a + 2h - 3 - (2a - 3)}{h} = \dfrac{2a + 2h - 3 - 2a + 3}{h} = \dfrac{2h}{h} = 2$

82. Finding the function values:

$$f(a) = a^2 - 2a \qquad\qquad f(a+h) = (a+h)^2 - 2(a+h) = a^2 + 2ah + h^2 - 2a - 2h$$

The average rate of change is: $\dfrac{f(a+h) - f(a)}{(a+h) - a} = \dfrac{a^2 + 2ah + h^2 - 2a - 2h - \left(a^2 - 2a\right)}{h} = \dfrac{2ah + h^2 - 2h}{h} = 2a + h - 2$

83. **a.** Finding $(f+g)(x)$: $(f+g)(x) = f(x) + g(x) = (4x^2 + 1) + (x+1) = 4x^2 + x + 2$

The domain is all real numbers, or $(-\infty, \infty)$.

b. Finding $(f-g)(x)$: $(f-g)(x) = f(x) - g(x) = (4x^2 + 1) - (x+1) = 4x^2 + 1 - x - 1 = 4x^2 - x$

The domain is all real numbers, or $(-\infty, \infty)$.

c. Finding $(fg)(x)$: $(fg)(x) = f(x) \cdot g(x) = (4x^2 + 1)(x+1) = 4x^3 + 4x^2 + x + 1$

The domain is all real numbers, or $(-\infty, \infty)$.

d. Finding $\left(\dfrac{f}{g}\right)(x)$: $\left(\dfrac{f}{g}\right)(x) = \dfrac{f(x)}{g(x)} = \dfrac{4x^2 + 1}{x+1}$

The domain is all real numbers $x \neq -1$, or $(-\infty, -1) \cup (-1, \infty)$.

84. **a.** Finding $(f+g)(x)$: $(f+g)(x) = (3x-1) + (x^2 - 4) = x^2 + 3x - 5$

The domain is all real numbers, or $(-\infty, \infty)$.

b. Finding $(f-g)(x)$: $(f-g)(x) = (3x-1) - (x^2 - 4) = -x^2 + 3x + 3$

The domain is all real numbers, or $(-\infty, \infty)$.

c. Finding $(fg)(x)$: $(fg)(x) = (3x-1)(x^2-4) = 3x^3 - 12x - x^2 + 4 = 3x^3 - x^2 - 12x + 4$

The domain is all real numbers, or $(-\infty, \infty)$.

d. Finding $\left(\dfrac{f}{g}\right)(x)$: $\left(\dfrac{f}{g}\right)(x) = \dfrac{f(x)}{g(x)} = \dfrac{3x-1}{x^2 - 4}$

The domain is all real numbers $x \neq -2, 2$, or $(-\infty, -2) \cup (-2, 2) \cup (2, \infty)$.

85. **a.** Finding $(f+g)(x)$: $(f+g)(x) = f(x) + g(x) = \dfrac{1}{2x} + \dfrac{1}{x^2 + 1} = \dfrac{x^2 + 2x + 1}{2x(x^2 + 1)}$

The domain is all real numbers $x \neq 0$, or $(-\infty, 0) \cup (0, \infty)$.

b. Finding $(f-g)(x)$: $(f-g)(x) = f(x) - g(x) = \dfrac{1}{2x} - \dfrac{1}{x^2 + 1} = \dfrac{(x^2 + 1) - 2x}{2x(x^2 + 1)} = \dfrac{x^2 - 2x + 1}{2x(x^2 + 1)}$

The domain is all real numbers $x \neq 0$, or $(-\infty, 0) \cup (0, \infty)$.

c. Finding $(fg)(x)$: $(fg)(x) = f(x) \cdot g(x) = \dfrac{1}{2x} \cdot \dfrac{1}{x^2 + 1} = \dfrac{1}{2x(x^2 + 1)}$

The domain is all real numbers $x \neq 0$, or $(-\infty, 0) \cup (0, \infty)$.

d. Finding $\left(\dfrac{f}{g}\right)(x)$: $\left(\dfrac{f}{g}\right)(x) = \dfrac{f(x)}{g(x)} = \dfrac{\frac{1}{2x}}{\frac{1}{x^2 + 1}} = \dfrac{x^2 + 1}{2x}$

The domain is all real numbers $x \neq 0$, or $(-\infty, 0) \cup (0, \infty)$.

86. **a.** Finding $(f+g)(x)$: $(f+g)(x) = \sqrt{x} + \dfrac{1}{\sqrt{x}} = \dfrac{x+1}{\sqrt{x}} = \dfrac{x+1}{\sqrt{x}} \cdot \dfrac{\sqrt{x}}{\sqrt{x}} = \dfrac{x\sqrt{x} + \sqrt{x}}{x}$

The domain is all real numbers $x > 0$, or $(0, \infty)$.

b. Finding $(f-g)(x)$: $(f-g)(x) = \sqrt{x} - \dfrac{1}{\sqrt{x}} = \dfrac{x-1}{\sqrt{x}} = \dfrac{x-1}{\sqrt{x}} \cdot \dfrac{\sqrt{x}}{\sqrt{x}} = \dfrac{x\sqrt{x} - \sqrt{x}}{x}$

The domain is all real numbers $x > 0$, or $(0, \infty)$.

c. Finding $(fg)(x)$: $(fg)(x) = \sqrt{x} \cdot \dfrac{1}{\sqrt{x}} = 1$

The domain is all real numbers $x > 0$, or $(0, \infty)$.

d. Finding $\left(\dfrac{f}{g}\right)(x)$: $\left(\dfrac{f}{g}\right)(x) = \dfrac{\sqrt{x}}{\dfrac{1}{\sqrt{x}}} = x$

The domain is all real numbers $x > 0$, or $(0, \infty)$.

87. a. Finding $(f+g)(x)$: $(f+g)(x) = f(x) + g(x) = \dfrac{2}{x-4} + 3x^2 = \dfrac{2 + 3x^2(x-4)}{x-4} = \dfrac{3x^3 - 12x^2 + 2}{x-4}$

The domain is all real numbers $x \neq 4$, or $(-\infty, 4) \cup (4, \infty)$.

b. Finding $(f-g)(x)$: $(f-g)(x) = f(x) - g(x) = \dfrac{2}{x-4} - 3x^2 = \dfrac{2 - 3x^2(x-4)}{x-4} = \dfrac{-3x^3 + 12x^2 + 2}{x-4}$

The domain is all real numbers $x \neq 4$, or $(-\infty, 4) \cup (4, \infty)$.

c. Finding $(fg)(x)$: $(fg)(x) = f(x) \cdot g(x) = \dfrac{2}{x-4} \cdot 3x^2 = \dfrac{6x^2}{x-4}$

The domain is all real numbers $x \neq 4$, or $(-\infty, 4) \cup (4, \infty)$.

d. Finding $\left(\dfrac{f}{g}\right)(x)$: $\left(\dfrac{f}{g}\right)(x) = \dfrac{f(x)}{g(x)} = \dfrac{\dfrac{2}{x-4}}{3x^2} = \dfrac{2}{3x^2(x-4)}$

The domain is all real numbers $x \neq 0, 4$, or $(-\infty, 0) \cup (0, 4) \cup (4, \infty)$.

88. a. Finding $(f+g)(x)$: $(f+g)(x) = \dfrac{2}{x+3} + \dfrac{x+1}{x-4} = \dfrac{2x - 8 + x^2 + 4x + 3}{(x+3)(x-4)} = \dfrac{x^2 + 6x - 5}{(x+3)(x-4)}$

The domain is all real numbers $x \neq -3, 4$, or $(-\infty, -3) \cup (-3, 4) \cup (4, \infty)$.

b. Finding $(f-g)(x)$: $(f-g)(x) = \dfrac{2}{x+3} - \dfrac{x+1}{x-4} = \dfrac{2x - 8 - x^2 - 4x - 3}{(x+3)(x-4)} = \dfrac{-x^2 - 2x - 11}{(x+3)(x-4)}$

The domain is all real numbers $x \neq -3, 4$, or $(-\infty, -3) \cup (-3, 4) \cup (4, \infty)$.

c. Finding $(fg)(x)$: $(fg)(x) = \dfrac{2}{x+3} \cdot \dfrac{x+1}{x-4} = \dfrac{2(x+1)}{(x+3)(x-4)}$

The domain is all real numbers $x \neq -3, 4$, or $(-\infty, -3) \cup (-3, 4) \cup (4, \infty)$.

d. Finding $\left(\dfrac{f}{g}\right)(x)$: $\left(\dfrac{f}{g}\right)(x) = \dfrac{\dfrac{2}{x+3}}{\dfrac{x+1}{x-4}} = \dfrac{2(x-4)}{(x+1)(x+3)}$

The domain is all real numbers $x \neq -3, -1, 4$, or $(-\infty, -3) \cup (-3, -1) \cup (-1, 4) \cup (4, \infty)$.

89. Evaluating the function: $(f \circ g)(-1) = f(g(-1)) = f(-2) = 0$

90. Evaluating the function: $(f \circ g)(0) = f(g(0)) = f(0) = 3$

91. Evaluating the function: $(g \circ f)(0) = g(f(0)) = g(3) = 5$

92. Evaluating the function: $(g \circ f)(-4) = g(f(-4)) = g(-1) = -2$

93. Finding the function and then the value:

$(f+g)(x) = f(x) + g(x) = (3x - 1) + \left(-2\sqrt{x}\right) = 3x - 2\sqrt{x} - 1$

$(f+g)(4) = 3(4) - 2\sqrt{4} - 1 = 7$

94. Finding the function and then the value:

$$(g-h)(x) = -2\sqrt{x} - 4x$$

$$(g-h)(9) = -2\sqrt{9} - 4(9) = -42$$

95. Finding the function and then the value:

$$\left(\frac{f}{h}\right)(x) = \frac{f(x)}{h(x)} = \frac{3x-1}{4x}$$

$$\left(\frac{f}{h}\right)(2) = \frac{3(2)-1}{4(2)} = \frac{5}{8}$$

96. Finding the function and then the value:

$$(f \cdot h)(x) = (3x-1)(4x) = 12x^2 - 4x$$

$$(f \cdot h)(3) = 12(3)^2 - 4(3) = 96$$

97. Finding the function and then the value:

$$(f \circ h)(x) = f(h(x)) = f(4x) = 3(4x) - 1 = 12x - 1$$

$$(f \circ h)(-1) = 12(-1) - 1 = -13$$

98. Finding the function and then the value:

$$(h \circ f)(x) = h(3x-1) = 4(3x-1) = 12x - 4$$

$$(h \circ f)(2) = 12(2) - 4 = 20$$

99. Finding the function and then the value:

$$(f \circ g)(x) = f(g(x)) = f(-2\sqrt{x}) = 3(-2\sqrt{x}) - 1 = -6\sqrt{x} - 1$$

$$(f \circ g)(9) = -6\sqrt{9} - 1 = -19$$

100. Finding the function and then the value:

$$(g \circ f)(x) = g(3x-1) = -2\sqrt{3x-1}$$

$$(g \circ f)(3) = -2\sqrt{3(3)-1} = -2\sqrt{8} = -4\sqrt{2}$$

101. Finding $(f \circ g)(x)$: $(f \circ g)(x) = f(g(x)) = f(x-2) = -(x-2)^2 + 4 = -(x^2 - 4x + 4) + 4 = -x^2 + 4x$

The domain is all real numbers, or $(-\infty, \infty)$.

Finding $(g \circ f)(x)$: $(g \circ f)(x) = g(f(x)) = g(-x^2 + 4) = (-x^2 + 4) - 2 = -x^2 + 2$

The domain is all real numbers, or $(-\infty, \infty)$.

102. Finding $(f \circ g)(x)$: $(f \circ g)(x) = f\left(\frac{x-5}{2}\right) = 2\left(\frac{x-5}{2}\right) + 5 = x - 5 + 5 = x$

The domain is all real numbers, or $(-\infty, \infty)$.

Finding $(g \circ f)(x)$: $(g \circ f)(x) = g(2x+5) = \frac{(2x+5)-5}{2} = x$

The domain is all real numbers, or $(-\infty, \infty)$.

103. Finding $(f \circ g)(x)$:

$$(f \circ g)(x) = f(g(x)) = f(x-3) = -(x-3)^2 + 3(x-3) = -(x^2 - 6x + 9) + 3x - 9 = -x^2 + 6x - 9 + 3x - 9 = -x^2 + 9x - 18$$

The domain is all real numbers, or $(-\infty, \infty)$.

Finding $(g \circ f)(x)$: $(g \circ f)(x) = g(f(x)) = g(-x^2 + 3x) = (-x^2 + 3x) - 3 = -x^2 + 3x - 3$

The domain is all real numbers, or $(-\infty, \infty)$.

104. Finding $(f \circ g)(x)$: $(f \circ g)(x) = f(x+5) = -\dfrac{2}{x+5}$

The domain is all real numbers $x \neq -5$, or $(-\infty, -5) \cup (-5, \infty)$.

Finding $(g \circ f)(x)$: $(g \circ f)(x) = g\left(-\dfrac{2}{x}\right) = -\dfrac{2}{x} + 5 = \dfrac{5x-2}{x}$

The domain is all real numbers $x \neq 0$, or $(-\infty, 0) \cup (0, \infty)$.

105. Finding $(f \circ g)(x)$: $(f \circ g)(x) = f(g(x)) = f(x^2 + x) = \dfrac{1}{x^2 + x - 2}$

For the domain, we must find where the denominator is equal to 0:
$$x^2 + x - 2 = 0$$
$$(x+2)(x-1) = 0$$
$$x = -2, 1$$

The domain is all real numbers $x \neq -2, 1$, or $(-\infty, -2) \cup (-2, 1) \cup (1, \infty)$.

Finding $(g \circ f)(x)$: $(g \circ f)(x) = g(f(x)) = g\left(\dfrac{1}{x-2}\right) = \left(\dfrac{1}{x-2}\right)^2 + \dfrac{1}{x-2} = \dfrac{1}{(x-2)^2} + \dfrac{1}{x-2} = \dfrac{x-1}{(x-2)^2}$

The domain is all real numbers $x \neq 2$, or $(-\infty, 2) \cup (2, \infty)$.

106. Finding $(f \circ g)(x)$: $(f \circ g)(x) = f(2x+1) = \sqrt{(2x+1)+2} = \sqrt{2x+3}$

The domain is all real numbers $x \geq -\dfrac{3}{2}$, or $\left[-\dfrac{3}{2}, \infty\right)$.

Finding $(g \circ f)(x)$: $(g \circ f)(x) = g\left(\sqrt{x+2}\right) = 2\sqrt{x+2} + 1$

The domain is all real numbers $x \geq -2$, or $[-2, \infty)$.

107. Finding $(f \circ g)(x)$: $(f \circ g)(x) = f(g(x)) = f(|x|) = \dfrac{|x|}{|x| + 3}$

The domain is all real numbers, or $(-\infty, \infty)$.

Finding $(g \circ f)(x)$: $(g \circ f)(x) = g(f(x)) = g\left(\dfrac{x}{x+3}\right) = \left|\dfrac{x}{x+3}\right|$

The domain is all real numbers $x \neq -3$, or $(-\infty, -3) \cup (-3, \infty)$.

108. Finding $(f \circ g)(x)$: $(f \circ g)(x) = f\left(\dfrac{1}{x}\right) = \left(\dfrac{1}{x}\right)^2 - 4\left(\dfrac{1}{x}\right) + 4 = \dfrac{1}{x^2} - \dfrac{4}{x} + 4 = \dfrac{4x^2 - 4x + 1}{x^2}$

The domain is all real numbers $x \neq 0$, or $(-\infty, 0) \cup (0, \infty)$.

Finding $(g \circ f)(x)$: $(g \circ f)(x) = g(x^2 - 4x + 4) = \dfrac{1}{x^2 - 4x + 4} = \dfrac{1}{(x-2)^2}$

The domain is all real numbers $x \neq 2$, or $(-\infty, 2) \cup (2, \infty)$.

109. First simplify the expression: $f(x+h) = 4(x+h) - 3 = 4x + 4h - 3$

Now finding the difference quotient: $\dfrac{f(x+h) - f(x)}{h} = \dfrac{4x + 4h - 3 - (4x-3)}{h} = \dfrac{4x + 4h - 3 - 4x + 3}{h} = \dfrac{4h}{h} = 4$

110. First simplify the expression: $f(x+h) = -3(x+h)^2 = -3(x^2 + 2xh + h^2) = -3x^2 - 6xh - 3h^2$

Now finding the difference quotient:
$$\dfrac{f(x+h) - f(x)}{h} = \dfrac{(-3x^2 - 6xh - 3h^2) - (-3x^2)}{h} = \dfrac{-3x^2 - 6xh - 3h^2 + 3x^2}{h} = \dfrac{-6xh - 3h^2}{h} = \dfrac{h(-6x - 3h)}{h} = -6x - 3h$$

111. The graph of $g(x)$ is the graph of $f(x) = |x|$ shifted down by 6 units. Sketching the graph:

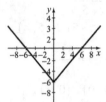

112. The graph of $F(s)$ is the graph of $f(s) = s^2$ shifted right by 5 units. Sketching the graph:

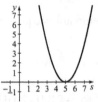

113. The graph of $H(x)$ is the graph of $h(x) = |x|$ shifted right by 1 unit and up by 2 units. Sketching the graph:

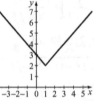

114. The graph of $G(x)$ is the graph of $g(x) = x^2$ shifted to the left by 4 units and down by 3 units. Sketching the graph:

115. The graph of $f(x)$ is the graph of $g(x) = \sqrt{x}$ stretched vertically away from x-axis by a factor of 2. Sketching the graph:

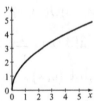

116. The graph of $H(s)$ is the graph of $h(s) = |s|$ reflected across the x-axis. Sketching the graph:

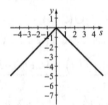

117. The graph of $F(s)$ is the graph of $f(s) = s^2$ reflected across the x-axis and shifted to the left by 4 units. Sketching the graph:

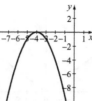

118. The graph of $P(x)$ is the graph of $f(x) = \sqrt{x}$ reflected across the x-axis and shifted up by 1 unit. Sketching the graph:

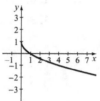

119. The graph of $f(x)$ is the graph of $g(x) = x^2$ reflected across the x-axis, stretched vertically away from the x-axis by a factor of 3, shifted left by 2 units, and shifted up by 1 unit. Sketching the graph:

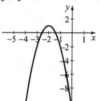

120. The graph of $h(x)$ is the graph of $f(x) = \sqrt{x}$ compressed horizontally toward the y-axis, scaled by a factor of $\dfrac{1}{3}$. Sketching the graph:

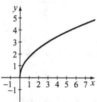

121. The graph of $h(x)$ is the graph of $f(x) = |x|$ compressed horizontally toward the y-axis by a scaling factor of $\dfrac{1}{2}$ and shifted down by 3 units. Sketching the graph:

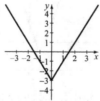

122. The graph of $h(x)$ is the graph of $g(x)=|x|$ compressed horizontally away from the y-axis by a scaling factor of 3. Sketching the graph:

123. The function is: $g(x)=|x-3|+1$

124. The function is: $f(x)=\sqrt{x-2}+3$

125. The function is: $g(x)=2(x+1)^2$

126. The function is: $g(x)=|2x|+2$

127. Sketching the graph:

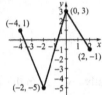

128. Sketching the graph:

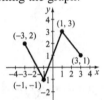

129. Sketching the graph:

130. Sketching the graph:

131. The first function translates $f(x)=x^2$ to the right by 1.5 units, whereas the second function translates $f(x)=x^2$ down by 1.5 units. Sketching the graphs:

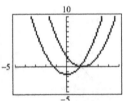

132. The graph of $y_1(x)=4|x+1.5|-2.5$ is the graph of $f(x)=|x|$ expanded vertically away from the x-axis, shifted to the left by 1.5 units, and shifted down by 2.5 units. Sketching the graph:

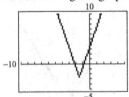

133. Using the points $(x_1,y_1)=(0,4)$ and $(x_2,y_2)=(3,6)$ in the slope formula: $m=\dfrac{6-4}{3-0}=\dfrac{2}{3}$

Using the point-slope form of a function: $f(x)=\dfrac{2}{3}(x-0)+4=\dfrac{2}{3}x+4$

134 Using the points $(x_1,y_1)=(-1,3)$ and $(x_2,y_2)=(4,-2)$ in the slope formula: $m=\dfrac{-2-3}{4-(-1)}=\dfrac{-5}{5}=-1$

Using the point-slope form of a function: $f(x)=-1(x-4)-2=-x+4=-x+2$

135. Substituting $x = 10$ and $y = 25$ in the variation equation:

$$y = kx$$

$$25 = k(10)$$

$$k = \frac{25}{10} = \frac{5}{2}$$

The variation equation is $y = \frac{5}{2}x$.

136. Substituting $x = 8$ and $y = 40$ in the variation equation:

$$y = kx$$

$$40 = k(8)$$

$$k = 5$$

The variation equation is $y = 5x$.

137. Substituting $x = 6$ and $y = 9$ in the variation equation:

$$y = \frac{k}{x}$$

$$9 = \frac{k}{6}$$

$$k = 54$$

The variation equation is $y = \frac{54}{x}$.

138. Substituting $x = 8$ and $y = 12$ in the variation equation:

$$y = \frac{k}{x}$$

$$12 = \frac{k}{8}$$

$$k = 96$$

The variation equation is $y = \frac{96}{x}$.

139. Let x represent the number of wallets sold and R represent the revenue. Substituting $x = 5,000$ and $R = 30,000$ in the variation equation:

$$R = kx$$

$$30,000 = k(5,000)$$

$$k = 6$$

The variation equation is $R = 6x$. Substituting $x = 800$: $R = 6(800) = \$4,800$

The revenue is $4,800 from selling 800 wallets.

140. Let p represent the price and D the demand. Substituting $p = 3$ and $D = 400$ in the variation equation:

$$D = \frac{k}{p}$$

$$400 = \frac{k}{3}$$

$$k = 3(400) = 1,200$$

The variation equation is $D = \frac{1,200}{p}$. Substituting $p = 2$: $D = \frac{1,200}{2} = 600$

The demand is 600 units when the price is $2.

141. **a.** Using the points $(2, 300)$ and $(4, 200)$ in the slope formula: $m = \dfrac{200 - 300}{4 - 2} = -50$

Using the point-slope formula:
$$y - 300 = -50(x - 2)$$
$$y - 300 = -50x + 100$$
$$y = -50x + 400$$

b. If $x = 0$, $y = 400$. The original purchase price was $400.

c. Substituting $y = 0$:
$$0 = -50x + 400$$
$$-400 = -50x$$
$$8 = x$$

The value will be $0 in 8 years, which corresponds to the year $2008 + 8 = 2016$.

142. **a.** The figures are generally decreasing.

b. Let x represent the years since 2009, and y represent the number of CDs sold (in millions).
The best fit line is: $f(x) = -23.2x + 277.3$

c. In 2014, $x = 2015 - 2009 = 6$. Substituting into the function: $f(6) = -23.2(6) + 277.3 = 138.1$
The predicted number of CDs sold in 2015 is $138.1 million.

Chapter 2 Test

1. **a.** Using the slope formula: $m = \dfrac{2 - (-5)}{4 - 2} = \dfrac{7}{2}$

b. Using the slope formula: $m = \dfrac{6 - 4}{-2 - (-2)} = \dfrac{2}{0}$, which is undefined

2. Using the point-slope formula:
$$y - 3 = -4(x - (-1))$$
$$y - 3 = -4(x + 1)$$
$$y - 3 = -4x - 4$$
$$y = -4x - 1$$

3. Finding the slope: $m = \dfrac{0 - (-2)}{3 - 5} = \dfrac{2}{-2} = -1$

Using the point-slope formula:
$$y - 0 = -1(x - 3)$$
$$y = -x + 3$$
$$x + y - 3 = 0$$

4. First solve for y to find the slope:
$$2y - x = 3$$
$$2y = x + 3$$
$$y = \dfrac{1}{2}x + \dfrac{3}{2}$$

So the perpendicular slope is -2. Using the point-slope formula:
$$y - 4 = -2(x - 1)$$
$$y - 4 = -2x + 2$$
$$y = -2x + 6$$

5. First solve for y to find the slope:
$$-4x - y = 6$$
$$-y = 4x + 6$$
$$y = -4x - 6$$

So the parallel slope is –4. Using the point-slope formula:
$$y - 0 = -4(x + 3)$$
$$y = -4x - 12$$

6. The equation of the horizontal line is $y = -5$.

7. The equation of the vertical line is $x = 7$.

8. Using the distance formula: $d = \sqrt{(-4-1)^2 + (3-2)^2} = \sqrt{25+1} = \sqrt{26}$

Using the midpoint formula: $\left(\dfrac{1+(-4)}{2}, \dfrac{2+3}{2}\right) = \left(-\dfrac{3}{2}, \dfrac{5}{2}\right)$

9. Writing the equation of the circle with center (2, 5) and radius 6:
$$(x-h)^2 + (y-k)^2 = r^2$$
$$(x-2)^2 + (y-5)^2 = 6^2$$
$$(x-2)^2 + (y-5)^2 = 36$$

10. First complete the square:
$$x^2 + 2x + y^2 - 4y = 4$$
$$(x^2 + 2x) + (y^2 - 4y) = 4$$
$$(x^2 + 2x + 1) + (y^2 - 4y + 4) = 4 + 1 + 4$$
$$(x+1)^2 + (y-2)^2 = 9$$

The center is (–1, 2) and the radius is $\sqrt{9} = 3$. Sketching the graph:

11. Sketching the graph:

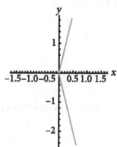

This in not a function, since its graph does not pass the vertical line test.

12. **a.** Evaluating the function: $f(-2) = -(-2)^2 + 2(-2) = -8$

b. Simplifying the value: $f(a-1) = -(a-1)^2 + 2(a-1) = -(a^2 - 2a + 1) + 2a - 2 = -a^2 + 2a - 1 + 2a - 2 = -a^2 + 4a - 3$

c. Evaluating the function: $g(3) = \sqrt{3+6} = \sqrt{9} = 3$

d. Evaluating the function: $g(10) = \sqrt{10+6} = \sqrt{16} = 4$

13. The domain is all real numbers, or $(-\infty, \infty)$.

14. The denominator is equal to 0 when $x = 5$, so the domain is all real numbers $x \neq 5$, or $(-\infty, 5) \cup (5, \infty)$.

15. The domain is all real numbers, or $(-\infty, \infty)$. Sketching the graph:

16. The domain is all real numbers $x \geq -3$, or $[-3, \infty)$. Sketching the graph:

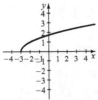

17. The domain is all real numbers, or $(-\infty, \infty)$, and the range is $(-\infty, 4]$. Sketching the graph:

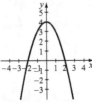

18. They do not represent a function, since there are two different y values for the value $x = 1$.

19. This does represent a function, since the graph passes the vertical line test.

20. **a.** Graphing the function:

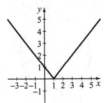

    b. The function in absolute value form is: $f(x) = |x - 1|$

21. Finding the values:
$$f(x) = 2x + 1$$
$$-f(x) = -(2x + 1) = -2x - 1$$
$$f(-x) = 2(-x) + 1 = -2x + 1$$

Since $f(-x) \neq f(x)$ and $f(-x) \neq -f(x)$, the function is neither even nor odd.

22. Finding the values:
$$f(x) = -3x^2 - 5$$
$$-f(x) = -(-3x^2 - 5) = 3x^2 + 5$$
$$f(-x) = -3(-x)^2 - 5 = -3x^2 - 5$$

Since $f(-x) = f(x)$, the function is even.

23. Finding the values:

$$f(x) = 2x^5 + x^3$$

$$-f(x) = -\left(2x^5 + x^3\right) = -2x^5 - x^3$$

$$f(-x) = 2(-x)^5 + (-x)^3 = -2x^5 - x^3$$

Since $f(-x) = -f(x)$, the function is odd.

24. **a.** The function is increasing on the interval $(0,2)$.

    b. The function is decreasing on the interval $(-5,0)$.

    c. The function is constant on the interval $(2,5)$.

25. Finding the average rate of change: $\dfrac{f(1) - f(-2)}{1 - (-2)} = \dfrac{0 - \frac{1}{2}}{3} = -\dfrac{1}{6}$

26. First simplify the expression: $f(x+h) = 4(x+h)^2 - 5 = 4\left(x^2 + 2xh + h^2\right) - 5 = 4x^2 + 8xh + 4h^2 - 5$

Now finding the difference quotient:

$$\frac{f(x+h) - f(x)}{h} = \frac{4x^2 + 8xh + 4h^2 - 5 - \left(4x^2 - 5\right)}{h}$$

$$= \frac{4x^2 + 8xh + 4h^2 - 5 - 4x^2 + 5}{h}$$

$$= \frac{8xh + 4h^2}{h}$$

$$= \frac{h(8x + 4h)}{h}$$

$$= 8x + 4h$$

27. Finding $(f+g)(x)$: $(f+g)(x) = f(x) + g(x) = \left(x^2 + 2x\right) + (2x - 1) = x^2 + 4x - 1$

The domain is all real numbers, or $(-\infty, \infty)$.

28. Finding $(g-f)(x)$: $(g-f)(x) = g(x) - f(x) = (2x - 1) - \left(x^2 + 2x\right) = 2x - 1 - x^2 - 2x = -x^2 - 1$

The domain is all real numbers, or $(-\infty, \infty)$.

29. Finding the function and then the value:

$$\left(\frac{f}{g}\right)(x) = \frac{f(x)}{g(x)} = \frac{x^2 + 2x}{2x - 1}$$

$$\left(\frac{f}{g}\right)(3) = \frac{(3)^2 + 2(3)}{2(3) - 1} = \frac{15}{5} = 3$$

30. Finding the function and then the value:

$$(f \cdot g)(x) = f(x) \cdot g(x) = \left(x^2 + 2x\right)(2x - 1) = 2x^3 - x^2 + 4x^2 - 2x = 2x^3 + 3x^2 - 2x$$

$$(f \cdot g)(-2) = 2(-2)^3 + 3(-2)^2 - 2(-2) = 0$$

31. Finding the function and then the value:

$$(f \circ g)(x) = f\left(g(x)\right) = f(2x - 1) = (2x - 1)^2 + 2(2x - 1) = 4x^2 - 4x + 1 + 4x - 2 = 4x^2 - 1$$

$$(f \circ g)(0) = 4(0)^2 - 1 = -1$$

32. Finding the function and then the value:

$$(g \circ f)(x) = g\left(f(x)\right) = g\left(x^2 + 2x\right) = 2\left(x^2 + 2x\right) - 1 = 2x^2 + 4x - 1$$

$$(g \circ f)(-1) = 2(-1)^2 + 4(-1) - 1 = -3$$

33. Finding the product: $(f \cdot g)(x) = f(x) \cdot g(x) = (x^2 + 2x)(2x - 1) = 2x^3 - x^2 + 4x^2 - 2x = 2x^3 + 3x^2 - 2x$

The domain is all real numbers, or $(-\infty, \infty)$.

34. Finding the quotient: $\left(\dfrac{f}{g}\right)(x) = \dfrac{f(x)}{g(x)} = \dfrac{x^2 + 2x}{2x - 1}$

The domain is all real numbers $x \neq \dfrac{1}{2}$, or $\left(-\infty, \dfrac{1}{2}\right) \cup \left(\dfrac{1}{2}, \infty\right)$.

35. Finding the composition: $(f \circ g)(x) = f(g(x)) = f(x^2 - 1) = \dfrac{1}{2(x^2 - 1)} = \dfrac{1}{2x^2 - 2}$

To find the domain, set the denominator equal to 0:
$$2x^2 - 2 = 0$$
$$2(x^2 - 1) = 0$$
$$2(x + 1)(x - 1) = 0$$
$$x = -1, 1$$

The domain is all real numbers $x \neq -1, 1$, or $(-\infty, -1) \cup (-1, 1) \cup (1, \infty)$.

36. The graph of $f(x)$ is the graph of $g(x) = |x|$ compressed horizontally away from the y-axis by a scaling factor of 2. Sketching the graph:

37. The graph of $f(x)$ is the graph of $g(x) = |x|$ compressed horizontally toward the y-axis by a scaling factor of $\dfrac{1}{3}$ and shifted down by 1 unit. Sketching the graph:

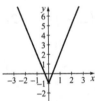

38. The graph of $f(x)$ is the graph of $g(x) = \sqrt{x}$ reflected across the x-axis, stretched vertically by a factor of 2, and shifted up by 3 units. Sketching the graph:

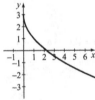

39. The graph of $f(x)$ is the graph of $g(x) = x^2$ reflected across the x-axis, shifted left by 2 units, and shifted down by 2 units. Sketching the graph:

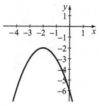

40. The function is: $g(x) = |x + 2| + 1$

41. The function is: $g(x) = (2x)^2 - 1$

42. Substituting $x = 8$ and $y = 36$ in the variation equation:

$$y = kx$$

$$36 = k(8)$$

$$k = \frac{36}{8} = \frac{9}{2}$$

The variation equation is $y = \frac{9}{2}x$.

43. Substituting $x = 7$ and $y = 10$ in the variation equation:

$$y = \frac{k}{x}$$

$$10 = \frac{k}{7}$$

$$k = 70$$

The variation equation is $y = \frac{70}{x}$.

44. **a.** The function is given by: $V(t) = 300{,}000 + 15{,}000t$

 b. Setting the function equal to 420,000:

$$420{,}000 = 300{,}000 + 15{,}000t$$

$$120{,}000 = 15{,}000t$$

$$8 = t$$

The house will have a value of \$420,000 in 8 years, which is the year 2006 + 8 = 2014.

Chapter 3
Polynomial and Rational Functions

3.1 Quadratic Functions and Their Graphs

1. The graph of $g(x) = f(x) + 2$ is the graph of f shifted up by 2 units.

3. Factoring the trinomial: $x^2 - 13x + 40 = (x - 8)(x - 5)$

5. Completing the square: $\left(x - \dfrac{3}{2}\right)^2 = x^2 - 3x + \dfrac{9}{4}$

Thus $c = \dfrac{9}{4}$.

7. The domain for both functions is $(-\infty, \infty)$, and the range for both functions is $(-\infty, 0]$. Sketching the graphs:

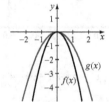

9. The domain for both functions is $(-\infty, \infty)$, the range for $f(x)$ is $[1, \infty)$, and the range for $g(x)$ is $[-1, \infty)$. Sketching both graphs:

11. **a.** The domain is $(-\infty, \infty)$ and the range is $(-\infty, 1]$.

  b. The maximum of f is attained when $x = -2$.

  c. The maximum value of f is 1.

  d. $f(x) = 0$ when $x = -3, -1$

13. This is the graph b. **15.** This is the graph a.

17. This is the graph e. **19.** This is the graph f.

---

21. The vertex is $\left(-2,-1\right)$. Sketching the graph:

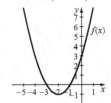

23. The vertex is $\left(-1,-1\right)$. Sketching the graph:

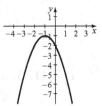

25. The vertex is $\left(-4,-2\right)$. Sketching the graph:

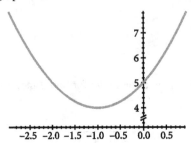

27. Completing the square: $g\left(x\right)=x^2+2x+5=\left(x^2+2x\right)+5=\left(x^2+2x+1-1\right)+5=\left(x^2+2x+1\right)-1+5=\left(x+1\right)^2+4$

The vertex is $\left(-1,4\right)$. Sketching the graph:

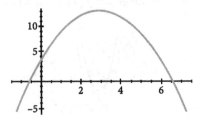

29. Completing the square:

$$w\left(x\right)=-x^2+6x+4=-\left(x^2-6x\right)+4=-\left(x^2-6x+9-9\right)+4=-\left(x^2-6x+9\right)+9+4=-\left(x-3\right)^2+13$$

The vertex is $\left(3,13\right)$. Sketching the graph:

31. Completing the square: $h(x) = x^2 + x - 3 = (x^2 + x) - 3 = \left(x^2 + x + \frac{1}{4} - \frac{1}{4}\right) - 3 = \left(x^2 + x + \frac{1}{4}\right) - \frac{1}{4} - 3 = \left(x + \frac{1}{2}\right)^2 - \frac{13}{4}$

The vertex is $\left(-\frac{1}{2}, -\frac{13}{4}\right)$. Sketching the graph:

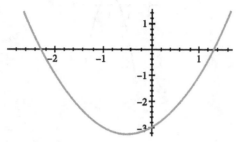

33. Completing the square:

$$f(x) = 3x^2 + 6x - 4 = 3(x^2 + 2x) - 4 = 3(x^2 + 2x + 1 - 1) - 4 = 3(x^2 + 2x + 1) - 3 - 4 = 3(x + 1)^2 - 7$$

The vertex is $(-1, -7)$. Sketching the graph:

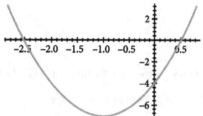

35. Finding the discriminant: $b^2 - 4ac = (-2)^2 - 4(1)(-1) = 8 > 0$

The graph of f has two x-intercepts, and the equation $f(x) = 0$ has two real solutions.

37. Finding the discriminant: $b^2 - 4ac = (1)^2 - 4(2)(1) = -7 < 0$

The graph of f has no x-intercepts, and the equation $f(x) = 0$ has no real solutions.

39. Finding the discriminant: $b^2 - 4ac = (2)^2 - 4(1)(1) = 0$

The graph of f has one x-intercept, and the equation $f(x) = 0$ has one real solution.

41. First find the vertex:

$$h = \frac{-b}{2a} = \frac{-4}{2(-2)} = 1$$

$$k = f(1) = -2(1)^2 + 4(1) - 1 = 1$$

Finding the x-intercepts by setting $f(x) = 0$: $x = \dfrac{-4 \pm \sqrt{(4)^2 - 4(-2)(-1)}}{2(-2)} = \dfrac{-4 \pm \sqrt{8}}{-4} = \dfrac{-4 \pm 2\sqrt{2}}{-4} = \dfrac{2 \pm \sqrt{2}}{2}$

The vertex is $(1,1)$, the axis of symmetry is $x = 1$, the x-intercepts are $\left(\dfrac{2 \pm \sqrt{2}}{2}, 0\right)$, the y-intercept is $(0,-1)$, and two

other points are $(2,-1)$ and $(3,-7)$. Sketching the graph:

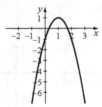

43.   First find the vertex:
$$h = \frac{-b}{2a} = \frac{-4}{2(-1)} = 2$$
$$k = g(2) = -(2)^2 + 4(2) - 3 = 1$$
Finding the x-intercepts by setting $g(x) = 0$:
$$-x^2 + 4x - 3 = 0$$
$$-(x^2 - 4x + 3) = 0$$
$$-(x - 3)(x - 1) = 0$$
$$x = 3, 1$$
The vertex is $(2,1)$, the axis of symmetry is $x = 2$, the x-intercepts are $(1,0)$ and $(3,0)$, the y-intercept is $(0,-3)$,

and two other points are $(4,-3)$ and $(5,-8)$. Sketching the graph:

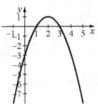

45.   First find the vertex:
$$\frac{-b}{2a} = \frac{-(-3)}{2(1)} = \frac{3}{2}$$
$$k = \left(\frac{3}{2}\right)^2 - 3\left(\frac{3}{2}\right) + 5 = \frac{11}{4}$$

Finding the x-intercepts by setting $h(x) = 0$: $x = \dfrac{3 \pm \sqrt{(-3)^2 - 4(1)(5)}}{2(1)} = \dfrac{3 \pm \sqrt{-11}}{2}$; no real solutions

The vertex is $\left(\dfrac{3}{2}, \dfrac{11}{4}\right)$, the axis of symmetry is $x = \dfrac{3}{2}$, there are no x-intercepts, the y-intercept is $(0,5)$, and

two other points are $(3,5)$ and $(-1,9)$. Sketching the graph:

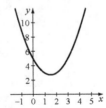

47. First find the vertex:

$$h = \frac{-b}{2a} = \frac{-0}{2(-16)} = 0$$

$$k = f(0) = -16(0)^2 + 100 = 100$$

Finding the x-intercepts by setting $f(t) = 0$:

$$-16t^2 + 100 = 0$$
$$-4(4t^2 - 25) = 0$$
$$-4(2t + 5)(2t - 5) = 0$$
$$t = -\frac{5}{2}, \frac{5}{2}$$

The vertex is $(0,100)$, the axis of symmetry is $t = 0$, the t-intercepts are $\left(\pm\frac{5}{2}, 0\right)$, the y-intercept is $(0,100)$, and two other points are $(2,36)$ and $(-2,36)$. Sketching the graph:

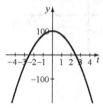

49. First find the vertex:

$$h = \frac{-b}{2a} = \frac{-(-6)}{2(1)} = 3$$

$$k = f(3) = -6(3) + (3)^2 + 5 = -4$$

Finding the x-intercepts by setting $G(x) = 0$:

$$-6x + x^2 + 5 = 0$$
$$x^2 - 6x + 5 = 0$$
$$(x - 5)(x - 1) = 0$$
$$x = 1, 5$$

The vertex is $(3,-4)$, the axis of symmetry is $x = 3$, the x-intercepts are $(1,0)$ and $(5,0)$, the y-intercept is $(0,5)$, and two other points are $(2,-3)$ and $(-1,12)$. Sketching the graph:

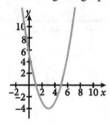

51. First find the vertex:

$$h = \frac{-b}{2a} = \frac{-3}{2(-2)} = \frac{3}{4}$$

$$k = f\left(\frac{3}{4}\right) = -2\left(\frac{3}{4}\right)^2 + 3\left(\frac{3}{4}\right) + 1 = \frac{17}{8}$$

Finding the s-intercepts by setting $f(s) = 0$: $s = \dfrac{-3 \pm \sqrt{(3)^2 - 4(-2)(1)}}{2(-2)} = \dfrac{-3 \pm \sqrt{17}}{-4} = \dfrac{3 \pm \sqrt{17}}{4}$

The vertex is $\left(\dfrac{3}{4}, \dfrac{7}{8}\right)$, the axis of symmetry is $s = \dfrac{3}{4}$, the s-intercepts are $\left(\dfrac{3 \pm \sqrt{17}}{4}, 0\right)$, the y-intercept is $(0,1)$,

and two other points are $(-1,4)$ and $(2,-1)$. Sketching the graph:

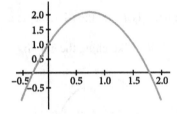

53. First find the vertex:

$$h = \frac{-b}{2a} = \frac{-1}{2(1)} = -\frac{1}{2}$$

$$k = g\left(-\frac{1}{2}\right) = \left(-\frac{1}{2}\right)^2 + \left(-\frac{1}{2}\right) + 1 = \frac{3}{4}$$

Finding the t-intercepts by setting $g(t) = 0$: $t = \dfrac{-1 \pm \sqrt{(1)^2 - 4(1)(1)}}{2(1)} = \dfrac{-1 \pm \sqrt{-3}}{2}$; no real solutions

The vertex is $\left(-\dfrac{1}{2}, \dfrac{3}{4}\right)$, the axis of symmetry is $t = -\dfrac{1}{2}$, there are no t-intercepts, the y-intercept is $(0,1)$,

and two other points are $(-1,1)$ and $(1,3)$. Sketching the graph:

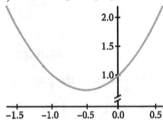

55. First find the vertex:

$$h = \frac{-b}{2a} = \frac{-(-3)}{2(1)} = \frac{3}{2}$$

$$k = f\left(\frac{3}{2}\right) = \frac{1}{3} - 3\left(\frac{3}{2}\right) + \left(\frac{3}{2}\right)^2 = -\frac{23}{12}$$

Finding the t-intercepts by setting $f(t) = 0$:

$$t^2 - 3t + \frac{1}{3} = 0$$

$$3t^2 - 9t + 1 = 0$$

$$t = \frac{9 \pm \sqrt{(-9)^2 - 4(3)(1)}}{2(3)} = \frac{9 \pm \sqrt{81 - 12}}{6} = \frac{9 \pm \sqrt{69}}{6}$$

The vertex is $\left(\frac{3}{2}, -\frac{23}{12}\right)$, the axis of symmetry is $t = \frac{3}{2}$, the t-intercepts are $\left(\frac{9 \pm \sqrt{69}}{6}, 0\right)$, the y-intercept is $\left(0, \frac{1}{3}\right)$,

and two other points are $\left(-1, \frac{13}{3}\right)$ and $\left(3, \frac{1}{3}\right)$. Sketching the graph:

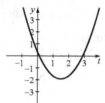

57. Finding the vertex:

$$h = \frac{-b}{2a} = \frac{-10}{2(-1)} = 5$$

$$k = f(5) = -(5)^2 + 10(5) - 8 = 17$$

The vertex is $(5, 17)$, the axis of symmetry is $x = 5$, the function is increasing on $(-\infty, 5)$ and decreasing on $(5, \infty)$, and the range is $(-\infty, 17]$. Sketching the graph:

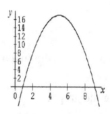

59. Finding the vertex:

$$h = \frac{-b}{2a} = \frac{-4}{2(2)} = -1$$

$$k = f(-1) = 2(-1)^2 + 4(-1) - 3 = -5$$

The vertex is $(-1,-5)$, the axis of symmetry is $x = -1$, the function is increasing on $(-1,\infty)$ and decreasing on $(-\infty,-1)$, and the range is $[-5,\infty)$. Sketching the graph:

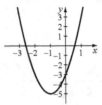

61. Finding the vertex:

$$h = \frac{-b}{2a} = \frac{-(0.4)}{2(-0.2)} = 1$$

$$k = f(1) = -0.2(1)^2 + 0.4(1) - 2.2 = -2$$

The vertex is $(1,-2)$, the axis of symmetry is $x = 1$, the function is increasing on $(-\infty,1)$ and decreasing on $(1,\infty)$, and the range is $(-\infty,-2]$. Sketching the graph:

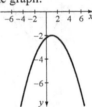

63. Finding the vertex:

$$h = \frac{-b}{2a} = \frac{-\dfrac{1}{2}}{2\left(\dfrac{1}{4}\right)} = -1$$

$$k = h(-1) = \frac{1}{4}(-1)^2 + \frac{1}{2}(-1) - 2 = -\frac{9}{4}$$

The vertex is $\left(-1,-\dfrac{9}{4}\right)$, the axis of symmetry is $x = -1$, the function is increasing on $(-1,\infty)$ and decreasing on $(-\infty,-1)$, and the range is $\left[-\dfrac{9}{4},\infty\right)$. Sketching the graph:

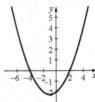

65. Since the graph opens downward, the leading coefficient is negative. The zeros are 3 and –1, therefore two factors are $x - 3$ and $x + 1$. Forming the function: $f(x) = -(x-3)(x+1) = -(x^2 - 2x - 3) = -x^2 + 2x + 3$

67. Since the vertex is the lowest point, the leading coefficient is positive. The zeros are –1 and 4, therefore two factors are $x + 1$ and $x - 4$. Forming the function: $f(x) = (x+1)(x-4) = x^2 - 3x - 4$

69. The vertex is $(0, 20)$. Sketching the graph:

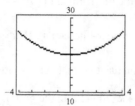

71. The vertex is $(-0.3536, 0.8232)$. Sketching the graph:

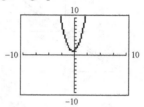

73. The vertex is $(0, 20)$. Sketching the graph:

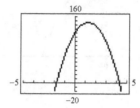

75. **a.** The axis of symmetry is $x = 2$.

    b. Since $x = 3$ is one unit to the right of $x = 2$, $x = 1$ will have the same y-coordinate. So a third point on the parabola is $(1, -1)$.

    c. Sketching the parabola:

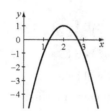

77. Using the vertex formula:

$$\frac{-b}{2a} = h$$

$$\frac{-b}{2(-2)} = 1$$

$$\frac{b}{4} = 1$$

$$b = 4$$

79. For the related function $f(x) = x^2 - x - k$, the discriminant is $b^2 - 4ac = (-1)^2 - 4(1)(-k) = 1 + 4k$. If $k < -\dfrac{1}{4}$, the function has no real zeros (and the graph has no x-intercepts). If $k = -\dfrac{1}{4}$, the function has one real zero (and the graph has one x-intercept). If $k > -\dfrac{1}{4}$, the function has two real zeros (and the graph has two x-intercepts). These correspond to the numbers of real solutions for $x^2 = x + k$. Sketching the graph:

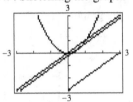

81. **a.** Sketching the graph:

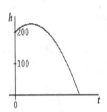

b. Using the vertex formula:
$$t = \frac{-b}{2a} = \frac{-40}{2(-16)} = 1.25$$
$$h(1.25) = -16(1.25)^2 + 40(1.25) + 200 = 220$$
The ball will reach its maximum height of 225 feet at 1.25 seconds.

83. Finding the function values:
$$p(49) = -0.387(49 - 45)^2 + 2.73(49 - 45) - 3.89 = -0.387(16) + 2.73(4) - 3.89 = 0.838$$
$$p(47) = -0.387(47 - 45)^2 + 2.73(47 - 45) - 3.89 = -0.387(4) + 2.73(2) - 3.89 = 0.022$$
At 49°F, 83.8% will hatch, and at 47°F, 2.2% will hatch.

85. **a.** In 1995, $t = 1995 - 1981 = 14$. Evaluating the function: $p(14) = 0.0489(14)^2 - 0.7815(14) + 10.31 = 8.9534$

An estimated 8.9534 million attended Broadway shows in 1995, which is within $\dfrac{9 - 8.9534}{9} \approx 0.005$ or

$\dfrac{1}{2}$% of the actual value of 9 million.

b. In 2006, $t = 2006 - 1981 = 25$. Evaluating the function: $p(25) = 0.0489(25)^2 - 0.7815(25) + 10.31 = 21.335$
An estimated 21.335 million attended Broadway shows in 2006.

c. Using the vertex formula:
$$t = \frac{-b}{2a} = \frac{-(-0.7815)}{2(0.0489)} = 7.991$$
$$p(7.991) = 0.0489(7.991)^2 - 0.7815(7.991) + 10.31 = 7.1876$$
The vertex is $(7.99, 7.1876)$. About 8 years after 1981 (1989), the attendance at Broadway shows was at a minimum of 7.18.

87. Using the perimeter formula:

$$4x + 3y = 400$$

$$3y = 400 - 4x$$

$$y = \frac{400}{3} - \frac{4}{3}x$$

The area is given by: $A(x) = xy = x\left(\frac{400}{3} - \frac{4}{3}x\right) = \frac{400}{3}x - \frac{4}{3}x^2$

This is a quadratic function whose graph opens downwards so its maximum occurs at the vertex:

$$x = \frac{-b}{2a} = \frac{-\frac{400}{3}}{2\left(-\frac{4}{3}\right)} = 50 \qquad\qquad y = \frac{400}{3} - \frac{4}{3}(50) = \frac{200}{3}$$

Each corral will be $\frac{200}{3}$ ft $\times$ 50 ft .

89. a. There is a constant change of 0.125 in. diameter but there is not a corresponding change in load.

b. Evaluating the function: $f(0.8) = 14{,}926(0.8)^2 + 148(0.8) - 51 = 9{,}620.04$

The load is 9,620 lb of concrete.

91. a. Since the maximum height of 144 feet is reached at $t = 3$ seconds, the vertex is $(h, k) = (3, 144)$.

Thus $d(t) = a(t - 3)^2 + 144$.

b. At $t = 0$, $d(t) = 0$, therefore:

$$0 = a(0 - 3)^2 + 144$$

$$-144 = 9a$$

$$-16 = a$$

c. The function is: $d(t) = -16(t - 3)^2 + 144$

d. The vertex is $(3, 144)$. Substituting the point $(0, 0)$:

$$0 = -16(0 - 3)^2 + 144$$

$$0 = 0$$

This checks our answer.

93. a. Drawing a scatter plot:

b. The best fit quadratic function is: $f(x) = 0.1945x^2 + 3.6454x + 11.8844$

c. Completing the table:

Year	Actual Returns (millions)	Predicted Returns (millions
1995	11.8	11.80
1998	24.6	24.58
2000	35.4	35.00
2003	52.9	53.56
2005	68.2	67.88

d. In 2004, $x = 2004 - 1995 = 0$. Evaluating the function: $f(9) = 0.1945(9)^2 + 3.6454(9) + 11.8844 = 60.52$

About 60.52 million tax returns were filed electronically in 2004.

e. Finding the percent error: $\dfrac{|61.2-60.52|}{61.2}\times100\% = \dfrac{0.68}{61.2}\times100\% = 0.011\times100\% = 1.1\%$

The number compares quite well, with a percent error of about 1%.

95. A linear function has a constant rate of change (slope) but a quadratic function does not. A linear function increases (or decreases) over its entire domain, but a quadratic function decreases and then increases (or increases and then decreases) over its domain.

97. **a.** Since the x-intercept $(4,0)$ is on the x-axis 5 units to the right of the vertex, the other x-intercept must be on the x-axis 5 units to the left of the vertex. This is $-1-5=-6$, so the other x-intercept is $(-6,0)$.

b. The form of the function is: $f(x) = a\big(x-(-1)\big)^2 + 2 = a(x+1)^2 + 2$

Using the point $(4,0)$:

$$f(x) = a(x+1)^2 + 2$$
$$0 = a(4+1)^2 + 2$$
$$-2 = 25a$$
$$-\frac{2}{25} = a$$

The equation is: $f(x) = -\dfrac{2}{25}(x+1)^2 + 2$

c. Sketching the graph:

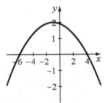

99. **a.** Since the vertex is $(2,8)$, then $h = 2$ and $k = 8$.

b. The form of the function is: $f(x) = a(x-2)^2 + 8$

c. Using the function value $f(4) = 0$:

$$0 = a(4-2)^2 + 8$$
$$-8 = 4a$$
$$-2 = a$$

d. The function is: $f(x) = -2(x-2)^2 + 8$

e. Sketching the graph:

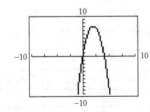

3.2 Polynomial Functions and Their Graphs

1. The graph of $f(x+2)$ is the same as the graph of $f(x)$ shifted to the left by 2 units.

3. For the x-intercept, set the function equal to 0:
$$-2x+4=0$$
$$-2x=-4$$
$$x=2$$

For the y-intercept, evaluate the function: $f(0)=-2(0)+4=4$

The x-intercept is $(2,0)$ and the y-intercept is $(0,4)$.

5. $f(x)=f(-x)$ for all x in the domain of f means that f is an even function. Thus, the graph of f has y-axis symmetry.

7. **a.** Factoring the function: $f(x)=-2x^3+18x=-2x(x^2-9)=-2x(x+3)(x-3)$

The factors are: $-2x, x+3, x-3$

b. Setting the function equal to 0:
$$-2x(x+3)(x-3)=0$$
$$x=0,-3,3$$

c. The x-intercepts are $(0,0),(-3,0),(3,0)$.

9. This is the graph of a polynomial function. The graph has no breaks, no corners, and has end behavior like a polynomial.

11. No, this is not the graph of a polynomial function. The graph has a corner (discontinuity).

13. This is a polynomial function of degree 3.

15. This is not a polynomial function. $f(t)=\sqrt{t}=t^{1/2}$ so this function cannot be written a sum of terms in which t is raised to a nonnegative-integer power.

17. This is a polynomial function of degree 0.

19. This is a polynomial function of degree 3:
$$f(x)=-(x+1)^3=-(x+1)(x+1)^2=-(x+1)(x^2+2x+1)=-(x^3+2x^2+x+x^2+2x+1)=-x^3-3x^2-3x-1$$

21. $f(x)=7x$ has leading term $7x$ (n odd, $a_n>0$). Thus $f(x)\to-\infty$ as $x\to-\infty$ and $f(x)\to\infty$ as $x\to\infty$.

23. $f(x)=-2x^3+4x-1$ has leading term $-2x^3$ (n odd, $a_n<0$). Thus $f(x)\to\infty$ as $x\to-\infty$ and $f(x)\to-\infty$ as $x\to\infty$.

25. $H(x)=-5x^4+3x^2+x-1$ has leading term $-5x^4$ (n even, $a_n<0$). Thus $H(x)\to-\infty$ as $x\to-\infty$ and $H(x)\to-\infty$ as $x\to\infty$.

27. $g(x)=-10x^3+3x^2+5x-2$ has leading term $-10x^3$ (n odd, $a_n<0$). Thus $g(x)\to\infty$ as $x\to-\infty$ and $g(x)\to-\infty$ as $x\to\infty$.

29. $f(s)=\dfrac{7}{2}s^5-14s^3+10s$ has leading term $\dfrac{7}{2}s^5$ (n odd, $a_n>0$). Thus $f(s)\to-\infty$ as $s\to-\infty$ and $f(s)\to\infty$ as $s\to\infty$.

31. The graph of $f(x)=x^3-2$ is the graph of $g(x)=x^3$ vertically shifted 2 units downward:

33. The graph of $f(x) = \dfrac{1}{2}x^3$ is the graph of $g(x) = x^3$ compressed vertically by a factor of $\dfrac{1}{2}$:

35. The graph of $g(x) = (x-2)^3$ is the graph of $f(x) = x^3$ shifted horizontally 2 units to the right:

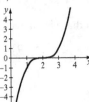

37. The graph of $h(x) = -2x^5 - 1$ is the graph of $f(x) = x^5$ stretched vertically by a factor of 2, reflected across the x-axis, and vertically shifted 1 unit downward:

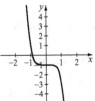

39. The graph of $f(x) = -(x+1)^3 - 2$ is the graph of $h(x) = x^3$ shifted horizontally 1 unit to the left, reflected across the x-axis, and vertically shifted 2 units downward:

41. The graph of $h(x) = -\dfrac{1}{2}(x+1)^3 - 2$ is the graph of $f(x) = x^3$ shifted horizontally 1 unit to the left, compressed vertically by a factor of $\dfrac{1}{2}$, reflected across the x-axis, and vertically shifted 2 units downward:

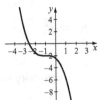

43. The function is $y = -5x^3$. Sketching both functions:

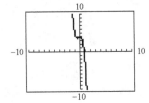

45. The function is $y = 1.5x^5$. Sketching both functions:

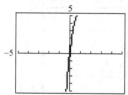 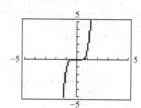

47. a. The function is $g(x) = -2x^3$.

b. Finding the value: $f(0) = -2(0)^3 + 8(0) = 0$

The y-intercept is $(0,0)$.

Finding the x-intercepts:

$$-2x^3 + 8x = 0$$
$$-2x(x^2 - 4) = 0$$
$$-2x(x+2)(x-2) = 0$$
$$x = 0, -2, 2$$

The x-intercepts are $(0,0), (-2,0), (2,0)$.

c. Completing the sign chart:

Interval	Test Value x	Function Value $f(x)$	Sign of $f(x)$
$(-\infty, -2)$	-3	30	$+$
$(-2, 0)$	-1	-6	$-$
$(0, 2)$	1	6	$+$
$(2, \infty)$	3	-30	$-$

The function is positive on $(-\infty, -2) \cup (0, 2)$.

d. The function is negative on $(-2, 0) \cup (2, \infty)$.

e. Sketching the graph:

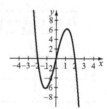

49. a. The function is $y = x^3$.

b. Finding the value: $g(0) = (0-3)(0+4)(0-1) = 12$

The y-intercept is $(0,12)$.

Finding the x-intercepts:

$$(x-3)(x+4)(x-1) = 0$$
$$x = 3, -4, 1$$

The x-intercepts are $(3,0), (-4,0), (1,0)$.

Interval	Test Value x	Function Value $g(x)$	Sign of $g(x)$
$(-\infty,-4)$	-5	-48	$-$
$(-4,1)$	0	12	$+$
$(1,3)$	2	-6	$-$
$(3,\infty)$	4	24	$+$

c. Completing the sign chart:

The function is positive on $(-4,1)\cup(3,\infty)$.

d. The function is negative on $(-\infty,-4)\cup(1,3)$.

e. Sketching the graph:

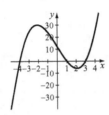

51. a. The function is $y=-\dfrac{1}{2}x^4$.

b. Finding the value: $f(0)=-\dfrac{1}{2}\left(0^2-4\right)\left(0^2-1\right)=-2$

The y-intercept is $(0,-2)$.

Finding the x-intercepts:

$$-\frac{1}{2}\left(x^2-4\right)\left(x^2-1\right)=0$$

$$-\frac{1}{2}(x+2)(x-2)(x+1)(x-1)=0$$

$$x=-2,2,-1,1$$

The x-intercepts are $(-2,0),(2,0),(-1,0),(1,0)$.

Interval	Test Value x	Function Value $f(x)$	Sign of $f(x)$
$(-\infty,-2)$	-3	-20	$-$
$(-2,-1)$	-1.5	1.094	$+$
$(-1,1)$	0	-2	$-$
$(1,2)$	1.5	1.094	$+$
$(2,\infty)$	3	-20	$-$

c. Completing the sign chart:

The function is positive on $(-2,-1)\cup(1,2)$.

d. The function is negative on $(-\infty,-2)\cup(-1,1)\cup(2,\infty)$.

e. Sketching the graph:

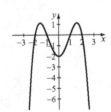

53. **a.** The function is $y = x^3$.

b. Finding the value: $f(0) = (0)^3 - 2(0)^2 - 3(0) = 0$

The y-intercept is $(0,0)$.

Finding the x-intercepts:
$$x^3 - 2x^2 - 3x = 0$$
$$x(x^2 - 2x - 3) = 0$$
$$x(x+1)(x-3) = 0$$
$$x = 0, -1, 3$$

The x-intercepts are $(0,0), (-1,0), (3,0)$.

c. Completing the sign chart:

Interval	Test Value x	Function Value $f(x)$	Sign of $f(x)$
$(-\infty,-1)$	-2	-10	$-$
$(-1,0)$	-0.5	0.875	$+$
$(0,3)$	1	-4	$-$
$(3,\infty)$	4	20	$+$

The function is positive on $(-1,0) \cup (3,\infty)$.

d. The function is negative on $(-\infty,-1) \cup (0,3)$.

e. Sketching the graph:

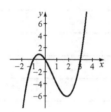

55. **a.** The function is $y = -2x^3$.

b. Finding the value: $f(0) = -0(2 \cdot 0 + 1)(0 - 3) = 0$

The y-intercept is $(0,0)$.

Finding the x-intercepts:
$$-x(2x+1)(x-3) = 0$$
$$x = 0, -\frac{1}{2}, 3$$

The x-intercepts are $(0,0), \left(-\frac{1}{2}, 0\right), (3,0)$.

c. Completing the sign chart:

Interval	Test Value x	Function Value $f(x)$	Sign of $f(x)$
$\left(-\infty, -\frac{1}{2}\right)$	-1	4	$+$
$\left(-\frac{1}{2}, 0\right)$	-0.25	-0.406	$-$
$(0,3)$	1	6	$+$
$(3,\infty)$	4	-36	$-$

The function is positive on $\left(-\infty, -\frac{1}{2}\right) \cup (0,3)$.

d. The function is negative on $\left(-\dfrac{1}{2},0\right)\cup(3,\infty)$.

e. Sketching the graph:

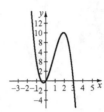

57. **a.** The function is $y=-x^4$.

b. Finding the value: $f(0)=-\left(0^2-1\right)(0-2)(0+3)=-6$

The y-intercept is $(0,-6)$.

Finding the x-intercepts:
$$-\left(x^2-1\right)(x-2)(x+3)=0$$
$$-(x+1)(x-1)(x-2)(x+3)=0$$
$$x=-1,1,2,-3$$

The x-intercepts are $(-1,0),(1,0),(2,0),(-3,0)$.

c. Completing the sign chart:

Interval	Test Value x	Function Value $f(x)$	Sign of $f(x)$
$(-\infty,-3)$	-4	-90	$-$
$(-3,-1)$	-2	12	$+$
$(-1,1)$	0	-6	$-$
$(1,2)$	1.5	6.563	$+$
$(2,\infty)$	3	-48	$-$

The function is positive on $(-3,1)\cup(1,2)$.

d. The function is negative on $(-\infty,-3)\cup(-1,1)\cup(2,\infty)$.

e. Sketching the graph:

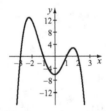

59. **a.** The function is $y=2x^3$.

b. Finding the value: $g(0)=2(0)^2(0+3)=0$

The y-intercept is $(0,0)$.

Finding the x-intercepts:
$$2x^2(x+3)=0$$
$$x=0,-3$$

The x-intercepts are $(0,0),(-3,0)$.

Interval	Test Value x	Function Value $f(x)$	Sign of $f(x)$
$(-\infty,-3)$	-4	-32	$-$
$(-3,0)$	-1	4	$+$
$(0,\infty)$	1	8	$+$

c. Completing the sign chart:

The function is positive on $(-3,0)\cup(0,\infty)$.

d. The function is negative on $(-\infty,-3)$.

e. Sketching the graph:

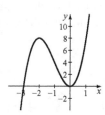

61. **a.** The function is $y=2x^4$.

b. Finding the value: $f(0)=(2\cdot0+1)(0-3)(0^2+1)=-3$

The y-intercept is $(0,-3)$.

Finding the x-intercepts:

$$(2x+1)(x-3)(x^2+1)=0$$

$$x=-\frac{1}{2},3$$

The x-intercepts are $\left(-\frac{1}{2},0\right),(3,0)$.

Interval	Test Value x	Function Value $f(x)$	Sign of $f(x)$
$\left(-\infty,-\frac{1}{2}\right)$	-1	8	$+$
$\left(-\frac{1}{2},3\right)$	0	-3	$-$
$(3,\infty)$	4	153	$+$

c. Completing the sign chart:

The function is positive on $\left(-\infty,-\frac{1}{2}\right)\cup(3,\infty)$.

d. The function is negative on $\left(-\frac{1}{2},3\right)$.

e. Sketching the graph:

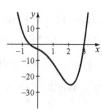

63. **a.** The x-intercept is $(-1,0)$.   **b.** The y-intercept is $(0,3)$.

   c. The power of the leading term is odd.   **d.** The sign of the leading coefficient is positive.

65. **a.** The x-intercepts are $(-1,0),(0,0)$, and $(1,0)$.   **b.** The y-intercept is $(0,0)$.

   c. The power of the leading term is odd.   **d.** The sign of the leading coefficient is negative.

67. The zero $x = 2$ has multiplicity 2; the graph just touches the x-axis.
The zero $x = -5$ has multiplicity 5; the graph passes through the x-axis.

69. The zero $t = 0$ has multiplicity 2; the graph just touches the t-axis.
The zero $t = 1$ has multiplicity 1; the graph passes through the t-axis.
The zero $t = -2$ has multiplicity 1; the graph passes through the t-axis.

71. Factoring the function: $f(x) = x^2 + 2x + 1 = (x+1)^2$

The zero $x = -1$ has multiplicity 2; the graph just touches the x-axis.

73. Factoring the function: $g(s) = 2s^3 + 4s^2 + 2s = 2s(s^2 + 2s + 1) = 2s(s+1)^2$

The zero $s = 0$ has multiplicity 1; the graph passes through the s-axis.
The zero $s = -1$ has multiplicity 2; the graph just touches the s-axis.

75. Finding the function values:
$$g(x) = x^4 + 2x^2 - 1$$
$$-g(x) = -(x^4 + 2x^2 - 1) = -x^4 - 2x^2 + 1$$
$$g(-x) = (-x)^4 + 2(-x)^2 - 1 = x^4 + 2x^2 - 1$$

Since $g(-x) = g(x)$, g is an even function and has y-axis symmetry.

77. Finding the function values:
$$f(x) = -3x^3 + 1$$
$$-f(x) = -(-3x^3 + 1) = 3x^3 - 1$$
$$f(-x) = -3(-x)^3 + 1 = 3x^3 + 1$$

Since $f(-x) \neq f(x)$ and $f(-x) \neq -f(x)$, f is neither an even or odd function and has no symmetry.

79. Finding the function values:
$$f(x) = -x^3 + 2x$$
$$-f(x) = -(-x^3 + 2x) = x^3 - 2x$$
$$f(-x) = -(-x)^3 + 2(-x) = x^3 - 2x$$

Since $f(-x) = -f(x)$, f is an odd function and has origin symmetry.

81. Finding the function values:
$$h(x) = -2x^4 + 3x^2 - 1$$
$$-h(x) = -(-2x^4 + 3x^2 - 1) = 2x^4 - 3x^2 + 1$$
$$h(-x) = -2(-x)^4 + 3(-x)^2 - 1 = -2x^4 + 3x^2 - 1$$

Since $h(-x) = h(x)$, h is an even function and has y-axis symmetry.

83. The zero at $x = -1$ has odd multiplicity, the zero at $x = 0$ has odd multiplicity, and the zero at $x = \dfrac{3}{2}$ has odd multiplicity.

85. The zero at $x = 0$ has even multiplicity and the zero at $x = 4$ has even multiplicity.

87. **a.** $f(x)$ behaves like $g(x) = x^3$ so $f(x) \to \infty$ as $x \to \infty$ and $f(x) \to -\infty$ as $x \to -\infty$

  b. Evaluating the function: $f(0) = (0)^2(0-1) = 0$. The y-intercept is $(0,0)$.

  c. The x-intercept at $(0,0)$ has multiplicity 2 and the x-intercept at $(1,0)$ has multiplicity 1.

  d. Finding the function values:
$$f(-x) = (-x)^2((-x)-1) = x^2(-x-1) = -x^2(x+1) \neq f(x)$$
$$-f(-x) = -(-x)^2((-x)-1) = -x^2(-x-1) = x^2(x+1) \neq f(x)$$

Thus f is neither even nor odd and has no symmetry.

Interval	Test Value x	Function Value $f(x)$	Sign of $f(x)$
$(-\infty,0)$	-1	-2	$-$
$(0,1)$	0.5	-0.125	$-$
$(1,\infty)$	2	4	$+$

e. Creating a sign chart:

Thus f is positive on $(1,\infty)$ and negative on $(-\infty,0)\cup(0,1)$. Sketching the graph:

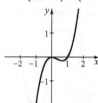

89. a. $f(x)$ behaves like $g(x)=x^3$ so $f(x)\to\infty$ as $x\to\infty$ and $f(x)\to-\infty$ as $x\to-\infty$

b. Evaluating the function: $f(0)=(0-2)^2(0+2)=8$

The y-intercept is $(0,8)$.

c. The x-intercept at $(2,0)$ has multiplicity 2 and the x-intercept at $(-2,0)$ has multiplicity 1.

d. Finding the function values:

$$f(-x)=(-x-2)^2(-x+2)=-(x+2)^2(x-2)\neq f(x)$$
$$-f(-x)=-(-x-2)^2(-x+2)=(x+2)^2(x-2)\neq f(x)$$

Thus f is neither even nor odd and has no symmetry.

Interval	Test Value x	Function Value $f(x)$	Sign of $f(x)$
$(-\infty,-2)$	-3	-25	$-$
$(-2,2)$	0	8	$+$
$(2,\infty)$	3	5	$+$

e. Creating a sign chart:

Thus f is positive on $(-2,2)\cup(2,\infty)$ and negative on $(-\infty,-2)$. Sketching the graph:

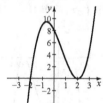

91. a. $g(x)$ behaves like $h(x)=x^4$ so $g(x)\to\infty$ as $x\to\infty$ and $g(x)\to\infty$ as $x\to-\infty$

b. Evaluating the function: $g(0)=(0+1)^2(0-2)(0+3)=-6$

The y-intercept is $(0,-6)$.

c. The x-intercept at $(-1,0)$ has multiplicity 2, the x-intercept at $(2,0)$ has multiplicity 1, and the x-intercept at $(-3,0)$ has multiplicity 1.

d. Finding the function values:

$$g(-x)=(-x+1)^2(-x-2)(-x+3)=(1-x)^2(x+2)(x-3)\neq g(x)$$
$$-g(-x)=-(-x+1)^2(-x-2)(-x+3)=-(1-x)^2(x+2)(x-3)\neq g(x)$$

Thus g is neither even nor odd and has no symmetry.

Interval	Test Value x	Function Value $g(x)$	Sign of $g(x)$
$(-\infty,-3)$	-4	54	$+$
$(-3,-1)$	-2	-4	$-$
$(-1,2)$	0	-6	$-$
$(2,\infty)$	3	96	$+$

e. Creating a sign chart:

Thus g is positive on $(-\infty,-3)\cup(2,\infty)$ and negative on $(-3,-1)\cup(-1,2)$. Sketching the graph:

93. **a.** $g(x)$ behaves like $h(x)=-x^4$ so $g(x)\to-\infty$ as $x\to\infty$ and $g(x)\to-\infty$ as $x\to-\infty$

b. Evaluating the function: $g(0)=-2(0+1)^2(0-3)^2=-18$

The y-intercept is $(0,-18)$.

c. The x-intercept at $(-1,0)$ has multiplicity 2 and the x-intercept at $(3,0)$ has multiplicity 2.

d. Finding the function values:

$$g(-x)=-2(-x+1)^2(-x-3)^2=-2(x-1)^2(x+3)^2\neq g(x)$$
$$-g(-x)=2(-x+1)^2(-x-3)^2=2(x-1)^2(x+3)^2\neq g(x)$$

Thus g is neither even nor odd and has no symmetry.

Interval	Test Value x	Function Value $g(x)$	Sign of $g(x)$
$(-\infty,-1)$	-2	-50	$-$
$(-1,3)$	0	-18	$-$
$(3,\infty)$	4	-50	$-$

e. Creating a sign chart:

Thus g is never positive and negative on $(-\infty,-1)\cup(-1,3)\cup(3,\infty)$. Sketching the graph:

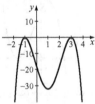

95. **a.** $f(x)$ behaves like $g(x)=x^3$ so $f(x)\to\infty$ as $x\to\infty$ and $f(x)\to-\infty$ as $x\to-\infty$

b. Evaluating the function: $f(0)=(0)^3+4(0)^2+4(0)=0$

The y-intercept is $(0,0)$.

c. Factoring the function: $f(x)=x^3+4x^2+4x=x(x^2+4x+4)=x(x+2)^2$

The x-intercept at $(-2,0)$ has multiplicity 2 and the x-intercept at $(0,0)$ has multiplicity 1.

d. Finding the function values:

$$f(-x)=(-x)^3+4(-x)^2+4(-x)=-x^3+4x^2-4x\neq f(x)$$
$$-f(-x)=-(-x)^3-4(-x)^2-4(-x)=x^3-4x^2+4x\neq f(x)$$

Thus f is neither even nor odd and has no symmetry.

e. Creating a sign chart:

Interval	Test Value x	Function Value $f(x)$	Sign of $f(x)$
$(-\infty,-2)$	-3	-3	$-$
$(-2,0)$	-1	-1	$-$
$(0,\infty)$	1	9	$+$

Thus f is positive on $(0,\infty)$ and negative on $(-\infty,-2)\cup(-2,0)$. Sketching the graph:

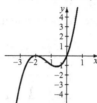

97. **a.** $h(x)$ behaves like $g(x)=-x^4$ so $h(x)\rightarrow -\infty$ as $x\rightarrow \infty$ and $h(x)\rightarrow -\infty$ as $x\rightarrow -\infty$

b. Evaluating the function: $h(0)=-2(0)^4+4(0)^3+2(0)^2=0$

The y-intercept is $(0,0)$.

c. Finding the x-intercepts:
$$-2x^4+4x^3+2x^2=0$$
$$-2x^2\left(x^2-2x-1\right)=0$$
$$x=0,\ \frac{2\pm\sqrt{(-2)^2-4(1)(-1)}}{2(1)}=\frac{2\pm\sqrt{8}}{2}=\frac{2\pm2\sqrt{2}}{2}=1\pm\sqrt{2}\approx 2.4,-0.4$$

The x-intercept at $(0,0)$ has multiplicity 2, the x-intercept at $\left(1-\sqrt{2},0\right)$ has multiplicity 1, and the x-intercept at $\left(1+\sqrt{2},0\right)$ has multiplicity 1.

d. Finding the function values:
$$h(-x)=-2(-x)^4+4(-x)^3+2(-x)^2=-2x^4-4x^3+2x^2\neq h(x)$$
$$-h(-x)=2(-x)^4-4(-x)^3-2(-x)^2=2x^4+4x^3-2x^2\neq h(x)$$

Thus h is neither even nor odd and has no symmetry.

e. Creating a sign chart:

Interval	Test Value x	Function Value $h(x)$	Sign of $h(x)$
$(-\infty,-0.4)$	-1	-4	$-$
$(-0.4,0)$	-0.2	0.045	$+$
$(0,2.4)$	1	4	$+$
$(2.4,\infty)$	3	-36	$-$

Thus h is positive on $\left(1-\sqrt{2},0\right)\cup\left(0,1+\sqrt{2}\right)$ and negative on $\left(-\infty,1-\sqrt{2}\right)\cup\left(1+\sqrt{2},\infty\right)$. Sketching the graph:

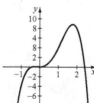

99. $x=-2, x=5,$ and $x=6$ zeros of multiplicity 1 gives factors $x-(-2)=x+2, x-5,$ and $x-6$.

Therefore the polynomial is: $f(x)=(x+2)(x-5)(x-6)$

101. $x = 2$ and $x = 4$ zeros of multiplicity 2 gives factors $(x-2)^2$ and $(x-4)^2$.

Therefore the polynomial is: $f(x) = (x-2)^2(x-4)^2$

103. $x = 2$ a zero of multiplicity 1 and $x = -3$ a zero of multiplicity 2 gives factors $x-2$ and $(x+3)^2$.

Therefore the polynomial is: $f(x) = (x-2)(x+3)^2$

105. $x = -2$ and $x = -1$ zeros of multiplicity 1 gives factors $x-(-2) = x+2$, and $x-(-1) = x+1$. The zero $x = 5$ of

multiplicity 3 yields the factor $(x-5)^3$. Therefore the polynomial is: $f(x) = (x+2)(x+1)(x-5)^3$

107. Sketching the graph:

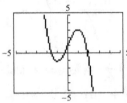

   a.   The x-intercepts are: $(-1.5321, 0), (-0.3473, 0), (1.8794, 0)$

   b.   The function is positive on $(-\infty, -1.5321) \cup (-0.3473, 1.8794)$, and negative on

       $(-1.5321, -0.3473) \cup (1.8794, \infty)$.

   c.   The local maximum is $(1, 3)$, and the local minimum is $(-1, -1)$.

   d.   There is no symmetry of the graph.

109. Sketching the graph:

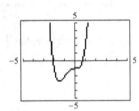

   a.   The x-intercepts are: $(0.7167, 0), (-2.1069, 0)$

   b.   The function is positive on $(-\infty, -2.1069) \cup (0.7167, \infty)$, and negative on $(-2.1069, 0.7167)$.

   c.   There is no local maximum, and the local minimum is $(-1.5, -2.6875)$.

   d.   There is no symmetry of the graph.

111. **a.**   Sketching the graph in the standard window $[-10, 10] \times [-10, 10]$:

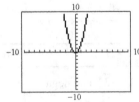

   Note the graph appears as a parabola.

   b.   Finding the x-intercepts:

$$0.001x^3 + 2x^2 = 0$$
$$x^2(0.001x + 2) = 0$$
$$x^2 = 0 \text{ or } 0.001x + 2 = 0$$
$$x = 0 \qquad 0.001x = -2$$
$$x = -2000$$

   The x-intercepts are: $(0, 0), (-2000, 0)$

Sketching the graph:

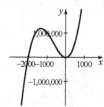

c. Sketching the graph in the window $[-3000, 2000] \times [-2000000, 2000000]$:

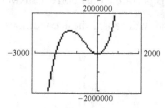

113. a. The relationship is:
$$h + d = 10$$
$$h = 10 - d$$
$$h = 10 - 2r$$

b. Finding the volume: $V = \pi r^2 (10 - 2r)$

c. Note that $r > 0$. For $h > 0$, we must have:
$$10 - 2r > 0$$
$$5 > r$$
This problem makes sense for $0 < r < 5$ in order for the height to be a positive value.

115. a. The base side is $h + 3$. Finding the volume: $V = lwh = s^2 h = (h+3)^2 h = h(h+3)^2$

b. Graphing the volume function:

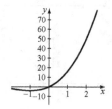

c. The volume makes sense for $h > 0$.

117. a. For 1934, $x = 1$: $g(1) = 0.294(1)^5 - 12.2(1)^4 + 169(1)^3 - 912(1)^2 + 2025(1) + 4508 \approx \$5,778$

For 1942, $x = 9$: $g(9) = 0.294(9)^5 - 12.2(9)^4 + 169(9)^3 - 912(9)^2 + 2025(9) + 4508 \approx \$9,378$

For 1949, $x = 16$: $g(16) = 0.294(16)^5 - 12.2(16)^4 + 169(16)^3 - 912(16)^2 + 2025(16) + 4508 \approx \$4,402$

From 1934 to 1942 the GNP rose, then from 1942 to 1949 it fell.

b. It would not be a good predictor since 2002 is too far outside the range of the data used to model the equation.

c. Graphing the function:

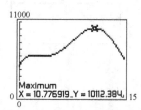

The maximum occurs at $x \approx 10.8$, which corresponds to the year 1943.

119. Many answers are possible. The graphed cubic $f(x) = x^2(x-2)$ has exactly two real zeros.

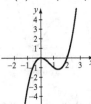

121. One answer is $f(x) = (x-2)(x-1)$. This is not the only correct answer. Any function of the form

$f(x) = a(x-2)^m (x-1)^n$, $a \neq 0, m, n$ odd, will satisfy these conditions.

123. **a.** A possible graph is:

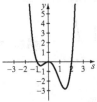

    b. The local minima are $(-0.693, -0.397)$ and $(1.443, -2.883)$.

    c. The polynomial is: $f(s) = s^2(s+1)(s-2)$

    d. Graphing the polynomial:

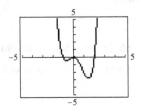

125. **a.** A possible graph is:

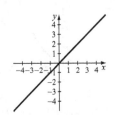

    b. There are no local extrema .

    c. The polynomial is: $q(x) = x$

    d. Graphing the polynomial:

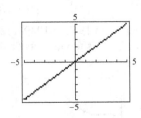

3.3 Division of Polynomials; the Remainder and Factor Theorems

1. Using synthetic division:

$$-5 \underline{)\, 2 \quad 13 \quad 15}$$
$$ -10 \quad -15$$
$$\overline{2 \quad\ \ 3 \quad\ \ 0}$$

The quotient is $q(x) = 2x + 3$ and the remainder is $r(x) = 0$.

3. Using long division:

$$
\begin{array}{r}
x^2 - 4 \\
2x-1 \overline{)\, 2x^3 - x^2 - 8x + 4} \\
\underline{2x^3 - x^2} \\
-8x + 4 \\
\underline{-8x + 4} \\
0
\end{array}
$$

The quotient is $q(x) = x^2 - 4$ and the remainder is $r(x) = 0$.

5. Using synthetic division:

$$-2 \underline{)\, 1 \quad -3 \quad\ \ 2 \quad\ \ -4}$$
$$ -2 \quad 10 \quad -24$$
$$\overline{1 \quad -5 \quad 12 \quad -28}$$

The quotient is $q(x) = x^2 - 5x + 12$ and the remainder is $r(x) = -28$.

7. Using long division:

$$
\begin{array}{r}
-x^3 - \dfrac{1}{3}x^2 + \dfrac{2}{9}x + \dfrac{2}{27} \\
3x-1 \overline{)\, -3x^4 + 0x^3 + x^2 + 0x - 2}\\
\underline{-3x^4 + x^3} \\
-x^3 + x^2 \\
\underline{-x^3 + \dfrac{1}{3}x^2} \\
\dfrac{2}{3}x^2 + 0x \\
\underline{\dfrac{2}{9}x^2 - \dfrac{2}{9}x} \\
\dfrac{2}{9}x - 2 \\
\underline{\dfrac{2}{9}x - \dfrac{2}{27}}\\
-\dfrac{52}{27}
\end{array}
$$

The quotient is $q(x) = -x^3 - \dfrac{1}{3}x^3 + \dfrac{2}{9}x + \dfrac{2}{27}$ and the remainder is $r(x) = -\dfrac{52}{27}$.

9. Using synthetic division:

$$\begin{array}{r|rrrrrrr} -1 & 1 & 0 & 0 & 0 & 0 & 0 & 1 \\ & & -1 & 1 & -1 & 1 & -1 & 1 \\ \hline & 1 & -1 & 1 & -1 & 1 & -1 & 2 \end{array}$$

The quotient is $q(x) = x^5 - x^4 + x^3 - x^2 + x - 1$ and the remainder is $r(x) = 2$.

11. Using long division:

$$\begin{array}{r} x+2 \\ x^2 - 2 \overline{) x^3 + 2x^2 + 0x - 5} \\ \underline{x^3 - 2x } \\ 2x^2 + 2x - 5 \\ \underline{2x^2 - 4} \\ 2x - 1 \end{array}$$

The quotient is $q(x) = x + 2$ and the remainder is $r(x) = 2x - 1$.

13. Using long division:

$$\begin{array}{r} x^2 - x + 1 \\ x^3 + x - 1 \overline{) x^5 - x^4 + 2x^3 + x^2 - x + 1} \\ \underline{x^5 + x^3 - x^2 } \\ -x^4 + x^3 + 2x^2 - x \\ \underline{-x^4 - x^2 + x } \\ x^3 + 3x^2 - 2x + 1 \\ \underline{x^3 + x - 1} \\ 3x^2 - 3x + 2 \end{array}$$

The quotient is $q(x) = x^2 - x + 1$ and the remainder is $r(x) = 3x^2 - 3x + 2$.

15. Using synthetic division:

$$\begin{array}{r|rrr} -1 & 1 & 1 & 1 \\ & & -1 & 0 \\ \hline & 1 & 0 & 1 \end{array}$$

Therefore: $\dfrac{x^2 + x + 1}{x + 1} = x + \dfrac{1}{x + 1}$

Written in the desired form: $x^2 + x + 1 = (x + 1)x + 1$

17. Using synthetic division:

$$\begin{array}{r|rrrr} 4 & 3 & 0 & 2 & -8 \\ & & 12 & 48 & 200 \\ \hline & 3 & 12 & 50 & 192 \end{array}$$

Therefore: $\dfrac{3x^3 + 2x - 8}{x - 4} = 3x^2 + 12x + 50 + \dfrac{192}{x - 4}$

Written in the desired form: $3x^3 + 2x - 8 = (x - 4)(3x^2 + 12x + 50) + 192$

19. Using long division:

$$
\begin{array}{r}
x^4 - 3x^3 - x^2 + 6x \\
x^2 + 2 \overline{)\,x^6 - 3x^5 + x^4 + 0x^3 - 2x^2 - 5x + 6} \\
\underline{x^6 \qquad\quad + 2x^4} \\
-3x^5 - x^4 + 0x^3 \\
\underline{-3x^5 \qquad\quad - 6x^3} \\
-x^4 + 6x^3 - 2x^2 \\
\underline{-x^4 \qquad\quad - 2x^2} \\
6x^3 \qquad\qquad - 5x \\
\underline{6x^3 \qquad\qquad + 12x} \\
-17x + 6
\end{array}
$$

Therefore: $\dfrac{x^6 - 3x^5 + x^4 - 2x^2 - 5x + 6}{x^2 + 2} = x^4 - 3x^3 - x^2 + 6x + \dfrac{6 - 17x}{x^2 + 2}$

Written in the desired form: $x^6 - 3x^5 + x^4 - 2x^2 - 5x + 6 = \left(x^2 + 2\right)\left(x^4 - 3x^3 - x^2 + 6x\right) + \left(-17x + 6\right)$

21. Using synthetic division with $x = 3$:

$$
\begin{array}{r|rrrr}
3 & 1 & 0 & -7 & 5 \\
  &   & 3 & 9 & 6 \\
\hline
  & 1 & 3 & 2 & 11
\end{array}
$$

Therefore: $f(3) = 11$

Using synthetic division with $x = 5$:

$$
\begin{array}{r|rrrr}
5 & 1 & 0 & -7 & 5 \\
  &   & 5 & 25 & 90 \\
\hline
  & 1 & 5 & 18 & 95
\end{array}
$$

Therefore: $f(5) = 95$

23. Using synthetic division with $x = -1$:

$$
\begin{array}{r|rrrrr}
-1 & -2 & -10 & 0 & -3 & 10 \\
   &   & 2 & 8 & -8 & 11 \\
\hline
   & -2 & -8 & 8 & -11 & 21
\end{array}
$$

Therefore: $f(-1) = 21$

Using synthetic division with $x = 2$:

$$
\begin{array}{r|rrrrr}
2 & -2 & -10 & 0 & -3 & 10 \\
  &   & -4 & -28 & -56 & -118 \\
\hline
  & -2 & -14 & -28 & -59 & -108
\end{array}
$$

Therefore: $f(2) = -108$

25. Using synthetic division with $x = 3$:

$$
\begin{array}{r|rrrrrr}
3 & 1 & 0 & -2 & 0 & 0 & 12 \\
  &   & 3 & 9 & 21 & 63 & 189 \\
\hline
  & 1 & 3 & 7 & 21 & 63 & 201
\end{array}
$$

Therefore: $f(3) = 201$

Using synthetic division with $x = -2$:

$$
\begin{array}{r|rrrrrr}
-2 & 1 & 0 & -2 & 0 & 0 & 12 \\
   &   & -2 & 4 & -4 & 8 & -16 \\
\hline
   & 1 & -2 & 2 & -4 & 8 & -4
\end{array}
$$

Therefore: $f(-2) = -4$

27. Using synthetic division with $x = \dfrac{1}{2}$:

$$
\begin{array}{r|rrrrr}
\frac{1}{2} & 1 & 0 & -2 & 0 & 1 \\
            &   & \frac{1}{2} & \frac{1}{4} & -\frac{7}{8} & -\frac{7}{16} \\
\hline
            & 1 & \frac{1}{2} & -\frac{7}{4} & -\frac{7}{8} & \frac{9}{16}
\end{array}
$$

Therefore: $f\left(\dfrac{1}{2}\right) = \dfrac{9}{16}$

29. Using synthetic division with $x = 3$:

$$
\begin{array}{r|rrrr}
3 & 1 & 0 & -7 & 6 \\
  &   & 3 & 9 & 6 \\
\hline
  & 1 & 3 & 2 & 12
\end{array}
$$

$q(x)$ is not a factor of $p(x)$, since $\dfrac{p(x)}{q(x)}$ has a nonzero remainder.

31. Using synthetic division with $x = -3$:

$$
\begin{array}{r|rrrr}
-3 & 1 & 0 & -7 & 6 \\
   &   & -3 & 9 & -6 \\
\hline
   & 1 & -3 & 2 & 0
\end{array}
$$

$q(x)$ is a factor of $p(x)$, since $\dfrac{p(x)}{q(x)}$ has no remainder.

33. Using synthetic division with $x = 4$:

$$
\begin{array}{r|rrrrrr}
4 & 1 & 0 & -3 & 0 & 2 & -8 \\
  &   & 4 & 16 & 52 & 208 & 840 \\
\hline
  & 1 & 4 & 13 & 52 & 210 & 832
\end{array}
$$

$q(x)$ is not a factor of $p(x)$, since $\dfrac{p(x)}{q(x)}$ has a nonzero remainder.

35. Using synthetic division with $x = 5$:

$$
\begin{array}{r|rrrrr}
5 & 1 & 0 & 0 & 0 & -50 \\
  &   & 5 & 25 & 125 & 625 \\
\hline
  & 1 & 5 & 25 & 125 & 575
\end{array}
$$

$q(x)$ is not a factor of $p(x)$, since $\dfrac{p(x)}{q(x)}$ has a nonzero remainder.

37. Rewriting $p(x)$: $p(x) = 3x^3 - 48x - 4x^2 + 64 = 3x^3 - 4x^2 - 48x + 64$

Using synthetic division with $x = -4$:

$$
\begin{array}{r|rrrr}
-4 & 3 & -4 & -48 & 64 \\
   &   & -12 & 64 & -64 \\
\hline
   & 3 & -16 & 16 & 0
\end{array}
$$

$q(x)$ is a factor of $p(x)$, since $\dfrac{p(x)}{q(x)}$ has no remainder.

39. The graph crosses the x-axis at $x = 1$, so $x = 1$ is a zero of multiplicity 1. Thus, $x - 1$ is a linear factor of $p(x)$.

41. If $p(x) = x^7 + 7$, then $p(1) = (1)^7 + 7 = 8$. By the Remainder Theorem, the remainder when $x^7 + 7$ is divided by $x - 1$ is 8.

43. Since $x - \dfrac{1}{2}$ a factor of $p(x)$, $x = \dfrac{1}{2}$ is a zero of $p(x)$. Thus $p\!\left(\dfrac{1}{2}\right) = 0$.

45. If $p(x) = x^3 - x^2 + kx + 3$, then $p(-1) = (-1)^3 - (-1)^2 + k(-1) + 3 = 1 - k$. Since $p(-1) = -2$, we have:

$$1 - k = -2$$
$$-k = -3$$
$$k = 3$$

3.4 Real Zeros of Polynomials; Solutions of Equations

1. A rational number is a number that can be expressed as a quotient of two integers.

3. False, since $0.1111... = \dfrac{1}{9}$, which is a rational number.

5. Finding the values:
$$p(6) = (6-10)^8 = (-4)^8 \neq 0$$
$$p(-10) = (-10-10)^8 = (-20)^8 \neq 0$$
$$p(10) = (10-10)^8 = (0)^8 = 0$$
Only $x = 10$ is a zero of $p(x)$.

7. Finding the values:
$$g(-2) = (-2)^2 + 4 = 4 + 4 = 8$$
$$g(2) = (2)^2 + 4 = 4 + 4 = 8$$
Neither are zeros of $g(x)$.

9. Finding the values:
$$f\left(\sqrt{3}\right) = \left(\sqrt{3}\right)^3 + 2\left(\sqrt{3}\right)^2 - 3\left(\sqrt{3}\right) - 6 = 3\sqrt{3} + 6 - 3\sqrt{3} - 6 = 0$$
$$f\left(-\sqrt{2}\right) = \left(-\sqrt{2}\right)^3 + 2\left(-\sqrt{2}\right)^2 - 3\left(-\sqrt{2}\right) - 6 = -2\sqrt{2} - 4 + 3\sqrt{2} - 6 \neq 0$$
Only $x = \sqrt{3}$ is a zero of $f(x)$.

11. Evaluating the polynomial: $p(2) = (2)^3 - 5(2)^2 + 8(2) - 4 = 8 - 20 + 16 - 4 = 0$
Using synthetic division:

$$
\begin{array}{r|rrrr}
2 & 1 & -5 & 8 & -4 \\
  &   & 2 & -6 & 4 \\
\hline
  & 1 & -3 & 2 & 0
\end{array}
$$

Factoring the polynomial: $p(x) = (x-2)(x^2 - 3x + 2) = (x-2)(x-2)(x-1) = (x-2)^2(x-1)$

13. Evaluating the polynomial: $p(1) = -(1)^4 - (1)^3 + 18(1)^2 + 16(1) - 32 = -1 - 1 + 18 + 16 - 32 = 0$
Using synthetic division:

$$
\begin{array}{r|rrrrr}
1 & -1 & -1 & 18 & 16 & -32 \\
  &   & -1 & -2 & 16 & 32 \\
\hline
  & -1 & -2 & 16 & 32 & 0
\end{array}
$$

Factoring the polynomial:
$$p(x) = (x-1)(-x^3 - 2x^2 + 16x + 32)$$
$$= -(x-1)(x^3 + 2x^2 - 16x - 32)$$
$$= -(x-1)\left[x^2(x+2) - 16(x+2)\right]$$
$$= -(x-1)(x+2)(x^2 - 16)$$
$$= -(x-1)(x+2)(x+4)(x-4)$$

15. Evaluating the polynomial: $p\left(\dfrac{2}{3}\right) = 3\left(\dfrac{2}{3}\right)^3 - 2\left(\dfrac{2}{3}\right)^2 + 3\left(\dfrac{2}{3}\right) - 2 = \dfrac{8}{9} - \dfrac{8}{9} + 2 - 2 = 0$

Using synthetic division:

$$\begin{array}{r|rrrr} \dfrac{2}{3} & 3 & -2 & 3 & -2 \\ & & 2 & 0 & 2 \\ \hline & 3 & 0 & 3 & 0 \end{array}$$

Factoring the polynomial: $p(x) = \left(x - \dfrac{2}{3}\right)(3x^2 + 3) = 3\left(x - \dfrac{2}{3}\right)(x^2 + 1) = (3x - 2)(x^2 + 1)$

17. Evaluating the polynomial: $p\left(-\dfrac{1}{3}\right) = 3\left(-\dfrac{1}{3}\right)^3 + \left(-\dfrac{1}{3}\right)^2 + 24\left(-\dfrac{1}{3}\right) + 8 = -\dfrac{1}{9} + \dfrac{1}{9} - 8 + 8 = 0$

Using synthetic division:

$$\begin{array}{r|rrrr} -\dfrac{1}{3} & 3 & 1 & 24 & 8 \\ & & -1 & 0 & -8 \\ \hline & 3 & 0 & 24 & 0 \end{array}$$

Factoring the polynomial: $p(x) = \left(x + \dfrac{1}{3}\right)(3x^2 + 24) = 3\left(x + \dfrac{1}{3}\right)(x^2 + 8) = (3x + 1)(x^2 + 8)$

19-21 Completing the table:

	Function	Zero	x-Intercept	Factor
19.	$f(x)$	-2	$(-2,0)$	$x + 2$
21.	$h(x)$	-4	$(-4,0)$	$x + 4$

23. The possible rational roots are: $\dfrac{\text{Factors of } -6}{\text{Factors of } 1} = \dfrac{\pm 1, \pm 2, \pm 3, \pm 6}{\pm 1} = \pm 1, \pm 2, \pm 3, \pm 6$

Evaluating the function (until we reach a 0):

$P(1) = (1)^3 + 2(1)^2 - 5(1) - 6 = -8$

$P(-1) = (-1)^3 + 2(-1)^2 - 5(-1) - 6 = 0$

Using synthetic division:

$$\begin{array}{r|rrrr} -1 & 1 & 2 & -5 & -6 \\ & & -1 & -1 & 6 \\ \hline & 1 & 1 & -6 & 0 \end{array}$$

Factoring the polynomial: $P(x) = (x + 1)(x^2 + x - 6) = (x + 1)(x + 3)(x - 2)$

The real zeros are: $x = -1, -3, 2$

25. First factoring out x: $P(x) = x^4 - 13x^2 - 12x = x(x^3 - 13x - 12)$

The possible rational roots are: $\dfrac{\text{Factors of } -12}{\text{Factors of } 1} = \dfrac{\pm 1, \pm 2, \pm 3, \pm 4, \pm 6, \pm 12}{\pm 1} = \pm 1, \pm 2, \pm 3, \pm 4, \pm 6, \pm 12$

Evaluating the function (until we reach a 0):

$f(1) = (1)^3 - 13(1) - 12 = -24$

$f(-1) = (-1)^3 - 13(-1) - 12 = 0$

Using synthetic division:

$$\begin{array}{r|rrrr} -1 & 1 & 0 & -13 & -12 \\ & & -1 & 1 & 12 \\ \hline & 1 & -1 & -12 & 0 \end{array}$$

Factoring the polynomial: $P(x) = x(x+1)(x^2 - x - 12) = x(x+1)(x+3)(x-4)$

The real zeros are: $x = 0, -1, -3, 4$

27. The possible rational roots are:

$$\frac{\text{Factors of } 36}{\text{Factors of } 4} = \frac{\pm 1, \pm 2, \pm 3, \pm 4, \pm 6, \pm 9, \pm 12, \pm 18, \pm 36}{\pm 1, \pm 2, \pm 4}$$

$$= \pm 1, \pm 2, \pm 3, \pm 4, \pm 6, \pm 9, \pm 12, \pm 18, \pm 36, \pm \frac{1}{2}, \pm \frac{1}{4}, \pm \frac{3}{2}, \pm \frac{3}{4}, \pm \frac{9}{2}, \pm \frac{9}{4}$$

Evaluating the function (until we reach a 0):

$$P(1) = 4(1)^4 - 25(1)^2 + 36 = 15$$

$$P(-1) = 4(-1)^4 - 25(-1)^2 + 36 = 15$$

$$P(2) = 4(2)^4 - 25(2)^2 + 36 = 0$$

Using synthetic division:

$$\begin{array}{r|rrrrr} 2 & 4 & 0 & -25 & 0 & 36 \\ & & 8 & 16 & -18 & -36 \\ \hline & 4 & 8 & -9 & -18 & 0 \end{array}$$

Factoring the polynomial:

$$\begin{aligned} P(s) &= (s-2)(4s^3 + 8s^2 - 9s - 18) \\ &= (s-2)[4s^2(s+2) - 9(s+2)] \\ &= (s-2)(s+2)(4s^2 - 9) \\ &= (s-2)(s+2)(2s+3)(2s-3) \end{aligned}$$

The real zeros are: $s = 2, -2, -\dfrac{3}{2}, \dfrac{3}{2}$

29. The possible rational roots are: $\dfrac{\text{Factors of } 3}{\text{Factors of } -4} = \dfrac{\pm 1, \pm 3}{\pm 1, \pm 2, \pm 4} = \pm 1, \pm 3, \pm \dfrac{1}{2}, \pm \dfrac{1}{4}, \pm \dfrac{3}{2}, \pm \dfrac{3}{4}$

Evaluating the function: $F(-3) = -4(-3)^4 - 11(-3)^3 - (-3)^2 - 11(-3) + 3 = 0$

Using synthetic division:

$$\begin{array}{r|rrrrr} -3 & -4 & -11 & -1 & -11 & 3 \\ & & 12 & -3 & 12 & -3 \\ \hline & -4 & 1 & -4 & 1 & 0 \end{array}$$

Factoring the polynomial:

$$\begin{aligned} F(x) &= (x+3)(-4x^3 + x^2 - 4x + 1) \\ &= (x+3)[-x^2(4x-1) - 1(4x-1)] \\ &= (x+3)(4x-1)(-x^2 - 1) \\ &= -(x+3)(4x-1)(x^2 + 1) \end{aligned}$$

The real zeros are: $x = -3, \dfrac{1}{4}$

31. The possible rational roots are: $\dfrac{\text{Factors of } 6}{\text{Factors of } 1} = \dfrac{\pm 1, \pm 2, \pm 3, \pm 6}{\pm 1} = \pm 1, \pm 2, \pm 3, \pm 6$

Evaluating the function: $f(1) = (1)^4 + 2(1)^3 - 5(1)^2 - 4(1) + 6 = 0$

Using synthetic division:

$$\begin{array}{r|rrrr} 1 & 1 & 2 & -5 & -4 & 6 \\ & & 1 & 3 & -2 & -6 \\ \hline & 1 & 3 & -2 & -6 & 0 \end{array}$$

Factoring the polynomial: $f(x) = (x-1)(x^3 + 3x^2 - 2x - 6) = (x-1)\left[x^2(x+3) - 2(x+3)\right] = (x-1)(x+3)(x^2-2)$

The real zeros are: $x = 1, -3, \pm\sqrt{2}$

33. The possible rational roots are: $\dfrac{\text{Factors of } 24}{\text{Factors of } 1} = \pm 1, \pm 2, \pm 3, \pm 4, \pm 6, \pm 8, \pm 12, \pm 24$

Evaluating the function: $h(3) = (3)^4 + 3(3)^3 - 8(3)^2 - 22(3) - 24 = 0$

Using synthetic division:

$$\begin{array}{r|rrrrr} 3 & 1 & 3 & -8 & -22 & -24 \\ & & 3 & 18 & 30 & 24 \\ \hline -4 & 1 & 6 & 10 & 8 & 0 \\ & & -4 & -8 & -8 & \\ \hline & 1 & 2 & 2 & 0 & \end{array}$$

Factoring the polynomial: $h(x) = (x-3)(x+4)(x^2 + 2x + 2)$

Using the quadratic formula: $x = \dfrac{-2 \pm \sqrt{(2)^2 - 4(1)(2)}}{2(1)} = \dfrac{-2 \pm \sqrt{-4}}{2}$; no real solutions

The real zeros are: $x = 3, -4$

35. Creating a function:

$$x^3 + 2x^2 + 2x = -1$$

$$x^3 + 2x^2 + 2x + 1 = 0$$

$$p(x) = x^3 + 2x^2 + 2x + 1$$

The possible rational roots are: ± 1

Using synthetic division:

$$\begin{array}{r|rrrr} -1 & 1 & 2 & 2 & 1 \\ & & -1 & -1 & -1 \\ \hline & 1 & 1 & 1 & 0 \end{array}$$

Factoring the polynomial: $p(x) = (x+1)(x^2 + x + 1)$

Using the quadratic formula: $x = \dfrac{-1 \pm \sqrt{(1)^2 - 4(1)(1)}}{2(1)} = \dfrac{-1 \pm \sqrt{-3}}{2}$; no real solutions

The only real solution is: $x = -1$

37. Creating a function:
$$x^3 - 6x^2 + 5x = -12$$
$$x^3 - 6x^2 + 5x + 12 = 0$$
$$p(x) = x^3 - 6x^2 + 5x + 12$$

The possible rational roots are: $\pm 1, \pm 2, \pm 3, \pm 4, \pm 6, \pm 12$

Evaluating the function: $p(-1) = (-1)^3 - 6(-1)^2 + 5(-1) + 12 = 0$

Using synthetic division:
```
-1│ 1   -6    5    12
        -1    7   -12
  ─────────────────────
    1   -7   12    0
```

Factoring the polynomial: $p(x) = x^3 - 6x^2 + 5x + 12 = (x+1)(x^2 - 7x + 12) = (x+1)(x-3)(x-4)$

The real solutions are: $x = -1, 3, 4$

39. Creating a function:
$$2x^3 - 3x^2 = 11x - 6$$
$$2x^3 - 3x^2 - 11x + 6 = 0$$
$$p(x) = 2x^3 - 3x^2 - 11x + 6$$

The possible rational roots are: $\pm 1, \pm 2, \pm 3, \pm 6, \pm \dfrac{1}{2}, \pm \dfrac{3}{2}$

Evaluating the function: $p(-2) = 2(-2)^3 - 3(-2)^2 - 11(-2) + 6 = 0$

Using synthetic division:
```
-2│ 2   -3   -11    6
        -4    14   -6
  ─────────────────────
    2   -7     3    0
```

Factoring the polynomial: $p(x) = (x+2)(2x^2 - 7x + 3) = (x+2)(2x-1)(x-3)$

The real solutions are: $x = -2, \dfrac{1}{2}, 3$

41. Solving the equation:
$$x^4 + x^3 - x = 1$$
$$x^4 + x^3 - x - 1 = 0$$
$$x^3(x+1) - 1(x+1) = 0$$
$$(x+1)(x^3 - 1) = 0$$
$$(x+1)(x-1)(x^2 + x + 1) = 0$$

Using the quadratic formula: $x = \dfrac{-1 \pm \sqrt{(1)^2 - 4(1)(1)}}{2(1)} = \dfrac{-1 \pm \sqrt{-3}}{2}$; no real solutions

The real solutions are: $x = -1, 1$

43. For $p(x) = 4x^4 - 5x^3 + 6x - 3$, there are 3 sign variations.

For $p(-x) = 4(-x)^4 - 5(-x)^3 + 6(-x) - 3 = 4x^4 + 5x^3 - 6x - 3$, there is 1 sign variation.

Positive zeros: 3 or 1; negative zeros: 1

45. For $p(x) = -2x^3 + x^2 - x + 1$, there are 3 sign variations.

For $p(-x) = -2(-x)^3 + (-x)^2 - (-x) + 1 = 2x^3 + x^2 + x + 1$, there are no sign variations.

Positive zeros: 3 or 1; negative zeros: 0

47. For $p(x) = 2x^4 - x^3 - 2x^2 + 2x + 5$, there are 2 sign variations.

For $p(-x) = 2(-x)^4 - (-x)^3 - 2(-x)^2 + 2(-x) + 5 = 2x^4 + x^3 - 2x^2 - 2x + 5$, there are 2 sign variations.

Positive zeros: 2 or 0; negative zeros: 2 or 0

49. For $p(x) = x^5 + 3x^4 - 4x^2 + 10$, there are 2 sign variations.

For $p(-x) = (-x)^5 + 3(-x)^4 - 4(-x)^2 + 10 = -x^5 + 3x^4 - 4x^2 + 10$, there are 3 sign variations.

Positive zeros: 2 or 0; negative zeros: 3 or 1

51. For $p(x) = x^6 + 4x^3 - 3x^2 + 7$, there are 2 sign variations.

For $p(-x) = (-x)^6 + 4(-x)^3 - 3(-x)^2 + 7 = x^6 - 4x^3 - 3x^2 + 7$, there are 2 sign variations.

Positive zeros: 2 or 0; negative zeros: 2 or 0

53. The zero is: $x = 4$

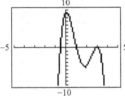

55. The zeros are: $x = -\dfrac{1}{2}, \dfrac{3}{2}, 2$

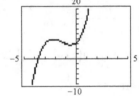

57. The zeros are: $x = -\dfrac{1}{2}, 1, 3$

59. The zero is: $x \approx -3.8265$

61. Let x represent the height, $x + 10$ represent the length, and $x + 5$ represent the width. Using the volume formula, the equation is:

$$V = 168 \text{ cubic in.}$$
$$l \cdot w \cdot h = 168$$
$$(x+10)(x+5)x = 168$$
$$(x^2 + 15x + 50)x = 168$$
$$x^3 + 15x^2 + 50x - 168 = 0$$

For $p(x) = x^3 + 15x^2 + 50x - 168$, the possible rational roots are:

$$\pm 1, \pm 2, \pm 3, \pm 4, \pm 7, \pm 8, \pm 12, \pm 14, \pm 21, \pm 24, \pm 42, \pm 56, \pm 84, \pm 168$$

Since $p(2) = (2)^3 + 15(2)^2 + 50(2) - 168 = 0$, the value of x is 2. The length is 12 in., the width is 7 in., and the height is 2 in.

63. Let r represent the radius and $r + 5$ represent the height. Using the volume formula:

$$V = 1000$$
$$\pi r^2 h = 1000$$
$$\pi r^2 (r + 5) = 1000$$
$$\pi r^3 + 5\pi r^2 = 1000$$
$$\pi r^3 + 5\pi r^2 - 1000 = 0$$

Solving graphically, the radius $r \approx 5.5047$ in. and the height is ≈ 10.5047 in.

65. Answers may vary. Two examples are $y = (x+1)(x^2+1)$ and $y = -(x+1)^3$.

3.5 Complex Numbers

1. Multiplying: $(2+3x)(-3+x) = -6 + 2x - 9x + 3x^2 = 3x^2 - 7x - 6$

3. Multiplying: $\left(x+\sqrt{2}\right)\left(x-\sqrt{3}\right) = x^2 - \sqrt{3}x + \sqrt{2}x - \sqrt{6} = x^2 + \left(\sqrt{2}-\sqrt{3}\right)x - \sqrt{6}$

5. Using the quadratic formula: $x = \dfrac{3 \pm \sqrt{(-3)^2 - 4(1)(0)}}{2(1)} = \dfrac{3 \pm \sqrt{9}}{2} = \dfrac{3 \pm 3}{2} = 3, 0$

7. Rewrite the equation as: $2x^2 - x - 1 = 0$

Using the quadratic formula: $x = \dfrac{1 \pm \sqrt{(-1)^2 - 4(2)(-1)}}{2(2)} = \dfrac{1 \pm \sqrt{9}}{4} = \dfrac{1 \pm 3}{4} = -\dfrac{1}{2}, 1$

9. Writing as an imaginary number: $\sqrt{-16} = i\sqrt{16} = 4i$

11. Writing as an imaginary number: $\sqrt{-12} = i\sqrt{12} = i\sqrt{4 \cdot 3} = 2i\sqrt{3}$

13. Writing as an imaginary number: $\sqrt{-\dfrac{4}{25}} = i\sqrt{\dfrac{4}{25}} = \dfrac{2}{5}i$

15. The real part is 2 and the imaginary part is 0.　　**17.** The real part is 0 and the imaginary part is $-\pi$.

19. The real part is $1+\sqrt{5}$ and the imaginary part is 0.

21. Writing the complex number: $1 + \sqrt{-5} = 1 + i\sqrt{5}$. The real part is 1 and the imaginary part is $\sqrt{5}$.

23. The complex conjugate of -2 is -2.　　**25.** Since $i - 1 = -1 + i$, the complex conjugate is $-1 - i$.

27. The complex conjugate of $3+\sqrt{2}$ is $3+\sqrt{2}$.　　**29.** Since $i^2 = -1$, the complex conjugate is -1.

31. Finding the values:

$$x + y = 3i + (2-i) = 2 + (3i - i) = 2 + 2i$$
$$x - y = 3i - (2-i) = 3i - 2 + i = -2 + 4i$$
$$xy = 3i(2-i) = 6i - 3i^2 = 6i - 3(-1) = 3 + 6i$$
$$\frac{x}{y} = \frac{3i}{2-i} = \frac{3i}{2-i} \cdot \frac{2+i}{2+i} = \frac{6i + 3i^2}{4 + 2i - 2i - i^2} = \frac{-3+6i}{5} = -\frac{3}{5} + \frac{6}{5}i$$

33. Finding the values:

$$x + y = (-3+5i) + (2-3i) = -1 + 2i$$
$$x - y = (-3+5i) - (2-3i) = -3 + 5i - 2 + 3i = -5 + 8i$$
$$xy = (-3+5i)(2-3i) = -6 + 9i + 10i - 15i^2 = -6 + 19i - 15(-1) = -6 + 19i + 15 = 9 + 19i$$
$$\frac{x}{y} = \frac{-3+5i}{2-3i} = \frac{-3+5i}{2-3i} \cdot \frac{2+3i}{2+3i} = \frac{-6 - 9i + 10i + 15i^2}{4 + 6i - 6i - 9i^2} = \frac{-21+i}{13} = -\frac{21}{13} + \frac{1}{13}i$$

35. Finding the values:

$$x + y = (4 - 5i) + (3 + 2i) = 7 - 3i$$

$$x - y = (4 - 5i) - (3 + 2i) = 4 - 5i - 3 - 2i = 1 - 7i$$

$$xy = (4 - 5i)(3 + 2i) = 12 + 8i - 15i - 10i^2 = 12 - 7i + 10 = 22 - 7i$$

$$\frac{x}{y} = \frac{4 - 5i}{3 + 2i} = \frac{4 - 5i}{3 + 2i} \cdot \frac{3 - 2i}{3 - 2i} = \frac{12 - 8i - 15i + 10i^2}{9 - 6i + 6i - 4i^2} = \frac{2 - 23i}{13} = \frac{2}{13} - \frac{23}{13}i$$

37. Finding the values:

$$x + y = \left(\frac{1}{2} - 3i\right) + \left(\frac{1}{5} + \frac{4}{3}i\right) = \frac{1}{2} + \frac{1}{5} - 3i + \frac{4}{3}i = \frac{7}{10} - \frac{5}{3}i$$

$$x - y = \left(\frac{1}{2} - 3i\right) - \left(\frac{1}{5} + \frac{4}{3}i\right) = \frac{1}{2} - \frac{1}{5} - 3i - \frac{4}{3}i = \frac{3}{10} - \frac{13}{3}i$$

$$xy = \left(\frac{1}{2} - 3i\right)\left(\frac{1}{5} + \frac{4}{3}i\right) = \frac{1}{10} + \frac{2}{3}i - \frac{3}{5}i - 4i^2 = \frac{1}{10} + \frac{1}{15}i + 4 = \frac{41}{10} + \frac{1}{15}i$$

$$\frac{x}{y} = \frac{\left(\frac{1}{2} - 3i\right) \cdot 30}{\left(\frac{1}{5} + \frac{4}{3}i\right) \cdot 30} = \frac{15 - 90i}{6 + 40i} \cdot \frac{6 - 40i}{6 - 40i} = \frac{90 - 600i - 540i + 3600i^2}{36 - 240i + 240i - 1600i^2} = \frac{-3510 - 1140i}{1636} = -\frac{1755}{818} - \frac{285}{409}i$$

39. Finding the values:

$$x + y = \left(-\frac{1}{3} + i\sqrt{5}\right) + \left(-\frac{1}{2} - 2i\sqrt{5}\right) = -\frac{1}{3} - \frac{1}{2} + i\sqrt{5} - 2i\sqrt{5} = -\frac{5}{6} - i\sqrt{5}$$

$$x - y = \left(-\frac{1}{3} + i\sqrt{5}\right) - \left(-\frac{1}{2} - 2i\sqrt{5}\right) = -\frac{1}{3} + \frac{1}{2} + i\sqrt{5} + 2i\sqrt{5} = \frac{1}{6} + 3i\sqrt{5}$$

$$xy = \left(-\frac{1}{3} + i\sqrt{5}\right)\left(-\frac{1}{2} - 2i\sqrt{5}\right) = \frac{1}{6} + \frac{2\sqrt{5}}{3}i - \frac{\sqrt{5}}{2}i - 2i^2(5) = \frac{1}{6} + \frac{\sqrt{5}}{6}i + 10 = \frac{61}{6} + \frac{\sqrt{5}}{6}i$$

$$\frac{x}{y} = \frac{\left(-\frac{1}{3} + i\sqrt{5}\right) \cdot 6}{\left(-\frac{1}{2} - 2i\sqrt{5}\right) \cdot 6}$$

$$= \frac{-2 + 6i\sqrt{5}}{-3 - 12i\sqrt{5}} \cdot \frac{-3 + 12i\sqrt{5}}{-3 + 12i\sqrt{5}}$$

$$= \frac{6 - 24i\sqrt{5} - 18i\sqrt{5} + 360i^2}{9 - 36i\sqrt{5} + 36i\sqrt{5} - 720i^2}$$

$$= \frac{6 - 42i\sqrt{5} - 360}{9 + 720}$$

$$= \frac{-354 - 42i\sqrt{5}}{729}$$

$$= -\frac{118}{243} - \frac{14\sqrt{5}}{243}i$$

41. Finding the values:

$$x+y=(-3+i)+\left(i+\frac{1}{2}\right)=-3+\frac{1}{2}+i+i=-\frac{5}{2}+2i$$

$$x-y=(-3+i)-\left(i+\frac{1}{2}\right)=-3-\frac{1}{2}+i-i=-\frac{7}{2}$$

$$xy=(-3+i)\left(i+\frac{1}{2}\right)=-3i-\frac{3}{2}+i^2+\frac{1}{2}i=-\frac{5}{2}i-\frac{3}{2}-1=-\frac{5}{2}-\frac{5}{2}i$$

$$\frac{x}{y}=\frac{(-3+i)\cdot 2}{\left(i+\frac{1}{2}\right)\cdot 2}=\frac{-6+2i}{1+2i}\cdot\frac{1-2i}{1-2i}=\frac{-6+12i+2i-4i^2}{2i-4i^2+1-2i}=\frac{-2+14i}{5}=-\frac{2}{5}+\frac{14}{5}i$$

43. Solving the equation:

$$x^2=-16$$
$$\sqrt{x^2}=\pm\sqrt{-16}$$
$$x=\pm 4i$$

45. Solving the equation:

$$-x^2=8$$
$$x^2=-8$$
$$\sqrt{x^2}=\pm\sqrt{-8}$$
$$x=\pm 2i\sqrt{2}$$

47. Solving the equation:

$$3x^2=-30$$
$$x^2=-10$$
$$\sqrt{x^2}=\pm\sqrt{-10}$$
$$x=\pm i\sqrt{10}$$

49. a. $f(x)=2(x^2+2)$ has no real zeros.

b. Solving the equation $f(x)=0$:

$$x^2+2=0$$
$$x^2=-2$$
$$x=\pm i\sqrt{2}$$

51. a. Using the quadratic formula: $x=\dfrac{-1\pm\sqrt{(1)^2-4(1)(1)}}{2(1)}=\dfrac{-1\pm\sqrt{-3}}{2}$. There are no real zeros.

b. Using the quadratic formula: $x=\dfrac{-1\pm\sqrt{(1)^2-4(1)(1)}}{2(1)}=\dfrac{-1\pm\sqrt{-3}}{2}=\dfrac{-1\pm i\sqrt{3}}{2}=-\dfrac{1}{2}\pm\dfrac{\sqrt{3}}{2}i$

53. Solving the equation:

$$2x^2+9=0$$
$$2x^2=-9$$
$$x^2=-\frac{9}{2}$$
$$x=\pm\frac{3}{\sqrt{2}}i=\pm\frac{3\sqrt{2}}{2}i$$

The zeros are: $x=\pm\dfrac{3\sqrt{2}}{2}i$

55. Using the quadratic formula: $x=\dfrac{1\pm\sqrt{(-1)^2-4(-1)(-1)}}{2(-1)}=\dfrac{1\pm\sqrt{-3}}{-2}=\dfrac{1\pm i\sqrt{3}}{-2}=-\dfrac{1}{2}\pm\dfrac{\sqrt{3}}{2}i$

The zeros are: $x=-\dfrac{1}{2}\pm\dfrac{\sqrt{3}}{2}i$

57. Using the quadratic formula: $t = \dfrac{2 \pm \sqrt{(-2)^2 - 4(3)(-9)}}{2(3)} = \dfrac{2 \pm \sqrt{112}}{6} = \dfrac{2 \pm \sqrt{16 \cdot 7}}{6} = \dfrac{2 \pm 4\sqrt{7}}{6} = \dfrac{1 \pm 2\sqrt{7}}{3}$

The zeros are: $t = \dfrac{1 \pm 2\sqrt{7}}{3}$

59. Using the quadratic formula: $x = \dfrac{-8 \pm \sqrt{(8)^2 - 4(3)(-16)}}{2(3)} = \dfrac{-8 \pm \sqrt{256}}{6} = \dfrac{-8 \pm 16}{6} = \dfrac{8}{6}, \dfrac{-24}{6} = \dfrac{4}{3}, -4$

The zeros are: $x = \dfrac{4}{3}, -4$

61. Using the quadratic formula: $x = \dfrac{-2 \pm \sqrt{(2)^2 - 4(1)(3)}}{2(1)} = \dfrac{-2 \pm \sqrt{-8}}{2} = \dfrac{-2 \pm 2i\sqrt{2}}{2} = -1 \pm i\sqrt{2}$

The zeros of $f(x) = x^2 + 2x + 3$ are $x = -1 + i\sqrt{2}$ and $x = -1 - i\sqrt{2}$.

63. Using the quadratic formula: $x = \dfrac{-2 \pm \sqrt{(2)^2 - 4(-3)(-4)}}{2(-3)} = \dfrac{-2 \pm \sqrt{-44}}{-6} = \dfrac{-2 \pm 2i\sqrt{11}}{-6} = \dfrac{1}{3} \pm \dfrac{\sqrt{11}}{3}i$

The zeros of $f(x) = -3x^2 + 2x - 4$ are $x = \dfrac{1}{3} + \dfrac{\sqrt{11}}{3}i$ and $x = \dfrac{1}{3} - \dfrac{\sqrt{11}}{3}i$.

65. Using the quadratic formula: $x = \dfrac{2 \pm \sqrt{(-2)^2 - 4(5)(3)}}{2(5)} = \dfrac{2 \pm \sqrt{-56}}{10} = \dfrac{2 \pm 2i\sqrt{14}}{10} = \dfrac{1}{5} \pm \dfrac{\sqrt{14}}{5}i$

The zeros of $f(x) = 5x^2 - 2x + 3$ are $x = \dfrac{1}{5} + \dfrac{\sqrt{14}}{5}i$ and $x = \dfrac{1}{5} - \dfrac{\sqrt{14}}{5}i$.

67. First write the equation as $5x^2 + 2x + 3 = 0$.

Using the quadratic formula: $x = \dfrac{-2 \pm \sqrt{(2)^2 - 4(5)(3)}}{2(5)} = \dfrac{-2 \pm \sqrt{-56}}{10} = \dfrac{-2 \pm 2i\sqrt{14}}{10} = -\dfrac{1}{5} \pm \dfrac{\sqrt{14}}{5}i$

The zeros of $f(x) = 5x^2 + 2x + 3$ are $x = -\dfrac{1}{5} + \dfrac{\sqrt{14}}{5}i$ and $x = -\dfrac{1}{5} - \dfrac{\sqrt{14}}{5}i$.

69. First write the equation as $-3x^2 + 8x - 16 = 0$.

Using the quadratic formula: $x = \dfrac{-8 \pm \sqrt{(8)^2 - 4(-3)(-16)}}{2(-3)} = \dfrac{-8 \pm \sqrt{-128}}{-6} = \dfrac{-8 \pm i\sqrt{64 \cdot 2}}{-6} = \dfrac{-8 \pm 8i\sqrt{2}}{-6} = \dfrac{4}{3} \pm \dfrac{4\sqrt{2}}{3}i$

The zeros of $f(x) = -3x^2 + 8x - 16$ are $x = \dfrac{4}{3} + \dfrac{4\sqrt{2}}{3}i$ and $x = \dfrac{4}{3} - \dfrac{4\sqrt{2}}{3}i$.

71. Multiply by 2 to write the equation as $-8t^2 + 2t - 1 = 0$.

Using the quadratic formula: $t = \dfrac{-2 \pm \sqrt{(2)^2 - 4(-8)(-1)}}{2(-8)} = \dfrac{-2 \pm \sqrt{-28}}{-16} = \dfrac{-2 \pm 2i\sqrt{7}}{-16} = \dfrac{1}{8} \pm \dfrac{\sqrt{7}}{8}i$

The zeros of $f(t) = -4t^2 + t - \dfrac{1}{2}$ are $t = \dfrac{1}{8} + \dfrac{\sqrt{7}}{8}i$ and $t = \dfrac{1}{8} - \dfrac{\sqrt{7}}{8}i$.

73.   First write the equation as:

$$\frac{2}{3}x^2 + x = -1$$

$$\frac{2}{3}x^2 + x + 1 = 0$$

$$2x^2 + 3x + 3 = 0$$

Using the quadratic formula: $x = \dfrac{-3 \pm \sqrt{(3)^2 - 4(2)(3)}}{2(2)} = \dfrac{-3 \pm \sqrt{-15}}{4} = \dfrac{-3 \pm i\sqrt{15}}{4} = -\dfrac{3}{4} \pm \dfrac{\sqrt{15}}{4}i$

The zeros of $f(x) = \dfrac{2}{3}x^2 + x + 1$ are $x = -\dfrac{3}{4} + \dfrac{\sqrt{15}}{4}i$ and $x = -\dfrac{3}{4} - \dfrac{\sqrt{15}}{4}i$.

75.   Solving the equation:

$$(x+1)^2 = -25$$

$$\sqrt{(x+1)^2} = \pm\sqrt{-25}$$

$$x + 1 = \pm 5i$$

$$x = -1 \pm 5i$$

The zeros of $f(x) = (x+1)^2 + 25 = x^2 + 2x + 26$ are $x = -1 - 5i$ and $x = -1 + 5i$.

77.   Showing each result:

$$z + \bar{z} = (a+bi) + (a-bi) = a + a + bi - bi = 2a$$

$$z - \bar{z} = (a+bi) - (a-bi) = a - a + bi + bi = 2bi$$

79.   Showing the result: $\dfrac{z + \bar{z}}{2} = \dfrac{(a+bi) + (a-bi)}{2} = \dfrac{a + a + bi - bi}{2} = \dfrac{2a}{2} = a$

81.   Finding the discriminant: $b^2 - 4ac = (2)^2 - 4(a)(1) = 4 - 4a$

83.   Since the discriminant must be equal to zero:

$$4 - 4a = 0$$

$$-4a = -4$$

$$a = 1$$

85.   Using a graphing calculator: $x \approx 2.28 \pm 2.191i$

87.   Using a graphing calculator: $t \approx 0.333 \pm 1.158i$

89.   **a.**   The vertex is above the x-axis and the parabola opens upward. Because the graph does not intersect the x-axis, there are no real zeros of the function.

   b.   Since $f(x) = a(x-h)^2 + k$ and $(0,4)$ is the vertex where $a > 0$, then $f(x) = 2x^2 + 4$ is a possible function.

   This is not the only possible quadratic function for this parabola, as using any $a > 0$ gives a possible function.

   c.   Setting the function equal to 0:

$$2x^2 + 4 = 0$$

$$2x^2 = -4$$

$$x^2 = -2$$

$$\sqrt{x^2} = \pm\sqrt{-2}$$

$$x = \pm i\sqrt{2}$$

The zeros are $x = \pm i\sqrt{2}$.

91. **a.** Multiplying: $(x+i)(x-i) = x^2 - i^2 = x^2 + 1$

b. Setting the function equal to 0:

$$x^2 + 1 = 0$$

$$x^2 = -1$$

$$\sqrt{x^2} = \pm\sqrt{-1}$$

$$x = \pm i$$

c. If we solve the equation by factoring from part **a**:

$$x^2 + 1 = 0$$

$$(x+i)(x-i) = 0$$

$$x = \pm i$$

Note the answers are the same.

d. Solving the equation:

$$x^2 + 9 = 0$$

$$x^2 = -9$$

$$\sqrt{x^2} = \pm\sqrt{-9}$$

$$x = \pm 3i$$

Thus the factoring is: $x^2 + 9 = (x + 3i)(x - 3i)$

e. The factoring is: $x^2 + c^2 = (x + ci)(x - ci)$

93. **a.** The line of symmetry for the associated parabola is $x = 0$, because $f(x) = f(-x)$ and so $(x, f(x))$ and $(-x, f(-x))$ are the same distance from $(0, f(0))$ for all x.

b. The minimum value is 1, which occurs at $x = 0$.

c. Sketching the graph:

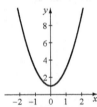

d. The function has two non-real zeros, since its graph doesn't intersect the x-axis.

3.6 The Fundamental Theorem of Algebra; Complex Zeros

1. For $x = 1$, the multiplicity is 3. For $x = 4$, the multiplicity is 5.

3. For $s = \pi$, the multiplicity is 10. For $s = -\pi$, the multiplicity is 3.

5. Finding the zeros:

$$2x^2 - 5x + 3 = 0$$

$$(2x - 3)(x - 1) = 0$$

$$x = 1, \frac{3}{2}$$

The zeros are: $x = 1, \frac{3}{2}$

The factored form is: $p(x) = (2x - 3)(x - 1)$

7. Finding the zeros:

$$x^2 - \pi^2 = 0$$

$$(x + \pi)(x - \pi) = 0$$

$$x = -\pi, \pi$$

The zeros are: $x = -\pi, \pi$

The factored form is: $p(x) = (x + \pi)(x - \pi)$

9. Finding the zeros:
$$x^2 + 9 = 0$$
$$(x + 3i)(x - 3i) = 0$$
$$x = -3i, 3i$$

The zeros are: $x = -3i, 3i$

The factored form is: $p(x) = (x + 3i)(x - 3i)$

11. Finding the zeros:
$$x^2 - 3 = 0$$
$$\left(x + \sqrt{3}\right)\left(x - \sqrt{3}\right) = 0$$
$$x = -\sqrt{3}, \sqrt{3}$$

The zeros are: $x = -\sqrt{3}, \sqrt{3}$

The factored form is: $p(x) = \left(x + \sqrt{3}\right)\left(x - \sqrt{3}\right)$

13. Finding the zeros:
$$x^3 + 3x = 0$$
$$x\left(x^2 + 3\right) = 0$$
$$x\left(x + i\sqrt{3}\right)\left(x - i\sqrt{3}\right) = 0$$
$$x = 0, -i\sqrt{3}, i\sqrt{3}$$

The zeros are: $x = 0, -i\sqrt{3}, i\sqrt{3}$

The factored form is: $p(x) = x\left(x + i\sqrt{3}\right)\left(x - i\sqrt{3}\right)$

15. Finding the zeros:
$$x^4 - 9 = 0$$
$$\left(x^2 - 3\right)\left(x^2 + 3\right) = 0$$
$$\left(x + \sqrt{3}\right)\left(x - \sqrt{3}\right)\left(x + i\sqrt{3}\right)\left(x - i\sqrt{3}\right) = 0$$
$$x = \pm\sqrt{3}, \pm i\sqrt{3}$$

The zeros are: $x = \pm\sqrt{3}, \pm i\sqrt{3}$

The factored form is:
$$p(x) = \left(x + \sqrt{3}\right)\left(x - \sqrt{3}\right)\left(x + i\sqrt{3}\right)\left(x - i\sqrt{3}\right)$$

17. Using synthetic division:

$$
\begin{array}{r|rrrr}
2 & 1 & -2 & 1 & -2 \\
  &   & 2 & 0 & 2 \\
\hline
  & 1 & 0 & 1 & 0
\end{array}
$$

The factorization is: $x^3 - 2x^2 + x - 2 = (x - 2)\left(x^2 + 1\right)$

19. Using synthetic division:

$$
\begin{array}{r|rrrr}
5 & 2 & -9 & -11 & 30 \\
  &   & 10 & 5 & -30 \\
\hline
  & 2 & 1 & -6 & 0
\end{array}
$$

The factorization is: $2x^3 - 9x^2 - 11x + 30 = (x - 5)\left(2x^2 + x - 6\right) = (x - 5)(2x - 3)(x + 2)$

21. Using synthetic division:

$$
\begin{array}{r|rrrrr}
3 & 1 & -5 & 7 & -5 & 6 \\
  &   & 3 & -6 & 3 & -6 \\
\hline
  & 1 & -2 & 1 & -2 & 0
\end{array}
$$

The factorization is:
$$x^4 - 5x^3 + 7x^2 - 5x + 6 = (x - 3)\left(x^3 - 2x^2 + x - 2\right) = (x - 3)\left[x^2(x - 2) + 1(x - 2)\right] = (x - 3)(x - 2)\left(x^2 + 1\right)$$

23. Using the results of problem 17: $x^3 - 2x^2 + x - 2 = (x - 2)\left(x^2 + 1\right) = (x - 2)(x + i)(x - i)$

25. Using synthetic division:

$$\begin{array}{r|rrrrr} -5 & 1 & 4 & -1 & 16 & -20 \\ & & -5 & 5 & -20 & 20 \\ \hline & 1 & -1 & 4 & -4 & 0 \end{array}$$

The factorization is:

$$\begin{aligned} x^4 + 4x^3 - x^2 + 16x - 20 &= (x+5)\left(x^3 - x^2 + 4x - 4\right) \\ &= (x+5)\left[x^2(x-1) + 4(x-1)\right] \\ &= (x+5)(x-1)\left(x^2+4\right) \\ &= (x+5)(x-1)(x+2i)(x-2i) \end{aligned}$$

27. Using the results of problem 21: $x^4 - 5x^3 + 7x^2 - 5x + 6 = (x-3)(x-2)\left(x^2+1\right) = (x-3)(x-2)(x+i)(x-i)$

29. Using synthetic division:

$$\begin{array}{r|rrrrr} 2 & 2 & -5 & 8 & -15 & 6 \\ & & 4 & -2 & 12 & -6 \\ \hline & 2 & -1 & 6 & -3 & 0 \end{array}$$

The factorization is:

$$\begin{aligned} 2x^4 - 5x^3 + 8x^2 - 15x + 6 &= (x-2)\left(2x^3 - x^2 + 6x - 3\right) \\ &= (x-2)\left[x^2(2x-1) + 3(2x-1)\right] \\ &= (x-2)(2x-1)\left(x^2+3\right) \\ &= (x-2)(2x-1)\left(x+i\sqrt{3}\right)\left(x-i\sqrt{3}\right) \end{aligned}$$

31. The polynomial is given as: $p(x) = (x-2)(x-(-1)) = (x-2)(x+1) = x^2 - x - 2$

33. The polynomial is given as: $p(x) = x(x-1)^2 = x\left(x^2 - 2x + 1\right) = x^3 - 2x^2 + x$

35. For $x = \dfrac{1}{3}$, we can use the factor $3x-1$. The polynomial is given as:

$$\begin{aligned} p(x) &= (x-1)^2(3x-1)^2 \\ &= \left(x^2 - 2x + 1\right)\left(9x^2 - 6x + 1\right) \\ &= 9x^4 - 6x^3 + x^2 - 18x^3 + 12x^2 - 2x + 9x^2 - 6x + 1 \\ &= 9x^4 - 24x^3 + 22x^2 - 8x + 1 \end{aligned}$$

37. The other zero is the complex conjugate $1-i$.

39. Each of these zeros would have to be of even multiplicity, and so the function would have to be at least a quartic (4th degree) function.

41. The polynomial must be at least degree 3. $x = -1$ is a zero of odd multiplicity and $x = 1$ is a zero of even multiplicity. Thus the minimum degree is $1 + 2 = 3$. A possible polynomial is:

$$p(x) = (x+1)(x-1)^2 = (x+1)\left(x^2 - 2x + 1\right) = x^3 - x^2 - x + 1$$

3.7 Rational Functions

1. This is false. Evaluating the expression: $\dfrac{1}{1+x^2} = \dfrac{1}{1+(-1)^2} = \dfrac{1}{2}$

3. This statement is false. x is not a factor in the denominator.

5. Finding when the denominator is equal to 0:
    $$x + 6 = 0$$
    $$x = -6$$
    The domain is $(-\infty,-6)\cup(-6,\infty)$. The vertical asymptote is $x = -6$, and the horizontal asymptote is $y = 0$.

7. Finding when the denominator is equal to 0:
    $$x^2 - 4 = 0$$
    $$x^2 = 4$$
    $$x = \pm 2$$
    The domain is $(-\infty,-2)\cup(-2,2)\cup(2,\infty)$. The vertical asymptotes are $x = -2$ and $x = 2$, and the horizontal asymptote is $y = 0$.

9. Factoring the numerator and denominator: $f(x) = \dfrac{-x^2+9}{-2x^2+8} = \dfrac{x^2-9}{2x^2-8} = \dfrac{(x+3)(x-3)}{2(x+2)(x-2)}$

    The domain is $(-\infty,-2)\cup(-2,2)\cup(2,\infty)$. The vertical asymptotes are $x = -2$ and $x = 2$, and the horizontal asymptote is $y = \dfrac{1}{2}$.

11. The denominator is equal to 0 when $x = 2$, so the domain is $(-\infty,2)\cup(2,\infty)$. The vertical asymptote is $x = 2$, and the horizontal asymptote is $y = 0$.

13. The denominator is equal to 0 when $x = -1$, so the domain is $(-\infty,-1)\cup(-1,\infty)$. The vertical asymptote is $x = -1$, and there is no horizontal asymptote.

15. Factoring the numerator and denominator: $f(x) = \dfrac{2x+7}{2x^2+5x-3} = \dfrac{2x+7}{(x+3)(2x-1)}$

    The domain is $(-\infty,-3)\cup\left(-3,\dfrac{1}{2}\right)\cup\left(\dfrac{1}{2},\infty\right)$. The vertical asymptotes are $x = -3$ and $x = \dfrac{1}{2}$, and the horizontal asymptote is $y = 0$.

17. Since $x^2 + 1 = 0$ has no real zeros, the domain is $(-\infty,\infty)$. There are no vertical asymptotes, and the horizontal asymptote is $y = 0$.

19. The domain is $(-\infty,2)\cup(2,\infty)$. The vertical asymptote is $x = 2$, and the horizontal asymptote is $y = 3$.
    The x-intercept is $(0,0)$, and the y-intercept is $(0,0)$.

21. The domain is $(-\infty,-2)\cup(-2,1)\cup(1,\infty)$. The vertical asymptotes are $x = -2$ and $x = 1$, and the horizontal asymptote is $y = 0$. The x-intercept is $(-3,0)$, and the y-intercept is $\left(0,-\dfrac{3}{2}\right)$.

23. **a.** Completing the table:

x	-1.5	-1.1	-1.01	-0.99	-0.9	-0.5
$f(x)$	-4	-20	-200	200	20	4

As $x \to -1$ from the left, $f(x) \to -\infty$, and as $x \to -1$ from the right, $f(x) \to \infty$.

b. Completing the table:

x	10	50	100	1000
$f(x)$	$\dfrac{2}{11}$	$\dfrac{2}{51}$	$\dfrac{2}{101}$	$\dfrac{2}{1001}$

As $x \to \infty$, $f(x) \to 0$.

c. Completing the table:

x	-1000	-100	-50	-10
$f(x)$	$\dfrac{2}{999}$	$\dfrac{2}{99}$	$\dfrac{2}{49}$	$\dfrac{2}{9}$

As $x \to -\infty$, $f(x) \to 0$.

25. **a.** Completing the table:

x	-0.5	-0.1	-0.01	0.01	0.1	0.5
$f(x)$	-2	-98	-9998	-9998	-98	-2

As $x \to 0$ from the left, $f(x) \to -\infty$, and as $x \to 0$ from the right, $f(x) \to -\infty$.

b. Completing the table:

x	10	50	100	1000
$f(x)$	1.99	1.9996	1.9999	1.999999

As $x \to \infty$, $f(x) \to 2$.

c. Completing the table:

x	-1000	-100	-50	-10
$f(x)$	1.999999	1.9999	1.9996	1.99

As $x \to -\infty$, $f(x) \to 2$.

27. The vertical asymptote is $x = 2$, the horizontal asymptote is $y = 0$, there is no x-intercept, and the y-intercept is $\left(0, -\dfrac{1}{2}\right)$. Sketching the graph:

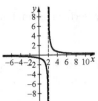

29. The vertical asymptote is $x = -6$, the horizontal asymptote is $y = 0$, there is no x-intercept, and the y-intercept is $(0, -2)$. Sketching the graph:

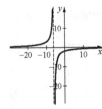

31. The vertical asymptote is $x = 4$, the horizontal asymptote is $y = 0$, there is no x-intercept, and the y-intercept is $(0,2)$. Sketching the graph:

33. The vertical asymptote is $x = -1$, the horizontal asymptote is $y = 0$, there is no x-intercept, and the y-intercept is $(0,3)$. Sketching the graph:

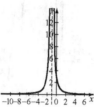

35. The vertical asymptote is $x = -4$, the horizontal asymptote is $y = -1$, the x-intercept is $(3,0)$, and the y-intercept is $\left(0,\dfrac{3}{4}\right)$. Sketching the graph:

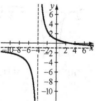

37. The vertical asymptotes are $x = 1$ and $x = -4$, the horizontal asymptote is $y = 0$, the x-intercept is $(0,0)$, and the y-intercept is $(0,0)$. Sketching the graph:

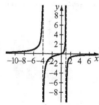

39. Factoring the denominator: $f(x) = \dfrac{3x^2}{x^2 - x - 2} = \dfrac{3x^2}{(x+1)(x-2)}$

The vertical asymptotes are $x = -1$ and $x = 2$, the horizontal asymptote is $y = 3$, the x-intercept is $(0,0)$, and the y-intercept is $(0,0)$. Sketching the graph:

41. Factoring the denominator: $f(x) = \dfrac{x-1}{2x^2 - 5x - 3} = \dfrac{x-1}{(2x+1)(x-3)}$

The vertical asymptotes are $x = -\dfrac{1}{2}$ and $x = 3$, the horizontal asymptote is $y = 0$, the x-intercept is $(1,0)$, and the

y-intercept is $\left(0, \dfrac{1}{3}\right)$. Sketching the graph:

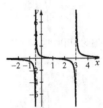

43. Factoring the numerator and denominator: $f(x) = \dfrac{x^2 + x - 6}{x^2 - 1} = \dfrac{(x+3)(x-2)}{(x+1)(x-1)}$

The vertical asymptotes are $x = -1$ and $x = 1$, the horizontal asymptote is $y = 1$, the x-intercepts are $(-3,0)$ and $(2,0)$, and the y-intercept is $(0,6)$. Sketching the graph:

45. There is no vertical asymptote, the horizontal asymptote is $y = 0$, there are no x-intercepts, and the y-intercept is $(0,1)$. Sketching the graph:

47. Using synthetic division:

```
-4| 1    0    0
        -4   16
   ─────────────
    1   -4   16
```

The function can be written as: $g(x) = \dfrac{x^2}{x+4} = x - 4 + \dfrac{16}{x+4}$

The vertical asymptote is $x = -4$, there is no horizontal asymptote, the slant asymptote is $y = x - 4$, the x-intercept is $(0,0)$, and the y-intercept is $(0,0)$. Sketching the graph:

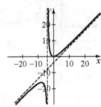

49. Using synthetic division:

$$\begin{array}{r|rrr} 3 & -1 & 0 & 0 \\ & & -3 & -9 \\ \hline & -1 & -3 & -9 \end{array}$$

The function can be written as: $h(x) = \dfrac{-x^2}{x-3} = -x - 3 - \dfrac{9}{x-3}$

The vertical asymptote is $x = 3$, there is no horizontal asymptote, the slant asymptote is $y = -x - 3$, the x-intercept is $(0,0)$, and the y-intercept is $(0,0)$. Sketching the graph:

51. The function can be written as: $h(x) = \dfrac{4 - x^2}{x} = \dfrac{4}{x} - \dfrac{x^2}{x} = -x + \dfrac{4}{x}$

The vertical asymptote is $x = 0$, there is no horizontal asymptote, the slant asymptote is $y = -x$, the x-intercepts are $(-2,0)$ and $(2,0)$, and there is no y-intercept (since $x \neq 0$). Sketching the graph:

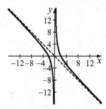

53. Using synthetic division:

$$\begin{array}{r|rrr} 1 & 1 & 1 & 1 \\ & & 1 & 2 \\ \hline & 1 & 2 & 3 \end{array}$$

The function can be written as: $h(x) = \dfrac{x^2 + x + 1}{x - 1} = x + 2 + \dfrac{3}{x-1}$

The vertical asymptote is $x = 1$, there is no horizontal asymptote, the slant asymptote is $y = x + 2$, there are no x-intercepts (since $x^2 + x + 1 \neq 0$), and the y-intercept is $(0,-1)$. Sketching the graph:

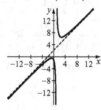

55. Using synthetic division:

$$-1\,|\begin{array}{ccc} 3 & 5 & -2 \\ & -3 & -2 \\ \hline 3 & 2 & -4 \end{array}$$

The function can be written as: $h(x) = \dfrac{3x^2 + 5x - 2}{x+1} = \dfrac{(3x-1)(x+2)}{x+1} = 3x + 2 - \dfrac{4}{x+1}$

The vertical asymptote is $x = -1$, there is no horizontal asymptote, the slant asymptote is $y = 3x + 2$, the x-intercepts are $\left(\dfrac{1}{3}, 0\right)$ and $(-2, 0)$, and the y-intercept is $(0, -2)$. Sketching the graph:

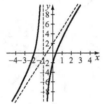

57. Using long division:

$$\begin{array}{r} x - 3 \\ x^2 + 3x\,\overline{)\,x^3 + 0x^2 + 0x + 1} \\ \underline{x^3 + 3x^2} \\ -3x^2 + 0x \\ \underline{-3x^2 - 9x} \\ 9x + 1 \end{array}$$

The function can be written as: $h(x) = \dfrac{x^3 + 1}{x^2 + 3x} = \dfrac{(x+1)(x^2 - x + 1)}{x(x+3)} = x - 3 + \dfrac{9x + 1}{x^2 + 3x}$

The vertical asymptotes are $x = 0$ and $x = -3$, there is no horizontal asymptote, the slant asymptote is $y = x - 3$, the x-intercept is $(-1, 0)$, and there is no y-intercept (since $x \neq 0$). Sketching the graph:

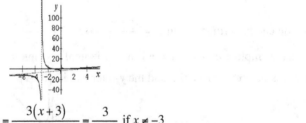

59. The function can be written as: $f(x) = \dfrac{3x + 9}{x^2 - 9} = \dfrac{3(x+3)}{(x+3)(x-3)} = \dfrac{3}{x-3}$ if $x \neq -3$

The vertical asymptote is $x = 3$, the horizontal asymptote is $y = 0$, there is no x-intercept, and the y-intercept is $(0, -1)$. Sketching the graph:

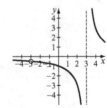

61. The function can be written as: $f(x) = \dfrac{x^2 + x - 2}{x^2 + 2x - 3} = \dfrac{(x+2)(x-1)}{(x+3)(x-1)} = \dfrac{x+2}{x+3}$ if $x \neq 1$

The vertical asymptote is $x = -3$, the horizontal asymptote is $y = 1$, the x-intercept is $(-2, 0)$, and the y-intercept is $\left(0, \dfrac{2}{3}\right)$. Sketching the graph:

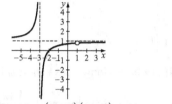

63. The function can be written as: $f(x) = \dfrac{x^2 + 3x - 10}{x - 2} = \dfrac{(x+5)(x-2)}{x - 2} = x + 5$ if $x \neq 2$

There is no vertical asymptote, there is no horizontal asymptote, the x-intercept is $(-5, 0)$, and the y-intercept is $(0, 5)$. Sketching the graph:

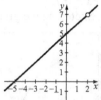

65. a. Evaluating the function: $C(8) = \dfrac{10(8)}{1 + (8)^2} = \dfrac{80}{65} \approx 1.2308$ mg per liter

b. The horizontal asymptote is $C = 0$. As time increases, the concentration will approach 0.

67. Let x represent the number of miles driven per day. The average cost function is given by:

$$C(x) = \dfrac{15 + 0.25x}{x} = 0.25 + \dfrac{15}{x}$$

Evaluating when $x = 50$: $C(50) = 0.25 + \dfrac{15}{50} = 0.55$

The average cost of driving 50 miles per day is $0.55 per mile.

69. a. The average cost function is: $C(x) = \dfrac{30}{x}$ if $0 < x < 250$

b. If $x > 250$, the extra charge is: $0.60(x - 250)$

Therefore the average cost function is: $C(x) = \dfrac{30}{x} + \dfrac{0.60(x - 250)}{x}$ if $x \geq 250$

c. Evaluating when $x = 600$: $C(600) = \dfrac{30}{600} + \dfrac{0.60(600 - 250)}{600} = 0.40$

The average cost is $0.40 per minute.

71. Let x represent the amount of pure gold. The equation is:

$$x + 0.25(2) = 0.60(x + 2)$$
$$x + 0.5 = 0.6x + 1.2$$
$$0.4x = 0.7$$
$$x = \dfrac{7}{4} = 1.75$$

1.75 ounces of pure gold should be added.

73. **a.** Since x is cut out, the width is $3 - 2x$, the length is $5 - 2x$, and the height is x. The volume is given by:

$$V(x) = \text{length} \cdot \text{width} \cdot \text{height} = (5 - 2x)(3 - 2x)x = x(5 - 2x)(3 - 2x)$$

The width gives the appropriate restriction on x:

$$3 - 2x > 0$$

$$-2x > -3$$

$$x < \frac{3}{2}$$

The domain is $0 < x < \frac{3}{2}$, or $\left(0, \frac{3}{2}\right)$.

b. Finding the surface area: $S(x) = \text{base} + \text{long sides} + \text{short sides} = (5 - 2x)(3 - 2x) + 2x(5 - 2x) + 2x(3 - 2x)$

c. The ratio of volume to surface area is given by: $r(x) = \dfrac{V(x)}{S(x)} = \dfrac{x(5 - 2x)(3 - 2x)}{(5 - 2x)(3 - 2x) + 2x(5 - 2x) + 2x(3 - 2x)}$

d. Completing the table:

x	0.2	0.4	0.6	0.8	1.0	1.2	1.4
$r(x)$	0.1612	0.2574	0.3027	0.3061	0.2727	0.2026	0.0860

e. It increases for $x < 0.7$ and decreases for $x > 0.7$.

f. The maximum occurs when $x \approx 0.7170$. Sketching the graph:

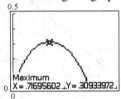

75. One possible rational function is $r(x) = \dfrac{-2x(x - 2)}{(x - 1)^2}$. Sketching the graph:

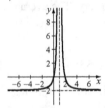

77. One possible rational function is $r(x) = \dfrac{1}{x}$.

79. The graph doesn't show the behavior of the graph near the vertical asymptote $x = 10$.

3.8 Quadratic, Polynomial, and Rational Inequalities

1. Factoring the inequality:

$$x^2 - 1 \le 0$$

$$(x+1)(x-1) \le 0$$

Creating a sign chart:

Interval	Test value	Sign of $x+1$	Sign of $x-1$	Sign of $(x+1)(x-1)$
$(-\infty,-1)$	-2	$-$	$-$	$+$
$(-1,1)$	0	$+$	$-$	$-$
$(1,\infty)$	2	$+$	$+$	$+$

The inequality is satisfied on the interval $(-1,1)$. Since the endpoints are included, the solution is $[-1,1]$.

3. Factoring the inequality:

$$2x^2 + 3x - 5 \ge 0$$

$$(2x+5)(x-1) \ge 0$$

Creating a sign chart:

Interval	Test value	Sign of $2x+5$	Sign of $x-1$	Sign of $(2x+5)(x-1)$
$\left(-\infty,-\dfrac{5}{2}\right)$	-3	$-$	$-$	$+$
$\left(-\dfrac{5}{2},1\right)$	0	$+$	$-$	$-$
$(1,\infty)$	2	$+$	$+$	$+$

The inequality is satisfied on the interval $\left(-\infty,-\dfrac{5}{2}\right) \cup (1,\infty)$. Since the endpoints are included, the solution is

$\left(-\infty,-\dfrac{5}{2}\right] \cup [1,\infty)$.

5. Factoring the inequality:

$$2x^2 < x+1$$

$$2x^2 - x - 1 < 0$$

$$(2x+1)(x-1) < 0$$

Creating a sign chart:

Interval	Test value	Sign of $2x+1$	Sign of $x-1$	Sign of $(2x+1)(x-1)$
$\left(-\infty,-\dfrac{1}{2}\right)$	-1	$-$	$-$	$+$
$\left(-\dfrac{1}{2},1\right)$	0	$+$	$-$	$-$
$(1,\infty)$	2	$+$	$+$	$+$

The inequality is satisfied on the interval $\left(-\dfrac{1}{2},1\right)$. Since the endpoints are not included, the solution is $\left(-\dfrac{1}{2},1\right)$.

7. Factoring the inequality:
$$5x^2 - 8x \geq 4$$
$$5x^2 - 8x - 4 \geq 0$$
$$(5x+2)(x-2) \geq 0$$

Creating a sign chart:

Interval	Test value	Sign of $5x+2$	Sign of $x-2$	Sign of $(5x+2)(x-2)$
$\left(-\infty, -\dfrac{2}{5}\right)$	-1	$-$	$-$	$+$
$\left(-\dfrac{2}{5}, 2\right)$	0	$+$	$-$	$-$
$(2, \infty)$	3	$+$	$+$	$+$

The inequality is satisfied on the interval $\left(-\infty, -\dfrac{2}{5}\right) \cup (2, \infty)$. Since the endpoints are included, the solution is

$$\left(-\infty, -\dfrac{2}{5}\right] \cup [2, \infty).$$

9. Creating a sign chart:

Interval	Test value	Sign of $x+5$	Sign of $2x$	Sign of $x-3$	Sign of $2x(x+5)(x-3)$
$(-\infty, -5)$	-6	$-$	$-$	$-$	$-$
$(-5, 0)$	-1	$+$	$-$	$-$	$+$
$(0, 3)$	2	$+$	$+$	$-$	$-$
$(3, \infty)$	4	$+$	$+$	$+$	$+$

The inequality is satisfied on the interval $(-5, 0) \cup (3, \infty)$. Since the endpoints are included, the solution is

$$[-5, 0] \cup [3, \infty).$$

11. Factoring the inequality:
$$x^3 - 16x < 0$$
$$x(x^2 - 16) < 0$$
$$x(x+4)(x-4) < 0$$

Creating a sign chart:

Interval	Test value	Sign of $x+4$	Sign of x	Sign of $x-4$	Sign of $x(x+4)(x-4)$
$(-\infty, -4)$	-6	$-$	$-$	$-$	$-$
$(-4, 0)$	-2	$+$	$-$	$-$	$+$
$(0, 4)$	2	$+$	$+$	$-$	$-$
$(4, \infty)$	6	$+$	$+$	$+$	$+$

The inequality is satisfied on the interval $(-\infty, -4) \cup (0, 4)$. Since the endpoints are not included, the solution is

$$(-\infty, -4) \cup (0, 4).$$

13. Factoring the inequality:

$$x^3 - 4x > 0$$
$$x(x^2 - 4) > 0$$
$$x(x+2)(x-2) > 0$$

Creating a sign chart:

Interval	Test value	Sign of $x+2$	Sign of x	Sign of $x-2$	Sign of $x(x+2)(x-2)$
$(-\infty,-2)$	-3	$-$	$-$	$-$	$-$
$(-2,0)$	-1	$+$	$-$	$-$	$+$
$(0,2)$	1	$+$	$+$	$-$	$-$
$(2,\infty)$	3	$+$	$+$	$+$	$+$

The inequality is satisfied on the interval $(-2,0) \cup (2,\infty)$. Since the endpoints are not included, the solution is $(-2,0) \cup (2,\infty)$.

15. Factoring the inequality:

$$(x-2)(x^2-4) < 0$$
$$(x-2)(x-2)(x+2) < 0$$
$$(x+2)(x-2)^2 < 0$$

Creating a sign chart:

Interval	Test value	Sign of $(x+2)$	Sign of $(x-2)^2$	Sign of $(x+2)(x-2)^2$
$(-\infty,-2)$	-3	$-$	$+$	$-$
$(-2,2)$	0	$+$	$+$	$+$
$(2,\infty)$	3	$+$	$+$	$+$

The inequality is satisfied on the interval $(-\infty,-2)$. Since the endpoints are not included, the solution is $(-\infty,-2)$.

17. Factoring the inequality:

$$(x+2)(x^2-5x+4) \geq 0$$
$$(x+2)(x-1)(x-4) \geq 0$$

Creating a sign chart:

Interval	Test value	Sign of $x+2$	Sign of $x-1$	Sign of $x-4$	Sign of $(x+2)(x-1)(x-4)$
$(-\infty,-2)$	-3	$-$	$-$	$-$	$-$
$(-2,1)$	0	$+$	$-$	$-$	$+$
$(1,4)$	3	$+$	$+$	$-$	$-$
$(4,\infty)$	5	$+$	$+$	$+$	$+$

The inequality is satisfied on the interval $(-2,1) \cup (4,\infty)$. Since the endpoints are included, the solution is $[-2,1] \cup [4,\infty)$.

19. Re-writing the inequality:
$$x^4 - x^2 > 3$$
$$x^4 - x^2 - 3 > 0$$

Using the quadratic formula: $x^2 = \dfrac{1 \pm \sqrt{(-1)^2 - 4(1)(-3)}}{2(1)} = \dfrac{1 \pm \sqrt{1+12}}{2} = \dfrac{1 \pm \sqrt{13}}{2} \approx -1.302, 2.303$

Therefore: $x \approx \pm\sqrt{2.303} \approx \pm 1.5175$

Creating a sign chart:

Interval	Test value	Sign of $x^4 - x^2 - 3$
$(-\infty, -1.5175)$	-2	$+$
$(-1.5175, 1.5175)$	0	$-$
$(1.5175, \infty)$	2	$+$

The inequality is satisfied on the interval $(-\infty, -1.5175) \cup (1.5175, \infty)$. Since the endpoints are not included, the solution is $(-\infty, -1.5175) \cup (1.5175, \infty)$.

21. Factoring the inequality:
$$x^3 - 4x \le -x^2 + 4$$
$$x^3 + x^2 - 4x - 4 \le 0$$
$$x^2(x+1) - 4(x+1) \le 0$$
$$(x+1)(x^2 - 4) \le 0$$
$$(x+1)(x+2)(x-2) \le 0$$

Creating a sign chart:

Interval	Test value	Sign of $x+2$	Sign of $x+1$	Sign of $x-2$	Sign of $(x+2)(x+1)(x-2)$
$(-\infty, -2)$	-3	$-$	$-$	$-$	$-$
$(-2, -1)$	-1.5	$+$	$-$	$-$	$+$
$(-1, 2)$	0	$+$	$+$	$-$	$-$
$(2, \infty)$	3	$+$	$+$	$+$	$+$

The inequality is satisfied on the interval $(-\infty, -2) \cup (-1, 2)$. Since the endpoints are included, the solution is $(-\infty, -2] \cup [-1, 2]$.

23. Factoring the inequality:
$$x^3 \le 4x$$
$$x^3 - 4x \le 0$$
$$x(x^2 - 4) \le 0$$
$$x(x+2)(x-2) \le 0$$

Creating a sign chart:

Interval	Test value	Sign of $x+2$	Sign of x	Sign of $x-2$	Sign of $x(x+2)(x-2)$
$(-\infty, -2)$	-3	$-$	$-$	$-$	$-$
$(-2, 0)$	-1	$+$	$-$	$-$	$+$
$(0, 2)$	1	$+$	$+$	$-$	$-$
$(2, \infty)$	3	$+$	$+$	$+$	$+$

The inequality is satisfied on the interval $(-\infty, -2) \cup (0, 2)$. Since the endpoints are included, the solution is $(-\infty, -2] \cup [0, 2]$.

25. Factoring the inequality:
$$x^3 < 2x^2 + 3x$$
$$x^3 - 2x^2 - 3x < 0$$
$$x\left(x^2 - 2x - 3\right) < 0$$
$$x(x+1)(x-3) < 0$$

Creating a sign chart:

Interval	Test value	Sign of $x+1$	Sign of x	Sign of $x-3$	Sign of $x(x+1)(x-3)$
$(-\infty, -1)$	-2	$-$	$-$	$-$	$-$
$(-1, 0)$	-0.5	$+$	$-$	$-$	$+$
$(0, 3)$	1	$+$	$+$	$-$	$-$
$(3, \infty)$	4	$+$	$+$	$+$	$+$

The inequality is satisfied on the interval $(-\infty, -1) \cup (0, 3)$. Since the endpoints are not included, the solution is $(-\infty, -1) \cup (0, 3)$.

27. Creating a sign chart:

Interval	Test value	Sign of $x+2$	Sign of $x-1$	Sign of $\dfrac{x+2}{x-1}$
$(-\infty, -2)$	-3	$-$	$-$	$+$
$(-2, 1)$	0	$+$	$-$	$-$
$(1, \infty)$	2	$+$	$+$	$+$

The inequality is satisfied on the interval $(-2, 1)$. Since the value $x = -2$ is included, the solution is $[-2, 1)$.

29. Factoring the inequality:
$$\frac{x^2 - 4}{x - 3} \le 0$$
$$\frac{(x+2)(x-2)}{x-3} \le 0$$

Creating a sign chart:

Interval	Test value	Sign of $x+2$	Sign of $x-2$	Sign of $x-3$	Sign of $\dfrac{(x+2)(x-2)}{x-3}$
$(-\infty, -2)$	-2	$-$	$-$	$-$	$-$
$(-2, 2)$	0	$+$	$-$	$-$	$+$
$(2, 3)$	2.5	$+$	$+$	$-$	$-$
$(3, \infty)$	4	$+$	$+$	$+$	$+$

The inequality is satisfied on the interval $(-\infty, -2) \cup (2, 3)$. Since the values $x = \pm 2$ are included, the solution is $(-\infty, -2] \cup [2, 3)$.

31.   Creating a sign chart:

Interval	Test value	Sign of $1+x^2$	Sign of $x+1$	Sign of x	Sign of $\dfrac{x(x+1)}{1+x^2}$
$(-\infty,-1)$	-2	$+$	$-$	$-$	$+$
$(-1,0)$	-0.5	$+$	$+$	$-$	$-$
$(0,\infty)$	1	$+$	$+$	$+$	$+$

The inequality is satisfied on the interval $(-\infty,-1)\cup(0,\infty)$. Since the values $x=-1,0$ are included, the solution is $(-\infty,-1]\cup[0,\infty)$.

33.   Solving and factoring the inequality:

$$\frac{4-x}{x-1} > x$$

$$\frac{4-x}{x-1} - x > 0$$

$$\frac{4-x-x(x-1)}{x-1} > 0$$

$$\frac{4-x^2}{x-1} > 0$$

$$\frac{(2+x)(2-x)}{x-1} > 0$$

Creating a sign chart:

Interval	Test value	Sign of $2+x$	Sign of $x-1$	Sign of $2-x$	Sign of $\dfrac{(2+x)(2-x)}{x-1}$
$(-\infty,-2)$	-3	$-$	$-$	$+$	$+$
$(-2,1)$	0	$+$	$-$	$+$	$-$
$(1,2)$	0.5	$+$	$-$	$-$	$+$
$(2,\infty)$	3	$+$	$+$	$-$	$-$

The inequality is satisfied on the interval $(-\infty,-2)\cup(1,2)$. Since the endpoints are not included, the solution is $(-\infty,-2)\cup(1,2)$.

35.   Solving and factoring the inequality:

$$\frac{1}{x} \le \frac{1}{2x-1}$$

$$\frac{1}{x} - \frac{1}{2x-1} \le 0$$

$$\frac{2x-1-x}{x(2x-1)} \le 0$$

$$\frac{x-1}{x(2x-1)} \le 0$$

Creating a sign chart:

Interval	Test value	Sign of x	Sign of $2x-1$	Sign of $x-1$	Sign of $\dfrac{x-1}{x(2x-1)}$
$(-\infty,0)$	-1	$-$	$-$	$-$	$-$
$\left(0,\dfrac{1}{2}\right)$	0.25	$+$	$-$	$-$	$+$
$\left(\dfrac{1}{2},1\right)$	0.75	$+$	$+$	$-$	$-$
$(1,\infty)$	2	$+$	$+$	$+$	$+$

The inequality is satisfied on the interval $(-\infty,0)\cup\left(\dfrac{1}{2},1\right)$. Since the value $x=1$ is included, the solution is

$(-\infty,0)\cup\left(\dfrac{1}{2},1\right]$.

37. Solving and factoring the inequality:

$$\frac{3}{x-1}\le 2$$

$$\frac{3}{x-1}-2\le 0$$

$$\frac{3-2(x-1)}{x-1}\le 0$$

$$\frac{5-2x}{x-1}\le 0$$

Creating a sign chart:

Interval	Test value	Sign of $x-1$	Sign of $5-2x$	Sign of $\dfrac{5-2x}{x-1}$
$(-\infty,1)$	0	$-$	$+$	$-$
$\left(1,\dfrac{5}{2}\right)$	2	$+$	$+$	$+$
$\left(\dfrac{5}{2},\infty\right)$	3	$+$	$-$	$-$

The inequality is satisfied on the interval $(-\infty,1)\cup\left(\dfrac{5}{2},\infty\right)$. Since the value $x=\dfrac{5}{2}$ is included, the solution is

$(-\infty,1)\cup\left[\dfrac{5}{2},\infty\right)$.

39. Creating a sign chart:

Interval	Test value	Sign of $x+2$	Sign of $x-1$	Sign of $\dfrac{x-1}{x+2}$
$(-\infty,-2)$	-3	$-$	$-$	$+$
$(-2,1)$	0	$+$	$-$	$-$
$(1,\infty)$	2	$+$	$+$	$+$

The inequality is satisfied on the interval $(-\infty,-2)\cup(1,\infty)$. Since the value $x=1$ is included, the solution is
$(-\infty,-2)\cup[1,\infty)$.

41. Creating a sign chart:

Interval	Test value	Sign of $2x+1$	Sign of $\dfrac{1}{2x+1}$
$\left(-\infty,-\dfrac{1}{2}\right)$	-1	$-$	$-$
$\left(-\dfrac{1}{2},\infty\right)$	0	$+$	$+$

The inequality is satisfied on the interval $\left(-\infty,-\dfrac{1}{2}\right)$. Since the value $x=-\dfrac{1}{2}$ is not included, the solution is $\left(-\infty,-\dfrac{1}{2}\right)$.

43. Factoring the inequality:
$$\frac{x+1}{x^2-9}<0$$
$$\frac{x+1}{(x+3)(x-3)}<0$$

Creating a sign chart:

Interval	Test value	Sign of $x+3$	Sign of $x+1$	Sign of $x-3$	Sign of $\dfrac{x+1}{(x+3)(x-3)}$
$(-\infty,-3)$	-4	$-$	$-$	$-$	$-$
$(-3,-1)$	-2	$+$	$-$	$-$	$+$
$(-1,3)$	0	$+$	$+$	$-$	$-$
$(3,\infty)$	4	$+$	$+$	$+$	$+$

The inequality is satisfied on the interval $(-\infty,-3)\cup(-1,3)$. Since the endpoints are not included, the solution is $(-\infty,-3)\cup(-1,3)$.

45. Solving and factoring the inequality:
$$\frac{x+1}{x-3}\le\frac{x-2}{x+4}$$
$$\frac{x+1}{x-3}-\frac{x-2}{x+4}\le0$$
$$\frac{(x+1)(x+4)-(x-3)(x-2)}{(x-3)(x+4)}\le0$$
$$\frac{(x^2+5x+4)-(x^2-5x+6)}{(x-3)(x+4)}\le0$$
$$\frac{10x-2}{(x-3)(x+4)}\le0$$
$$\frac{2(5x-1)}{(x-3)(x+4)}\le0$$

Creating a sign chart:

Interval	Test value	Sign of $x+4$	Sign of $5x-1$	Sign of $x-3$	Sign of $\dfrac{2(5x-1)}{(x-3)(x+4)}$
$(-\infty,-4)$	-5	$-$	$-$	$-$	$-$
$\left(-4,\dfrac{1}{5}\right)$	0	$+$	$-$	$-$	$+$
$\left(\dfrac{1}{5},3\right)$	1	$+$	$+$	$-$	$-$
$(3,\infty)$	4	$+$	$+$	$+$	$+$

The inequality is satisfied on the interval $(-\infty,-4)\cup\left(\dfrac{1}{5},3\right)$. Since the value $x=\dfrac{1}{5}$ is included, the solution is

$(-\infty,-4)\cup\left[\dfrac{1}{5},3\right)$.

47. The volume is given by: $V=(x)(x)(x-2)=x^3-2x^2$
    Solving and factoring the inequality:
    $$x^3-2x^2\geq 32$$
    $$x^3-2x^2-32\geq 0$$
    $$(x-4)\left(x^2+2x+8\right)\geq 0 \quad\longleftarrow\quad \text{Using rational roots theorem and synthetic division.}$$

    Creating a sign chart (note that $x^2+2x+8\neq 0$):

Interval	Test value	Sign of $x-4$	Sign of x^2+2x+8	Sign of $(x-4)\left(x^2+2x+8\right)$
$(-\infty,4)$	0	$-$	$+$	$-$
$(4,\infty)$	5	$+$	$+$	$+$

    The inequality is satisfied on the interval $(4,\infty)$. Since the endpoint is included, the solution is $[4,\infty)$.

    Lengths of the base greater than or equal to 4 inches will produce a volume greater than or equal to 32 cubic inches.

49. Solving and factoring the inequality:
    $$\frac{4t}{3+t^2}>1$$
    $$\frac{4t}{3+t^2}-1>0$$
    $$\frac{4t-\left(3+t^2\right)}{3+t^2}>0$$
    $$\frac{-t^2+4t-3}{3+t^2}>0$$
    $$\frac{-\left(t^2-4t+3\right)}{3+t^2}>0$$
    $$\frac{-(t-1)(t-3)}{3+t^2}>0$$

Creating a sign chart:

Interval	Test value	Sign of $3+t^2$	Sign of $t-1$	Sign of $t-3$	Sign of $\dfrac{-(t-1)(t-3)}{3+t^2}$
$(-\infty,1)$	0	+	–	–	–
$(1,3)$	2	+	+	–	+
$(3,\infty)$	4	+	+	+	–

The inequality is satisfied on the interval $(1,3)$. Since the endpoints are not included, the solution is $(1,3)$.

51. Each term doesn't necessarily have to be less than 2 for the product of the terms to be less than 2. The student should expand the product and bring the constant term to the left-hand side before attempting to factor to find the zeros.

53. One example is: $p(x)=x(x-1)(x-3)$

Chapter 3 Review Exercises

1. The vertex is $(-3,-1)$. Sketching the graph:

2. The vertex is $(1,4)$. Sketching the graph:

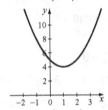

3. The vertex is $(0,-1)$. Sketching the graph:

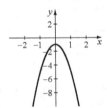

4. The vertex is $(-1,3)$. Sketching the graph:

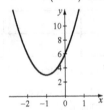

5. Completing the square: $f(x)=x^2-4x+3=\left(x^2-4x\right)+3=\left(x^2-4x+4-4\right)+3=\left(x^2-4x+4\right)-4+3=\left(x-2\right)^2-1$

The vertex is $(2,-1)$, which is a minimum point.

6. Completing the square: $g(x)=3-6x+x^2=\left(x^2-6x\right)+3=\left(x^2-6x+9-9\right)+3=\left(x^2-6x+9\right)-9+3=\left(x-3\right)^2-6$

The vertex is $(3,-6)$, which is a minimum point.

7. Completing the square: $f(x)=4x^2+8x-1=4\left(x^2+2x\right)-1=4\left(x^2+2x+1-1\right)-1=4\left(x^2+2x+1\right)-4-1=4\left(x+1\right)^2-5$

The vertex is $(-1,-5)$, which is a minimum point.

8. Completing the square:
$$g(x)=-3x^2+12x+5=-3\left(x^2-4x\right)+5=-3\left(x^2-4x+4-4\right)+5=-3\left(x^2-4x+4\right)+12+5=-3\left(x-2\right)^2+17$$
The vertex is $(2,17)$, which is a maximum point.

9. First find the vertex:

$$h = \frac{-b}{2a} = \frac{2}{2(1)} = 1$$

$$k = f(1) = (1)^2 - 2(1) + 1 = 0$$

Finding the x-intercepts by setting $f(x) = 0$:

$$x^2 - 2x + 1 = 0$$

$$(x-1)^2 = 0$$

$$x = 1$$

The vertex is $(1,0)$, the axis of symmetry is $x = 1$, the x-intercept is $(1,0)$, and the y-intercept is $(0,1)$. The function is increasing on $(1,\infty)$ and decreasing on $(-\infty,1)$, and the range is $[0,\infty)$. Sketching the graph:

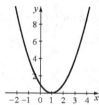

10. First find the vertex:

$$h = \frac{-b}{2a} = \frac{3}{2(-2)} = -\frac{3}{4}$$

$$k = g\left(-\frac{3}{4}\right) = -2\left(-\frac{3}{4}\right)^2 - 3\left(-\frac{3}{4}\right) = -\frac{9}{8} + \frac{9}{4} = \frac{9}{8}$$

Finding the x-intercepts by setting $g(x) = 0$:

$$-2x^2 - 3x = 0$$

$$-x(2x+3) = 0$$

$$x = -\frac{3}{2}, 0$$

The vertex is $\left(-\frac{3}{4}, \frac{9}{8}\right)$, the axis of symmetry is $x = -\frac{3}{4}$, the x-intercepts are $\left(-\frac{3}{2}, 0\right)$ and $(0,0)$, and the y-intercept is $(0,0)$. The function is increasing on $\left(-\infty, -\frac{3}{4}\right)$ and decreasing on $\left(-\frac{3}{4}, \infty\right)$, and the range is $\left(-\infty, \frac{9}{8}\right]$.

Sketching the graph:

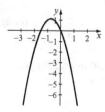

11. First find the vertex:

$$h = \frac{-b}{2a} = \frac{3}{2(-1)} = -\frac{3}{2}$$

$$k = f\left(-\frac{3}{2}\right) = -\left(-\frac{3}{2}\right)^2 - 3\left(-\frac{3}{2}\right) + 1 = -\frac{9}{4} + \frac{9}{2} + 1 = \frac{13}{4}$$

Finding the x-intercepts by setting $f(x) = 0$ and using the quadratic formula:

$$x = \frac{3 \pm \sqrt{(-3)^2 - 4(-1)(1)}}{2(-1)} = \frac{3 \pm \sqrt{13}}{-2} = \frac{-3 \pm \sqrt{13}}{2}$$

The vertex is $\left(-\frac{3}{2}, \frac{13}{4}\right)$, the axis of symmetry is $x = -\frac{3}{2}$, the x-intercepts are $\left(\frac{-3-\sqrt{13}}{2}, 0\right)$ and $\left(\frac{-3+\sqrt{13}}{2}, 0\right)$, and

the y-intercept is $(0,1)$. The function is increasing on $\left(-\infty, -\frac{3}{2}\right)$ and decreasing on $\left(-\frac{3}{2}, \infty\right)$, and the range is

$\left(-\infty, \frac{13}{4}\right]$. Sketching the graph:

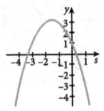

12. First find the vertex:

$$h = \frac{-b}{2a} = \frac{4}{2(3)} = \frac{2}{3}$$

$$k = f\left(\frac{2}{3}\right) = 1 - 4\left(\frac{2}{3}\right) + 3\left(\frac{2}{3}\right)^2 = 1 - \frac{8}{3} + \frac{4}{3} = -\frac{1}{3}$$

Finding the x-intercepts by setting $f(x) = 0$:

$$1 - 4x + 3x^2 = 0$$
$$3x^2 - 4x + 1 = 0$$
$$(3x - 1)(x - 1) = 0$$
$$x = \frac{1}{3}, 1$$

The vertex is $\left(\frac{2}{3}, -\frac{1}{3}\right)$, the axis of symmetry is $x = \frac{2}{3}$, the x-intercepts are $\left(\frac{1}{3}, 0\right)$ and $(1, 0)$, and the y-intercept is

$(0,1)$. The function is increasing on $\left(\frac{2}{3}, \infty\right)$ and decreasing on $\left(-\infty, \frac{2}{3}\right)$, and the range is $\left[-\frac{1}{3}, \infty\right)$.

Sketching the graph:

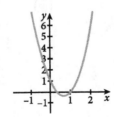

13. First find the vertex:

$$h = \frac{-b}{2a} = \frac{2}{2\left(\frac{1}{2}\right)} = 2$$

$$k = g(2) = \frac{1}{2}(2)^2 - 2(2) + 5 = 2 - 4 + 5 = 3$$

Finding the x-intercepts by setting $g(x) = 0$ and using the quadratic formula:

$$x = \frac{2 \pm \sqrt{(-2)^2 - 4\left(\frac{1}{2}\right)(5)}}{2\left(\frac{1}{2}\right)} = \frac{2 \pm \sqrt{-6}}{1}, \text{ no real solutions}$$

The vertex is $(2,3)$, the axis of symmetry is $x = 2$, there are no x-intercepts, and the y-intercept is $(0,5)$. The function is increasing on $(2,\infty)$ and decreasing on $(-\infty,2)$, and the range is $(3,\infty]$. Sketching the graph:

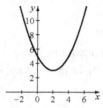

14. First find the vertex:

$$h = \frac{-b}{2a} = \frac{-1}{2\left(-\frac{2}{3}\right)} = \frac{3}{4}$$

$$k = f\left(\frac{3}{4}\right) = -\frac{2}{3}\left(\frac{3}{4}\right)^2 + \frac{3}{4} - 1 = -\frac{3}{8} + \frac{3}{4} - 1 = -\frac{5}{8}$$

Finding the x-intercepts by setting $f(x) = 0$ and using the quadratic formula:

$$x = \frac{-1 \pm \sqrt{(1)^2 - 4\left(-\frac{2}{3}\right)(-1)}}{2\left(-\frac{2}{3}\right)} = \frac{-1 \pm \sqrt{-\frac{5}{3}}}{-\frac{4}{3}}, \text{ no real solutions}$$

The vertex is $\left(\frac{3}{4}, -\frac{5}{8}\right)$, the axis of symmetry is $x = \frac{3}{4}$, there are no x-intercepts, and the y-intercept is $(0,-1)$. The function is increasing on $\left(-\infty, \frac{3}{4}\right)$ and decreasing on $\left(\frac{3}{4}, \infty\right)$, and the range is $\left(-\infty, -\frac{5}{8}\right]$. Sketching the graph:

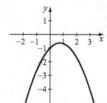

15. Finding the discriminant: $b^2 - 4ac = (-6)^2 - 4(1)(4) = 36 - 16 = 20 > 0$

The graph of f has two x-intercepts, and $f(x) = 0$ has two real solutions.

16. Finding the discriminant: $b^2 - 4ac = (-7)^2 - 4(-2)(0) = 49 - 0 = 49 > 0$

The graph of f has two x-intercepts, and $f(x) = 0$ has two real solutions.

17. Finding the discriminant: $b^2 - 4ac = (-6)^2 - 4(1)(9) = 36 - 36 = 0$

The graph of f has one x-intercept, and $f(x) = 0$ has one real solution.

18. Finding the discriminant: $b^2 - 4ac = (-1)^2 - 4(-1)(-2) = 1 - 8 = -7 < 0$

The graph of f has no x-intercepts, and $f(x) = 0$ has no real solutions.

19. Let w represent the width and l represent the length. Since the total fencing is 120, we have:
$$2w + l = 120$$
$$l = 120 - 2w$$
The area is given by: $A(w) = lw = (120 - 2w)w = -2w^2 + 120w$

Using the vertex formula:
$$w = \frac{-b}{2a} = \frac{-120}{2(-2)} = \frac{-120}{-4} = 30$$
$$l = 120 - 2w = 120 - 2(30) = 120 - 60 = 60$$

Dimensions of 30 feet by 60 feet will yield the maximum area.

20. **a.** The y-intercept is $(0, 2.90)$. In 1980, 2.9% of the total operating expenses incurred by airlines was for food.

b. Using the vertex formula: $t = \frac{-b}{2a} = \frac{-0.116}{2(-0.0055)} = \frac{-0.116}{-0.011} = 10.545$

The expenditure for airline food was a maximum after 10 years, in the year $1980 + 10 = 1990$.

c. Note that the graph of $f(t)$ is a downward facing parabola. It is not a reliable long-term indicator because as t increases, the value of $f(t)$ decreases, eventually passing 0 and becoming negative.

21. This is a polynomial function. Its degree is 3, the coefficients are $-1, -6, 5$, and the leading coefficient is -1.

22. This is a polynomial function. Its degree is 5, the coefficients are $1, 6, -1$, and the leading coefficient is 1.

23. This is not a polynomial function, since it is a radical.

24. This is not a polynomial function, since it is a rational function.

25. $f(x) = -3x^3 + 5x + 9$ has leading term $-3x^3$ (n odd, $a_n < 0$). Thus $f(x) \to \infty$ as $x \to -\infty$ and $f(x) \to -\infty$ as $x \to \infty$.

26. $g(t) = 5t^4 - 6t^2 + 1$ has leading term $5t^4$ (n even, $a_n > 0$). Thus $g(t) \to \infty$ as $t \to -\infty$ and $g(t) \to \infty$ as $t \to \infty$.

27. $H(s) = -6s^4 - 3s$ has leading term $-6s^4$ (n even, $a_n < 0$). Thus $H(s) \to -\infty$ as $s \to -\infty$ and $H(s) \to -\infty$ as $s \to \infty$.

28. $g(x) = -x^3 + 2x - 1$ has leading term $-x^3$ (n odd, $a_n < 0$). Thus $g(x) \to \infty$ as $x \to -\infty$ and $g(x) \to -\infty$ as $x \to \infty$.

29. $h(s) = 10s^5 - 2s^2$ has leading term $10s^5$ (n odd, $a_n > 0$). Thus $h(s) \to -\infty$ as $s \to -\infty$ and $h(s) \to \infty$ as $s \to \infty$.

30. $f(x) = 7x^2 - 4$ has leading term $7x^2$ (n even, $a_n > 0$). Thus $f(x) \to \infty$ as $x \to -\infty$ and $f(x) \to \infty$ as $x \to \infty$.

31. **a.** The leading term is $-x^3$. Thus $f(x) \to \infty$ as $x \to -\infty$ and $f(x) \to -\infty$ as $x \to \infty$.

b. Finding the value: $f(0) = -(0-1)(0+2)(0+4) = 8$

The y-intercept is $(0, 8)$.

Finding the x-intercepts:
$$-(x-1)(x+2)(x+4) = 0$$
$$x = -4, -2, 1$$

The x-intercepts are $(-4, 0), (-2, 0), (1, 0)$.

Interval	Test Value x	Function Value $f(x)$	Sign of $f(x)$
$(-\infty,-4)$	-5	18	$+$
$(-4,-2)$	-3	-4	$-$
$(-2,1)$	0	8	$+$
$(1,\infty)$	2	-24	$-$

c. Completing the sign chart:

The function is positive on $(-\infty,-4)\cup(-2,1)$.

d. The function is negative on $(-4,-2)\cup(1,\infty)$.

e. Sketching the graph:

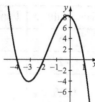

32. **a.** The leading term is x^3. Thus $g(x) \to -\infty$ as $x \to -\infty$ and $g(x) \to \infty$ as $x \to \infty$.

b. Finding the value: $g(0) = (0-3)(0-4)(0-1) = -12$

The y-intercept is $(0,-12)$.

Finding the x-intercepts:
$$(x-3)(x-4)(x-1) = 0$$
$$x = 1, 3, 4$$

The x-intercepts are $(1,0),(3,0),(4,0)$.

Interval	Test Value x	Function Value $g(x)$	Sign of $g(x)$
$(-\infty,1)$	0	-12	$-$
$(1,3)$	2	2	$+$
$(3,4)$	3.5	-0.625	$-$
$(4,\infty)$	5	8	$+$

c. Completing the sign chart:

The function is positive on $(1,3)\cup(4,\infty)$.

d. The function is negative on $(-\infty,1)\cup(3,4)$.

e. Sketching the graph:

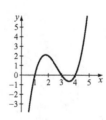

33. **a.** The leading term is $3t^3$. Thus $f(t) \to -\infty$ as $t \to -\infty$ and $f(t) \to \infty$ as $t \to \infty$.

b. Finding the value: $f(0) = 0(0-1)(0+4) = 0$

The y-intercept is $(0,0)$.

Finding the t-intercepts:
$$t(3t-1)(t+4) = 0$$
$$t = 0, \frac{1}{3}, -4$$

The t-intercepts are $(0,0), \left(\frac{1}{3},0\right), (-4,0)$.

c. Completing the sign chart:

Interval	Test Value x	Function Value $f(t)$	Sign of $f(t)$
$(-\infty,-4)$	-5	-80	$-$
$(-4,0)$	-2	28	$+$
$\left(0,\frac{1}{3}\right)$	0.25	-0.27	$-$
$\left(\frac{1}{3},\infty\right)$	1	10	$+$

The function is positive on $(-4,0) \cup \left(\frac{1}{3},\infty\right)$.

d. The function is negative on $(-\infty,-4) \cup \left(0,\frac{1}{3}\right)$.

e. Sketching the graph:

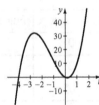

34. **a.** The leading term is $2t^3$. Thus $g(t) \to -\infty$ as $t \to -\infty$ and $g(t) \to \infty$ as $t \to \infty$.

b. Finding the value: $g(0) = 0(0+4)\left(0+\frac{3}{2}\right) = 0$

The y-intercept is $(0,0)$.

Finding the t-intercepts:
$$2t(t+4)\left(t+\frac{3}{2}\right) = 0$$
$$t = 0, -4, -\frac{3}{2}$$

The t-intercepts are $(0,0), \left(-\frac{3}{2},0\right), (-4,0)$.

Interval	Test Value t	Function Value $g(t)$	Sign of $g(t)$
$(-\infty,-4)$	-5	-35	$-$
$\left(-4,-\dfrac{3}{2}\right)$	-2	4	$+$
$\left(-\dfrac{3}{2},0\right)$	-1	-3	$-$
$(0,\infty)$	1	25	$+$

c. Completing the sign chart:

The function is positive on $\left(-4,-\dfrac{3}{2}\right)\cup(0,\infty)$.

d. The function is negative on $(-\infty,-4)\cup\left(-\dfrac{3}{2},0\right)$.

e. Sketching the graph:

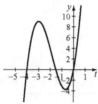

35. **a.** The leading term is $2x^3$. Thus $f(x)\to -\infty$ as $x\to -\infty$ and $f(x)\to \infty$ as $x\to \infty$.

b. Finding the value: $f(0)=2(0)^3+(0)^2-0=0$

The y-intercept is $(0,0)$.

Finding the x-intercepts:

$$2x^3+x^2-x=0$$
$$x\left(2x^2+x-1\right)=0$$
$$x(2x-1)(x+1)=0$$
$$x=0,-1,\frac{1}{2}$$

The x-intercepts are $(0,0),(-1,0),\left(\dfrac{1}{2},0\right)$.

Interval	Test Value x	Function Value $f(x)$	Sign of $f(x)$
$(-\infty,-1)$	-2	-10	$-$
$(-1,0)$	-0.5	0.5	$+$
$\left(0,\dfrac{1}{2}\right)$	0.25	-0.16	$-$
$\left(\dfrac{1}{2},\infty\right)$	1	2	$+$

c. Completing the sign chart:

The function is positive on $(-1,0)\cup\left(\dfrac{1}{2},\infty\right)$.

d. The function is negative on $(-\infty,-1)\cup\left(0,\dfrac{1}{2}\right)$.

e. Sketching the graph:

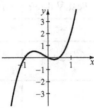

36. **a.** The leading term is $-x^3$. Thus $g(x) \to \infty$ as $x \to -\infty$ and $g(x) \to -\infty$ as $x \to \infty$.

b. Finding the value: $g(0) = -(0)^3 - 6(0)^2 + 7(0) = 0$

The y-intercept is $(0,0)$.

Finding the x-intercepts:

$$-x^3 - 6x^2 + 7x = 0$$
$$-x(x^2 + 6x - 7) = 0$$
$$-x(x-1)(x+7) = 0$$
$$x = 0, 1, -7$$

The x-intercepts are $(0,0), (1,0), (-7,0)$.

c. Completing the sign chart:

Interval	Test Value x	Function Value $g(x)$	Sign of $g(x)$
$(-\infty,-7)$	-8	72	$+$
$(-7,0)$	-1	-12	$-$
$(0,1)$	0.5	1.875	$+$
$(1,\infty)$	2	-18	$-$

The function is positive on $(-\infty,-7) \cup (0,1)$.

d. The function is negative on $(-7,0) \cup (1,\infty)$.

e. Sketching the graph:

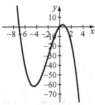

37. The zero $x = -2$ has multiplicity 3; the graph passes through the x-axis.
The zero $x = -7$ has multiplicity 2; the graph just touches the x-axis.

38. The zero $s = -8$ has multiplicity 5; the graph passes through the s-axis.
The zero $s = 1$ has multiplicity 2; the graph just touches the s-axis.

39. The zero $t = 0$ has multiplicity 2; the graph just touches the t-axis.
The zero $t = -1$ has multiplicity 1; the graph passes through the t-axis.
The zero $t = 2$ has multiplicity 1; the graph passes through the t-axis.

40. Factoring the function: $g(x) = -x^3(x^2 - 16) = -x^3(x+4)(x-4)$

The zero $x = 0$ has multiplicity 3; the graph passes through the x-axis.
The zero $x = -4$ has multiplicity 1; the graph passes through the x-axis.
The zero $x = 4$ has multiplicity 1; the graph passes through the x-axis.

41. Factoring the function: $f(x) = x^3 + 2x^2 + x = x(x^2 + 2x + 1) = x(x+1)^2$

The zero $x = 0$ has multiplicity 1; the graph passes through the x-axis.
The zero $x = -1$ has multiplicity 2; the graph just touches the x-axis.

42. Factoring the function: $h(s) = s^7 - 16s^3 = s^3(s^4 - 16) = s^3(s^2 + 4)(s^2 - 4) = s^3(s^2 + 4)(s + 2)(s - 2)$

The zero $s = 0$ has multiplicity 3; the graph passes through the s-axis.
The zero $s = -2$ has multiplicity 1; the graph passes through the s-axis.
The zero $s = 2$ has multiplicity 1; the graph passes through the s-axis.

43. **a.** Given the function: $f(x) = x^2(2x + 1)$

Evaluating the function: $f(0) = (0)^2(0 + 1) = 0$

The y-intercept is $(0,0)$. The x-intercepts are $(0,0)$ and $\left(-\frac{1}{2}, 0\right)$.

b. The zero at $x = 0$ has multiplicity 2, and the zero at $x = -\frac{1}{2}$ has multiplicity 1.

c. $f(x)$ behaves like $y = 2x^3$ so $f(x) \to -\infty$ as $x \to -\infty$ and $f(x) \to \infty$ as $x \to \infty$

d. Creating a sign chart:

Interval	Test Value x	Function Value $f(x)$	Sign of $f(x)$
$\left(-\infty, -\frac{1}{2}\right)$	-1	-1	$-$
$\left(-\frac{1}{2}, 0\right)$	-0.25	0.031	$+$
$(0, \infty)$	1	3	$+$

Thus f is positive on $\left(-\frac{1}{2}, 0\right) \cup (0, \infty)$ and f is negative on $\left(-\infty, -\frac{1}{2}\right)$. Sketching the graph:

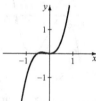

44. **a.** Given the function: $h(t) = -t(t + 4)^2$

Evaluating the function: $h(0) = 0(0 + 4)^2 = 0$

The y-intercept is $(0,0)$. The t-intercepts are $(0,0)$ and $(-4,0)$.

b. The zero at $t = 0$ has multiplicity 1, and the zero at $t = -4$ has multiplicity 2.

c. $h(t)$ behaves like $y = -t^3$ so $h(t) \to \infty$ as $t \to -\infty$ and $h(t) \to -\infty$ as $t \to \infty$

d. Creating a sign chart:

Interval	Test Value t	Function Value $h(t)$	Sign of $h(t)$
$(-\infty, -4)$	-5	5	$+$
$(-4, 0)$	-1	9	$+$
$(0, \infty)$	1	-25	$-$

Thus h is positive on $(-\infty, -4) \cup (-4, 0)$ and h is negative on $(0, \infty)$. Sketching the graph:

45. a. Given the function: $f(x) = \left(x - \dfrac{1}{2}\right)^2 (x-4)$

Evaluating the function: $f(0) = \left(0 - \dfrac{1}{2}\right)^2 (0-4) = -1$

The y-intercept is $(0, -1)$. The x-intercepts are $(4, 0)$ and $\left(\dfrac{1}{2}, 0\right)$.

b. The zero at $x = 4$ has multiplicity 1, and the zero at $x = \dfrac{1}{2}$ has multiplicity 2.

c. $f(x)$ behaves like $y = x^3$ so $f(x) \to -\infty$ as $x \to -\infty$ and $f(x) \to \infty$ as $x \to \infty$

d. Creating a sign chart:

Interval	Test Value x	Function Value $f(x)$	Sign of $f(x)$
$\left(-\infty, \dfrac{1}{2}\right)$	0	-1	$-$
$\left(\dfrac{1}{2}, 4\right)$	1	-0.75	$-$
$(4, \infty)$	5	20.25	$+$

Thus f is positive on $(4, \infty)$ and f is negative on $\left(-\infty, \dfrac{1}{2}\right) \cup \left(\dfrac{1}{2}, 4\right)$. Sketching the graph:

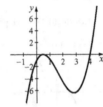

46. a. Given the function: $f(x) = (x-7)^2 (x+2)(x-3)$

Evaluating the function: $f(0) = (0-7)^2 (0+2)(0-3) = -294$

The y-intercept is $(0, -294)$. The x-intercepts are $(7, 0)$, $(-2, 0)$, and $(3, 0)$.

b. The zero at $x = 7$ has multiplicity 2, the zero at $x = -2$ has multiplicity 1, and the zero at $x = 3$ has multiplicity 1.

c. $f(x)$ behaves like $y = x^4$ so $f(x) \to \infty$ as $x \to -\infty$ and $f(x) \to \infty$ as $x \to \infty$

d. Creating a sign chart:

Interval	Test Value x	Function Value $f(x)$	Sign of $f(x)$
$(-\infty, -2)$	-3	600	$+$
$(-2, 3)$	0	-294	$-$
$(3, 7)$	4	54	$+$
$(7, \infty)$	8	50	$+$

Thus f is positive on $(-\infty, -2) \cup (3, 7) \cup (7, \infty)$ and f is negative on $(-2, 3)$. Sketching the graph:

47. **a.** Given the function: $f(t) = (t+2)(t-1)(t^2+1)$

Evaluating the function: $f(0) = (0+2)(0-1)(0^2+1) = -2$

The y-intercept is $(0,-2)$. The t-intercepts are $(-2,0)$ and $(1,0)$.

b. The zero at $t = -2$ has multiplicity 1, and the zero at $t = 1$ has multiplicity 1.

c. $f(t)$ behaves like $y = t^4$ so $f(t) \to \infty$ as $t \to -\infty$ and $f(t) \to \infty$ as $t \to \infty$

d. Creating a sign chart:

Interval	Test Value t	Function Value $f(t)$	Sign of $f(t)$
$(-\infty,-2)$	-3	40	$+$
$(-2,1)$	0	-2	$-$
$(1,\infty)$	2	20	$+$

Thus f is positive on $(-\infty,-2) \cup (1,\infty)$ and f is negative on $(-2,1)$. Sketching the graph:

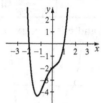

48. **a.** Given the function: $g(s) = \left(s - \dfrac{1}{2}\right)(s+3)(s^2+4)$

Evaluating the function: $g(0) = \left(0 - \dfrac{1}{2}\right)(0+3)(0^2+4) = -6$

The y-intercept is $(0,-6)$. The s-intercepts are $\left(\dfrac{1}{2},0\right)$ and $(-3,0)$.

b. The zero at $s = \dfrac{1}{2}$ has multiplicity 1, and the zero at $s = -3$ has multiplicity 1.

c. $g(s)$ behaves like $y = s^4$ so $g(s) \to \infty$ as $s \to -\infty$ and $g(s) \to \infty$ as $s \to \infty$

d. Creating a sign chart:

Interval	Test Value s	Function Value $g(s)$	Sign of $g(s)$
$(-\infty,-3)$	-4	90	$+$
$\left(-3,\dfrac{1}{2}\right)$	0	-6	$-$
$\left(\dfrac{1}{2},\infty\right)$	1	10	$+$

Thus g is positive on $(-\infty,-3) \cup \left(\dfrac{1}{2},\infty\right)$ and g is negative on $\left(-3,\dfrac{1}{2}\right)$. Sketching the graph:

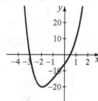

49.　**a.**　Given the function: $g(x) = x^4 - 3x^3 - 18x^2 = x^2(x^2 - 3x - 18) = x^2(x+3)(x-6)$

Evaluating the function: $g(0) = (0)^2(0+3)(0-6) = 0$

The y-intercept is $(0,0)$. The x-intercepts are $(0,0)$, $(-3,0)$, and $(6,0)$.

b.　The zero at $x = 0$ has multiplicity 2, the zero at $x = -3$ has multiplicity 1, and the zero at $x = 6$ has multiplicity 1.

c.　$g(x)$ behaves like $y = x^4$ so $g(x) \to \infty$ as $x \to -\infty$ and $g(x) \to \infty$ as $x \to \infty$

d.　Creating a sign chart:

Interval	Test Value x	Function Value $g(x)$	Sign of $g(x)$
$(-\infty,-3)$	-4	160	$+$
$(-3,0)$	-1	-14	$-$
$(0,6)$	1	-20	$-$
$(6,\infty)$	7	490	$+$

Thus g is positive on $(-\infty,-3) \cup (6,\infty)$ and g is negative on $(-3,0) \cup (0,6)$. Sketching the graph:

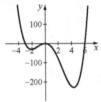

50.　**a.**　Given the function: $h(t) = -2t^5 + 4t^4 + 2t^3 = -2t^3(t^2 - 2t - 1)$

Evaluating the function: $h(0) = -2(0)^3(0^2 - 0 - 1) = 0$

The y-intercept is $(0,0)$. Using the quadratic formula:

$$t = \frac{2 \pm \sqrt{(-2)^2 - 4(1)(-1)}}{2(1)} = \frac{2 \pm \sqrt{8}}{2} = \frac{2 \pm 2\sqrt{2}}{2} = 1 \pm \sqrt{2} \approx -0.4, 2.4$$

The t-intercepts are $(0,0)$, $(1-\sqrt{2},0)$, and $(1+\sqrt{2},0)$.

b.　The zero at $t = 0$ has multiplicity 3, the zero at $t = 1-\sqrt{2}$ has multiplicity 1, and the zero at $t = 1+\sqrt{2}$ has multiplicity 1.

c.　$h(t)$ behaves like $y = -2t^5$ so $h(t) \to \infty$ as $t \to -\infty$ and $h(t) \to -\infty$ as $t \to \infty$

d.　Creating a sign chart:

Interval	Test Value t	Function Value $h(t)$	Sign of $h(t)$
$(-\infty,-0.4)$	-1	4	$+$
$(-0.4,0)$	-0.1	-0.002	$-$
$(0,2.4)$	1	4	$+$
$(2.4,\infty)$	3	-108	$-$

Thus h is positive on $(-\infty,1-\sqrt{2}) \cup (0,1+\sqrt{2})$ and h is negative on $(1-\sqrt{2},0) \cup (1+\sqrt{2},6)$.

Sketching the graph:

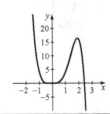

51. a. The length is given by 11 − 2x and the width is 8 − 2x, so the volume is given by:
$$V(x) = lwh = (11-2x)(8-2x)(x) = x(11-2x)(8-2x)$$

b. Clearly $x > 0$, and the largest x can be is 4 inches. Thus the values are $0 < x < 4$.

c. The value is $x \approx 1.5252$ inches:

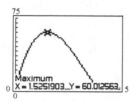

52. a. Since $r + h = 8$, $h = 8 - r$, so the volume is given by: $V(r) = \pi r^2 h = \pi r^2 (8 - r)$

b. Clearly $r > 0$, and the largest r can be is 8 inches. Thus the values are $0 < r < 8$.

c. The value is $r \approx 5.3333$ inches:

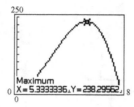

53. Using synthetic division:

$$\begin{array}{r|rrr} 4 & -4 & 1 & -7 \\ & & -16 & -60 \\ \hline & -4 & -15 & -67 \end{array}$$

Therefore: $\dfrac{-4x^2 + x - 7}{x - 4} = -4x - 15 + \dfrac{-67}{x-4}$. Written in the desired form: $-4x^2 + x - 7 = (x-4)(-4x-15) - 67$

54. Using synthetic division:

$$\begin{array}{r|rrrr} -2 & 5 & 0 & 2 & 4 \\ & & -10 & 20 & -44 \\ \hline & 5 & -10 & 22 & -40 \end{array}$$

Therefore: $\dfrac{5x^3 + 2x + 4}{x + 2} = 5x^2 - 10x + 22 + \dfrac{-40}{x+2}$

Written in the desired form: $5x^3 + 2x + 4 = (x+2)(5x^2 - 10x + 22) - 40$

55. Using long division:

$$\require{enclose}\begin{array}{r} x^3 - x^2 - 3x + 4 \\ x^2 + 3 \enclose{longdiv}{x^5 - x^4 + 0x^3 + x^2 - 3x + 1} \\ \underline{x^5 \phantom{{}-x^4} + 3x^3} \\ -x^4 - 3x^3 + x^2 \\ \underline{-x^4 \phantom{{}-3x^3} - 3x^2} \\ -3x^3 + 4x^2 - 3x \\ \underline{-3x^3 \phantom{{}+4x^2} - 9x} \\ 4x^2 + 6x + 1 \\ \underline{4x^2 \phantom{{}+6x} + 12} \\ 6x - 11 \end{array}$$

Therefore: $\dfrac{x^5 - x^4 + x^2 - 3x + 1}{x^2 + 3} = x^3 - x^2 - 3x + 4 + \dfrac{6x - 11}{x^2 + 3}$

Written in the desired form: $x^5 - x^4 + x^2 - 3x + 1 = (x^2 + 3)(x^3 - x^2 - 3x + 4) + (6x - 11)$

56. Using long division:

$$
\begin{array}{r}
-2x^2 + \dfrac{1}{2}x + \dfrac{3}{4} \\[4pt]
2x+1\overline{\smash{\big)}\,-4x^3 - x^2 + 2x + 1} \\[2pt]
\underline{-4x^3 - 2x^2} \\[2pt]
x^2 + 2x \\[2pt]
\underline{x^2 + \dfrac{1}{2}x} \\[2pt]
\dfrac{3}{2}x + 1 \\[2pt]
\underline{\dfrac{3}{2}x + \dfrac{3}{4}} \\[2pt]
\dfrac{1}{4}
\end{array}
$$

Therefore: $\dfrac{-4x^3 - x^2 + 2x + 1}{2x+1} = -2x^2 + \dfrac{1}{2}x + \dfrac{3}{4} + \dfrac{\frac{1}{4}}{2x+1}$

Written in the desired form: $-4x^3 - x^2 + 2x + 1 = (2x+1)\left(-2x^2 + \dfrac{1}{2}x + \dfrac{3}{4}\right) + \dfrac{1}{4}$

57. Using synthetic division with $x = -1$:

$$
\begin{array}{r|rrrr}
-1 & -1 & 0 & 7 & 6 \\
   &   & 1 & -1 & -6 \\
\hline
   & -1 & 1 & 6 & 0
\end{array}
$$

The remainder is 0. $d(x)$ is a factor of $p(x)$, since $\dfrac{p(x)}{d(x)}$ has no remainder.

58. Using synthetic division with $x = -2$:

$$
\begin{array}{r|rrrr}
-2 & 2 & 1 & 8 & 0 \\
   &   & -4 & 6 & -28 \\
\hline
   & 2 & -3 & 14 & -28
\end{array}
$$

The remainder is -28. $d(x)$ is not a factor of $p(x)$, since $\dfrac{p(x)}{d(x)}$ has a nonzero remainder.

59. Using synthetic division with $x = -3$:

$$
\begin{array}{r|rrrr}
-3 & 1 & 0 & -7 & 6 \\
   &   & -3 & 9 & -6 \\
\hline
   & 1 & -3 & 2 & 0
\end{array}
$$

The remainder is 0. $d(x)$ is a factor of $p(x)$, since $\dfrac{p(x)}{d(x)}$ has no remainder.

60. Evaluating the function: $p(1) = 1^{10} - 1 = 1 - 1 = 0$

By the remainder theorem, the remainder is 0. $d(x)$ is a factor of $p(x)$, since $\dfrac{p(x)}{d(x)}$ has no remainder.

61. Evaluating the function: $p(2) = (2)^3 - 6(2)^2 + 3(2) + 10 = 8 - 24 + 6 + 10 = 0$

Using synthetic division with $x = 2$:

$$
\begin{array}{r|rrrr}
2 & 1 & -6 & 3 & 10 \\
  &   & 2 & -8 & -10 \\
\hline
  & 1 & -4 & -5 & 0
\end{array}
$$

Factoring: $p(x) = (x-2)(x^2 - 4x - 5) = (x-2)(x+1)(x-5)$

62. Evaluating the function: $p(-1) = -(-1)^3 - 7(-1) - 8 = 1 + 7 - 8 = 0$

Using synthetic division with $x = -1$:

$$
\begin{array}{r|rrrr}
-1 & -1 & 0 & -7 & -8 \\
   &   & 1 & -1 & 8 \\
\hline
   & -1 & 1 & -8 & 0
\end{array}
$$

Factoring: $p(x) = (x+1)(-x^2 + x - 8) = -(x+1)(x^2 - x + 8)$

63. Evaluating the function: $p(3) = -(3)^4 + (3)^3 + 4(3)^2 + 5(3) + 3 = -81 + 27 + 36 + 15 + 3 = 0$

Using synthetic division with $x = 3$:

$$
\begin{array}{r|rrrrr}
3 & -1 & 1 & 4 & 5 & 3 \\
  &   & -3 & -6 & -6 & -3 \\
\hline
  & -1 & -2 & -2 & -1 & 0
\end{array}
$$

Factoring: $p(x) = (x-3)(-x^3 - 2x^2 - 2x - 1) = -(x-3)(x^3 + 2x^2 + 2x + 1)$

To further factor, note that:
$$
\begin{aligned}
x^3 + 2x^2 + 2x + 1 &= (x^3 + 1) + (2x^2 + 2x) \\
&= (x+1)(x^2 - x + 1) + 2x(x+1) \\
&= (x+1)(x^2 - x + 1 + 2x) \\
&= (x+1)(x^2 + x + 1)
\end{aligned}
$$

Therefore: $p(x) = -(x-3)(x^3 + 2x^2 + 2x + 1) = -(x-3)(x+1)(x^2 + x + 1)$

64. Evaluating the function: $p(-2) = (-2)^4 - (-2)^2 + 6(-2) = 16 - 4 - 12 = 0$

Using synthetic division with $x = -2$:

$$
\begin{array}{r|rrrrr}
-2 & 1 & 0 & -1 & 6 & 0 \\
   &   & -2 & 4 & -6 & 0 \\
\hline
   & 1 & -2 & 3 & 0 & 0
\end{array}
$$

Factoring: $p(x) = (x+2)(x^3 - 2x^2 + 3x) = x(x+2)(x^2 - 2x + 3)$

65. The possible rational roots are: $\dfrac{\text{Factors of } 3}{\text{Factors of } 2} = \dfrac{\pm 1, \pm 3}{\pm 1, \pm 2} = \pm 1, \pm 3, \pm \dfrac{1}{2}$

Evaluating the function (until we reach a 0): $P(1) = 2(1)^3 - 3(1)^2 - 2(1) + 3 = 0$

Using synthetic division:

$$
\begin{array}{r|rrrr}
1 & 2 & -3 & -2 & 3 \\
  &   & 2 & -1 & -3 \\
\hline
  & 2 & -1 & -3 & 0
\end{array}
$$

Factoring the polynomial: $P(x) = (x-1)(2x^2 - x - 3) = (x-1)(2x-3)(x+1)$

The real zeros are: $x = 1, \dfrac{3}{2}, -1$

66. The possible rational roots are: $\dfrac{\text{Factors of } 20}{\text{Factors of } -1} = \dfrac{\pm 1, \pm 2, \pm 4, \pm 5, \pm 10, \pm 20}{\pm 1} = \pm 1, \pm 2, \pm 4, \pm 5, \pm 10, \pm 20$

Evaluating the function (until we reach a 0):
$$P(1) = -(1)^3 - 5(1)^2 + 4(1) + 20 = 18$$
$$P(2) = -(2)^3 - 5(2)^2 + 4(2) + 20 = 0$$

Using synthetic division:

```
2 | -1   -5    4    20
   |      -2  -14  -20
   -------------------
     -1   -7  -10    0
```

Factoring the polynomial: $P(t) = (t-2)(-t^2 - 7t - 10) = -(t-2)(t^2 + 7t + 10) = -(t-2)(t+2)(t+5)$

The real zeros are: $t = 2, -2, -5$

67. The possible rational roots are: $\dfrac{\text{Factors of } -3}{\text{Factors of } 1} = \dfrac{\pm 1, \pm 3}{\pm 1} = \pm 1, \pm 3$

Evaluating the function (until we reach a 0):
$$h(1) = (1)^3 - 3(1)^2 + 1 - 3 = -4$$
$$h(3) = (3)^3 - 3(3)^2 + 3 - 3 = 0$$

Using synthetic division:

```
3 | 1   -3    1   -3
  |       3    0    3
  ------------------
    1    0    1    0
```

Factoring the polynomial: $h(x) = (x-3)(x^2 + 1)$. The real zero is: $x = 3$

68. The possible rational roots are: $\dfrac{\text{Factors of } 5}{\text{Factors of } 1} = \dfrac{\pm 1, \pm 5}{\pm 1} = \pm 1, \pm 5$

Evaluating the function (until we reach a 0): $f(1) = (1)^3 + 3(1)^2 - 9(1) + 5 = 0$

Using synthetic division:

```
1 | 1    3   -9    5
  |      1    4   -5
  ------------------
    1    4   -5    0
```

Factoring the polynomial: $f(x) = (x-1)(x^2 + 4x - 5) = (x-1)(x+5)(x-1) = (x+5)(x-1)^2$

The real zeros are: $x = 1, -5$

69. Creating a function:
$$2x^3 + 9x^2 - 6x = 5$$
$$2x^3 + 9x^2 - 6x - 5 = 0$$
$$p(x) = 2x^3 + 9x^2 - 6x - 5$$

The possible rational roots are: $\pm 1, \pm 5, \pm \dfrac{1}{2}, \pm \dfrac{5}{2}$. Using synthetic division:

```
1 | 2    9   -6   -5
  |      2   11    5
  ------------------
    2   11    5    0
```

Factoring the polynomial: $p(x) = (x-1)(2x^2 + 11x + 5) = (x-1)(2x+1)(x+5)$

The real solutions are: $x = 1, -\dfrac{1}{2}, -5$

70. Creating a function:
$$x^3 = 21x - 20$$
$$x^3 - 21x + 20 = 0$$
$$p(x) = x^3 - 21x + 20$$

The possible rational roots are: $\pm 1, \pm 2, \pm 4, \pm 5, \pm 10, \pm 20$

Using synthetic division:

$$\underline{1|}\ \begin{array}{rrrr} 1 & 0 & -21 & 20 \\ & 1 & 1 & -20 \\ \hline 1 & 1 & -20 & 0 \end{array}$$

Factoring the polynomial: $p(x) = (x-1)(x^2 + x - 20) = (x-1)(x-4)(x+5)$

The real solutions are: $x = 1, 4, -5$

71. Creating a function:
$$x^3 - 7x^2 = -14x + 8$$
$$x^3 - 7x^2 + 14x - 8 = 0$$
$$p(x) = x^3 - 7x^2 + 14x - 8$$

The possible rational roots are: $\pm 1, \pm 2, \pm 4, \pm 8$

Using synthetic division:

$$\underline{1|}\ \begin{array}{rrrr} 1 & -7 & 14 & -8 \\ & 1 & -6 & 8 \\ \hline 1 & -6 & 8 & 0 \end{array}$$

Factoring the polynomial: $p(x) = (x-1)(x^2 - 6x + 8) = (x-1)(x-2)(x-4)$

The real solutions are: $x = 1, 2, 4$

72. Creating a function:
$$x^4 - 9x^2 - 2x^3 + 2x = -8$$
$$x^4 - 2x^3 - 9x^2 + 2x + 8 = 0$$
$$p(x) = x^4 - 2x^3 - 9x^2 + 2x + 8$$

The possible rational roots are: $\pm 1, \pm 2, \pm 4, \pm 8$

Using synthetic division:

$$\underline{1|}\ \begin{array}{rrrrr} 1 & -2 & -9 & 2 & 8 \\ & 1 & -1 & -10 & -8 \\ \hline 1 & -1 & -10 & -8 & 0 \end{array}$$

Factoring the polynomial: $p(x) = (x-1)(x^3 - x^2 - 10x - 8)$

Using synthetic division again:

$$\underline{-1|}\ \begin{array}{rrrr} 1 & -1 & -10 & -8 \\ & -1 & 2 & 8 \\ \hline 1 & -2 & -8 & 0 \end{array}$$

Factoring the polynomial: $p(x) = (x-1)(x+1)(x^2 - 2x - 8) = (x-1)(x+1)(x-4)(x+2)$

The real solutions are: $x = 1, -1, 4, -2$

73. For $p(x) = -x^4 + 2x^3 - 7x - 4$, there are 2 sign variations.

For $p(-x) = -(-x)^4 + 2(-x)^3 - 7(-x) - 4 = -x^4 - 2x^3 + 7x - 4$, there are 2 sign variations.

Positive zeros: 2 or 0; negative zeros: 2 or 0

74. For $p(x) = x^5 + 3x^4 - 8x^2 - x - 3$, there is 1 sign variation.

For $p(-x) = (-x)^5 + 3(-x)^4 - 8(-x)^2 - (-x) - 3 = -x^5 + 3x^4 - 8x^2 + x - 3$, there are 4 sign variations.

Positive zeros: 1; negative zeros: 4, 2 or 0

75. Let h represent the height, $h + 3$ represent the length, and $h + 4$ represent the width. Using the volume formula:
$$V(h) = lwh = (h+3)(h+4)(h) = h(h^2 + 7h + 12) = h^3 + 7h^2 + 12h$$

The equation to solve is:
$$h^3 + 7h^2 + 12h = 60$$
$$h^3 + 7h^2 + 12h - 60 = 0$$

The possible rational roots are: $\pm 1, \pm 2, \pm 3, \pm 4, \pm 5, \pm 6, \pm 10, \pm 12, \pm 15, \pm 20, \pm 30, \pm 60$

Using synthetic division:

$$\begin{array}{r|rrrr} 2 & 1 & 7 & 12 & -60 \\ & & 2 & 18 & 60 \\ \hline & 1 & 9 & 30 & 0 \end{array}$$

Factoring the polynomial: $V(h) = (h-2)(h^2 + 9h + 30)$

The solution is $h = 2$. The height is 2 inches.

76. The real part is $\sqrt{3}$ and the imaginary part is 0.

77. The real part is 0 and the imaginary part is $-\dfrac{3}{2}$.

78. The real part is 7 and the imaginary part is –2.

79. Writing the complex number: $-1 - \sqrt{-5} = -1 - i\sqrt{5}$. The real part is –1 and the imaginary part is $-\sqrt{5}$.

80. The complex conjugate of $\dfrac{1}{2}$ is $\dfrac{1}{2}$.

81. The complex conjugate of $3 - i$ is $3 + i$.

82. Since $i + 4 = 4 + i$, the complex conjugate is $4 - i$.

83. The complex conjugate of $1 - \sqrt{2} + 3i$ is $1 - \sqrt{2} - 3i$.

84. Finding the values:
$$x + y = (1 + 4i) + (2 - 3i) = (1 + 2) + (4i - 3i) = 3 + i$$
$$x - y = (1 + 4i) - (2 - 3i) = (1 - 2) + (4i + 3i) = -1 + 7i$$
$$xy = (1 + 4i)(2 - 3i) = 2 - 3i + 8i - 12i^2 = 2 + 5i - 12(-1) = 14 + 5i$$
$$\frac{x}{y} = \frac{1 + 4i}{2 - 3i} = \frac{1 + 4i}{2 - 3i} \cdot \frac{2 + 3i}{2 + 3i} = \frac{2 + 3i + 8i + 12i^2}{4 + 6i - 6i - 9i^2} = \frac{-10 + 11i}{13} = -\frac{10}{13} + \frac{11}{13}i$$

85. Finding the values:
$$x + y = (3 + 2i) + (-4 + 3i) = (3 - 4) + (2i + 3i) = -1 + 5i$$
$$x - y = (3 + 2i) - (-4 + 3i) = (3 + 4) + (2i - 3i) = 7 - i$$
$$xy = (3 + 2i)(-4 + 3i) = -12 + 9i - 8i + 6i^2 = -12 + i + 6(-1) = -18 + i$$
$$\frac{x}{y} = \frac{3 + 2i}{-4 + 3i} = \frac{3 + 2i}{-4 + 3i} \cdot \frac{-4 - 3i}{-4 - 3i} = \frac{-12 - 9i - 8i - 6i^2}{16 + 12i - 12i - 9i^2} = \frac{-6 - 17i}{25} = -\frac{6}{25} - \frac{17}{25}i$$

86. Finding the values:
$$x + y = (1.5 - 3i) + (-1 + 2i) = (1.5 - 1) + (-3i + 2i) = 0.5 - i$$
$$x - y = (1.5 - 3i) - (-1 + 2i) = (1.5 + 1) + (-3i - 2i) = 2.5 - 5i$$
$$xy = (1.5 - 3i)(-1 + 2i) = -1.5 + 3i + 3i - 6i^2 = -1.5 + 6i - 6(-1) = 4.5 + 6i$$
$$\frac{x}{y} = \frac{1.5 - 3i}{-1 + 2i} = \frac{1.5 - 3i}{-1 + 2i} \cdot \frac{-1 - 2i}{-1 - 2i} = \frac{-1.5 - 3i + 3i + 6i^2}{1 + 2i - 2i - 4i^2} = \frac{-7.5}{5} = -1.5$$

87. Finding the values:

$$x + y = \left(-\sqrt{2} + i\right) + (-3) = \left(-3 - \sqrt{2}\right) + i$$

$$x - y = \left(-\sqrt{2} + i\right) - (-3) = \left(3 - \sqrt{2}\right) + i$$

$$xy = \left(-\sqrt{2} + i\right)(-3) = 3\sqrt{2} - 3i$$

$$\frac{x}{y} = \frac{-\sqrt{2} + i}{-3} = \frac{\sqrt{2}}{3} - \frac{1}{3}i$$

88. Finding the values:

$$x + y = \left(-1 + \frac{1}{2}i\right) + \left(\frac{3}{2} + i\right) = \left(-1 + \frac{3}{2}\right) + \left(\frac{1}{2}i + i\right) = \frac{1}{2} + \frac{3}{2}i$$

$$x - y = \left(-1 + \frac{1}{2}i\right) - \left(\frac{3}{2} + i\right) = \left(-1 - \frac{3}{2}\right) + \left(\frac{1}{2}i - i\right) = -\frac{5}{2} - \frac{1}{2}i$$

$$xy = \left(-1 + \frac{1}{2}i\right)\left(\frac{3}{2} + i\right) = -\frac{3}{2} - i + \frac{3}{4}i + \frac{1}{2}i^2 = -\frac{3}{2} - \frac{1}{4}i + \frac{1}{2}(-1) = -2 - \frac{1}{4}i$$

$$\frac{x}{y} = \frac{-1 + \frac{1}{2}i}{\frac{3}{2} + i} = \frac{-2 + i}{3 + 2i} \cdot \frac{3 - 2i}{3 - 2i} = \frac{-6 + 4i + 3i - 2i^2}{9 - 6i + 6i - 4i^2} = \frac{-4 + 7i}{13} = -\frac{4}{13} + \frac{7}{13}i$$

89. Finding the values:

$$x + y = (-i) + \left(-\sqrt{-3} + 1\right) = (-i) + \left(1 - i\sqrt{3}\right) = 1 - \left(1 + \sqrt{3}\right)i$$

$$x - y = (-i) - \left(-\sqrt{-3} + 1\right) = (-i) - \left(1 - i\sqrt{3}\right) = -1 + \left(\sqrt{3} - 1\right)i$$

$$xy = (-i)\left(-\sqrt{-3} + 1\right) = (-i)\left(-i\sqrt{3} + 1\right) = i^2\sqrt{3} - i = -\sqrt{3} - i$$

$$\frac{x}{y} = \frac{-i}{-\sqrt{-3} + 1} = \frac{-i}{1 - i\sqrt{3}} \cdot \frac{1 + i\sqrt{3}}{1 + i\sqrt{3}} = \frac{-i - i^2\sqrt{3}}{1 + i\sqrt{3} - i\sqrt{3} - 3i^2} = \frac{\sqrt{3} - i}{4} = \frac{\sqrt{3}}{4} - \frac{1}{4}i$$

90. Using the quadratic formula: $x = \dfrac{-1 \pm \sqrt{(1)^2 - 4(-1)(-3)}}{2(-1)} = \dfrac{-1 \pm \sqrt{-11}}{-2} = \dfrac{1}{2} \pm \dfrac{\sqrt{11}}{2}i$

   The zeros of $f(x) = -x^2 + x - 3$ are $x = \dfrac{1}{2} + \dfrac{\sqrt{11}}{2}i$ and $x = \dfrac{1}{2} - \dfrac{\sqrt{11}}{2}i$.

91. First write the equation as $2x^2 - x + 1 = 0$.

   Using the quadratic formula: $x = \dfrac{1 \pm \sqrt{(-1)^2 - 4(2)(1)}}{2(2)} = \dfrac{1 \pm \sqrt{-7}}{4} = \dfrac{1 \pm i\sqrt{7}}{4} = \dfrac{1}{4} \pm \dfrac{\sqrt{7}}{4}i$

   The zeros of $f(x) = 2x^2 - x + 1$ are $x = \dfrac{1}{4} + \dfrac{\sqrt{7}}{4}i$ and $x = \dfrac{1}{4} - \dfrac{\sqrt{7}}{4}i$.

92. First write the equation as $t^2 + \dfrac{4}{5}t + 1 = 0$.

   Using the quadratic formula: $t = \dfrac{-\frac{4}{5} \pm \sqrt{\left(\frac{4}{5}\right)^2 - 4(1)(1)}}{2(1)} = \dfrac{-\frac{4}{5} \pm \sqrt{-\frac{84}{25}}}{2} = \dfrac{-\frac{4}{5} \pm \frac{2i\sqrt{21}}{5}}{2} = \dfrac{-4 \pm 2i\sqrt{21}}{10} = -\dfrac{2}{5} \pm \dfrac{\sqrt{21}}{5}i$

   The zeros of $f(t) = t^2 + \dfrac{4}{5}t + 1$ are $t = -\dfrac{2}{5} + \dfrac{\sqrt{21}}{5}i$ and $t = -\dfrac{2}{5} - \dfrac{\sqrt{21}}{5}i$.

93. First write the equation as $2t^2 - t - \sqrt{13} = 0$.

Using the quadratic formula: $t = \dfrac{1 \pm \sqrt{(-1)^2 - 4(2)(-\sqrt{13})}}{2(2)} = \dfrac{1 \pm \sqrt{1 + 8\sqrt{13}}}{4}$

The zeros of $f(t) = 2t^2 - t - \sqrt{13}$ are $t = \dfrac{1 + \sqrt{1 + 8\sqrt{13}}}{4}$ and $t = \dfrac{1 - \sqrt{1 + 8\sqrt{13}}}{4}$.

94. Solving the equation:

$x^2 + 25 = 0$

$x^2 = -25$

$x = \pm\sqrt{-25} = \pm 5i$

The zeros are $x = \pm 5i$, so $p(x) = (x + 5i)(x - 5i)$.

95. Solving the equation:

$x^3 + x - 4x^2 - 4 = 0$

$x^3 - 4x^2 + x - 4 = 0$

$x^2(x - 4) + 1(x - 4) = 0$

$(x - 4)(x^2 + 1) = 0$

$x = 4, \pm i$

The zeros are $x = 4, \pm i$, so $p(x) = (x - 4)(x + i)(x - i)$.

96. Solving the equation:

$x^3 + 2x^2 + 4x + 8 = 0$

$x^2(x + 2) + 4(x + 2) = 0$

$(x + 2)(x^2 + 4) = 0$

$x = -2, \pm 2i$

The zeros are $x = -2, \pm 2i$, so $p(x) = (x + 2)(x + 2i)(x - 2i)$.

97. Solving the equation:

$x^4 - 8x^2 - 9 = 0$

$(x^2 - 9)(x^2 + 1) = 0$

$(x + 3)(x - 3)(x^2 + 1) = 0$

$x = -3, 3, \pm i$

The zeros are $x = -3, 3, \pm i$, so $p(x) = (x + 3)(x - 3)(x + i)(x - i)$.

98. **a.** Completing the table:

x	-1.5	-1.1	-1.01	-0.99	-0.9	-0.5
$f(x)$	4	100	10,000	10,000	100	4

As $x \to -1$ from the left, $f(x) \to \infty$, and as $x \to -1$ from the right, $f(x) \to \infty$.

b. Completing the table:

x	10	50	100	1000
$f(x)$	0.008264	0.000384	0.00009803	0.000000998

As $x \to \infty$, $f(x) \to 0$.

c. Completing the table:

x	-1000	-100	-50	-10
$f(x)$	0.000001002	0.0001020	0.0004165	0.01235

As $x \to -\infty$, $f(x) \to 0$.

99. **a.** Completing the table:

x	2.5	2.9	2.99	3.01	3.1	3.5
$f(x)$	4	100	10,000	10,000	100	4

As $x \to 3$ from the left, $f(x) \to \infty$, and as $x \to 3$ from the right, $f(x) \to \infty$.

b. Completing the table:

x	10	50	100	1000
$f(x)$	0.0204	0.0004527	0.0001063	0.000001006

As $x \to \infty$, $f(x) \to 0$.

c. Completing the table:

x	-1000	-100	-50	-10
$f(x)$	0.000000994	0.00009426	0.000356	0.005917

As $x \to -\infty$, $f(x) \to 0$.

100. The vertical asymptote is $x = 1$, the horizontal asymptote is $y = 0$, there is no x-intercept, and the y-intercept is $(0,-2)$. Sketching the graph:

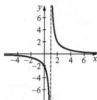

101. The vertical asymptote is $x = -5$, the horizontal asymptote is $y = 3$, the x-intercept is $(0,0)$, and the y-intercept is $(0,0)$. Sketching the graph:

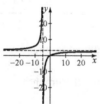

102. Factoring the denominator: $h(x) = \dfrac{1}{x^2 - 4} = \dfrac{1}{(x+2)(x-2)}$

The vertical asymptotes are $x = -2$ and $x = 2$, the horizontal asymptote is $y = 0$, there is no x-intercept, and the y-intercept is $\left(0,-\dfrac{1}{4}\right)$. Sketching the graph:

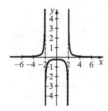

103. Factoring the denominator: $g(x) = \dfrac{2x^2}{x^2 - 1} = \dfrac{2x^2}{(x+1)(x-1)}$

The vertical asymptotes are $x = -1$ and $x = 1$, the horizontal asymptote is $y = 2$, the x-intercept is $(0,0)$, and the y-intercept is $(0,0)$. Sketching the graph:

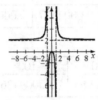

104. Factoring the denominator: $g(x) = \dfrac{x-2}{x^2 - 2x - 3} = \dfrac{x-2}{(x+1)(x-3)}$

The vertical asymptotes are $x = -1$ and $x = 3$, the horizontal asymptote is $y = 0$, the x-intercept is $(2,0)$, and the y-intercept is $\left(0, \dfrac{2}{3}\right)$. Sketching the graph:

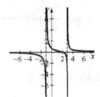

105. Factoring the numerator and denominator: $h(x) = \dfrac{x^2 - 2}{x^2 - 4} = \dfrac{\left(x+\sqrt{2}\right)\left(x-\sqrt{2}\right)}{(x+2)(x-2)}$

The vertical asymptotes are $x = -2$ and $x = 2$, the horizontal asymptote is $y = 1$, the x-intercepts are $\left(-\sqrt{2},0\right)$ and $\left(\sqrt{2},0\right)$, and the y-intercept is $\left(0, \dfrac{1}{2}\right)$. Sketching the graph:

106. Using synthetic division:

$$\begin{array}{r|rrr} -2 & 1 & 0 & -1 \\ & & -2 & 4 \\ \hline & 1 & -2 & 3 \end{array}$$

The function can be written as: $h(x) = \dfrac{x^2 - 1}{x + 2} = \dfrac{(x+1)(x-1)}{x+2} = x - 2 + \dfrac{3}{x+2}$

The vertical asymptote is $x = -2$, there is no horizontal asymptote, the slant asymptote is $y = x - 2$, the x-intercepts are $(-1,0)$ and $(1,0)$, and the y-intercept is $\left(0, -\dfrac{1}{2}\right)$. Sketching the graph:

107. Using synthetic division:

$$\begin{array}{r|rrr} 1 & 1 & 0 & -4 \\ & & 1 & 1 \\ \hline & 1 & 1 & -3 \end{array}$$

The function can be written as: $p(x) = \dfrac{x^2 - 4}{x-1} = \dfrac{(x+2)(x-2)}{x-1} = x+1 - \dfrac{3}{x-1}$

The vertical asymptote is $x = 1$, there is no horizontal asymptote, the slant asymptote is $y = x+1$, the x-intercepts are $(-2,0)$ and $(2,0)$, and the y-intercept is $(0,4)$. Sketching the graph:

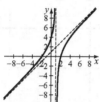

108. a. Let x represent the number of miles driven per day. The average cost function is given by:

$$C(x) = \frac{20 + 0.25x}{x} = 0.25 + \frac{20}{x}$$

b. Evaluating when $x = 100$: $C(100) = 0.25 + \dfrac{20}{100} = 0.45$

The average cost of driving 100 miles per day is $0.45 per mile.

c. The horizontal asymptote is $C = 0.25$. The cost per mile approaches $0.25 as the mileage increases.

109. Factoring the inequality:

$$4x^2 + 21x + 5 \le 0$$

$$(4x+1)(x+5) \le 0$$

Creating a sign chart:

Interval	Test value	Sign of $x+5$	Sign of $4x+1$	Sign of $(4x+1)(x+5)$
$(-\infty,-5)$	-6	$-$	$-$	$+$
$\left(-5,-\dfrac{1}{4}\right)$	-1	$+$	$-$	$-$
$\left(-\dfrac{1}{4},\infty\right)$	0	$+$	$+$	$+$

The inequality is satisfied on the interval $\left(-5,-\dfrac{1}{4}\right)$. Since the endpoints are included, the solution is $\left[-5,-\dfrac{1}{4}\right]$.

110. Factoring the inequality:

$$x^2 - 5x - 6 > 0$$

$$(x+1)(x-6) > 0$$

Creating a sign chart:

Interval	Test value	Sign of $x+1$	Sign of $x-6$	Sign of $(x+1)(x-6)$
$(-\infty,-1)$	-2	$-$	$-$	$+$
$(-1,6)$	0	$+$	$-$	$-$
$(6,\infty)$	7	$+$	$+$	$+$

The inequality is satisfied on the interval $(-\infty,-1) \cup (6,\infty)$. Since the endpoints are not included, the solution is $(-\infty,-1) \cup (6,\infty)$.

111. Factoring the inequality:

$$-6x^2 - 5x > -4$$
$$-6x^2 - 5x + 4 > 0$$
$$6x^2 + 5x - 4 < 0$$
$$(3x+4)(2x-1) < 0$$

Creating a sign chart:

Interval	Test value	Sign of $3x+4$	Sign of $2x-1$	Sign of $(3x+4)(2x-1)$
$\left(-\infty, -\dfrac{4}{3}\right)$	-2	$-$	$-$	$+$
$\left(-\dfrac{4}{3}, \dfrac{1}{2}\right)$	0	$+$	$-$	$-$
$\left(\dfrac{1}{2}, \infty\right)$	1	$+$	$+$	$+$

The inequality is satisfied on the interval $\left(-\dfrac{4}{3}, \dfrac{1}{2}\right)$. Since the endpoints are not included, the solution is $\left(-\dfrac{4}{3}, \dfrac{1}{2}\right)$.

112. Factoring the inequality:

$$2x^2 - 11x \le -12$$
$$2x^2 - 11x + 12 \le 0$$
$$(2x-3)(x-4) \le 0$$

Creating a sign chart:

Interval	Test value	Sign of $2x-3$	Sign of $x-4$	Sign of $(2x-3)(x-4)$
$\left(-\infty, \dfrac{3}{2}\right)$	0	$-$	$-$	$+$
$\left(\dfrac{3}{2}, 4\right)$	2	$+$	$-$	$-$
$(4, \infty)$	5	$+$	$+$	$+$

The inequality is satisfied on the interval $\left(\dfrac{3}{2}, 4\right)$. Since the endpoints are included, the solution is $\left[\dfrac{3}{2}, 4\right]$.

113. Factoring the inequality:

$$-x(x+1)(x^2-9) > 0$$
$$-x(x+1)(x+3)(x-3) > 0$$

Creating a sign chart:

Interval	Test value	Sign of $x+3$	Sign of $x+1$	Sign of $-x$	Sign of $x-3$	Sign of $f(x)$
$(-\infty, -3)$	-4	$-$	$-$	$+$	$-$	$-$
$(-3, -1)$	-2	$+$	$-$	$+$	$-$	$+$
$(-1, 0)$	-0.5	$+$	$+$	$+$	$-$	$-$
$(0, 3)$	1	$+$	$+$	$-$	$-$	$+$
$(3, \infty)$	4	$+$	$+$	$-$	$+$	$-$

The inequality is satisfied on the interval $(-3, -1) \cup (0, 3)$. Since the endpoints are not included, the solution is $(-3, -1) \cup (0, 3)$.

114. Creating a sign chart:

Interval	Test value	Sign of $x+2$	Sign of x^2	Sign of $x-3$	Sign of $x^2(x+2)(x-3)$
$(-\infty,-2)$	-3	$-$	$+$	$-$	$+$
$(-2,0)$	-1	$+$	$+$	$-$	$-$
$(0,3)$	1	$+$	$+$	$-$	$-$
$(3,\infty)$	4	$+$	$+$	$+$	$+$

The inequality is satisfied on the interval $(-2,0)\cup(0,3)$. Since the endpoints are included, the solution is $[-2,3]$.

115. Factoring the inequality:
$$x^3+4x^2\le -x+6$$
$$x^3+4x^2+x-6\le 0$$
$$(x-1)(x^2+5x+6)\le 0 \quad \longleftarrow \quad \text{Using rational roots theorem and synthetic division.}$$
$$(x-1)(x+3)(x+2)\le 0$$

Creating a sign chart:

Interval	Test value	Sign of $x+3$	Sign of $x+2$	Sign of $x-1$	Sign of $(x-1)(x+3)(x+2)$
$(-\infty,-3)$	-4	$-$	$-$	$-$	$-$
$(-3,-2)$	-2.5	$+$	$-$	$-$	$+$
$(-2,1)$	0	$+$	$+$	$-$	$-$
$(1,\infty)$	2	$+$	$+$	$+$	$+$

The inequality is satisfied on the interval $(-\infty,-3)\cup(-2,1)$. Since the endpoints are included, the solution is $(-\infty,-3]\cup[-2,1]$.

116. Factoring the inequality:
$$9x^3-x>-9x^2+1$$
$$9x^3+9x^2-x-1>0$$
$$9x^2(x+1)-1(x+1)>0$$
$$(x+1)(9x^2-1)>0$$
$$(x+1)(3x+1)(3x-1)>0$$

Creating a sign chart:

Interval	Test value	Sign of $x+1$	Sign of $3x+1$	Sign of $3x-1$	Sign of $(x-1)(x+3)(x+2)$
$(-\infty,-1)$	-2	$-$	$-$	$-$	$-$
$\left(-1,-\dfrac{1}{3}\right)$	$-\dfrac{2}{3}$	$+$	$-$	$-$	$+$
$\left(-\dfrac{1}{3},\dfrac{1}{3}\right)$	0	$+$	$+$	$-$	$-$
$\left(\dfrac{1}{3},\infty\right)$	1	$+$	$+$	$+$	$+$

The inequality is satisfied on the interval $\left(-1,-\dfrac{1}{3}\right)\cup\left(\dfrac{1}{3},\infty\right)$. Since the endpoints are not included, the solution is $\left(-1,-\dfrac{1}{3}\right)\cup\left(\dfrac{1}{3},\infty\right)$.

117. Factoring the inequality:

$$\frac{x^2 - 1}{x + 1} \le 0$$

$$\frac{(x+1)(x-1)}{x+1} \le 0$$

$$x - 1 \le 0 \qquad (x \ne -1)$$

$$x \le 1 \qquad (x \ne -1)$$

The inequality is satisfied on the interval $(-\infty, -1) \cup (-1, 1)$. Since the value $x = 1$ is included, the solution is $(-\infty, -1) \cup (-1, 1]$.

118. Factoring the inequality:

$$\frac{x^2 + 2x - 3}{x - 3} \le 0$$

$$\frac{(x+3)(x-1)}{x-3} \le 0$$

Creating a sign chart:

Interval	Test value	Sign of $x+3$	Sign of $x-1$	Sign of $x-3$	Sign of $\dfrac{(x+3)(x-1)}{x-3}$
$(-\infty, -3)$	-4	$-$	$-$	$-$	$-$
$(-3, 1)$	0	$+$	$-$	$-$	$+$
$(1, 3)$	2	$+$	$+$	$-$	$-$
$(3, \infty)$	4	$+$	$+$	$+$	$+$

The inequality is satisfied on the interval $(-\infty, -3) \cup (1, 3)$. Since the values $x = -3$ and $x = 1$ are included, the solution is $(-\infty, -3] \cup [1, 3)$.

119. Solving and factoring the inequality:

$$\frac{4x - 2}{3x - 1} > 2$$

$$\frac{4x - 2}{3x - 1} - 2 > 0$$

$$\frac{4x - 2 - 2(3x - 1)}{3x - 1} > 0$$

$$\frac{-2x}{3x - 1} > 0$$

Creating a sign chart:

Interval	Test value	Sign of $-2x$	Sign of $3x-1$	Sign of $\dfrac{-2x}{3x-1}$
$(-\infty, 0)$	-1	$+$	$-$	$-$
$\left(0, \dfrac{1}{3}\right)$	$\dfrac{1}{6}$	$-$	$-$	$+$
$\left(\dfrac{1}{3}, \infty\right)$	1	$-$	$+$	$-$

The inequality is satisfied on the interval $\left(0, \dfrac{1}{3}\right)$. Since the value $x = 0$ is not included, the solution is $\left(0, \dfrac{1}{3}\right)$.

120. Solving and factoring the inequality:

$$-\frac{2}{x+3} \le x$$

$$-\frac{2}{x+3} - x \le 0$$

$$\frac{-2 - x(x+3)}{x+3} \le 0$$

$$\frac{-x^2 - 3x - 2}{x+3} \le 0$$

$$\frac{-(x^2 + 3x + 2)}{x+3} \le 0$$

$$\frac{x^2 + 3x + 2}{x+3} \ge 0$$

$$\frac{(x+2)(x+1)}{x+3} \ge 0$$

Creating a sign chart:

Interval	Test value	Sign of $x+3$	Sign of $x+2$	Sign of $x+1$	Sign of $\dfrac{(x+2)(x+1)}{x+3}$
$(-\infty, -3)$	-4	$-$	$-$	$-$	$-$
$(-3, -2)$	-2.5	$+$	$-$	$-$	$+$
$(-2, -1)$	-1.5	$+$	$+$	$-$	$-$
$(-1, \infty)$	0	$+$	$+$	$+$	$+$

The inequality is satisfied on the interval $(-3, -2) \cup (-1, \infty)$. Since the values $x = -2$ and $x = -1$ are included, the solution is $(-3, -2] \cup [-1, \infty)$.

121. The volume is given by: $V = (x)(x)(x-1) = x^3 - x^2$

Solving and factoring the inequality:

$$x^3 - x^2 \ge 48$$

$$x^3 - x^2 - 48 \ge 0$$

$$(x-4)(x^2 + 3x + 12) \ge 0 \quad \longleftarrow \quad \text{Using rational roots theorem and synthetic division.}$$

Creating a sign chart (note that $x^2 + 3x + 12 \ne 0$):

Interval	Test value	Sign of $x-4$	Sign of $x^2 + 3x + 12$	Sign of $(x-4)(x^2 + 3x + 12)$
$(-\infty, 4)$	0	$-$	$+$	$-$
$(4, \infty)$	5	$+$	$+$	$+$

The inequality is satisfied on the interval $(4, \infty)$. Since the endpoint is included, the solution is $[4, \infty)$.

Lengths of the base greater than or equal to 4 inches will produce a volume greater than or equal to 48 cubic inches.

Chapter 3 Test

1. Completing the square: $f(x) = 2x^2 - 4x + 1 = 2(x^2 - 2x) + 1 = 2(x^2 - 2x + 1 - 1) + 1 = 2(x^2 - 2x + 1) - 2 + 1 = 2(x-1)^2 - 1$

    The vertex is $(1, -1)$, which is a minimum point.

2. The vertex is $(1, 2)$, the axis of symmetry is $x = 1$, and the range is $(-\infty, 2]$. Sketching the graph:

    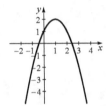

3. Completing the square: $f(x) = x^2 + 4x + 2 = (x^2 + 4x) + 2 = (x^2 + 4x + 4 - 4) + 2 = (x^2 + 4x + 4) - 4 + 2 = (x+2)^2 - 2$

    The vertex is $(-2, -2)$, the axis of symmetry is $x = -2$, and the range is $[-2, \infty)$. Sketching the graph:

    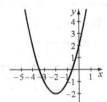

4. Completing the square:

    $$f(x) = -2x^2 + 8x - 4 = -2(x^2 - 4x) - 4 = -2(x^2 - 4x + 4 - 4) - 4 = -2(x^2 - 4x + 4) + 8 - 4 = -2(x-2)^2 + 4$$

    The vertex is $(2, 4)$, the axis of symmetry is $x = 2$, and the range is $(-\infty, 4]$. Sketching the graph:

5. First find the vertex:

    $$h = \frac{-b}{2a} = \frac{-6}{2(3)} = -1$$

    $$k = f(-1) = 3(-1)^2 + 6(-1) = -3$$

    Finding the x-intercepts by setting $f(x) = 0$:

    $$3x^2 + 6x = 0$$
    $$3x(x+2) = 0$$
    $$x = -2, 0$$

The vertex is $(-1,-3)$, the axis of symmetry is $x=-1$, the x-intercepts are $(-2,0)$ and $(0,0)$, and the y-intercept is $(0,0)$. The function is increasing on $(-1,\infty)$ and decreasing on $(-\infty,-1)$. Sketching the graph:

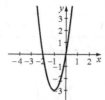

6. The degree is 5, the coefficients are $3, 4, -1, 7$, and the leading coefficient is 3.

7. $p(x) = -8x^4 + 3x - 1$ has leading term $-8x^4$ (n even, $a_n < 0$). Thus $p(x) \to -\infty$ as $x \to -\infty$ and $p(x) \to -\infty$ as $x \to \infty$.

8. Factoring the function: $p(x) = -2x^2(x^2 - 9) = -2x^2(x+3)(x-3)$

   The zero $x = 0$ has multiplicity 2; the graph touches the x-axis at $(0,0)$.

   The zero $x = -3$ has multiplicity 1; the graph passes through the x-axis at $(-3,0)$.

   The zero $x = 3$ has multiplicity 1; the graph passes through the x-axis at $(3,0)$.

9. **a.** Given the function: $f(x) = -2x(x-2)(x+1)$

   Evaluating the function: $f(0) = -2(0)(0-2)(0+1) = 0$

   The y-intercept is $(0,0)$. The x-intercepts are $(0,0)$, $(-1,0)$, and $(2,0)$.

   b. The zero at $x = 0$ has multiplicity 1, the zero at $x = -1$ has multiplicity 1, and the zero at $x = 2$ has multiplicity 1.

   c. $f(x)$ behaves like $y = -2x^3$ so $f(x) \to \infty$ as $x \to -\infty$ and $f(x) \to -\infty$ as $x \to \infty$

   d. Creating a sign chart:

Interval	Test Value x	Function Value $f(x)$	Sign of $f(x)$
$(-\infty,-1)$	-2	16	$+$
$(-1,0)$	-0.5	-1.25	$-$
$(0,2)$	1	4	$+$
$(2,\infty)$	3	-108	$-$

   Thus f is positive on $(-\infty,-1) \cup (0,2)$ and f is negative on $(-1,0) \cup (2,\infty)$. Sketching the graph:

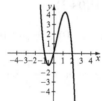

10. **a.** Given the function: $f(x) = (x+1)(x-2)^2$

   Evaluating the function: $f(0) = (0+1)(0-2)^2 = 4$

   The y-intercept is $(0,4)$. The x-intercepts are $(-1,0)$ and $(2,0)$.

   b. The zero at $x = -1$ has multiplicity 1 and the zero at $x = 2$ has multiplicity 2.

   c. $f(x)$ behaves like $y = x^3$ so $f(x) \to -\infty$ as $x \to -\infty$ and $f(x) \to \infty$ as $x \to \infty$

d. Creating a sign chart:

Interval	Test Value x	Function Value $f(x)$	Sign of $f(x)$
$(-\infty,-1)$	-2	-16	$-$
$(-1,2)$	0	4	$+$
$(2,\infty)$	3	4	$+$

Thus f is positive on $(-1,2)\cup(2,\infty)$ and f is negative on $(-\infty,-1)$. Sketching the graph:

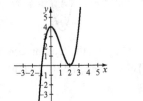

11. a. Factoring the function: $f(x)=-3x^3-6x^2-3x=-3x\left(x^2+2x+1\right)=-3x(x+1)^2$

Evaluating the function: $f(0)=-3(0)(0+1)^2=0$

The y-intercept is $(0,0)$. The x-intercepts are $(-1,0)$ and $(0,0)$.

b. The zero at $x=0$ has multiplicity 1 and the zero at $x=-1$ has multiplicity 2.

c. $f(x)$ behaves like $y=-3x^3$ so $f(x)\to\infty$ as $x\to-\infty$ and $f(x)\to-\infty$ as $x\to\infty$

d. Creating a sign chart:

Interval	Test Value x	Function Value $f(x)$	Sign of $f(x)$
$(-\infty,-1)$	-2	6	$+$
$(-1,0)$	-0.5	0.375	$+$
$(0,\infty)$	1	-12	$-$

Thus f is positive on $(-\infty,-1)\cup(-1,0)$ and f is negative on $(0,\infty)$. Sketching the graph:

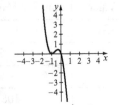

12. a. Factoring the function: $f(x)=2x^4+5x^3+2x^2=x^2\left(2x^2+5x+2\right)=x^2(2x+1)(x+2)$

Evaluating the function: $f(0)=(0)^2(0+1)(0+2)=0$

The y-intercept is $(0,0)$. The x-intercepts are $(0,0)$, $(-2,0)$ and $\left(-\dfrac{1}{2},0\right)$.

b. The zero at $x=0$ has multiplicity 2, the zero at $x=-\dfrac{1}{2}$ has multiplicity 1, and the zero at $x=-2$ has multiplicity 1.

c. $f(x)$ behaves like $y=2x^4$ so $f(x)\to\infty$ as $x\to-\infty$ and $f(x)\to\infty$ as $x\to\infty$

Interval	Test Value x	Function Value $f(x)$	Sign of $f(x)$
$(-\infty,-2)$	-3	45	$+$
$\left(-2,-\dfrac{1}{2}\right)$	-1	-1	$-$
$\left(-\dfrac{1}{2},0\right)$	-0.25	0.055	$+$
$(0,\infty)$	1	0	$+$

d. Creating a sign chart:

Thus f is positive on $(-\infty,-2)\cup\left(-\dfrac{1}{2},0\right)\cup(0,\infty)$ and f is negative on $\left(-2,-\dfrac{1}{2}\right)$. Sketching the graph:

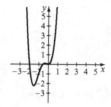

13. Using long division:

$$
\begin{array}{r}
3x^2-9 \\
x^2+1\overline{\smash{)}3x^4+0x^3-6x^2+x-1} \\
\underline{3x^4\qquad\ +3x^2} \\
-9x^2+x-1 \\
\underline{-9x^2\qquad-9} \\
x+8
\end{array}
$$

Therefore: $\dfrac{3x^4-6x^2+x-1}{x^2+1}=3x^2-9+\dfrac{x+8}{x^2+1}$

Written in the desired form: $3x^4-6x^2+x-1=\left(x^2+1\right)\left(3x^2-9\right)+(x+8)$

14. Using synthetic division:

$$
\begin{array}{r|rrrrr}
1 & -2 & 1 & 0 & -4 & 0 & 3 \\
& & -2 & -1 & -1 & -5 & -5 \\
\hline
& -2 & -1 & -1 & -5 & -5 & -2
\end{array}
$$

Therefore: $\dfrac{-2x^5+x^4-4x^2+3}{x-1}=-2x^4-x^3-x^2-5x-5+\dfrac{-2}{x-1}$

Written in the desired form: $-2x^5+x^4-4x^2+3=(x-1)\left(-2x^4-x^3-x^2-5x-5\right)-2$

15. Evaluating the function: $p(2)=(2)^4+2-2(2)^3-2=0$

The remainder is 0, so $x-2$ is a factor of $p(x)$ by the factor theorem.

16. First write $p(x)=x^4-3x^3-x+3$.

Using synthetic division:

$$
\begin{array}{r|rrrrr}
3 & 1 & -3 & 0 & -1 & 3 \\
& & 3 & 0 & 0 & -3 \\
\hline
& 1 & 0 & 0 & -1 & 0
\end{array}
$$

Therefore: $p(x)=(x-3)\left(x^3-1\right)=(x-3)(x-1)\left(x^2+x+1\right)$

17. Factoring: $p(x) = x^3 - 3x - 2x^2 + 6 = x(x^2 - 3) - 2(x^2 - 3) = (x^2 - 3)(x - 2)$

   The real zeros are: $x = 2, \pm\sqrt{3}$

18. The possible rational roots are: $\dfrac{\text{Factors of 2}}{\text{Factors of 2}} = \dfrac{\pm 1, \pm 2}{\pm 1, \pm 2} = \pm 1, \pm 2, \pm\dfrac{1}{2}$

   Using synthetic division:

   ```
   -1| 2    9    14    9    2
           -2   -7   -7   -2
      ─────────────────────────
       2    7    7    2    0
   ```

   Factoring the polynomial: $p(x) = (x+1)(2x^3 + 7x^2 + 7x + 2)$

   Using synthetic division again:

   ```
   -1| 2    7    7    2
           -2   -5   -2
      ──────────────────
       2    5    2    0
   ```

   Factoring the polynomial: $p(x) = (x+1)(x+1)(2x^2 + 5x + 2) = (x+1)^2(2x+1)(x+2)$

   The real zeros are: $x = -1, -\dfrac{1}{2}, -2$

19. Creating a function:
$$2x^3 + 5x^2 = 2 - x$$
$$2x^3 + 5x^2 + x - 2 = 0$$
$$p(x) = 2x^3 + 5x^2 + x - 2$$

   The possible rational roots are: $\pm 1, \pm 2, \pm\dfrac{1}{2}$

   Using synthetic division:

   ```
   -1| 2    5    1    -2
           -2   -3    2
      ──────────────────
       2    3   -2    0
   ```

   Factoring the polynomial: $p(x) = (x+1)(2x^2 + 3x - 2) = (x+1)(2x-1)(x+2)$

   The real solutions are: $x = -1, \dfrac{1}{2}, -2$

20. Creating a function:
$$x^4 - 4x^3 + 2x^2 + 4x = 3$$
$$x^4 - 4x^3 + 2x^2 + 4x - 3 = 0$$
$$p(x) = x^4 - 4x^3 + 2x^2 + 4x - 3$$

   The possible rational roots are: $\pm 1, \pm 3$

   Using synthetic division:

   ```
   1| 1   -4    2    4   -3
           1   -3   -1    3
      ────────────────────────
       1   -3   -1    3    0
   ```

Factoring the polynomial:
$$p(x) = (x-1)(x^3 - 3x^2 - x + 3)$$
$$= (x-1)(x^2(x-3) - 1(x-3))$$
$$= (x-1)(x-3)(x^2 - 1)$$
$$= (x-1)(x-3)(x+1)(x-1)$$
$$= (x-1)^2(x-3)(x+1)$$
The real solutions are: $x = 1, 3, -1$

21. For $p(x) = -x^5 + 4x^4 - 3x^2 + x + 8$, there are 3 sign variations.

For $p(-x) = -(-x)^5 + 4(-x)^4 - 3(-x)^2 + (-x) + 8 = x^5 + 4x^4 - 3x^2 - x + 8$, there are 2 sign variations.
Positive zeros: 3 or 1; negative zeros: 2 or 0

22. Writing the complex number: $4 - \sqrt{-2} = 4 - i\sqrt{2}$. The real part is 4 and the imaginary part is $-\sqrt{2}$.

23. Performing the operations: $(5 + 4i) - (6 + 2i) = (5 - 6) + (4i - 2i) = -1 + 2i$

24. Performing the operations: $(3 - 4i)(-2 + i) = -6 + 3i + 8i - 4i^2 = -6 + 11i - 4(-1) = -2 + 11i$

25. Performing the operations: $\dfrac{2+i}{3-2i} = \dfrac{2+i}{3-2i} \cdot \dfrac{3+2i}{3+2i} = \dfrac{6+4i+3i+2i^2}{9+6i-6i-4i^2} = \dfrac{4+7i}{13} = \dfrac{4}{13} + \dfrac{7}{13}i$

26. Using the quadratic formula: $x = \dfrac{-2 \pm \sqrt{(2)^2 - 4(1)(3)}}{2(1)} = \dfrac{-2 \pm \sqrt{-8}}{2} = \dfrac{-2 \pm 2i\sqrt{2}}{2} = -1 \pm i\sqrt{2}$

The zeros are $x = -1 + i\sqrt{2}$ and $x = -1 - i\sqrt{2}$.

27. Using the quadratic formula: $x = \dfrac{-1 \pm \sqrt{(1)^2 - 4(-2)(-1)}}{2(-2)} = \dfrac{-1 \pm \sqrt{-7}}{-4} = \dfrac{1 \pm i\sqrt{7}}{4} = \dfrac{1}{4} \pm \dfrac{\sqrt{7}}{4}i$

The zeros are $x = \dfrac{1}{4} + \dfrac{\sqrt{7}}{4}i$ and $x = \dfrac{1}{4} - \dfrac{\sqrt{7}}{4}i$.

28. Solving the equation:
$$x^5 - 16x = 0$$
$$x(x^4 - 16) = 0$$
$$x(x^2 - 4)(x^2 + 4) = 0$$
$$x(x+2)(x-2)(x^2 + 4) = 0$$
$$x = 0, \pm 2, \pm 2i$$
The zeros are $x = 0, \pm 2, \pm 2i$, so $p(x) = x(x+2)(x-2)(x+2i)(x-2i)$.

29. The possible rational roots are: $\pm 1, \pm 2, \pm 3, \pm 4, \pm 6, \pm 8, \pm 12, \pm 24$
Using synthetic division:

```
-2 | 1   -1   -2    -4   -24
   |     -2    6    -8    24
   ----------------------------
     1   -3    4   -12     0
```

Factoring the polynomial:
$$p(x) = (x+2)(x^3 - 3x^2 + 4x - 12) = (x+2)(x^2(x-3) + 4(x-3)) = (x+2)(x-3)(x^2 + 4)$$
The zeros are $x = -2, 3, \pm 2i$, so $p(x) = (x+2)(x-3)(x+2i)(x-2i)$.

30. The vertical asymptote is $x = -3$, the horizontal asymptote is $y = 0$, there is no x-intercept, and the y-intercept is $(0,-1)$. Sketching the graph:

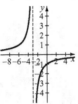

31. The vertical asymptote is $x = 2$, the horizontal asymptote is $y = -2$, the x-intercept is $(0,0)$, and the y-intercept is $(0,0)$. Sketching the graph:

32. Factoring the denominator: $f(x) = \dfrac{2}{2x^2 - 3x - 2} = \dfrac{2}{(2x+1)(x-2)}$

The vertical asymptotes are $x = 2$ and $x = -\dfrac{1}{2}$, the horizontal asymptote is $y = 0$, there is no x-intercept, and the y-intercept is $(0,-1)$. Sketching the graph:

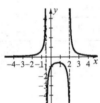

33. Factoring the inequality:
$$3x^2 - 4x - 15 < 0$$
$$(3x+5)(x-3) < 0$$
Creating a sign chart:

Interval	Test value	Sign of $3x+5$	Sign of $x-3$	Sign of $(3x+5)(x-3)$
$\left(-\infty, -\dfrac{5}{3}\right)$	-2	$-$	$-$	$+$
$\left(-\dfrac{5}{3}, 3\right)$	0	$+$	$-$	$-$
$(3, \infty)$	4	$+$	$+$	$+$

The inequality is satisfied on the interval $\left(-\dfrac{5}{3}, 3\right)$. Since the endpoints are not included, the solution is $\left(-\dfrac{5}{3}, 3\right)$.

34. Factoring the inequality:
$$\left(x^2-4\right)(x+3)\le 0$$
$$(x+2)(x-2)(x+3)\le 0$$
Creating a sign chart:

Interval	Test value	Sign of $x+3$	Sign of $x+2$	Sign of $x-2$	Sign of $(x+2)(x-2)(x+3)$
$(-\infty,-3)$	-4	$-$	$-$	$-$	$-$
$(-3,-2)$	-2.5	$+$	$-$	$-$	$+$
$(-2,2)$	0	$+$	$+$	$-$	$-$
$(2,\infty)$	3	$+$	$+$	$+$	$+$

The inequality is satisfied on the interval $(-\infty,-3)\cup(-2,2)$. Since the endpoints are included, the solution is $(-\infty,-3]\cup[-2,2]$.

35. Factoring the inequality:
$$\frac{x^2-4x-5}{x+2}>0$$
$$\frac{(x+1)(x-5)}{x+2}>0$$
Creating a sign chart:

Interval	Test value	Sign of $x+2$	Sign of $x+1$	Sign of $x-5$	Sign of $\dfrac{(x+1)(x-5)}{x+2}$
$(-\infty,-2)$	-3	$-$	$-$	$-$	$-$
$(-2,-1)$	-1.5	$+$	$-$	$-$	$+$
$(-1,5)$	0	$+$	$+$	$-$	$-$
$(5,\infty)$	6	$+$	$+$	$+$	$+$

The inequality is satisfied on the interval $(-2,-1)\cup(5,\infty)$. Since the endpoints are not included, the solution is $(-2,-1)\cup(5,\infty)$.

36. Solving and factoring the inequality:
$$\frac{4}{3x+1}\ge 2$$
$$\frac{4}{3x+1}-2\ge 0$$
$$\frac{4-2(3x+1)}{3x+1}\ge 0$$
$$\frac{2-6x}{3x+1}\ge 0$$
$$\frac{2(1-3x)}{3x+1}\ge 0$$

Creating a sign chart:

Interval	Test value	Sign of $1-3x$	Sign of $3x+1$	Sign of $\dfrac{2(1-3x)}{3x+1}$
$\left(-\infty, -\dfrac{1}{3}\right)$	-1	$+$	$-$	$-$
$\left(-\dfrac{1}{3}, \dfrac{1}{3}\right)$	0	$+$	$+$	$+$
$\left(\dfrac{1}{3}, \infty\right)$	1	$-$	$+$	$-$

The inequality is satisfied on the interval $\left(-\dfrac{1}{3}, \dfrac{1}{3}\right)$. Since the value $x = \dfrac{1}{3}$ is included, the solution is $\left(-\dfrac{1}{3}, \dfrac{1}{3}\right]$.

37. Given that $r = h + 2$, the volume is given by: $V = \dfrac{1}{3}\pi r^2 h = \dfrac{1}{3}\pi(h+2)^2 h = \dfrac{1}{3}\pi h(h+2)^2$

This results in the equation:

$$\frac{1}{3}\pi h(h+2)^2 = 48\pi$$
$$h(h+2)^2 = 144$$
$$h(h^2 + 4h + 4) = 144$$
$$h^3 + 4h^2 + 4h = 144$$
$$h^3 + 4h^2 + 4h - 144 = 0$$
$$(h-4)(h^2 + 8h + 36) \geq 0 \quad \longleftarrow \quad \text{Using rational roots theorem and synthetic division.}$$

Note that $h^2 + 8h + 36 \neq 0$, so $h = 4$. The height of the cone is 4 inches.

38. a. Let x represent the number of miles driven per day. The average cost function is given by:

$$C(x) = \frac{50 + 0.25x}{x} = 0.25 + \frac{50}{x}$$

b. Evaluating when $x = 250$: $C(250) = 0.25 + \dfrac{50}{250} = 0.45$

The average cost of driving 250 miles per day is $0.45 per mile.

Chapter 4
Exponential and Logarithmic Functions

4.1 Inverse Functions

1. This statement is true.

3. Finding the composition: $(f \circ g)(x) = f[g(x)] = f(x-1) = (x-1)^2 = x^2 - 2x + 1$

5. Simplifying: $2\left(\dfrac{1}{2}x+1\right) - 2 = x + 2 - 2 = x$

7. **a.** Evaluating: $f(3) = (3)^3 = 27$ **b.** Evaluating: $f^{-1}(3) = \sqrt[3]{3}$

     c. Evaluating: $(f(3))(f^{-1}(3)) = 27\sqrt[3]{3}$

     d. Evaluating: $(f \circ f^{-1})(3) = f[f^{-1}(3)] = f(\sqrt[3]{3}) = (\sqrt[3]{3})^3 = 3$

9. Verifying that $(f \circ g)(x) = x$ and $(g \circ f)(x) = x$:

$$f(g(x)) = f(x+2) = (x+2) - 2 = x + 2 - 2 = x \qquad g(f(x)) = g(x-2) = (x-2) + 2 = x - 2 + 2 = x$$

11. Verifying that $(f \circ g)(x) = x$ and $(g \circ f)(x) = x$:

$$f(g(x)) = f\left(\dfrac{1}{6}x\right) = 6\left(\dfrac{1}{6}x\right) = x \qquad g(f(x)) = g(6x) = \dfrac{1}{6}(6x) = x$$

13. Verifying that $(f \circ g)(x) = x$ and $(g \circ f)(x) = x$:

$$f(g(x)) = f\left(-\dfrac{1}{3}x + \dfrac{8}{3}\right) = -3\left(-\dfrac{1}{3}x + \dfrac{8}{3}\right) + 8 = x - 8 + 8 = x$$

$$g(f(x)) = g(-3x+8) = -\dfrac{1}{3}(-3x+8) + \dfrac{8}{3} = x - \dfrac{8}{3} + \dfrac{8}{3} = x$$

15. Verifying that $(f \circ g)(x) = x$ and $(g \circ f)(x) = x$:

$$f(g(x)) = f(\sqrt[3]{x+2}) = (\sqrt[3]{x+2})^3 - 2 = x + 2 - 2 = x \qquad g(f(x)) = g(x^3 - 2) = \sqrt[3]{(x^3-2)+2} = \sqrt[3]{x^3} = x$$

17. Verifying that $(f \circ g)(x) = x$ and $(g \circ f)(x) = x$:

$$f(g(x)) = f\left(\dfrac{1}{x}\right) = \dfrac{1}{(1/x)} = x \qquad g(f(x)) = g\left(\dfrac{1}{x}\right) = \dfrac{1}{(1/x)} = x$$

19. The function is one-to-one because there are no values of a and b in the chart such that $f(a) = f(b)$, where $a \neq b$.

21. The function is not one-to-one because there are values of a and b in the chart such that $f(a) = f(b)$, where $a \neq b$. Here, $f(0) = f(2) = 9$.

23. The function is not one-to-one, as it fails the horizontal line test.
25. The function is one-to-one, as it passes the horizontal line test.
27. The function is not one-to-one, as it fails the horizontal line test.

29. Testing for one-to-one using the definition:

$$f(a) = f(b)$$
$$-3a + 2 = -3b + 2$$
$$-3a = -3b$$
$$a = b$$

The function is one-to-one.

31. Testing for one-to-one using the definition:

$$f(a) = f(b)$$
$$2a^2 - 3 = 2b^2 - 3$$
$$2a^2 = 2b^2$$
$$a^2 = b^2$$
$$a = \pm b$$

The function is not one-to-one. For example: $f(3) = f(-3) = 15$

33. Testing for one-to-one using the definition:

$$f(a) = f(b)$$
$$-2a^3 + 4 = -2b^3 + 4$$
$$-2a^3 = -2b^3$$
$$a^3 = b^3$$
$$a = b$$

The function is one-to-one.

35. Finding the inverse:

$$f(x) = -\frac{2}{3}x$$
$$y = -\frac{2}{3}x$$
$$x = -\frac{2}{3}y$$
$$-\frac{3}{2}x = y$$
$$f^{-1}(x) = -\frac{3}{2}x$$

Sketching the two functions on the same axes:

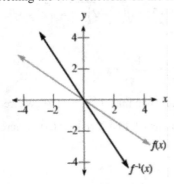

37. Finding the inverse:

$$f(x) = -4x + \frac{1}{5}$$
$$y = -4x + \frac{1}{5}$$
$$x = -4y + \frac{1}{5}$$
$$5x = -20y + 1$$
$$5x - 1 = -20y$$
$$\frac{5x - 1}{-20} = y$$
$$f^{-1}(x) = -\frac{1}{4}x + \frac{1}{20}$$

Sketching the two functions on the same axes:

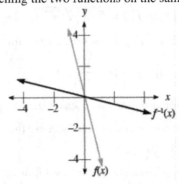

39. Finding the inverse:

$$f(x) = x^3 - 6$$
$$y = x^3 - 6$$
$$x = y^3 - 6$$
$$x + 6 = y^3$$
$$\sqrt[3]{x+6} = y$$
$$f^{-1}(x) = \sqrt[3]{x+6}$$

Sketching the two functions on the same axes:

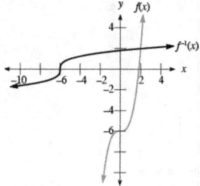

41. Finding the inverse:

$$g(x) = -x^2 + 8, \ x \geq 0$$
$$y = -x^2 + 8$$
$$x = -y^2 + 8, \ y \geq 0$$
$$x - 8 = -y^2$$
$$8 - x = y^2$$
$$\sqrt{8-x} = y, \text{ since } y \geq 0$$
$$g^{-1}(x) = \sqrt{8-x}$$

Sketching the two functions on the same axes:

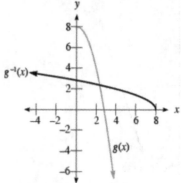

43. Finding the inverse:

$$f(x) = -2x^3 + 7$$
$$y = -2x^3 + 7$$
$$x = -2y^3 + 7$$
$$x - 7 = -2y^3$$
$$\frac{x-7}{-2} = y^3$$
$$\sqrt[3]{\frac{7-x}{2}} = y$$
$$f^{-1}(x) = \sqrt[3]{\frac{7-x}{2}}$$

Sketching the two functions on the same axes:

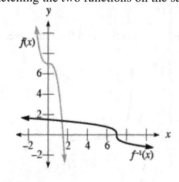

45. Finding the inverse:

$$f(x) = -4x^5 + 9$$
$$y = -4x^5 + 9$$
$$x = -4y^5 + 9$$
$$x - 9 = -4y^5$$
$$\frac{x-9}{-4} = y^5$$
$$\sqrt[5]{\frac{9-x}{4}} = y$$
$$f^{-1}(x) = \sqrt[5]{\frac{9-x}{4}}$$

Sketching the two functions on the same axes:

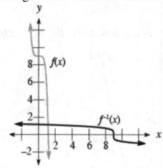

47. Finding the inverse:

$$f(x) = \frac{1}{3}x$$

$$y = \frac{1}{3}x$$

$$x = \frac{1}{3}y$$

$$3x = y$$

$$f^{-1}(x) = 3x$$

Sketching the two functions on the same axes:

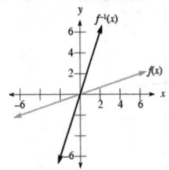

49. Finding the inverse:

$$g(x) = (x-1)^2, \ x \geq 1$$

$$y = (x-1)^2$$

$$x = (y-1)^2, \ y \geq 1$$

$$\sqrt{x} = y - 1, \text{ since } y \geq 1$$

$$1 + \sqrt{x} = y$$

$$g^{-1}(x) = 1 + \sqrt{x}$$

Sketching the two functions on the same axes:

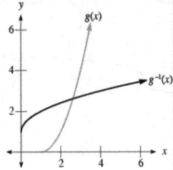

51. Finding the inverse:

$$f(x) = \sqrt{x+3}, \ x \geq -3 \ (y \geq 0)$$

$$y = \sqrt{x+3}$$

$$x = \sqrt{y+3}, \ y \geq -3 \ (x \geq 0)$$

$$x^2 = y + 3$$

$$x^2 - 3 = y$$

$$f^{-1}(x) = x^2 - 3, x \geq 0$$

Sketching the two functions on the same axes:

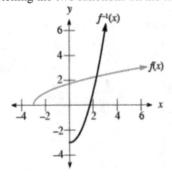

53. Finding the inverse:

$$f(x) = \frac{2x}{x-1}$$

$$y = \frac{2x}{x-1}$$

$$x = \frac{2y}{y-1}$$

$$x(y-1) = 2y$$

$$xy - x = 2y$$

$$xy - 2y = x$$

$$y(x-2) = x$$

$$y = \frac{x}{x-2}$$

$$f^{-1}(x) = \frac{x}{x-2}$$

Sketching the two functions on the same axes:

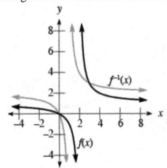

55. Finding the inverse:

$$f(x) = 2x$$
$$y = 2x$$
$$x = 2y$$
$$\frac{x}{2} = y$$
$$f^{-1}(x) = \frac{1}{2}x$$

Sketching the two functions on the same axes:

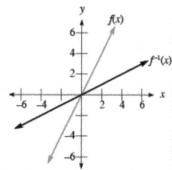

57. Finding the inverse:

$$f(x) = -3x + 3$$
$$y = -3x + 3$$
$$x = -3y + 3$$
$$x - 3 = -3y$$
$$\frac{x-3}{-3} = y$$
$$f^{-1}(x) = -\frac{1}{3}x + 1$$

Sketching the two functions on the same axes:

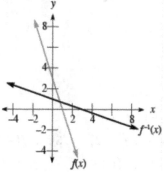

59. Finding the inverse:

$$f(x) = 8x^3$$
$$y = 8x^3$$
$$x = 8y^3$$
$$\frac{x}{8} = y^3$$
$$\sqrt[3]{\frac{x}{8}} = y$$
$$f^{-1}(x) = \frac{\sqrt[3]{x}}{2} = \frac{1}{2}\sqrt[3]{x}$$

Sketching the two functions on the same axes:

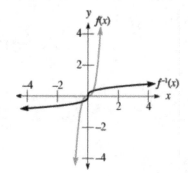

61. Finding the inverse:

$$f(x) = x^2 + 2, \ x \geq 0$$
$$y = x^2 + 2$$
$$x = y^2 + 2, \ y \geq 0$$
$$x - 2 = y^2$$
$$\sqrt{x-2} = y, \text{ since } y \geq 0$$
$$f^{-1}(x) = \sqrt{x-2}$$

Sketching the two functions on the same axes:

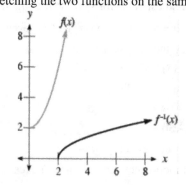

63. The domain of f is $[-3, 3]$, and the range of f is $[0, 4]$. The domain of f^{-1} is $[0, 4]$, and the range of f^{-1} is $[-3, 3]$. Sketching the graphs:

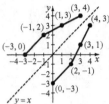

65. The domain of f is $[-3, 2]$, and the range of f is $[-5, 5]$. The domain of f^{-1} is $[-5, 5]$, and the range of f^{-1} is $[-3, 2]$. Sketching the graphs:

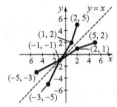

67. Since $f(-2) = 1$, $f^{-1}(1) = -2$.

69. Since $f(2) = -2$, $f^{-1}(-2) = 2$. Since $f(-1) = 2$, $f^{-1}(f^{-1}(-2)) = f^{-1}(2) = -1$.

71. Since $f(0) = 1$, $f^{-1}(1) = 0$.

73. Since $f(-2) = -3$, $f^{-1}(-3) = -2$. Since $f(-1.5) = -2$, $f^{-1}(f^{-1}(-3)) = f^{-1}(-2) = -1.5$.

75. The function is $f(x) = 4x$, where x is the number of gallons and $f(x)$ is the number of quarts in x gallons. The inverse, $f^{-1}(x) = \dfrac{1}{4}x$, gives the number of gallons, where x is the number of quarts.

77. Solving for q:
$$p = 100 - 0.1q$$
$$p - 100 = -0.1q$$
$$\frac{p - 100}{-0.1} = q$$
$$q = 1000 - 10p$$

79. **a.** The smallest value for s is 2 so the smallest value for $f(s)$ is $2 + 30 = 32$. Similarly the largest value for $f(s)$ is $24 + 30 = 54$. Thus the range of f is even integers in the interval $[32, 54]$.

  b. Finding the inverse:
$$f(s) = s + 30$$
$$y = s + 30$$
$$s = y + 30$$
$$s - 30 = y$$
$$f^{-1}(s) = s - 30$$
This function converts a woman's dress size in France to American size.

81.   **a.**   Since $f(-2)=1$, the value is $x=-2$.

     b.   Since 2 is the input of the inverse function g, it is the output of the function f. Looking at $y=2$ on the graph of f we see that it corresponds to the input $x=1$. Thus $g(2)=1$.

     c.   Sketching the graph:

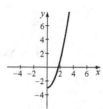

83.   No. If f is symmetric with respect to the y-axis, then $f(a)=f(-a)$. This statement does not meet the criteria for a one-to-one function; in this case, if $f(a)=f(b)$, then $a \neq b$.

85.   The simplest function that is its own inverse is $f(x)=x$. Another example is $f(x)=\dfrac{1}{x}$.

4.2 Exponential Functions

1.   Evaluating the expression: $4^3 = 64$

3.   Evaluating the expression: $3^{-2} = \dfrac{1}{3^2} = \dfrac{1}{9}$

5.   Evaluating the expression: $4(2^3) = 4(8) = 32$

7.   Evaluating the expression: $2.1^{1/3} \approx 1.2806$

9.   Evaluating the expression: $4^{1.6} \approx 9.1896$

11.   Evaluating the expression: $3^{\sqrt{2}} \approx 4.7288$

13.   Evaluating the expression: $e^3 \approx 20.0855$

15.   Evaluating the expression: $e^{-2.5} \approx 0.0821$

17.   **a.**   Evaluating the functions: $f(3) = 2^3 = 8$, $g(3) = 3^2 = 9$

     b.   Evaluating the functions: $f(-2) = 2^{-2} = \dfrac{1}{2^2} = \dfrac{1}{4}$, $g(-2) = (-2)^2 = 4$

     c. $f(x) = 2^x$ has a horizontal asymptote.

     d. $g(x) = x^2$ has range $[0, \infty)$.

19.   Sketching the graph:

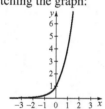

21.   Sketching the graph:

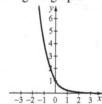

23.   Sketching the graph:

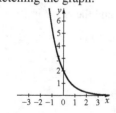

25.   Sketching the graph:

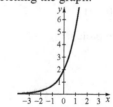

27. Sketching the graph:

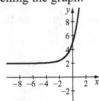

29. Sketching the graph:

31. Sketching the graph:

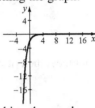

33. Sketching the graph:

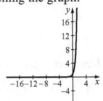

35. Sketching the graph:

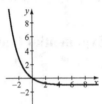

37. **a.** The y-intercept is $(0,-1)$.

c. The horizontal asymptote is $y=0$.

b. The domain is $(-\infty,\infty)$, and the range is $(-\infty,0)$.

d. $f(x)\to 0$ as $x\to-\infty$ and $f(x)\to-\infty$ as $x\to\infty$

39. **a.** The y-intercept is $(0,2)$.

c. The horizontal asymptote is $y=3$.

b. The domain is $(-\infty,\infty)$, and the range is $(-\infty,3)$.

d. $f(x)\to 3$ as $x\to-\infty$ and $f(x)\to-\infty$ as $x\to\infty$

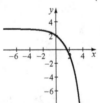

41. **a.** The y-intercept is $(0,7)$.

c. The horizontal asymptote is $y=0$.

b. The domain is $(-\infty,\infty)$, and the range is $(0,\infty)$.

d. $f(x)\to 0$ as $x\to-\infty$ and $f(x)\to\infty$ as $x\to\infty$

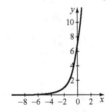

43. **a.** The y-intercept is $(0,-1)$.

    b. The domain is $(-\infty,\infty)$, and the range is $(-4,\infty)$.

    c. The horizontal asymptote is $y=-4$.

    d. $f(x)\to\infty$ as $x\to-\infty$ and $f(x)\to-4$ as $x\to\infty$

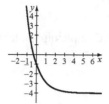

45. **a.** The y-intercept is $(0,-3)$.

    b. The domain is $(-\infty,\infty)$, and the range is $(-\infty,1)$.

    c. The horizontal asymptote is $y=1$.

    d. $f(x)\to1$ as $x\to-\infty$ and $f(x)\to-\infty$ as $x\to\infty$

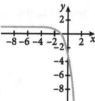

47. This graph does not represent an exponential function since it does not include a horizontal asymptote.

49. This graph does not represent an exponential function since it includes a vertical asymptote.

51. The solution is: $x\approx1.4650$

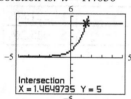

53. The solution is: $x\approx-3.3219$

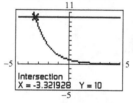

55. The solution is: $x\approx11.5525$

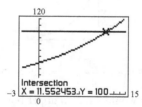

57. **a.** Sketching the graph:

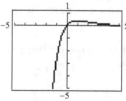

    b. The domain is $(-\infty,\infty)$, and the range is $(-\infty,0.3679]$.

    c. The x-intercept is $(0,0)$, and the y-intercept is $(0,0)$.

    d. $f(x)\to-\infty$ as $x\to-\infty$ and $f(x)\to0$ as $x\to\infty$

59. Finding the amount: $A=1{,}500\left(1+\dfrac{0.06}{1}\right)^{(1)(5)}=\$2{,}007.34$

61. Finding the amount: $A=1{,}500\left(1+\dfrac{0.06}{12}\right)^{(12)(5)}=\$2{,}023.28$

63. Finding the amount: $A=1{,}500e^{0.06(3)}=\$1{,}795.83$

65. Finding the amount: $A = 1,500e^{0.0325(5.5)} = \$1,793.58$

67. The function is given by $S(t) = 10,000(1.05)^t$. Completing the table:

Years at Work	Annual Salary
0	$10,000.00
1	$10,500.00
2	$11,025.00
3	$11,576.25
4	$12,155.06

69. The function is given by $V(t) = 20,000(0.9)^t$. Completing the table:

Years Since Purchase	Value
0	$20,000
1	$18,000
2	$16,200
3	$14,580
4	$13,122

71. The function is given by $V(t) = 18,000(0.7)^t$. Completing the table:

Years Since Purchase	Value
1	$12,600.00
2	$8,820.00
3	$6,174.00
4	$4,321.80
5	$3,025.26

Sketching the graph:

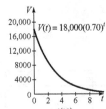

73. The value after 10 years is given by $A = 1,000\left(1 + \dfrac{0.03}{4}\right)^{4(10)} = 1,348.35$. The bond would be worth $1,348.35. If the bonds continued paying interest, their value would have no upper bound. Thus it would be financially onerous for the government to guarantee this rate over a long period of time. For instance, after 80 years, a bond purchased for $1,000 would be worth $10,924.90, nearly 11 times its purchase price.

75.
a. Evaluating when $t = 0$: $C(0) = 4.5(0)e^{-1.275(0)} = 0$

This answer makes sense because the drug has not yet been ingested.

b. Evaluating when $t = 1$: $C(1) = 4.5(1)e^{-1.275(1)} \approx 3.4181$ mg/L

c. Sketching the graph:

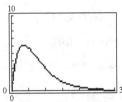

d. $C(t) \to 0$ as $t \to \infty$. This makes sense because the concentration of a drug decreases over time after reaching a maximum value.

e. The concentration reaches its maximum about 3.6 hours after the drug is administered. Sketching the graph:

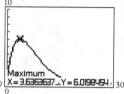

f. The concentration reaches 3 mg/L for the second time about 9.8 hours after the drug is administered. Sketching the graph:

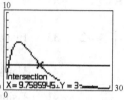

77. Because when $a = 1$ for $f(x) = Ca^x$, the function is a horizontal line.

79. **a.** Since $f(0) = C$ and the curve passes through the point $(0, 12)$, $C = 12$.

b. Based on the given points, as x increases from 0 to 2, the function is decreasing.

c. Substituting the value $f(2) = 3$:

$$12a^2 = 3;$$

$$a^2 = \frac{1}{4}$$

$$a = \frac{1}{2} \quad (\text{since } a > 0)$$

81. $f(x) = 2^x$ has no vertical asymptotes because the function is defined for every value in its domain, which has no restrictions – that is, $x \in (-\infty, \infty)$.

4.3 Logarithmic Functions

1. Writing with a rational exponent: $\sqrt{13} = 13^{1/2}$

3. Writing with a rational exponent: $\sqrt[3]{e} = e^{1/3}$

5. This statement is true.

7. This statement is false, since $f(x) = 4$ has no inverse.

9. Writing in scientific notation: $0.036 = 3.6 \times 10^{-2}$

11. Completing the table:

Logarithmic Statement	Exponential Statement
$\log_3 1 = 0$	$3^0 = 1$
$\log 10 = 1$	$10^1 = 10$
$\log_5 \frac{1}{5} = -1$	$5^{-1} = \frac{1}{5}$
$\log_a x = b, a > 0, a \neq 1$	$a^b = x$

13. Completing the table:

Exponential Statement	Logarithmic Statement
$3^4 = 81$	$\log_3 81 = 4$
$5^{1/3} = \sqrt[3]{5}$	$\log_5 \sqrt[3]{5} = \frac{1}{3}$
$6^{-1} = \frac{1}{6}$	$\log_6 \frac{1}{6} = -1$
$a^v = u, a > 0, a \neq 1$	$\log_a u = v, a > 0$

15. Since $10^4 = 10,000$, we get $\log 10,000 = 4$.

17. Since $10^{1/3} = \sqrt[3]{10}$, we get $\log \sqrt[3]{10} = \dfrac{1}{3}$.

19. Since $e^2 = e^2$, we get $\ln e^2 = 2$.

21. Since $e^{1/3} = e^{1/3}$, we get $\ln e^{1/3} = \dfrac{1}{3}$.

23. Evaluating the logarithm: $\log 10^{x+y} = x + y$

25. Evaluating the logarithm: $\log 10^k = k$

27. Evaluating the logarithm: $\log_2 \sqrt{2} = \log_2 2^{1/2} = \dfrac{1}{2}$

29. Evaluating the logarithm: $\log_3 \dfrac{1}{81} = \log_3 \dfrac{1}{3^4} = \log_3 3^{-4} = -4$

31. Evaluating the logarithm: $\log_{1/2} 4 = \log_{1/2} \left(\dfrac{1}{2}\right)^{-2} = -2$

33. Evaluating the logarithm: $\log_4 4^{x^2+1} = x^2 + 1$

35. Using a calculator: $2\log 4 \approx 1.2041$

37. Using a calculator: $\ln \sqrt{2} \approx 0.3466$

39. Using a calculator: $\log 1400 \approx 3.1461$

41. Using a calculator: $2\ln \dfrac{1}{5} \approx -3.2189$

43. Using the change of base formula and a calculator: $\log_3 1.25 = \dfrac{\ln 1.25}{\ln 3} \approx 0.2031$

45. Using the change of base formula and a calculator: $\log_5 0.5 = \dfrac{\ln 0.5}{\ln 5} \approx -0.4307$

47. Using the change of base formula and a calculator: $\log_2 12 = \dfrac{\ln 12}{\ln 2} \approx 3.5850$

49. Using the change of base formula and a calculator: $\log_7 150 = \dfrac{\ln 150}{\ln 7} \approx 2.5750$

51. Solving for x:
$$\log_2 x = 3$$
$$x = 2^3$$
$$x = 8$$

53. Solving for x:
$$\log_3 x = \dfrac{1}{3}$$
$$x = 3^{1/3}$$
$$x = \sqrt[3]{3}$$

55. Solving for x:
$$\log_x 216 = 3$$
$$x^3 = 216$$
$$x = \sqrt[3]{216} = 6$$

57. The domain is $(0, \infty)$, the vertical asymptote is $x = 0$, the x-intercept is $(1, 0)$, and there is no y-intercept.

Sketching the graph:

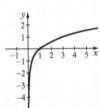

59. The domain is $(0, \infty)$, the vertical asymptote is $x = 0$, the x-intercept is $(1, 0)$, and there is no y-intercept. Sketching the graph:

61. The domain is $(0, \infty)$, the vertical asymptote is $x = 0$, and there is no y-intercept. Finding the x-intercept:

$$\log x - 3 = 0$$
$$\log x = 3$$
$$x = 10^3 = 1000$$

The x-intercept is $(1000, 0)$. Sketching the graph:

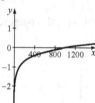

63. The domain is $(-1, \infty)$, the vertical asymptote is $x = -1$, and the y-intercept is $(0, 0)$. Finding the x-intercept:

$$\log_4 (x + 1) = 0$$
$$x + 1 = 4^0$$
$$x = 0$$

The x-intercept is $(0, 0)$. Sketching the graph:

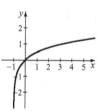

65. The domain is $(-4, \infty)$, the vertical asymptote is $x = -4$, and the y-intercept is $(0, \ln 4)$. Finding the x-intercept:

$$\ln (x + 4) = 0$$
$$x + 4 = e^0$$
$$x + 4 = 1$$
$$x = -3$$

The x-intercept is $(-3, 0)$. Sketching the graph:

67. The domain is $(1, \infty)$, the vertical asymptote is $x = 1$, and there is no y-intercept. Finding the x-intercept:

$$2\log_3(x-1) = 0$$
$$\log_3(x-1) = 0$$
$$x - 1 = 10^0$$
$$x - 1 = 1$$
$$x = 2$$

The x-intercept is $(2, 0)$. Sketching the graph:

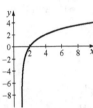

69. The domain is $(0, \infty)$, the vertical asymptote is $t = 0$, the t-intercept is $(1, 0)$, and there is no y-intercept. Sketching the graph:

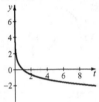

71. The domain is $(-\infty, 0) \cup (0, \infty)$, the vertical asymptote is $x = 0$, and there is no y-intercept. Finding the x-intercepts:

$$\log|x| = 0$$
$$|x| = 10^0$$
$$|x| = 1$$
$$x = \pm 1$$

The x-intercepts are $(-1, 0)$ and $(1, 0)$. Sketching the graph:

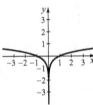

73. The value is $\log 7 \approx 0.85$. The graph corresponds to $f(x) = 10^x$, so $\log f(x) = \log 10^x = x$. In this case, when $f(x) = 7$, $x \approx 0.85$.

75. The correct graph is c.

77. The correct graph is b.

79. The value is $t = \log 7 \approx 0.8451$:

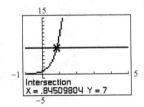

81. The value is $t = \log\left(\dfrac{20}{4}\right) = \log 5 \approx 0.6990$:

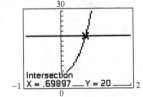

83. Solving when $I = 10{,}000I_0$: $R(I) = \log\left(\dfrac{10{,}000I_0}{I_0}\right) = \log(10{,}000) = 4$

85. Solving when $R(I) = 7.8$:

$$R(I) = \log\left(\frac{I}{I_0}\right)$$

$$7.8 = \log\left(\frac{I}{I_0}\right)$$

$$\frac{I}{I_0} = 10^{7.8} = 63{,}095{,}734.45$$

$$I = 63{,}095{,}734.45 I_0$$

87. Finding the intensity for each Richter number:

$R = 7.1$:

$$7.1 = \log\left(\frac{I}{I_0}\right)$$

$$\frac{I}{I_0} = 10^{7.1}$$

$$I = 10^{7.1} I_0$$

$R = 4.2$:

$$4.2 = \log\left(\frac{I}{I_0}\right)$$

$$\frac{I}{I_0} = 10^{4.2}$$

$$I = 10^{4.2} I_0$$

Comparing the two intensities: $\dfrac{10^{7.1} I_0}{10^{4.2} I_0} = 10^{2.9} \approx 794.33$

The ratio is approximately 794.33 to 1.

89. Finding the pH: $\text{pH} = -\log\left[H^+\right] = -\log 10^{-4} = -(-4) = 4$

91. **a.** The bubble sort has $100^2 = 10{,}000$ operations. The heap sort has $100\log 100 = 100 \cdot 2 = 200$ operations.

b. Completing the table:

n	Number of operations $\left(n^2\right)$
5	25
10	100
15	225
20	400

The corresponding increase would be 300 operations.

c. Completing the table:

n	Number of operations $\left(n \log n\right)$
5	3.49
10	10
15	17.64
20	26.02

The corresponding increase would be 16 operations.

d. The heap sort is more efficient because n^2 grows faster than $n \log n$.

e. The graph shows that n^2 grows faster than $n \log n$.

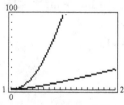

93. Because $10^2 = 100$ and $10^3 = 1000$, the value of x for which $10^x = 400$ is between 2 and 3, as is the value of $\log 400$.

95. Let $\log 1000 = x$ where $f(x) = 10^x$ and $f(x) = 1000$, so $x = 3$.

97. Let $\log 0.5 = x$ where $f(x) = 10^x$ and $f(x) = 0.5$, so $x = -0.3010$.

99. Using the point $(10, 3)$:

$$3 = a \log 10$$
$$3 = a$$

So $f(x) = 3\log x$. Sketching the graph:

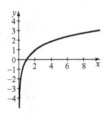

101. The graphs of the two functions are identical:

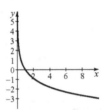

4.4 Properties of Logarithms

1. Writing using rational exponents: $\sqrt[3]{x} = x^{1/3}$

3. Writing using rational exponents: $\sqrt[4]{x^3} = x^{3/4}$

5. Using properties of logarithms: $\log 35 = \log(5 \times 7) = \log 5 + \log 7 \approx 0.6990 + 0.8451 = 1.5441$

7. Using properties of logarithms: $\log\dfrac{2}{5} = \log 2 - \log 5 \approx 0.3010 - 0.6990 = -0.3980$

9. Using properties of logarithms: $\log\sqrt{2} = \log 2^{1/2} = \dfrac{1}{2}\log 2 \approx \dfrac{1}{2}(0.3010) = 0.1505$

11. Using properties of logarithms: $\log 125 = \log 5^3 = 3\log 5 \approx 3(0.6990) = 2.097$

13. Using properties of logarithms: $\log(xy^3) = \log x + \log y^3 = \log x + 3\log y$

15. Using properties of logarithms: $\log\left(\sqrt[3]{x}\sqrt[4]{y}\right) = \log\sqrt[3]{x} + \log\sqrt[4]{y} = \log x^{1/3} + \log y^{1/4} = \dfrac{1}{3}\log x + \dfrac{1}{4}\log y$

17. Using properties of logarithms: $\log\dfrac{\sqrt[4]{x}}{y^{-1}} = \log\left(y\sqrt[4]{x}\right) = \log y + \log\sqrt[4]{x} = \log y + \log x^{1/4} = \log y + \dfrac{1}{4}\log x$

19. Using properties of logarithms: $\log\dfrac{x^2 y^5}{10} = \log x^2 y^5 - \log 10 = \log x^2 + \log y^5 - 1 = 2\log x + 5\log y - 1$

21. Using properties of logarithms: $\ln\dfrac{\sqrt[3]{x^2}}{e^2} = \ln\sqrt[3]{x^2} - \ln e^2 = \ln x^{2/3} - 2 = \dfrac{2}{3}\ln x - 2$

23. Using properties of logarithms: $\log_a\dfrac{\sqrt{x^2+y}}{a^3} = \log_a\sqrt{x^2+y} - \log_a a^3 = \log_a(x^2+y)^{1/2} - 3 = \dfrac{1}{2}\log_a(x^2+y) - 3$

25. Using properties of logarithms:

$$\log_a \sqrt{\frac{x^6}{y^3 z^5}} = \log_a \frac{\sqrt{x^6}}{\sqrt{y^3 z^5}}$$

$$= \log_a \sqrt{x^6} - \log_a \sqrt{y^3 z^5}$$

$$= \log_a x^3 - \log_a y^{3/2} z^{5/2}$$

$$= 3\log_a x - \left(\log_a y^{3/2} + \log_a z^{5/2}\right)$$

$$= 3\log_a x - \frac{3}{2}\log_a y - \frac{5}{2}\log_a z$$

27. Using properties of logarithms:

$$\log \sqrt[3]{\frac{xy^3}{z^5}} = \frac{1}{3}\log \frac{xy^3}{z^5}$$

$$= \frac{1}{3}\left(\log xy^3 - \log z^5\right)$$

$$= \frac{1}{3}\left(\log x + 3\log y - 5\log z\right)$$

$$= \frac{1}{3}\log x + \log y - \frac{5}{3}\log z$$

29. Using properties of logarithms: $\log 6.3 - \log 3 = \log \frac{6.3}{3} = \log 2.1$

31. Using properties of logarithms: $\log 3 + \log x + \log \sqrt{y} = \log 2x + \log \sqrt{y} = \log\left(3x\sqrt{y}\right)$

33. Using properties of logarithms: $\ln 4 - 1 = \ln 4 - \ln e = \ln \frac{4}{e}$

35. Using properties of logarithms: $3\log x + 2 = \log x^3 + \log 100 = \log\left(100x^3\right)$

37. Using properties of logarithms: $\frac{1}{3}\log_4 8x^9 - \log_4 x^2 = \log_4 \sqrt[3]{8x^9} - \log_4 x^2 = \log_4 2x^3 - \log_4 x^2 = \log_4 \frac{2x^3}{x^2} = \log_4\left(2x\right)$

39. Using properties of logarithms: $\ln\left(x^2 - 9\right) - \ln\left(x + 3\right) = \ln \frac{x^2 - 9}{x + 3} = \ln \frac{(x+3)(x-3)}{x+3} = \ln\left(x - 3\right)$

41. Using properties of logarithms:

$$\frac{1}{2}\left[\log\left(x^2 - 1\right) - \log\left(x + 1\right)\right] + \log x = \frac{1}{2}\log \frac{x^2 - 1}{x + 1} + \log x$$

$$= \frac{1}{2}\log \frac{(x+1)(x-1)}{x+1} + \log x$$

$$= \frac{1}{2}\log\left(x - 1\right) + \log x$$

$$= \log \sqrt{x - 1} + \log x$$

$$= \log x\sqrt{x - 1}$$

43. Using properties of logarithms:

$$\frac{3}{2}\log 16x^4 - \frac{1}{2}\log y^8 = \log\left(\sqrt{16x^4}\right)^3 - \log \sqrt{y^8} = \log\left(4x^2\right)^3 - \log y^4 = \log 64x^6 - \log y^4 = \log \frac{64x^6}{y^4}$$

45. Writing in terms of b: $\log 10k = \log 10 + \log k = 1 + b$

47. Writing in terms of b: $\log k^3 = 3\log k = 3b$

49. Writing in terms of b: $\log \frac{1}{k} = \log 1 - \log k = 0 - b = -b$

51. Simplifying: $\log 10^{\sqrt{2}} = \sqrt{2}\log 10 = \sqrt{2} \cdot 1 = \sqrt{2}$

53. Simplifying: $\ln e^{(x+2)} = (x+2)\ln e = (x+2)\cdot 1 = x + 2$

55. Simplifying: $10^{\log(3x+1)} = 3x + 1$

57. Simplifying: $e^{\ln\left(x^2+1\right)} = x^2 + 1$

59. Simplifying: $\log_a \sqrt[5]{a^2} = \log_a a^{2/5} = \frac{2}{5}\log_a a = \frac{2}{5}\cdot 1 = \frac{2}{5}$

61. Using properties of logarithms: $f(x) = \log 10x = \log 10 + \log x = 1 + g(x)$

So $f(x) = 1 + g(x)$. Sketching the graphs:

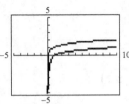

63. Using properties of logarithms: $f(x) = \ln e^2 x = \ln e^2 + \ln x = 2 + g(x)$

So $f(x) = 2 + g(x)$. Sketching the graphs:

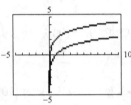

65. For solution A:

$$pH = -\log[H^+]$$
$$5 = -\log[H^+]$$
$$-5 = \log[H^+]$$
$$[H^+] = 10^{-5}$$

For solution B:

$$pH = -\log[H^+]$$
$$9 = -\log[H^+]$$
$$-9 = \log[H^+]$$
$$[H^+] = 10^{-9}$$

Finding the ratio: $\dfrac{10^{-5}}{10^{-9}} = \dfrac{10^9}{10^5} = 10^4 = 10,000$

The ratio in concentrations is 10,000 to 1.

67. Finding the pH:

$$pH = -\log[H^+] = -\log(6 \times 10^{-8}) = -(\log 6 + \log 10^{-8}) = -(\text{lo } 6 - 8\log 10) = -(\log 6 - 8) = -(0.778 - 8) = 7.2$$

69. Finding $[H^+]$:

$$pH = -\log[H^+]$$
$$3.4 = -\log[H^+]$$
$$-3.4 = \log[H^+]$$
$$[H^+] = 10^{-3.4}$$

71. Finding the relative value: $D = 10\log \dfrac{P_1}{P_2} = 10\log \dfrac{10\,W}{0.5\,W} = 10\log 20 = 13.01 \text{ dB}$

73. **a.** Sketching the graph:

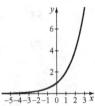

b. The domain is $(-\infty, \infty)$ and the range is $(0, \infty)$.

c.   Graphing the inverse:

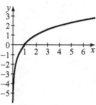

d.   The domain is $(0, \infty)$ and the range is $(-\infty, \infty)$.

75. a.   The domain of $f(x) = e^{\ln x}$ is $(0, \infty)$, and the domain of $g(x) = x$ is $(-\infty, \infty)$.

b.   The functions agree for all real values of $x > 0$. Sketching the graphs:

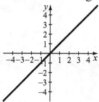

77. No, because there is no real value of y for which a^y is equal to a negative number, in this case $x = -3$.

4.5 Exponential and Logarithmic Equations

1.   This statement is true.

3.   This statement is true.

5.   Solving the equation:
$$5^x = 125$$
$$5^x = 5^3$$
$$x = 3$$

7.   Solving the equation:
$$10^x = 10,000$$
$$10^x = 10^4$$
$$x = 4$$

9.   Solving the equation:
$$4^x = \frac{1}{16}$$
$$4^x = \frac{1}{4^2}$$
$$4^x = 4^{-2}$$
$$x = -2$$

11. Solving the equation:
$$4e^x = 36$$
$$e^x = 9$$
$$\ln e^x = \ln 9$$
$$x \ln e = \ln 9$$
$$x = \ln 9 \approx 2.197$$

13. Solving the equation:
$$3(1.3^x) = 5$$
$$1.3^x = \frac{5}{3}$$
$$\ln 1.3^x = \ln \frac{5}{3}$$
$$x \ln 1.3 = \ln 5 - \ln 3$$
$$x = \frac{\ln 5 - \ln 3}{\ln 1.3} \approx 1.947$$

15. Solving the equation:
$$10^x = 2^{-x+4}$$
$$\log 10^x = \log 2^{-x+4}$$
$$x \log 10 = (-x+4) \log 2$$
$$x = -x \log 2 + 4 \log 2$$
$$x + x \log 2 = 4 \log 2$$
$$x(1 + \log 2) = \log 2^4$$
$$x = \frac{\log 16}{1 + \log 2} \approx 0.926$$

17. Solving the equation:
$$3^{-2x-1} = 2^x$$
$$\ln 3^{-2x-1} = \ln 2^x$$
$$(-2x-1)\ln 3 = x\ln 2$$
$$-2x\ln 3 - \ln 3 = x\ln 2$$
$$-2x\ln 3 - x\ln 2 = \ln 3$$
$$-x(2\ln 3 + \ln 2) = \ln 3$$
$$x = \frac{-\ln 3}{2\ln 3 + \ln 2} \approx -0.380$$

19. Solving the equation:
$$1000e^{0.04x} = 2000$$
$$e^{0.04x} = 2$$
$$\ln e^{0.04x} = \ln 2$$
$$0.04x\ln e = \ln 2$$
$$0.04x = \ln 2$$
$$x = \frac{\ln 2}{0.04} \approx 17.329$$

21. Solving the equation:
$$5e^x + 7 = 32$$
$$5e^x = 25$$
$$e^x = 5$$
$$\ln e^x = \ln 5$$
$$x\ln e = \ln 5$$
$$x = \ln 5 \approx 1.609$$

23. Solving the equation:
$$2(0.8^x) - 3 = 8$$
$$2(0.8^x) = 11$$
$$0.8^x = \frac{11}{2}$$
$$\ln 0.8^x = \ln\frac{11}{2}$$
$$x\ln 0.8 = \ln 11 - \ln 2$$
$$x = \frac{\ln 11 - \ln 2}{\ln 0.8} \approx -7.640$$

25. Solving the equation:
$$e^{x^2+1} - 2 = 3$$
$$e^{x^2+1} = 5$$
$$\ln e^{x^2+1} = \ln 5$$
$$x^2 + 1 = \ln 5$$
$$x^2 = \ln 5 - 1$$
$$x = \pm\sqrt{\ln 5 - 1} \approx \pm 0.781$$

27. The solution is $x \approx 1.302$. Sketching the graph:

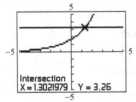

29. The solution is $x \approx 0.524$. Sketching the graph:

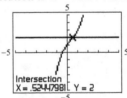

31. Solving the equation:
$$\log x = 0$$
$$10^{\log x} = 10^0$$
$$x = 1$$

33. Solving the equation:
$$\ln(x-1) = 2$$
$$e^{\ln(x-1)} = e^2$$
$$x - 1 = e^2$$
$$x = e^2 + 1 \approx 8.389$$

35. Solving the equation:
$$\log(x+3) = 1$$
$$10^{\log(x+3)} = 10^1$$
$$x + 3 = 10$$
$$x = 7$$

37. Solving the equation:
$$\log_3(x+4) = 2$$
$$3^{\log_3(x+4)} = 3^2$$
$$x + 4 = 9$$
$$x = 5$$

39. Solving the equation:

$$\log(x+1)+\log(x-1)=0$$
$$\log\left[(x+1)(x-1)\right]=0$$
$$\log\left(x^2-1\right)=0$$
$$10^{\log\left(x^2-1\right)}=10^0$$
$$x^2-1=1$$
$$x^2=2$$
$$x=\sqrt{2},\;\cancel{-\sqrt{2}}$$

41. Solving the equation:

$$\log x+\log(x+3)=1$$
$$\log\left[x(x+3)\right]=1$$
$$\log\left(x^2+3x\right)=1$$
$$10^{\log\left(x^2+3x\right)}=10^1$$
$$x^2+3x=10$$
$$x^2+3x-10=0$$
$$(x+5)(x-2)=0$$
$$\cancel{x=-5},\;x=2$$

43. Solving the equation:

$$\log_2 x=2-\log_2(x-3)$$
$$\log_2 x+\log_2(x-3)=2$$
$$\log_2\left(x^2-3x\right)=2$$
$$2^{\log_2\left(x^2-3x\right)}=2^2$$
$$x^2-3x=4$$
$$x^2-3x-4=0$$
$$(x+1)(x-4)=0$$
$$\cancel{x=-1},\;x=4$$

45. Solving the equation:

$$\ln(2x)=1+\ln(x+3)$$
$$\ln(2x)-\ln(x+3)=1$$
$$\ln\frac{2x}{x+3}=1$$
$$e^{\ln\frac{2x}{x+3}}=e^1$$
$$\frac{2x}{x+3}=e$$
$$2x=e(x+3)$$
$$2x=ex+3e$$
$$2x-ex=3e$$
$$x(2-e)=3e$$
$$x=\frac{3e}{2-e}\approx-11.353$$

There is no solution (x can't be negative).

47. Solving the equation:

$$\log(3x+1)-\log\left(x^2+1\right)=0$$
$$\log\frac{3x+1}{x^2+1}=0$$
$$10^{\log\frac{3x+1}{x^2+1}}=10^0$$
$$\frac{3x+1}{x^2+1}=1$$
$$3x+1=x^2+1$$
$$0=x^2-3x$$
$$0=x(x-3)$$
$$x=0,\;x=3$$

49. Solving the equation:
$$\log(2x+5)+\log(x+1)=1$$
$$\log[(2x+5)(x+1)]=1$$
$$\log(2x^2+7x+5)=1$$
$$10^{\log(2x^2+7x+5)}=10^1$$
$$2x^2+7x+5=10$$
$$2x^2+7x-5=0$$
$$x=\frac{-7\pm\sqrt{(7)^2-4(2)(-5)}}{2(2)}=\frac{-7\pm\sqrt{89}}{4}\approx 0.608,\ \cancel{-4.108}$$
$$x=\frac{-7+\sqrt{89}}{4}$$

51. Solving the equation:
$$\log_2(x+5)=\log_2(x)+\log_2(x-3)$$
$$\log_2(x+5)=\log_2(x^2-3x)$$
$$2^{\log_2(x+5)}=2^{\log_2(x^2-3x)}$$
$$x+5=x^2-3x$$
$$0=x^2-4x-5$$
$$0=(x+1)(x-5)$$
$$\cancel{x=-1},\ x=5$$

53. The solution is $x\approx 3.186$. Sketching the graph:

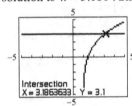

55. The solution is $x\approx 5.105,\ -3.105$. Sketching the graph:

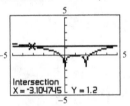

57. Finding the doubling time:
$$A=Pe^{rt}$$
$$3000=1500e^{0.06t}$$
$$2=e^{0.06t}$$
$$\ln 2=\ln e^{0.06t}$$
$$\ln 2=0.06t$$
$$t=\frac{\ln 2}{0.06}\approx 11.55 \text{ years}$$

59. Finding the doubling time:
$$A=Pe^{rt}$$
$$8{,}000=4{,}000e^{0.0575t}$$
$$2=e^{0.0575t}$$
$$\ln 2=\ln e^{0.0575t}$$
$$\ln 2=0.0575t$$
$$t=\frac{\ln 2}{0.0575}\approx 12.05 \text{ years}$$

61. Finding the doubling time:

$$A = Pe^{rt}$$

$$5{,}400 = 2{,}700e^{0.75t}$$

$$2 = e^{0.075t}$$

$$\ln 2 = \ln e^{0.075t}$$

$$\ln 2 = 0.075t$$

$$t = \frac{\ln 2}{0.075} \approx 9.24 \text{ years}$$

63. Finding the interest rate:

$$A = Pe^{rt}$$

$$2{,}000 = 1{,}500e^{r(5)}$$

$$\frac{4}{3} = e^{5r}$$

$$\ln\frac{4}{3} = \ln e^{5r}$$

$$\ln\frac{4}{3} = 5r$$

$$r = \frac{\ln\frac{4}{3}}{5} = 0.05754$$

$$r = 5.75\%$$

65. Finding the interest rate:

$$A = Pe^{rt}$$

$$6{,}000 = 4{,}000e^{r(8)}$$

$$1.5 = e^{8r}$$

$$\ln 1.5 = \ln e^{8r}$$

$$\ln 1.5 = 8r$$

$$r = \frac{\ln 1.5}{8} = 0.05068$$

$$r = 5.07\%$$

67. Finding the interest rate:

$$A = Pe^{rt}$$

$$10{,}000 = 8{,}500e^{r(5)}$$

$$\frac{20}{17} = e^{5r}$$

$$\ln\frac{20}{17} = \ln e^{5r}$$

$$\ln\frac{20}{17} = 5r$$

$$r = \frac{\ln\frac{20}{17}}{5} = 0.03250$$

$$r = 3.25\%$$

69. Finding the growth constant k:

$$P = P_0 e^{kt}$$

$$2{,}000{,}000 = 1{,}000{,}000e^{k(12)}$$

$$2 = e^{12k}$$

$$\ln 2 = \ln e^{12k}$$

$$\ln 2 = 12k$$

$$k = \frac{\ln 2}{12} \approx 0.0578$$

Finding the time to reach a population of 4 million:

$$P = e^{0.0578t}$$

$$4 = e^{0.0578t}$$

$$\ln 4 = \ln e^{0.0578t}$$

$$\ln 4 = 0.0578t$$

$$t = \frac{\ln 4}{0.0578} \approx 24 \text{ hr}$$

Finding the time to reach a population of 8 million:

$$P = e^{0.0578t}$$

$$8 = e^{0.0578t}$$

$$\ln 8 = \ln e^{0.0578t}$$

$$\ln 8 = 0.0578t$$

$$t = \frac{\ln 8}{0.0578} \approx 36 \text{ hr}$$

71. **a.** Evaluating the function: $s(0) = 2297.1e^{0.3316(0)} = 2,297.1$

In 1971, there were about 2,297 transistors per chip.

b. Finding the doubling time:

$$s(t) = 2297.1e^{0.3316t}$$

$$4,594.2 = 2,297.1e^{0.3316t}$$

$$2 = e^{0.3316t}$$

$$\ln 2 = \ln e^{0.3316t}$$

$$\ln 2 = 0.3316t$$

$$t = \frac{\ln 2}{0.3316} \approx 2.09 \text{ years}$$

73. Finding the time for the revenue to reach $140 million:

$$R(x) = 26.203\ln x + 90.798$$

$$140 = 26.203\ln x + 90.798$$

$$49.202 = 26.203\ln x$$

$$\frac{49.202}{26.203} = \ln x$$

$$e^{\frac{49.202}{26.203}} = e^{\ln x}$$

$$x = e^{\frac{49.202}{26.203}} \approx 6.54 \text{ weeks}$$

75. Finding the hydrogen ion concentration:

$$pH = -\log[H^+]$$

$$6.2 = -\log[H^+]$$

$$-6.2 = \log[H^+]$$

$$10^{-6.2} = 10^{\log[H^+]}$$

$$[H^+] = 10^{-6.2} \text{ moles per liter}$$

77. Solving for P_1:

$$D = 10\log\frac{P_1}{P_2}$$

$$0.7 = 10\log\frac{P_1}{75\,W}$$

$$0.07 = \log\frac{P_1}{75\,W}$$

$$10^{0.07} = 10^{\log\frac{P_1}{75\,W}}$$

$$10^{0.07} = \frac{P_1}{75\,W}$$

$$P_1 = 10^{0.07}(75\,W) \approx 88\,W$$

79. The initial deposit is $5,000.

81. The investment doubles in slightly less than 12 years.

83. No. Solving each equation:

$$\ln x^2 = 1$$
$$x^2 = e$$
$$x = \pm\sqrt{e}$$

$$2\ln x = 1$$
$$\ln x = \frac{1}{2}$$
$$x = e^{1/2} = \sqrt{e}$$

The two equations share a solution, but the first equation has an additional negative solution because the logarithm is taken after x is squared. This allows for a non-positive solution.

85. The step incorrectly uses the properties of addition of logarithms of the same base. Instead, the step should read:

$$\log x + \log(x+1) = 0 \implies \log(x(x+1)) = 0 \implies x(x+1) = 1$$

87. Solving the equation:

$$\ln(\log x) = 1$$
$$e^{\ln(\log x)} = e^1$$
$$\log x = e$$
$$10^{\log x} = 10^e$$
$$x = 10^e$$

89. Solving the equation:

$$\log_5|x-2| = 2$$
$$|x-2| = 5^2$$
$$|x-2| = 25$$
$$x-2 = -25, 25$$
$$x = -23, 27$$

4.6 Exponential, Logistic, and Logarithmic Models

1. Evaluating the function: $f(0) = 10e^0 = 10 \cdot 1 = 10$

3. Solving the equation:

$$5 = 10e^{-t}$$
$$0.5 = e^{-t}$$
$$\ln 0.5 = \ln e^{-t}$$
$$\ln 0.5 = -t$$
$$t = -\ln 0.5 \approx 0.6931$$

5. Evaluating the function: $f(1) = 4e^1 = 4e \approx 10.8731$

7. Solving the equation:

$$8 = 4e^t$$
$$2 = e^t$$
$$\ln 2 = \ln e^t$$
$$\ln 2 = t$$
$$t = \ln 2 \approx 0.6391$$

9. Evaluating the function: $f(0) = \dfrac{0.3}{1+10e^{-2(0)}} = \dfrac{0.3}{1+10(1)} = \dfrac{0.3}{11} = \dfrac{3}{110}$

11. Evaluating the function: $f(10) = \dfrac{0.3}{1+10e^{-2(10)}} = \dfrac{0.3}{1+10e^{-20}} \approx 0.3000$

13. Evaluating the function: $f(e) = 3\ln e - 4 = 3(1) - 4 = -1$

15. Solving the equation:

$$2 = 3\ln x - 4$$
$$6 = 3\ln x$$
$$2 = \ln x$$
$$e^2 = e^{\ln x}$$
$$x = e^2 \approx 7.3891$$

17. The correct graph is c.

19. The correct graph is a.

21. a. Finding the exponential decay model:

$$A(t) = A_0 e^{kt}$$

$$\frac{1}{2}A_0 = A_0 e^{5700k}$$

$$\frac{1}{2} = e^{5700k}$$

$$\ln\frac{1}{2} = 5700k$$

$$k = \frac{\ln\frac{1}{2}}{5700} \approx -0.0001216$$

$$A(t) = A_0 e^{-0.0001216t}$$

b. Finding the time:

$$A(t) = A_0 e^{-0.0001216t}$$

$$\frac{1}{3}A_0 = A_0 e^{-0.0001216t}$$

$$\frac{1}{3} = e^{-0.0001216t}$$

$$\ln\frac{1}{3} = -0.0001216t$$

$$t = \frac{\ln\frac{1}{3}}{-0.0001216} \approx 9{,}035 \text{ years}$$

23. a. Finding the exponential growth model:

$$P(t) = 282 e^{kt}$$

$$335 = 282 e^{k(20)}$$

$$\frac{335}{282} = e^{20k}$$

$$\ln\frac{335}{282} = 20k$$

$$k = \frac{\ln\frac{335}{282}}{20} \approx 0.008611$$

$$P(t) = 282 e^{0.008611t}$$

b. Finding the time:

$$P(t) = 282 e^{0.008611t}$$

$$350 = 282 e^{0.008611t}$$

$$\frac{175}{141} = e^{0.008611t}$$

$$\ln\frac{175}{141} = 0.008611t$$

$$t = \frac{\ln\frac{175}{141}}{0.008611} \approx 25.0872 \text{ years}$$

The year is: $2000 + 25 = 2025$

25. a. Finding the exponential growth model:

$$P(t) = 175{,}000 e^{kt}$$

$$280{,}000 = 175{,}000 e^{7k}$$

$$1.6 = e^{7k}$$

$$\ln 1.6 = 7k$$

$$k = \frac{\ln 1.6}{7} \approx 0.06714$$

$$P(t) = 175{,}000 e^{0.06714t}$$

b. The model assumes exponential growth and does not take into account other factors such as economic conditions.

27. a. Evaluating the function: $N(0) = \dfrac{300}{1+14e^{-0.05(0)}} = \dfrac{300}{1+14(1)} = 20$ deer

b. Evaluating the function: $N(10) = \dfrac{300}{1+14e^{-0.05(10)}} \approx 32$ deer

29. a. Finding the exponential decay model:

$$A(t) = A_0 e^{kt}$$
$$A(t) = 5e^{kt}$$
$$2.5 = 5e^{8k}$$
$$0.5 = e^{8k}$$
$$8k = \ln 0.5$$
$$k = \frac{\ln 0.5}{8} \approx -0.087$$
$$A(t) = 5e^{-0.087t}$$

b. Finding the exponential decay model:

$$B(t) = A_0 e^{kt}$$
$$B(t) = 5e^{kt}$$
$$2.5 = 5e^{3k}$$
$$0.5 = e^{3k}$$
$$3k = \ln 0.5$$
$$k = \frac{\ln 0.5}{3} \approx -0.231$$
$$B(t) = 5e^{-0.231t}$$

c. Solving the equation:

$$A(t) = 5e^{-0.087t}$$
$$3 = 5e^{-0.087t}$$
$$0.6 = e^{-0.087t}$$
$$-0.087t = \ln 0.6$$
$$t = \frac{\ln 0.6}{-0.087} \approx 5.87 \text{ days}$$

$$B(t) = 5e^{-0.231t}$$
$$3 = 5e^{-0.231t}$$
$$0.6 = e^{-0.231t}$$
$$-0.231t = \ln 0.6$$
$$t = \frac{\ln 0.6}{-0.231} \approx 2.21 \text{ days}$$

d. The solution produced with water that has a pH of 6.0 should be used because more malathion will remain after several days than will remain in the solution produced with water that has a pH of 7.0.

e. The graphs show that one function decreases more quickly than the other:

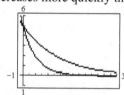

31. a. The function is $f(x) = 53.366(1.064)^x$. Sketching a scatter plot:

b. This is a growth model, thus $a > 1$.

c. For the year 2015, $t = 2015 - 1970 = 45$. Evaluating the function: $f(45) = 53.366(1.064)^{45} \approx \$870.238$ billion

d. No. Eventually the revenue growth will slow down, or may even decline.

33. a. A logistic function suits this data well because the number of cases is confined to the upper limit of the population.

b. The logistic function is $f(x) = \dfrac{264.8933}{1 + 6.0071e^{-0.6329x}}$. Sketching a scatter plot:

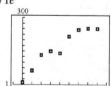

c. c signifies the greatest value that the model can produce.

d. According to this model, the greatest number of SARS cases is about 265 cases. By July, that number will have been effectively achieved.

35. **a.** As time increases, the percentage of women who smoke during pregnancy decreases.

b. The logarithmic function is: $p(t) = -1.3705 \ln t + 14.823$

a must be negative so that the value of $a \ln t + b$ decreases as t increases. Sketching a scatter plot:

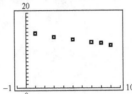

c. For the year 2007, $t = 2007 - 1993 = 14$. Evaluating the function: $p(14) = -1.3705 \ln 14 + 14.823 \approx 11.2\%$

37. The term refers to the upper bound of the function as x increases, which is c. The function can be used to model the maximum number of individual that a given environment can support, which is referred to as that environment's "carrying capacity."

39. If a and c are positive, the numerator is clearly positive, and the denominator is the sum of a positive number and the product of two positive numbers (since e^{-bx} is positive for any value of b). Thus, $\dfrac{c}{1 + ae^{-bx}}$ is the quotient of two positive numbers, so $f(x) > 0$.

Chapter 4 Review Exercises

1. Verifying that $(f \circ g)(x) = x$ and $(g \circ f)(x) = x$:

$$f(g(x)) = f\left(\frac{x-7}{2}\right) = 2\left(\frac{x-7}{2}\right) + 7 = x - 7 + 7 = x$$

$$g(f(x)) = g(2x+7) = \frac{(2x+7)-7}{2} = \frac{2x}{2} = x$$

2. Verifying that $(f \circ g)(x) = x$ and $(g \circ f)(x) = x$:

$$f(g(x)) = f(-x+3) = -(-x+3) + 3 = x - 3 + 3 = x$$

$$g(f(x)) = g(-x+3) = -(-x+3) + 3 = x - 3 + 3 = x$$

3. Verifying that $(f \circ g)(x) = x$ and $(g \circ f)(x) = x$:

$$f(g(x)) = f\left(\frac{\sqrt[3]{x}}{2}\right) = 8\left(\frac{\sqrt[3]{x}}{2}\right)^3 = 8\left(\frac{x}{8}\right) = x$$

$$g(f(x)) = g(8x^3) = \frac{\sqrt[3]{8x^3}}{2} = \frac{2x}{2} = x$$

4. Verifying that $(f \circ g)(x) = x$ and $(g \circ f)(x) = x$:

$$f(g(x)) = f(\sqrt{1-x}) = -(\sqrt{1-x})^2 + 1 = -(1-x) + 1 = x$$

$$g(f(x)) = g(-x^2+1) = \sqrt{1 - (-x^2+1)} = \sqrt{x^2} = x$$

5. Finding the inverse:

$$f(x) = -\frac{4}{5}x$$

$$y = -\frac{4}{5}x$$

$$x = -\frac{4}{5}y$$

$$-\frac{5}{4}x = y$$

$$f^{-1}(x) = -\frac{5}{4}x$$

6. Finding the inverse:

$$g(x) = \frac{2}{3}x$$

$$y = \frac{2}{3}x$$

$$x = \frac{2}{3}y$$

$$\frac{3}{2}x = y$$

$$g^{-1}(x) = \frac{3}{2}x$$

7. Finding the inverse:

$$f(x) = -3x + 6$$

$$y = -3x + 6$$

$$x = -3y + 6$$

$$x - 6 = -3y$$

$$\frac{x-6}{-3} = y$$

$$f^{-1}(x) = \frac{6-x}{3}$$

8. Finding the inverse:

$$f(x) = -2x - \frac{5}{3}$$

$$y = -2x - \frac{5}{3}$$

$$x = -2y - \frac{5}{3}$$

$$3x = -6y - 5$$

$$3x + 5 = -6y$$

$$\frac{3x+5}{-6} = y$$

$$f^{-1}(x) = -\frac{1}{2}x - \frac{5}{6}$$

9. Finding the inverse:

$$f(x) = x^3 + 8$$

$$y = x^3 + 8$$

$$x = y^3 + 8$$

$$x - 8 = y^3$$

$$\sqrt[3]{x-8} = y$$

$$f^{-1}(x) = \sqrt[3]{x-8}$$

10. Finding the inverse:

$$f(x) = -2x^3 + 4$$

$$y = -2x^3 + 4$$

$$x = -2y^3 + 4$$

$$x - 4 = -2y^3$$

$$\frac{x-4}{-2} = y^3$$

$$\sqrt[3]{\frac{x-4}{-2}} = y$$

$$f^{-1}(x) = \sqrt[3]{\frac{4-x}{2}}$$

11. Finding the inverse:

$$g(x) = -x^2 + 8, \ x \geq 0, \ y \leq 8$$
$$y = -x^2 + 8$$
$$x = -y^2 + 8, \ y \geq 0, \ x \leq 8$$
$$x - 8 = -y^2$$
$$8 - x = y^2$$
$$\pm\sqrt{8 - x} = y$$
$$\sqrt{8 - x} = y$$
$$g^{-1}(x) = \sqrt{8 - x}, \ x \leq 8$$

12. Finding the inverse:

$$g(x) = 3x^2 - 5, \ x \geq 0, \ y \geq -5$$
$$y = 3x^2 - 5$$
$$x = 3y^2 - 5, \ y \geq 0, \ x \geq -5$$
$$x + 5 = 3y^2$$
$$\frac{x + 5}{3} = y^2$$
$$\sqrt{\frac{x + 5}{3}} = y$$
$$g^{-1}(x) = \sqrt{\frac{x + 5}{3}}, \ x \geq -5$$

13. Finding the inverse:

$$f(x) = -x - 7$$
$$y = -x - 7$$
$$x = -y - 7$$
$$x + 7 = -y$$
$$-x - 7 = y$$
$$f^{-1}(x) = -x - 7$$

Sketching the graph of both functions:

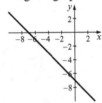

14. Finding the inverse:

$$f(x) = 2x + 1$$
$$y = 2x + 1$$
$$x = 2y + 1$$
$$x - 1 = 2y$$
$$\frac{x - 1}{2} = y$$
$$f^{-1}(x) = \frac{x - 1}{2}$$

Sketching the graph of both functions:

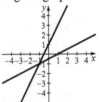

15. Finding the inverse:

$$f(x) = -x^3 + 1$$
$$y = -x^3 + 1$$
$$x = -y^3 + 1$$
$$x - 1 = -y^3$$
$$1 - x = y^3$$
$$\sqrt[3]{1 - x} = y$$
$$f^{-1}(x) = \sqrt[3]{1 - x}$$

Sketching the graph of both functions:

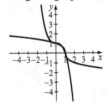

16. Finding the inverse:

$$f(x) = x^2 - 3, \ x \geq 0, \ y \geq -3$$
$$y = x^2 - 3$$
$$x = y^2 - 3, \ y \geq 0, \ x \geq -3$$
$$x + 3 = y^2$$
$$\sqrt{x + 3} = y$$
$$f^{-1}(x) = \sqrt{x + 3}, \ x \geq -3$$

Sketching the graph of both functions:

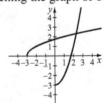

17. The y-intercept is $(0, -1)$, two other points are $(1, -4)$ and $(2, -16)$, the domain is $(-\infty, \infty)$, and the range is $(-\infty, 0)$. As $x \rightarrow -\infty$, $f(x) \rightarrow 0$, and as $x \rightarrow \infty$, $f(x) \rightarrow -\infty$. Sketching the graph:

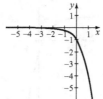

18. The y-intercept is $(0, -1)$, two other points are $(1, -3)$ and $(2, -9)$, the domain is $(-\infty, \infty)$, and the range is $(-\infty, 0)$. As $x \rightarrow -\infty$, $f(x) \rightarrow 0$, and as $x \rightarrow \infty$, $f(x) \rightarrow -\infty$. Sketching the graph:

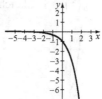

19. The y-intercept is $(0, 1)$, two other points are $\left(1, \dfrac{2}{3}\right)$ and $\left(-1, \dfrac{3}{2}\right)$, the domain is $(-\infty, \infty)$, and the range is $(0, \infty)$. As $x \rightarrow -\infty$, $g(x) \rightarrow \infty$, and as $x \rightarrow \infty$, $g(x) \rightarrow 0$. Sketching the graph:

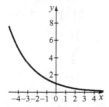

20. The y-intercept is $(0, 1)$, two other points are $\left(1, \dfrac{3}{5}\right)$ and $\left(-1, \dfrac{5}{3}\right)$, the domain is $(-\infty, \infty)$, and the range is $(0, \infty)$. As $x \rightarrow -\infty$, $g(x) \rightarrow \infty$, and as $x \rightarrow \infty$, $g(x) \rightarrow 0$. Sketching the graph:

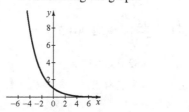

21. The y-intercept is $(0, 4)$, two other points are $(1, 4e)$ and $\left(-1, \dfrac{4}{e}\right)$, the domain is $(-\infty, \infty)$, and the range is $(0, \infty)$. As $x \rightarrow -\infty$, $f(x) \rightarrow 0$, and as $x \rightarrow \infty$, $f(x) \rightarrow \infty$. Sketching the graph:

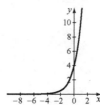

22. The y-intercept is $(0,-1)$, two other points are $(1, 2-3e)$ and $(2, 2-3e^2)$, the domain is $(-\infty, \infty)$, and the range is $(-\infty, 2)$. As $x \to -\infty$, $g(x) \to 2$, and as $x \to \infty$, $g(x) \to -\infty$. Sketching the graph:

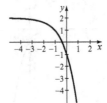

23. The y-intercept is $(0,3)$, two other points are $\left(1, \dfrac{2}{e}+1\right)$ and $(-1, 2e+1)$, the domain is $(-\infty, \infty)$, and the range is $(1, \infty)$. As $x \to -\infty$, $g(x) \to \infty$, and as $x \to \infty$, $g(x) \to 1$. Sketching the graph:

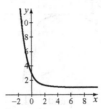

24. The y-intercept is $(0,2)$, two other points are $\left(1, \dfrac{5}{e}-3\right)$ and $(-1, 5e-3)$, the domain is $(-\infty, \infty)$, and the range is $(-3, \infty)$. As $x \to -\infty$, $h(x) \to \infty$, and as $x \to \infty$, $h(x) \to -3$. Sketching the graph:

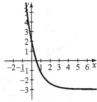

25. Finding the amount: $A = 1,500\left(1+\dfrac{0.05}{4}\right)^{4(6)} = \$2,021.03$

26. Finding the amount: $A = 1,500\left(1+\dfrac{0.08}{2}\right)^{2(6)} = \$2,401.55$

27. Finding the amount: $A = 1,500e^{0.08(4)} = \$2,065.69$

28. Finding the amount: $A = 1,500e^{0.035(5)} = \$1,786.87$

29. Completing the table:

Years Since Purchase	Value
1	$12,750.00
2	$9,562.50
3	$7,171.88
4	$5,378.91
5	$4,034.18

The depreciation function is $V(t) = 17,000(0.75)^t$. Sketching the graph:

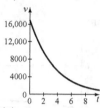

30. Evaluating the function: $A = 4,000\left(1 + \dfrac{0.04}{12}\right)^{12(18)} = \$8,207.90$

31. Completing the table:

Logarithmic Statement	Exponential Statement
$\log_3 9 = 2$	$3^2 = 9$
$\log 0.1 = -1$	$10^{-1} = 0.1$
$\log_5 \dfrac{1}{25} = -2$	$5^{-2} = \dfrac{1}{25}$

32. Completing the table:

Exponential Statement	Logarithmic Statement
$3^5 = 243$	$\log_3 243 = 5$
$4^{1/5} = \sqrt[5]{4}$	$\log_4 \sqrt[5]{4} = \dfrac{1}{5}$
$8^{-1} = \dfrac{1}{8}$	$\log_8 \dfrac{1}{8} = -1$

33. Evaluating the logarithm: $\log_5 625 = \log_5 5^4 = 4$

34. Evaluating the logarithm: $\log_6 \dfrac{1}{36} = \log_6 \dfrac{1}{6^2} = \log_6 6^{-2} = -2$

35. Evaluating the logarithm: $\log_9 81 = \log_9 9^2 = 2$

36. Evaluating the logarithm: $\log_7 \dfrac{1}{7} = \log_7 7^{-1} = -1$

37. Evaluating the logarithm: $\log \sqrt{10} = \log 10^{1/2} = \dfrac{1}{2}$

38. Evaluating the logarithm: $\ln e^{1/2} = \dfrac{1}{2}$

39. Evaluating the logarithm: $\ln \sqrt[3]{e} = \ln e^{1/3} = \dfrac{1}{3}$

40. Evaluating the logarithm: $\ln e^{-1} = -1$

41. Evaluating the logarithm: $\log 10^{x+2} = x + 2$

42. Evaluating the logarithm: $\ln e^{5x} = 5x$

43. Evaluating the logarithm: $4 \log 2 \approx 1.2041$

44. Evaluating the logarithm: $-6 \log 7.3 \approx -5.1799$

45. Evaluating the logarithm: $\ln \sqrt{8} \approx 1.0397$

46. Evaluating the logarithm: $\ln\left(\dfrac{\pi}{2}\right) \approx 0.4516$

47. Using the change-of-base formula: $\log_3 4.3 = \dfrac{\ln 4.3}{\ln 3} \approx 1.3277$

48. Using the change-of-base formula: $\log_4 6.52 = \dfrac{\ln 6.52}{\ln 4} \approx 1.3524$

49. Using the change-of-base formula: $\log_6 0.75 = \dfrac{\ln 0.75}{\ln 6} \approx -0.1606$

50. Using the change-of-base formula: $\log_5 0.85 = \dfrac{\ln 0.85}{\ln 5} \approx -0.1010$

51. The domain is $(0, \infty)$, there is no y-intercept, and the vertical asymptote is $x = 0$. Finding the x-intercept:

$$0 = \log x - 6$$
$$6 = \log x$$
$$x = 10^6$$

The x-intercept is $\left(10^6, 0\right)$. Sketching the graph:

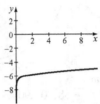

52. The domain is $(4, \infty)$, there is no y-intercept, and the vertical asymptote is $x = 4$. Finding the x-intercept:

$$0 = \ln(x - 4)$$
$$x - 4 = e^0$$
$$x = 5$$

The x-intercept is $(5, 0)$. Sketching the graph:

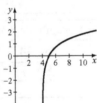

53. The domain is $(0, \infty)$, there is no y-intercept, and the vertical asymptote is $x = 0$. Finding the x-intercept:

$$0 = 3\log_4 x$$
$$0 = \log_4 x$$
$$x = 4^0 = 1$$

The x-intercept is $(1, 0)$. Sketching the graph:

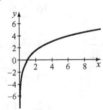

54. The domain is $(0, \infty)$, there is no y-intercept, and the vertical asymptote is $x = 0$. Finding the x-intercept:

$$0 = \log_5 x + 4$$
$$-4 = \log_5 x$$
$$x = 5^{-4} = \frac{1}{625}$$

The x-intercept is $\left(\dfrac{1}{625}, 0\right)$. Sketching the graph:

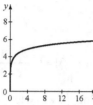

55. Finding the magnitude: $R(10 I_0) = \log\left(\dfrac{10 I_0}{I_0}\right) = \log 10 = 1$

56. Finding the intensity:

$$R(I) = \log\left(\frac{I}{I_0}\right)$$
$$7.6 = \log\left(\frac{I}{I_0}\right)$$
$$10^{7.6} = \frac{I}{I_0}$$
$$I = 10^{7.6} I_0$$

57. Evaluating the logarithm: $\log 21 = \log(7 \cdot 3) = \log 7 + \log 3 \approx 0.8451 + 0.4771 = 1.3222$

58. Evaluating the logarithm: $\log 15 = \log(5 \cdot 3) = \log 5 + \log 3 \approx 0.6990 + 0.4771 = 1.1761$

59. Evaluating the logarithm: $\log\left(\dfrac{5}{3}\right) = \log 5 - \log 3 \approx 0.6990 - 0.4771 = 0.2219$

60. Evaluating the logarithm: $\log \sqrt{3} = \log 3^{1/2} = \dfrac{1}{2}\log 3 \approx \dfrac{1}{2}(0.4771) = 0.23855$

61. Using properties of logarithms: $\log\left(\sqrt[4]{x}\sqrt[3]{y}\right) = \log\sqrt[4]{x} + \log\sqrt[3]{y} = \log x^{1/4} + \log y^{1/3} = \dfrac{1}{4}\log x + \dfrac{1}{3}\log y$

62. Using properties of logarithms: $\ln\left(\sqrt[3]{x^5}\sqrt{y^3}\right) = \ln\sqrt[3]{x^5} + \ln\sqrt{y^3} = \ln x^{5/3} + \ln y^{3/2} = \dfrac{5}{3}\ln x + \dfrac{3}{2}\ln y$

63. Using properties of logarithms:

$$\log_a \sqrt{\frac{x^6}{y^3 z^5}} = \log_a \frac{x^3}{y^{3/2} z^{5/2}} = \log_a x^3 - \log_a\left(y^{3/2} z^{5/2}\right) = \log_a x^3 - \left(\log_a y^{3/2} + \log_a z^{5/2}\right) = 3\log_a x - \frac{3}{2}\log_a y - \frac{5}{2}\log_a z$$

64. Using properties of logarithms:

$$\log_a \sqrt{\frac{z^5}{xy^4}} = \log_a \frac{z^{5/2}}{x^{1/2} y^2} = \log_a z^{5/2} - \log_a\left(x^{1/2} y^2\right) = \log_a z^{5/2} - \left(\log_a x^{1/2} + \log_a y^2\right) = \frac{5}{2}\log_a z - \frac{1}{2}\log_a x - 2\log_a y$$

65. Using properties of logarithms: $\ln\sqrt[3]{\dfrac{xy^3}{z^5}} = \ln\dfrac{x^{1/3} y}{z^{5/3}} = \ln\left(x^{1/3} y\right) - \ln z^{5/3} = \ln x^{1/3} + \ln y - \ln z^{5/3} = \dfrac{1}{3}\ln x + \ln y - \dfrac{5}{3}\ln z$

66. Using properties of logarithms:

$$\log \sqrt[3]{\frac{x^3 z^5}{10 y^2}} = \log \frac{x z^{5/3}}{10^{1/3} y^{2/3}}$$

$$= \log\left(x z^{5/3}\right) - \log\left(10^{1/3} y^{2/3}\right)$$

$$= \log x + \log z^{5/3} - \left(\log 10^{1/3} + \log y^{2/3}\right)$$

$$= \log x + \frac{5}{3}\log z - \frac{1}{3}\log 10 - \frac{2}{3}\log y$$

$$= \log x + \frac{5}{3}\log z - \frac{1}{3} - \frac{2}{3}\log y$$

67. Using properties of logarithms: $\ln\left(x^2 - 3x\right) - \ln\left(x - 3\right) = \ln\frac{x^2 - 3x}{x - 3} = \ln\frac{x(x-3)}{x-3} = \ln x$

68. Using properties of logarithms: $\log_a\left(x^2 - 4\right) - \log_a\left(x + 2\right) = \log_a\frac{x^2 - 4}{x + 2} = \log_a\frac{(x+2)(x-2)}{x+2} = \log_a\left(x - 2\right)$

69. Using properties of logarithms:

$$\frac{1}{4}\left[\log\left(x^2 - 1\right) - \log\left(x + 1\right)\right] + 3\log x = \frac{1}{4}\log\frac{x^2 - 1}{x + 1} + 3\log x$$

$$= \frac{1}{4}\log\frac{(x+1)(x-1)}{x+1} + 3\log x$$

$$= \frac{1}{4}\log\left(x - 1\right) + 3\log x$$

$$= \log\sqrt[4]{x - 1} + \log x^3$$

$$= \log\left(x^3\sqrt[4]{x - 1}\right)$$

70. Using properties of logarithms:

$$\frac{2}{3}\log\left(9x^3\right) - \frac{1}{4}\log\left(16y^8\right) = \log\left(9x^3\right)^{2/3} - \log\left(16y^8\right)^{1/4}$$

$$= \log\sqrt[3]{81x^6} - \log\sqrt[4]{16y^8}$$

$$= \log\left(3x^2\sqrt[3]{3}\right) - \log\left(2y^2\right)$$

$$= \log\frac{3x^2\sqrt[3]{3}}{2y^2}$$

71. Using properties of logarithms:

$$2\log_3 x^2 - \frac{1}{3}\log_3\sqrt{x} = \log_3\left(x^2\right)^2 - \log_3\left(\sqrt{x}\right)^{1/3}$$

$$= \log_3 x^4 - \log_3\left(x^{1/2}\right)^{1/3}$$

$$= \log_3 x^4 - \log_3 x^{1/6}$$

$$= \log_3\frac{x^4}{x^{1/6}}$$

$$= \log_3 x^{23/6}$$

72. Using properties of logarithms:

$$2\ln\left(x^2+1\right)+\frac{1}{2}\ln x^4-3\ln x=\ln\left(x^2+1\right)^2+\ln\sqrt{x^4}-\ln x^3$$

$$=\ln\left(x^2+1\right)^2+\ln x^2-\ln x^3$$

$$=\ln\left(x^2\left(x^2+1\right)^2\right)-\ln x^3$$

$$=\ln\frac{x^2\left(x^2+1\right)^2}{x^3}$$

$$=\ln\frac{\left(x^2+1\right)^2}{x}$$

73. Solving the equation:

$$5^x=625$$
$$5^x=5^4$$
$$x=4$$

74. Solving the equation:

$$6^{2x}=1296$$
$$6^{2x}=6^4$$
$$2x=4$$
$$x=2$$

75. Solving the equation:

$$7^x=\frac{1}{49}$$
$$7^x=\frac{1}{7^2}$$
$$7^x=7^{-2}$$
$$x=-2$$

76. Solving the equation:

$$4e^x+6=38$$
$$4e^x=32$$
$$e^x=8$$
$$x=\ln 8\approx 2.0794$$

77. Solving the equation:

$$25e^{0.04x}=100$$
$$e^{0.04x}=4$$
$$0.04x=\ln 4$$
$$x=\frac{\ln 4}{0.04}\approx 34.6574$$

78. Solving the equation:

$$3\left(1.5^x\right)-2=9$$
$$3\left(1.5^x\right)=11$$
$$1.5^x=\frac{11}{3}$$
$$\ln 1.5^x=\ln\frac{11}{3}$$
$$x\ln 1.5=\ln 11-\ln 3$$
$$x=\frac{\ln 11-\ln 3}{\ln 1.5}\approx 3.2044$$

79. Solving the equation:

$$4^{2x+3}=16$$
$$4^{2x+3}=4^2$$
$$2x+3=2$$
$$2x=-1$$
$$x=-\frac{1}{2}$$

80. Solving the equation:

$$5^{3x+2}=\frac{1}{5}$$
$$5^{3x+2}=5^{-1}$$
$$3x+2=-1$$
$$3x=-3$$
$$x=-1$$

81. Solving the equation:

$$e^{2x+1} = 4$$
$$2x+1 = \ln 4$$
$$2x = \ln 4 - 1$$
$$x = \frac{\ln 4 - 1}{2} \approx 0.1931$$

82. Solving the equation:

$$2^{x-1} = 10$$
$$\log 2^{x-1} = \log 10$$
$$(x-1)\log 2 = 1$$
$$x \log 2 - \log 2 = 1$$
$$x \log 2 = 1 + \log 2$$
$$x = \frac{1 + \log 2}{\log 2} \approx 4.3219$$

83. Solving the equation:

$$\ln(2x-1) = 0$$
$$e^{\ln(2x-1)} = e^0$$
$$2x-1 = 1$$
$$2x = 2$$
$$x = 1$$

84. Solving the equation:

$$\log(x+3) - \log(2x-4) = 0$$
$$\log \frac{x+3}{2x-4} = 0$$
$$10^{\log \frac{x+3}{2x-4}} = 10^0$$
$$\frac{x+3}{2x-4} = 1$$
$$x+3 = 2x-4$$
$$-x = -7$$
$$x = 7$$

85. Solving the equation:

$$\ln x^{1/2} = 2$$
$$\frac{1}{2}\ln x = 2$$
$$\ln x = 4$$
$$e^{\ln x} = e^4$$
$$x = e^4 \approx 54.5982$$

86. Solving the equation:

$$2\log_3 x = -4$$
$$\log_3 x = -2$$
$$3^{\log_3 x} = 3^{-2}$$
$$x = \frac{1}{9}$$

87. Solving the equation:

$$\log x + \log(2x-1) = 1$$
$$\log[x(2x-1)] = 1$$
$$\log(2x^2 - x) = 1$$
$$2x^2 - x = 10^1$$
$$2x^2 - x - 10 = 0$$
$$(2x-5)(x+2) = 0$$
$$x = \frac{5}{2}, \cancel{x = -2}$$

88. Solving the equation:

$$\log(x+6) = \log x^2$$
$$\log(x+6) - \log x^2 = 0$$
$$\log \frac{x+6}{x^2} = 0$$
$$\frac{x+6}{x^2} = 10^0$$
$$x+6 = x^2$$
$$0 = x^2 - x - 6$$
$$0 = (x+2)(x-3)$$
$$x = -2, x = 3$$

89. Solving the equation:

$$\log(3x+1) - \log(x^2+1) = 0$$

$$\log\frac{3x+1}{x^2+1} = 0$$

$$\frac{3x+1}{x^2+1} = 10^0$$

$$3x+1 = x^2+1$$

$$0 = x^2 - 3x$$

$$0 = x(x-3)$$

$$x = 0, x = 3$$

90. Solving the equation:

$$\log_3 x + \log_3(x+8) = 2$$

$$\log_3[x(x+8)] = 2$$

$$\log_3(x^2+8x) = 2$$

$$3^{\log_3(x^2+8x)} = 3^2$$

$$x^2+8x = 9$$

$$x^2+8x-9 = 0$$

$$(x+9)(x-1) = 0$$

$$x = -9, x = 1$$

91. Solving the equation:

$$\log_4 x + \log_4(x+3) = 1$$

$$\log_4[x(x+3)] = 1$$

$$\log_4(x^2+3x) = 1$$

$$4^{\log_4(x^2+3x)} = 4^1$$

$$x^2+3x = 4$$

$$x^2+3x-4 = 0$$

$$(x+4)(x-1) = 0$$

$$x = -4, x = 1$$

92. Solving the equation:

$$\log(3x+10) = 2\log x$$

$$\log(3x+10) = \log x^2$$

$$\log(3x+10) - \log x^2 = 0$$

$$\log\frac{3x+10}{x^2} = 0$$

$$\frac{3x+10}{x^2} = 10^0$$

$$3x+10 = x^2$$

$$0 = x^2 - 3x - 10$$

$$0 = (x+2)(x-5)$$

$$x = -2, x = 5$$

93. Evaluating the function:

$$f(0) = 4e^{-2.5(0)} = 4 \qquad f(3) = 4e^{-2.5(3)} \approx 0.0022$$

94. Evaluating the function:

$$f(0) = 30e^{1.2(0)} = 30 \qquad f(3) = 30^{1.2(3)} \approx 1097.9470$$

95. Evaluating the function:

$$f(0) = 20\ln(0+2)+1 = 20\ln 2+1 \approx 14.8629 \qquad f(3) = 20\ln(3+2)+1 = 20\ln 5+1 \approx 33.1888$$

96. Evaluating the function:

$$f(0) = 10\ln(2(0)+1)-2 = 10\ln 1-2 = -2 \qquad f(3) = 10\ln(2(3)+1)-2 = 10\ln 7-2 \approx 17.4591$$

97. Evaluating the function:

$$f(0) = \frac{0.2}{1+100e^{-4(0)}} = \frac{0.2}{1+100(1)} \approx 0.0020 \qquad f(3) = \frac{0.2}{1+100e^{-4(3)}} \approx 0.1999$$

98. Evaluating the function:

$$f(0) = \frac{0.5}{1+200e^{-5(0)}} = \frac{0.5}{1+200(1)} \approx 0.0025 \qquad f(3) = \frac{0.5}{1+200e^{-5(3)}} \approx 0.5000$$

99. The function is $P(t) = 2.5(1.07)^t$, where $P(t)$ is the purchasing power in trillions of dollars.

100. **a.** The exponential function is $f(x) = 0.4627(1.8887)^x$. Sketching a scatter plot:

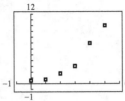

b. For the year 2007, $x = 2007 - 2000 = 7$. Evaluating the function:

$$f(7) = 0.4627(1.8887)^7 \approx 39.668 \text{ million players}$$

c. Solving the equation:

$$21 = 0.4627(1.8887)^x$$

$$\frac{21}{0.4627} = (1.8887)^x$$

$$\ln\frac{21}{0.4627} = \ln(1.8887)^x$$

$$\ln\frac{21}{0.4627} = x\ln 1.8887$$

$$x = \frac{\ln\dfrac{21}{0.4627}}{\ln 1.8887} \approx 6$$

The sales of portable music players equals 21 million in the year $2000 + 6 = 2006$.

101. **a.** Evaluating the function: $N(0) = \dfrac{450}{1+9e^{-0.3(0)}} = \dfrac{450}{1+9(1)} = 45$ trout

b. Evaluating the function: $N(15) = \dfrac{450}{1+9e^{-0.3(15)}} \approx 409$ trout

c. As t increases, the number of trout in the pond increases, but at an increasingly slower rate.
The graph is asymptotic to $N(t) = 450$. Sketching the graph:

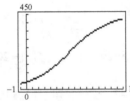

d. The number of trout in the pond will reach 400 after approximately 14.3 months. Sketching the graph:

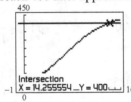

Chapter 4 Test

1. Verifying that $(f \circ g)(x) = x$ and $(g \circ f)(x) = x$:

$$f(g(x)) = f\left(\frac{x+1}{3}\right) = 3\left(\frac{x+1}{3}\right) - 1 = x + 1 - 1 = x$$

$$g(f(x)) = g(3x-1) = \frac{(3x-1)+1}{3} = \frac{3x}{3} = x$$

2. Finding the inverse:

$$f(x) = 4x^3 - 1$$

$$y = 4x^3 - 1$$

$$x = 4y^3 - 1$$

$$x + 1 = 4y^3$$

$$\frac{x+1}{4} = y^3$$

$$\sqrt[3]{\frac{x+1}{4}} = y$$

$$f^{-1}(x) = \sqrt[3]{\frac{x+1}{4}}$$

3. Finding the inverse:

$$f(x) = x^2 - 2, \; x \ge 0, \; y \ge -2$$

$$y = x^2 - 2$$

$$x = y^2 - 2, \; y \ge 0, \; x \ge -2$$

$$x + 2 = y^2$$

$$\sqrt{x+2} = y$$

$$f^{-1}(x) = \sqrt{x+2}, \; x \ge -2$$

Sketching the graph of both functions:

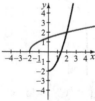

4. As $x \to -\infty$, $f(x) \to 1$, and as $x \to \infty$, $f(x) \to -\infty$. Sketching the graph:

5. As $x \to -\infty$, $f(x) \to \infty$, and as $x \to \infty$, $f(x) \to -3$. Sketching the graph:

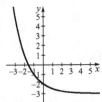

6. As $x \to -\infty$, $f(x) \to \infty$, and as $x \to \infty$, $f(x) \to 0$. Sketching the graph:

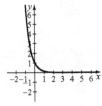

7. Writing in exponential form: $6^{-3} = \dfrac{1}{216}$

8. Writing in logarithmic form: $\log_2 32 = 5$

9. Evaluating the logarithm: $\log_8 \dfrac{1}{64} = \log_8 \dfrac{1}{8^2} = \log_8 8^{-2} = -2$

10. Evaluating the logarithm: $\ln e^{3.2} = 3.2$

11. Using the change-of-base formula: $\log_7 4.91 = \dfrac{\ln 4.91}{\ln 7} \approx 0.8178$

12. The domain is $(-2, \infty)$, the y-intercept is $(0, \ln 2)$, and the vertical asymptote is $x = -2$. Finding the x-intercept:

$$0 = \ln(x+2)$$
$$x + 2 = e^0$$
$$x = -1$$

The x-intercept is $(-1, 0)$. Sketching the graph:

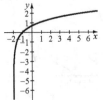

13. Using properties of logarithms: $\log \sqrt[3]{x^2 y^4} = \log\left(x^{2/3} y^{4/3}\right) = \log x^{2/3} + \log y^{4/3} = \dfrac{2}{3}\log x + \dfrac{4}{3}\log y$

14. Using properties of logarithms: $\ln\left(e^2 x^2 y\right) = \ln e^2 + \ln x^2 + \ln y = 2 + 2\ln x + \ln y$

15. Using properties of logarithms:

$$\ln\left(x^2 - 4\right) - \ln(x-2) + \ln x = \ln\dfrac{x^2 - 4}{x-2} + \ln x = \ln\dfrac{(x+2)(x-2)}{x-2} + \ln x = \ln(x+2) + \ln x = \ln\left[x(x+2)\right]$$

16. Using properties of logarithms: $4\log_2 x^{1/3} + 2\log_2 x^{1/3} = \log_2 x^{4/3} + \log_2 x^{2/3} = \log_2\left(x^{4/3} x^{2/3}\right) = \log_2 x^2$

17. Solving the equation:
$$6^{2x} = 36^{3x-1}$$
$$6^{2x} = \left(6^2\right)^{3x-1}$$
$$6^{2x} = 6^{6x-2}$$
$$2x = 6x - 2$$
$$-4x = -2$$
$$x = \frac{1}{2}$$

18. Solving the equation:
$$4^x = 7.1$$
$$\ln 4^x = \ln 7.1$$
$$x \ln 4 = \ln 7.1$$
$$x = \frac{\ln 7.1}{\ln 4} \approx 1.4139$$

19. Solving the equation:
$$4e^{x+2} - 6 = 10$$
$$4e^{x+2} = 16$$
$$e^{x+2} = 4$$
$$x + 2 = \ln 4$$
$$x = \ln 4 - 2 \approx -0.6137$$

20. Solving the equation:
$$200e^{0.2t} = 800$$
$$e^{0.2t} = 4$$
$$0.2t = \ln 4$$
$$t = \frac{\ln 4}{0.2} \approx 6.9315$$

21. Solving the equation:
$$\ln(4x+1) = 0$$
$$e^{\ln(4x+1)} = e^0$$
$$4x + 1 = 1$$
$$4x = 0$$
$$x = 0$$

22. Solving the equation:
$$\log x + \log(x+3) = 1$$
$$\log[x(x+3)] = 1$$
$$\log(x^2 + 3x) = 1$$
$$10^{\log(x^2+3x)} = 10^1$$
$$x^2 + 3x = 10$$
$$x^2 + 3x - 10 = 0$$
$$(x+5)(x-2) = 0$$
$$\cancel{x = -5}, x = 2$$

23. Evaluating the function: $A = 3000\left(1 + \dfrac{0.05}{4}\right)^{4(6)} = \$4{,}042.05$

24. Evaluating the function: $A = 4000e^{0.07(3)} = \$4{,}934.71$

25. The exponential function is $f(t) = 900(0.6)^t$.

26. Finding the intensity:
$$R(I) = \log\left(\frac{I}{I_0}\right)$$
$$6.2 = \log\left(\frac{I}{I_0}\right)$$
$$10^{6.2} = \frac{I}{I_0}$$
$$I = 10^{6.2} I_0 \text{ or about } \left(1.585 \times 10^6\right) I_0$$

27. **a.** Evaluating the function: $N(0) = \dfrac{120}{1 + 3e^{-0.4(0)}} = \dfrac{120}{1 + 3(1)} = 30$ students

   b. Evaluating the function: $N(10) = \dfrac{120}{1 + 3e^{-0.4(10)}} = \dfrac{120}{1 + 3e^{-4}} \approx 114$ students

28. Finding the decay rate k:

$$32{,}000 = 28{,}000e^{2k}$$

$$\frac{8}{7} = e^{2k}$$

$$\ln\frac{8}{7} = 2k$$

$$k = \frac{\ln\dfrac{8}{7}}{2} \approx 0.06677$$

The exponential function is $P(t) = 28{,}000e^{0.06677t}$.

Chapter 5
Trigonometric Functions

5.1 Angles and Their Measures

1. The point lies in quadrant III.   **3.** The point lies in quadrant IV.

5. This statement is false. The degree units (°) need to be included.

7. The terminal side lies in quadrant II.

9. Sketching the angle: **11.** Sketching the angle:

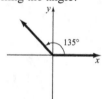

13. Sketching the angle: **15.** Sketching the angle:

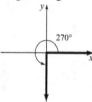   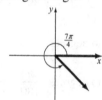

17. Sketching the angle: **19.** Sketching the angle:

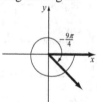

21. Finding the two angles:
$$140° + 360° = 500°$$ $$140° + 2(360°) = 140° + 720° = 860°$$

23. Finding the two angles:
$$-55° + 360° = 305°$$ $$-55° + 2(360°) = -55° + 720° = 665°$$

25. Finding the two angles:
$$60° + 360° = 420°$$ $$60° + 2(360°) = 60° + 720° = 780°$$

27. Finding the two angles:
$$210° + 360° = 570°$$ $$210° + 2(360°) = 210° + 720° = 930°$$

29. Finding the two angles:
$$\frac{\pi}{3} - 2\pi = \frac{\pi}{3} - \frac{6\pi}{3} = -\frac{5\pi}{3}$$ $$\frac{\pi}{3} + 2\pi = \frac{\pi}{3} + \frac{6\pi}{3} = \frac{7\pi}{3}$$

31. Finding the two angles:
$$-\frac{\pi}{6} - 2\pi = -\frac{\pi}{6} - \frac{12\pi}{6} = -\frac{13\pi}{6} \qquad\qquad -\frac{\pi}{6} + 2\pi = -\frac{\pi}{6} + \frac{12\pi}{6} = \frac{11\pi}{6}$$

33. Finding the two angles:
$$140° + 360° = 500° \qquad\qquad\qquad 140° - 360° = -220°$$

35. Finding the two angles:
$$-65° + 360° = 295° \qquad\qquad\qquad -65° - 360° = -425°$$

37. Finding the two angles:
$$\frac{\pi}{6} + 2\pi = \frac{\pi}{6} + \frac{12\pi}{6} = \frac{13\pi}{6} \qquad\qquad \frac{\pi}{6} - 2\pi = \frac{\pi}{6} - \frac{12\pi}{6} = -\frac{11\pi}{6}$$

39. The complementary angle is: $90° - 57° = 33°$ 41. The complementary angle is: $90° - 48° = 42°$

43. The complementary angle is: $90° - 15° = 75°$ 45. The supplementary angle is: $180° - 105° = 75°$

47. The supplementary angle is: $180° - 89° = 91°$ 49. The supplementary angle is: $180° - 130° = 50°$

51. Converting from degrees to radians: $240° = 240°\left(\dfrac{\pi}{180°}\right) = \dfrac{4\pi}{3}$ radians

53. Converting from degrees to radians: $-150° = -150°\left(\dfrac{\pi}{180°}\right) = -\dfrac{5\pi}{6}$ radians

55. Converting from degrees to radians: $270° = 270°\left(\dfrac{\pi}{180°}\right) = \dfrac{3\pi}{2}$ radians

57. Converting from degrees to radians: $-270° = -270°\left(\dfrac{\pi}{180°}\right) = -\dfrac{3\pi}{2}$ radians

59. Converting from degrees to radians: $720° = 720°\left(\dfrac{\pi}{180°}\right) = 4\pi$ radians

61. Converting from degrees to radians: $390° = 390°\left(\dfrac{\pi}{180°}\right) = \dfrac{13\pi}{6}$ radians

63. Converting from radians to degrees: $3\pi = 3\pi\left(\dfrac{180°}{\pi}\right) = 540°$

65. Converting from radians to degrees: $\dfrac{\pi}{180} = \dfrac{\pi}{180}\left(\dfrac{180°}{\pi}\right) = 1°$

67. Converting from radians to degrees: $-\dfrac{2\pi}{5} = -\dfrac{2\pi}{5}\left(\dfrac{180°}{\pi}\right) = -72°$

69. The angle is: $\theta = \dfrac{10}{60}$ rev $\cdot \dfrac{360°}{\text{rev}} = 60°$ or $\dfrac{\pi}{3}$ radians

71. The angle is: $\theta = \dfrac{1.5 \text{ min}}{2 \text{ min/rev}} \cdot \dfrac{360°}{\text{rev}} = 0.75(360°) = 270°$ or $\dfrac{3\pi}{2}$ radians

73. The angle is: $\theta = \dfrac{1}{24}$ rev $\cdot \dfrac{360°}{\text{rev}} = 15°$

75. Finding the angle: $\theta = 80° = 80°\left(\dfrac{\pi}{180°}\right) = \dfrac{4\pi}{9}$

Now finding the arc length: $s = r\theta = 7\left(\dfrac{4\pi}{9}\right) = \dfrac{28\pi}{9} \approx 9.77$

The trim is about 9.8 inches long.

77. The angle is given by: $\theta = 40° - 20° = 20° = 20°\left(\dfrac{\pi}{180°}\right) = \dfrac{\pi}{9}$

Finding the arc length: $s = r\theta = 3900\left(\dfrac{\pi}{9}\right) = \dfrac{1300\pi}{3} \approx 1360.3$

The bird traveled about 1,360.3 miles.

79. The angular speed is given by: $\omega = \dfrac{1 \text{ rev}}{3 \text{ sec}} \cdot \dfrac{2\pi \text{ rads}}{\text{rev}} = \dfrac{2\pi}{3}$ rads/sec

Finding the linear speed: $v = r\omega = (4 \text{ in}) \cdot \left(\dfrac{2\pi}{3} \dfrac{\text{rads}}{\text{sec}}\right) = \left(\dfrac{4}{12} \text{ ft}\right)\left(\dfrac{2\pi}{3} \dfrac{\text{rads}}{\text{sec}}\right) = \dfrac{2\pi}{9}$ ft/sec

81. Converting the linear speed units: $v = \dfrac{20 \text{ mi}}{\text{hr}} = \dfrac{20 \text{ mi}}{3600 \text{ sec}} = \dfrac{1 \text{ mi}}{180 \text{ sec}}$

Converting the radius to miles: $r = 18 \text{ in} = \dfrac{18 \text{ in}}{1} \cdot \dfrac{1 \text{ ft}}{12 \text{ in}} \cdot \dfrac{1 \text{ mi}}{5280 \text{ ft}} = \dfrac{1}{3520}$ mi

Now finding the angular speed: $\omega = \dfrac{v}{r} = \dfrac{1 \text{ mi}}{180 \text{ sec}} \div \dfrac{1}{3520} \text{ mi} = \dfrac{3520}{180 \text{ sec}} = \dfrac{176 \text{ rads}}{9 \text{ sec}} \approx 19.56 \text{ rads}/\text{sec}$

Converting the units: $\dfrac{176 \text{ rads}}{9 \text{ sec}} = \dfrac{\dfrac{176}{9}\left(\dfrac{180°}{\pi}\right)}{\text{sec}} = \dfrac{3520}{\pi}$ degrees/sec

The angular speed is 19.56 rads/sec, or $\dfrac{3520}{\pi} \approx 1120.45$ deg/sec.

83. Finding the angular speed: $\omega = \dfrac{1 \text{ rev}}{10 \text{ min}} \cdot \dfrac{2\pi \text{ rads}}{\text{rev}} = \dfrac{\pi}{5}$ rads/min

Finding the linear speed: $v = r\omega = (20 \text{ ft}) \cdot \left(\dfrac{\pi \text{ rads}}{5 \text{ min}}\right) = 4\pi$ ft/min ≈ 12.6 ft/min

85. Finding the angle:
$s = r\theta$
$6 = 10\theta$
$\theta = \dfrac{3}{5} = \dfrac{3}{5}\left(\dfrac{180°}{\pi}\right) \approx 34.38°$

87. Finding the arc length:
$v = \dfrac{s}{t}$
$5 = \dfrac{s}{1}$
$s = 5$

Finding the angle in radians: $\theta = \dfrac{1 \text{ rev}}{3 \text{ sec}} \cdot \dfrac{2\pi \text{ rads}}{\text{rev}} \cdot 1 \text{ sec} = \dfrac{2\pi}{3}$

Finding the radius:
$s = r\theta$
$5 = r\left(\dfrac{2\pi}{3}\right)$
$r = \dfrac{15}{2\pi} \approx 2.38732$

You are sitting $\dfrac{15}{2\pi}$ (or about 2.39) feet from center of the car.

89. Finding the linear speed: $v = rw = (2\text{ ft})\left(\dfrac{1\text{ rev}}{\text{sec}} \cdot \dfrac{2\pi\text{ rads}}{\text{rev}}\right) = \dfrac{4\pi\text{ ft}}{\text{sec}} \approx 12.6$ ft/sec

91. **a.** Finding the angular speed: $\omega = \dfrac{1\text{ rev}}{24\text{ hr}} \cdot \dfrac{360°}{\text{rev}} = 15°$ per hr

Converting to radians: $\omega = 15°$ per hr $= 15° \cdot \dfrac{\pi}{180°} = \dfrac{\pi}{12}$ radians per hr

b. Finding the arc length: $s = r\theta = 3900\text{ mi} \cdot \left(\dfrac{\pi}{12} \cdot 8\right) = 2600\pi \approx 8{,}168.1$ miles

c. Finding the linear speed: $v = r\omega = 3900\text{ mi} \cdot \dfrac{\pi}{12\text{ hr}} = 325\pi\ \dfrac{\text{mi}}{\text{hr}} \approx 1{,}021\ \dfrac{\text{mi}}{\text{hr}}$

93. Since $1\text{ radian} = 1 \cdot \dfrac{180°}{\pi} \approx 57.3°$, then 1 radian is larger.

95. The angle is: $\theta = \dfrac{1}{4}(-2\pi) = -\dfrac{\pi}{2}$

97. The angle is: $\theta = \dfrac{1}{3}(2\pi) = \dfrac{2\pi}{3}$

99. The angle is: $\theta = 2(-2\pi) = -4\pi$

5.2 Trigonometric Functions Using the Unit Circle

1. Substituting into the unit circle:
$$x^2 + y^2 = 1$$
$$0^2 + (-1)^2 = 1$$
$$1 = 1$$

Yes, $(0,-1)$ lies on the unit circle.

3. Substituting into the unit circle:
$$x^2 + y^2 = 1$$
$$(-0.3)^2 + (0.7)^2 = 1$$
$$0.09 + 0.49 = 1$$
$$0.58 \neq 1$$

No, $(-0.3, 0.7)$ does not lie on the unit circle.

5. Finding the quadrant: $t = \dfrac{4\pi}{3} = \left(1\dfrac{1}{3}\right)\pi = \pi + \dfrac{\pi}{3}$ is in Quadrant III

7. Finding the quadrant: $t = -\dfrac{11\pi}{3} = -\left(3 + \dfrac{2}{3}\right)\pi = -3\pi - \dfrac{2\pi}{3}$ is in Quadrant I

9. **a.** Since $t = \dfrac{5\pi}{3} = \left(1\dfrac{2}{3}\right)\pi = \pi + \dfrac{2\pi}{3}$ is in Quadrant IV, its reference angle is $2\pi - \dfrac{5\pi}{3} = \dfrac{\pi}{3}$.

b. A coterminal angle is $\dfrac{5\pi}{3} + 2\pi = \dfrac{11\pi}{3}$.

11. Since $t = \dfrac{7\pi}{6} = \pi + \dfrac{\pi}{6}$ is in Quadrant III, its reference angle is $\dfrac{7\pi}{6} - \pi = \dfrac{\pi}{6}$.

13. Since $t = -\dfrac{7\pi}{6} = -\left(\pi + \dfrac{\pi}{6}\right) = -\pi - \dfrac{\pi}{6}$ is in Quadrant II, its reference angle is $\dfrac{\pi}{6}$.

15. Since $t = \dfrac{3\pi}{4}$ is in Quadrant II, its reference angle is $\pi - \dfrac{3\pi}{4} = \dfrac{\pi}{4}$.

17. Since $t = -\dfrac{5\pi}{6}$ is in Quadrant III, its reference angle is $-\dfrac{5\pi}{6} + \pi = \dfrac{\pi}{6}$.

19. Since $t = \dfrac{7\pi}{8}$ is in Quadrant II, its reference angle is $\pi - \dfrac{7\pi}{8} = \dfrac{\pi}{8}$.

21. Since $t = -\dfrac{\pi}{5}$ is in Quadrant IV, its reference angle is $\dfrac{\pi}{5}$.

23. Note that $t = 5\pi = \pi + 4\pi$. Finding the trigonometric values:

$$\sin 5\pi = \sin(\pi + 4\pi) = \sin \pi = 0$$

$$\cos 5\pi = \cos(\pi + 4\pi) = \cos \pi = -1$$

$$\tan 5\pi = \frac{\sin 5\pi}{\cos 5\pi} = \frac{0}{-1} = 0$$

$$\cot 5\pi = \frac{1}{\tan 5\pi} \text{ is undefined}$$

$$\csc 5\pi = \frac{1}{\sin 5\pi} \text{ is undefined}$$

$$\sec 5\pi = \frac{1}{\cos 5\pi} = \frac{1}{-1} = -1$$

25. Note that $t = -3\pi = -\pi - 2\pi$. Finding the trigonometric values:

$$\sin(-3\pi) = \sin(-\pi - 2\pi) = \sin(-\pi) = \sin \pi = 0$$

$$\cos(-3\pi) = \cos(-\pi - 2\pi) = \cos(-\pi) = -\cos \pi = -1$$

$$\tan(-3\pi) = \frac{\sin(-3\pi)}{\cos(-3\pi)} = \frac{0}{-1} = 0$$

$$\cot(-3\pi) = \frac{1}{\tan(-3\pi)} \text{ is undefined}$$

$$\csc(-3\pi) = \frac{1}{\sin(-3\pi)} \text{ is undefined}$$

$$\sec(-3\pi) = \frac{1}{\cos(-3\pi)} = -1$$

27. Finding the trigonometric values:

$$\sin\left(-\frac{\pi}{3}\right) = -\sin\frac{\pi}{3} = -\frac{\sqrt{3}}{2}$$

$$\cos\left(-\frac{\pi}{3}\right) = \cos\frac{\pi}{3} = \frac{1}{2}$$

$$\tan\left(-\frac{\pi}{3}\right) = \frac{\sin\left(-\frac{\pi}{3}\right)}{\cos\left(-\frac{\pi}{3}\right)} = \frac{-\frac{\sqrt{3}}{2}}{\frac{1}{2}} = -\sqrt{3}$$

$$\cot\left(-\frac{\pi}{3}\right) = \frac{1}{\tan\left(-\frac{\pi}{3}\right)} = -\frac{1}{\sqrt{3}} = -\frac{\sqrt{3}}{3}$$

$$\csc\left(-\frac{\pi}{3}\right) = -\frac{2}{\sqrt{3}} = -\frac{2\sqrt{3}}{3}$$

$$\sec\left(-\frac{\pi}{3}\right) = 2$$

29. Finding the trigonometric values:

$$\sin\left(-\frac{\pi}{4}\right) = -\sin\frac{\pi}{4} = -\frac{\sqrt{2}}{2}$$

$$\cos\left(-\frac{\pi}{4}\right) = \cos\frac{\pi}{4} = \frac{\sqrt{2}}{2}$$

$$\tan\left(-\frac{\pi}{4}\right) = -\tan\frac{\pi}{4} = -1$$

$$\cot\left(-\frac{\pi}{4}\right) = -1$$

$$\csc\left(-\frac{\pi}{4}\right) = -\frac{2}{\sqrt{2}} = -\sqrt{2}$$

$$\sec\left(-\frac{\pi}{4}\right) = \frac{2}{\sqrt{2}} = \sqrt{2}$$

31. Note that $t = \frac{11\pi}{4} = \frac{3\pi}{4} + 2\pi$. Finding the trigonometric values:

$$\sin\frac{11\pi}{4} = \sin\frac{3\pi}{4} = \frac{\sqrt{2}}{2}$$

$$\cos\frac{11\pi}{4} = \cos\frac{3\pi}{4} = -\frac{\sqrt{2}}{2}$$

$$\tan\frac{11\pi}{4} = \frac{\sin\frac{11\pi}{4}}{\cos\frac{11\pi}{4}} = \frac{\frac{\sqrt{2}}{2}}{-\frac{\sqrt{2}}{2}} = -1$$

$$\cot\frac{11\pi}{4} = \frac{1}{\tan\frac{11\pi}{4}} = \frac{1}{-1} = -1$$

$$\csc\frac{11\pi}{4} = \frac{2}{\sqrt{2}} = \sqrt{2}$$

$$\sec\frac{11\pi}{4} = -\frac{2}{\sqrt{2}} = -\sqrt{2}$$

33. Note that $t = \dfrac{13\pi}{6} = \dfrac{\pi}{6} + 2\pi$. Finding the trigonometric values:

$$\sin\frac{13\pi}{6} = \sin\frac{\pi}{6} = \frac{1}{2}$$

$$\cos\frac{13\pi}{6} = \cos\frac{\pi}{6} = \frac{\sqrt{3}}{2}$$

$$\tan\frac{13\pi}{6} = \frac{\sin\dfrac{13\pi}{6}}{\cos\dfrac{13\pi}{6}} = \frac{\dfrac{1}{2}}{\dfrac{\sqrt{3}}{2}} = \frac{1}{\sqrt{3}} = \frac{\sqrt{3}}{3}$$

$$\cot\frac{13\pi}{6} = \frac{1}{\tan\dfrac{13\pi}{6}} = \frac{3}{\sqrt{3}} = \sqrt{3}$$

$$\csc\frac{13\pi}{6} = \frac{1}{\sin\dfrac{13\pi}{6}} = 2$$

$$\sec\frac{13\pi}{6} = \frac{1}{\cos\dfrac{13\pi}{6}} = \frac{2}{\sqrt{3}} = \frac{2\sqrt{3}}{3}$$

35. Note that $t = \dfrac{13\pi}{3} = \dfrac{\pi}{3} + 4\pi$. Finding the trigonometric values:

$$\sin\frac{13\pi}{3} = \sin\frac{\pi}{3} = \frac{\sqrt{3}}{2}$$

$$\cos\frac{13\pi}{3} = \cos\frac{\pi}{3} = \frac{1}{2}$$

$$\tan\frac{13\pi}{3} = \frac{\sin\dfrac{13\pi}{3}}{\cos\dfrac{13\pi}{3}} = \sqrt{3}$$

$$\cot\frac{13\pi}{3} = \frac{1}{\tan\dfrac{13\pi}{3}} = \frac{1}{\sqrt{3}} = \frac{\sqrt{3}}{3}$$

$$\csc\frac{13\pi}{3} = \frac{1}{\sin\dfrac{13\pi}{3}} = \frac{2}{\sqrt{3}} = \frac{2\sqrt{3}}{3}$$

$$\sec\frac{13\pi}{3} = \frac{1}{\cos\dfrac{13\pi}{3}} = 2$$

37. Note that $t = -\dfrac{10\pi}{3} = -\left(3\pi + \dfrac{\pi}{3}\right)$ is in Quadrant II with reference angle $\dfrac{\pi}{3}$. Finding the trigonometric values:

$$\sin\left(-\frac{10\pi}{3}\right) = \sin\frac{\pi}{3} = \frac{\sqrt{3}}{2}$$

$$\cos\left(-\frac{10\pi}{3}\right) = -\cos\frac{\pi}{3} = -\frac{1}{2}$$

$$\tan\left(-\frac{10\pi}{3}\right) = \frac{\sin\left(-\dfrac{10\pi}{3}\right)}{\cos\left(-\dfrac{10\pi}{3}\right)} = -\sqrt{3}$$

$$\cot\left(-\frac{10\pi}{3}\right) = \frac{1}{\tan\left(-\dfrac{10\pi}{3}\right)} = -\frac{1}{\sqrt{3}} = -\frac{\sqrt{3}}{3}$$

$$\csc\left(-\frac{10\pi}{3}\right) = \frac{1}{\sin\left(-\dfrac{10\pi}{3}\right)} = \frac{2}{\sqrt{3}} = \frac{2\sqrt{3}}{3}$$

$$\sec\left(-\frac{10\pi}{3}\right) = \frac{1}{\cos\left(-\dfrac{10\pi}{3}\right)} = -2$$

39. Using a calculator: $\cos 3 = -0.9900$

41. Using a calculator: $\sin(-3) = -0.1411$

43. Using a calculator: $\sin\dfrac{\pi}{12} = 0.2588$

45. Using a calculator: $\tan 2 = -2.1850$

47. Using a calculator: $\tan\dfrac{3\pi}{5} = -3.0777$

49. Using a calculator: $\tan(-0.5) = -0.5463$

51. Using a calculator: $\sec\dfrac{7\pi}{5} = \dfrac{1}{\cos\dfrac{7\pi}{5}} = -3.2361$

53. Using a calculator: $\sec(3.2) = \dfrac{1}{\cos(3.2)} = -1.0017$

55. Using a calculator: $\csc(-2.5) = \dfrac{1}{\sin(-2.5)} = -1.6709$

57. Using a calculator: $\sec(1.5) = \dfrac{1}{\cos(1.5)} = 14.1368$

59. Using a calculator: $\cot(-3.9) = \dfrac{1}{\tan(-3.9)} = -1.0555$

61. Finding the missing information:

$$\cos t = \frac{\sqrt{3}}{2}$$

$$\tan t = \frac{\sin t}{\cos t} = \frac{1}{\sqrt{3}} = \frac{\sqrt{3}}{3}$$

63. Finding the missing information:

$$\sin t = -\frac{\sqrt{2}}{2}$$

$$\cos t = -\frac{\sqrt{2}}{2}$$

65. Finding the missing information:

$$\sin t = \frac{\sqrt{3}}{2}$$

$$\tan t = \frac{\sin t}{\cos t} = \frac{\frac{\sqrt{3}}{2}}{-\frac{1}{2}} = -\sqrt{3}$$

67. First use the Pythagorean identity:

$$\sin^2 t + \cos^2 t = 1$$
$$(-0.6)^2 + \cos^2 t = 1$$
$$0.36 + \cos^2 t = 1$$
$$\cos^2 t = 0.64$$
$$\cos t = \pm 0.8$$

Since t is in Quadrant IV, finding the missing information:

$$\cos t = 0.8$$

$$\tan t = \frac{\sin t}{\cos t} = \frac{-0.6}{0.8} = -0.75$$

69. First use the Pythagorean identity:

$$\sin^2 t + \cos^2 t = 1$$
$$\sin^2 t + \left(-\frac{5}{13}\right)^2 = 1$$
$$\sin^2 t + \frac{25}{169} = 1$$
$$\sin^2 t = \frac{144}{169}$$
$$\sin t = \pm \frac{12}{13}$$

Since t is in Quadrant II, finding the missing information:

$$\sin t = \frac{12}{13}$$

$$\tan t = \frac{\sin t}{\cos t} = \frac{\frac{12}{13}}{-\frac{5}{13}} = -\frac{12}{5}$$

71. First use the Pythagorean identity:

$$1 + \tan^2 t = \sec^2 t$$
$$1 + (-2)^2 = \sec^2 t$$
$$5 = \sec^2 t$$
$$\sec t = \pm\sqrt{5}$$
$$\cos t = \pm\frac{1}{\sqrt{5}} = \pm\frac{\sqrt{5}}{5}$$

Since t is in Quadrant IV, $\cos t = \dfrac{\sqrt{5}}{5}$. Now using the Pythagorean identity:

$$\sin^2 t + \cos^2 t = 1$$

$$\sin^2 t + \left(\dfrac{\sqrt{5}}{5}\right)^2 = 1$$

$$\sin^2 t + \dfrac{1}{5} = 1$$

$$\sin^2 t = \dfrac{4}{5}$$

$$\sin t = -\dfrac{2}{\sqrt{5}} = -\dfrac{2\sqrt{5}}{5}$$

73. Using the negative-angle identities: $\sin\left(-\dfrac{2\pi}{3}\right) = -\sin\left(\dfrac{2\pi}{3}\right) = -\dfrac{\sqrt{3}}{2}$

75. Using the negative-angle identities: $\sec\left(-\dfrac{4\pi}{3}\right) = \sec\left(\dfrac{4\pi}{3}\right) = -\sec\left(\dfrac{\pi}{3}\right) = -\dfrac{1}{\cos\left(\dfrac{\pi}{3}\right)} = -2$

77. Using the negative-angle identities: $\tan\left(-\dfrac{7\pi}{3}\right) = -\tan\left(\dfrac{7\pi}{3}\right) = -\tan\left(\dfrac{\pi}{3}\right) = -\sqrt{3}$

79. Finding the exact value: $\sin\dfrac{\pi}{2} + \cos\pi = 1 + (-1) = 0$

81. Finding the exact value: $3\sin\dfrac{\pi}{4} + 2\cos\dfrac{3\pi}{4} = 3\left(\dfrac{\sqrt{2}}{2}\right) + 2\left(-\dfrac{\sqrt{2}}{2}\right) = \dfrac{3\sqrt{2}}{2} - \dfrac{2\sqrt{2}}{2} = \dfrac{\sqrt{2}}{2}$

83. Finding the exact value: $\sin\dfrac{\pi}{4}\cos\dfrac{\pi}{4} = \dfrac{\sqrt{2}}{2} \cdot \dfrac{\sqrt{2}}{2} = \dfrac{2}{4} = \dfrac{1}{2}$

85. Finding the exact value: $\tan\dfrac{\pi}{4}\sec\dfrac{\pi}{4} = \dfrac{\tan\dfrac{\pi}{4}}{\cos\dfrac{\pi}{4}} = \dfrac{1}{\left(\dfrac{\sqrt{2}}{2}\right)} = \dfrac{2}{\sqrt{2}} = \sqrt{2}$

87. Finding the exact value: $\csc\dfrac{\pi}{2} - 4\cot\dfrac{\pi}{2} = 1 - 4(0) = 1$

89. Finding the exact value: $\tan\dfrac{\pi}{3} - \cos\dfrac{\pi}{6} = \sqrt{3} - \dfrac{\sqrt{3}}{2} = \dfrac{\sqrt{3}}{2}$

91. Finding the values: $\sin t = 0$, $\cos t = -1$

93. Finding the values: $\sin t = \dfrac{3}{5}$, $\cos t = -\dfrac{4}{5}$

95. Finding the values: $\sin t = -\dfrac{5}{13}$, $\cos t = -\dfrac{12}{13}$

97. Note that $\cos\dfrac{\pi}{4} = \dfrac{\sqrt{2}}{2}$ and $\cos t > 0$ in Quadrants I and IV. In Quadrant IV, $s = 2\pi - \dfrac{\pi}{4} = \dfrac{7\pi}{4}$.

99. Note that $\cos\dfrac{4\pi}{3} = -\cos\dfrac{\pi}{3} = -\dfrac{1}{2}$ and $\cos t < 0$ in Quadrants II and III. $t = \dfrac{4\pi}{3}$ is in Quadrant III so in Quadrant II

$s = \pi - \dfrac{\pi}{3} = \dfrac{2\pi}{3}$.

101. Note that $\sin\pi = 0$ and $\sin 0 = 0$ so $s = 0$.

103. Note that $\sin \dfrac{2\pi}{3} = \sin \dfrac{\pi}{3} = \dfrac{\sqrt{3}}{2}$ so $s = \dfrac{\pi}{3}$.

105. Finding the values:

$$\cos(3 \cdot 0) = \cos 0 = 1 \qquad\qquad\qquad \cos\dfrac{0}{3} = \cos 0 = 1$$

107. Finding the values:

$$\cos\left(3 \cdot \left(-\dfrac{\pi}{2}\right)\right) = \cos\left(-\dfrac{3\pi}{2}\right) = \cos\dfrac{3\pi}{2} = 0 \qquad \cos\dfrac{\left(-\dfrac{\pi}{2}\right)}{3} = \cos\left(-\dfrac{\pi}{6}\right) = \cos\dfrac{\pi}{6} = \dfrac{\sqrt{3}}{2}$$

109. No; for example, when $t = \dfrac{\pi}{2}$, $\sin\left(\dfrac{\pi}{2} + \pi\right) = \sin\dfrac{3\pi}{2} = -1$ and $\sin\dfrac{\pi}{2} + \sin\pi = 1$.

111. First solving the equation:
$$\sin t = \cos t$$
$$\dfrac{\sin t}{\cos t} = 1$$
$$\tan t = 1$$
$$t = \dfrac{\pi}{4}$$

Since $\tan t > 0$ in Quadrants I and III so $t = \pi + \dfrac{\pi}{4} = \dfrac{5\pi}{4}$. Therefore $t = \dfrac{\pi}{4}, \dfrac{5\pi}{4}$.

113. For $t \in \left(0, \dfrac{\pi}{2}\right)$, $t + \pi$ will be in the interval $\left(0 + \pi, \dfrac{\pi}{2} + \pi\right) = \left(\pi, \dfrac{3\pi}{2}\right)$, which is Quadrant III.

Thus $\cos(t + \pi) = -\cos t$.

115. Deriving the identity:
$$\sin^2 t + \cos^2 t = 1$$
$$\dfrac{\sin^2 t}{\sin^2 t} + \dfrac{\cos^2 t}{\sin^2 t} = \dfrac{1}{\sin^2 t}$$
$$1 + \cot^2 t = \csc^2 t$$

5.3 Right Triangle Trigonometry

1. Using the Pythagorean theorem:
$$a^2 + b^2 = c^2$$
$$3^2 + 4^2 = c^2$$
$$25 = c^2$$
$$5 = c$$

3. Using the Pythagorean theorem:
$$a^2 + b^2 = c^2$$
$$2^2 + 3^2 = c^2$$
$$13 = c^2$$
$$\sqrt{13} = c$$

5. Using the Pythagorean theorem:
$$a^2 + b^2 = c^2$$
$$3^2 + b^2 = 6^2$$
$$9 + b^2 = 36$$
$$b^2 = 27$$
$$b = \sqrt{27} = 3\sqrt{3}$$

7. Using the Pythagorean theorem:
$$6^2 + 8^2 = c^2$$
$$36 + 64 = c^2$$
$$c^2 = 100$$
$$c = 10$$
The six trigonometric values are:

$$\sin\theta = \frac{8}{10} = \frac{4}{5} \qquad \cos\theta = \frac{6}{10} = \frac{3}{5} \qquad \tan\theta = \frac{8}{6} = \frac{4}{3}$$

$$\csc\theta = \frac{5}{4} \qquad \sec\theta = \frac{5}{3} \qquad \cot\theta = \frac{3}{4}$$

9. Using the Pythagorean theorem:
$$12^2 + b^2 = 37^2$$
$$144 + b^2 = 1369$$
$$b^2 = 1225$$
$$b = 35$$
The six trigonometric values are:

$$\sin\theta = \frac{12}{37} \qquad \cos\theta = \frac{35}{37} \qquad \tan\theta = \frac{12}{35}$$

$$\csc\theta = \frac{37}{12} \qquad \sec\theta = \frac{37}{35} \qquad \cot\theta = \frac{35}{12}$$

11. Using the Pythagorean theorem:
$$4^2 + 5^2 = c^2$$
$$16 + 25 = c^2$$
$$41 = c^2$$
$$c = \sqrt{41}$$
The six trigonometric values are:

$$\sin\theta = \frac{5}{\sqrt{41}} = \frac{5\sqrt{41}}{41} \qquad \cos\theta = \frac{4}{\sqrt{41}} = \frac{4\sqrt{41}}{41} \qquad \tan\theta = \frac{5}{4}$$

$$\csc\theta = \frac{\sqrt{41}}{5} \qquad \sec\theta = \frac{\sqrt{41}}{4} \qquad \cot\theta = \frac{4}{5}$$

13. Using the Pythagorean theorem:
$$4^2 + b^2 = \left(\sqrt{17}\right)^2$$
$$16 + b^2 = 17$$
$$b^2 = 1$$
$$b = 1$$
The six trigonometric values are:

$$\sin\theta = \frac{1}{\sqrt{17}} = \frac{\sqrt{17}}{17} \qquad \cos\theta = \frac{4}{\sqrt{17}} = \frac{4\sqrt{17}}{17} \qquad \tan\theta = \frac{1}{4}$$

$$\csc\theta = \sqrt{17} \qquad \sec\theta = \frac{\sqrt{17}}{4} \qquad \cot\theta = 4$$

15. If $\cos \theta = \dfrac{3}{5}$, choose $a = 3$ and $c = 5$ in the Pythagorean theorem:

$$3^2 + b^2 = 5^2$$
$$9 + b^2 = 25$$
$$b^2 = 16$$
$$b = 4$$

The six trigonometric values are:

$$\sin \theta = \dfrac{4}{5} \qquad \cos \theta = \dfrac{3}{5} \qquad \tan \theta = \dfrac{4}{3}$$
$$\csc \theta = \dfrac{5}{4} \qquad \sec \theta = \dfrac{5}{3} \qquad \cot \theta = \dfrac{3}{4}$$

17. If $\tan \theta = \dfrac{3}{2}$, choose $b = 3$ and $a = 2$ in the Pythagorean theorem:

$$2^2 + 3^2 = c^2$$
$$4 + 9 = c^2$$
$$13 = c^2$$
$$c = \sqrt{13}$$

The six trigonometric values are:

$$\sin \theta = \dfrac{3}{\sqrt{13}} = \dfrac{3\sqrt{13}}{13} \qquad \cos \theta = \dfrac{2}{\sqrt{13}} = \dfrac{2\sqrt{13}}{13} \qquad \tan \theta = \dfrac{3}{2}$$
$$\csc \theta = \dfrac{\sqrt{13}}{3} \qquad \sec \theta = \dfrac{\sqrt{13}}{2} \qquad \cot \theta = \dfrac{2}{3}$$

19. If $\sin \theta = 0.6 = \dfrac{3}{5}$, choose $b = 3$ and $c = 5$ in the Pythagorean theorem:

$$a^2 + 3^2 = 5^2$$
$$a^2 + 9 = 25$$
$$a^2 = 16$$
$$a = 4$$

The six trigonometric values are:

$$\sin \theta = \dfrac{3}{5} \qquad \cos \theta = \dfrac{4}{5} \qquad \tan \theta = \dfrac{3}{4}$$
$$\csc \theta = \dfrac{5}{3} \qquad \sec \theta = \dfrac{5}{4} \qquad \cot \theta = \dfrac{4}{3}$$

21. If $\cot \theta = 1.5 = \dfrac{3}{2}$, choose $a = 3$ and $b = 2$ in the Pythagorean theorem:

$$3^2 + 2^2 = c^2$$
$$9 + 4 = c^2$$
$$13 = c^2$$
$$c = \sqrt{13}$$

The six trigonometric values are:

$$\sin \theta = \dfrac{2}{\sqrt{13}} = \dfrac{2\sqrt{13}}{13} \qquad \cos \theta = \dfrac{3}{\sqrt{13}} = \dfrac{3\sqrt{13}}{13} \qquad \tan \theta = \dfrac{2}{3}$$
$$\csc \theta = \dfrac{\sqrt{13}}{2} \qquad \sec \theta = \dfrac{\sqrt{13}}{3} \qquad \cot \theta = \dfrac{3}{2}$$

23. If $\csc\theta = 2 = \dfrac{2}{1}$, choose $c = 2$ and $b = 1$ in the Pythagorean theorem:

$$a^2 + 1^2 = 2^2$$
$$a^2 + 1 = 4$$
$$a^2 = 3$$
$$a = \sqrt{3}$$

The six trigonometric values are:

$$\sin\theta = \frac{1}{2} \qquad\qquad \cos\theta = \frac{\sqrt{3}}{2} \qquad\qquad \tan\theta = \frac{1}{\sqrt{3}} = \frac{\sqrt{3}}{3}$$

$$\csc\theta = 2 \qquad\qquad \sec\theta = \frac{2}{\sqrt{3}} = \frac{2\sqrt{3}}{3} \qquad\qquad \cot\theta = \sqrt{3}$$

25. If $\cot\theta = 4 = \dfrac{4}{1}$, choose $a = 4$ and $b = 1$ in the Pythagorean theorem:

$$4^2 + 1^2 = c^2$$
$$16 + 1 = c^2$$
$$17 = c^2$$
$$c = \sqrt{17}$$

The six trigonometric values are:

$$\sin\theta = \frac{1}{\sqrt{17}} = \frac{\sqrt{17}}{17} \qquad\qquad \cos\theta = \frac{4}{\sqrt{17}} = \frac{4\sqrt{17}}{17} \qquad\qquad \tan\theta = \frac{1}{4}$$

$$\csc\theta = \sqrt{17} \qquad\qquad \sec\theta = \frac{\sqrt{17}}{4} \qquad\qquad \cot\theta = 4$$

27. Finding the exact value: $\cos 30° = \dfrac{\sqrt{3}}{2}$

29. Finding the exact value: $\sec 30° = \dfrac{1}{\cos 30°} = \dfrac{2}{\sqrt{3}} = \dfrac{2\sqrt{3}}{3}$

31. Finding the exact value: $\tan 60° = \sqrt{3}$

33. Finding the exact value: $\csc 30° = \dfrac{1}{\sin 30°} = \dfrac{2}{\sqrt{3}} = \dfrac{2\sqrt{3}}{3}$

35. Calculating the value: $\sin 38° = 0.6157$

37. Calculating the value: $\tan 65° = 2.1445$

39. Calculating the value: $\cos 83° = 0.1219$

41. Calculating the value: $\sec 15° = \dfrac{1}{\cos 15°} = 1.0353$

43. Calculating the value: $\cot 67° = \dfrac{1}{\tan 67°} = 0.4245$

45. Using a cofunction identity: $\sin 35° = \cos\left(90° - 35°\right) = \cos 55°$

47. Using a cofunction identity: $\tan 40° = \cot\left(90° - 40°\right) = \cot 50°$

49. Using a cofunction identity: $\sec 47° = \csc\left(90° - 47°\right) = \csc 43°$

51. Using a cofunction identity: $\cot 67° = \tan\left(90° - 67°\right) = \tan 23°$

53. The other angle is 45°. Finding side b:

$$\tan 45° = \frac{b}{a}$$

$$1 = \frac{b}{2}$$

$$b = 2$$

Using the Pythagorean theorem:

$$c^2 = 2^2 + 2^2$$

$$c^2 = 8$$

$$c = \sqrt{8} = 2\sqrt{2}$$

55. The other angle is 70°. Finding the other sides:

$$\tan 20° = \frac{b}{10}$$

$$b = 10\tan 20°$$

$$b \approx 3.6397$$

$$\cos 20° = \frac{10}{c}$$

$$c = \frac{10}{\cos 20°}$$

$$c \approx 10.6418$$

57. The other angle is 75°. Finding the other sides:

$$\cos 15° = \frac{a}{12}$$

$$a = 12\cos 15°$$

$$a \approx 11.5911$$

$$\sin 15° = \frac{b}{12}$$

$$b = 12\sin 15°$$

$$b \approx 3.1058$$

59. Since $\sin\theta = \frac{1}{2}$, $\theta = 30°$.

61. Since $\cos\theta = \frac{\sqrt{2}}{2}$, $\theta = 45°$.

63. Since $\sin\theta = \frac{\sqrt{2}}{2}$, $\theta = 45°$.

65. Finding the other trigonometric values:

$$\csc\alpha = \frac{1}{\sin\alpha} = \frac{1}{a} \qquad \cos(90° - \alpha) = \sin\alpha = a$$

67. Let y represent the height of the pole. The equation is:

$$\sin 30° = \frac{y}{20}$$

$$y = 20\sin 30°$$

$$y = 20\left(\frac{1}{2}\right) = 10 \text{ ft}$$

The pole is 10 feet tall.

69. Let d represent the distance from point A to the basket. The equation is:

$$\sin 10.5° = \frac{100}{d}$$

$$d\sin 10.5° = 100$$

$$d = \frac{100}{\sin 10.5°} \approx 548.7404 \text{ ft}$$

The distance from point A to the basket is approximately 548.7404 feet.

71. Let y represent the height of the tower and $x + 15$ represent the original distance from the point to the tower, with x representing the final distance from the point to the tower. Setting up the two equations:

$$\frac{y}{x} = \tan 42° \qquad\qquad\qquad \frac{y}{x+15} = \tan 38°$$

$$y = x \tan 42° \qquad\qquad\qquad y = (x+15) \tan 38°$$

Setting the two expressions equal:

$$x \tan 42° = (x+15) \tan 38°$$

$$x \tan 42° = x \tan 38° + 15 \tan 38°$$

$$x \tan 42° - x \tan 38° = 15 \tan 38°$$

$$x(\tan 42° - \tan 38°) = 15 \tan 38°$$

$$x = \frac{15 \tan 38°}{\tan 42° - \tan 38°} \approx 98.3835$$

$$y = x \tan 42° = 98.3835 \tan 42° \approx 88.5849$$

The height of the tower is approximately 88.5849 feet.

73. Let y represent the height above the surface of the lawn. The equation is:

$$\sin 68° = \frac{y}{16}$$

$$y = 16 \sin 68°$$

$$y \approx 14.8349$$

The top of the ladder is approximately 14.8349 feet above the surface of the lawn.

75. Let x represent the horizontal distance from the point to the top of the hill. The equation is:

$$\tan 10° = \frac{9}{x}$$

$$x = \frac{9}{\tan 10°}$$

$$x \approx 51.0415$$

The horizontal distance from the point to the top of the hill is approximately 51.0415 feet.

77. Let θ represent the angle of incline. The equation is:

$$\tan \theta = \frac{1}{8}$$

$$\theta = \tan^{-1}\left(\frac{1}{8}\right)$$

$$\theta \approx 7.1250°$$

The angle of incline is approximately 7.1250°.

79. Let x represent the distance from the point to the center of the base. The equation is:

$$\tan 50° = \frac{324}{x}$$

$$x \tan 50° = 324$$

$$x = \frac{324}{\tan 50°}$$

$$x \approx 271.8683 \text{ m}$$

The distance from the point to the center of the base is approximately 271.8683 meters.

81. Let θ represent the angle of depression from the camera. The equation is:
$$\tan\theta = \frac{10}{50} = \frac{1}{5}$$
$$\theta = \tan^{-1}\left(\frac{1}{5}\right)$$
$$\theta \approx 11.3099°$$
The angle of depression for the camera should be set at approximately $11.3099°$.

83. Let L represent the length of the surfboard. The equation is:
$$\tan 45° = \frac{L}{84}$$
$$L = 84\tan 45°$$
$$L = 84 \text{ inches}$$
The surfboard is 84 inches long.

85. Finding the value of the ratio:
$$\frac{F_y}{F_x} = \tan 36° = 0.7625$$

87. Let y represent the height of the building. The equation is:
$$\tan 57° = \frac{y}{180}$$
$$y = 180\tan 57°$$
$$y \approx 277.1757$$
The height of the building is approximately 277.1757 feet.

89. Let x represent the distance from the point to the center of the base. The equation is:
$$\tan 60° = \frac{555}{x}$$
$$x\tan 60° = 555$$
$$x = \frac{555}{\tan 60°}$$
$$x \approx 320.4294$$
The distance from the point to the center of the base is approximately 320.4294 feet.

91. Let d represent the distance traversed by the light rays. The equation is:
$$\sin 27° = \frac{25}{d}$$
$$d\sin 27° = 25$$
$$d = \frac{25}{\sin 27°}$$
$$d \approx 55.0672$$
The distance traversed by the light rays is approximately 55.0672 feet.

93. First find L:
$$\sin 55° = \frac{90}{L}$$
$$L\sin 55° = 90$$
$$L = \frac{90}{\sin 55°}$$
$$L \approx 109.8697 \text{ feet}$$

Let $x + 80$ represent the distance from the top to the road. The equation is:

$$\tan 55° = \frac{90}{x}$$
$$x \tan 55° = 90$$
$$x = \frac{90}{\tan 55°}$$
$$x \approx 63.0187$$
$$H = 80 + x \approx 80 + 63.0187 \approx 143.0187 \text{ feet}$$

95. a.   Let a, b, c represent the sides of the triangle. We have the relationships:

$$\tan 35° = \frac{b}{a}$$
$$b = a \tan 35°$$

$$\cos 35° = \frac{a}{c}$$
$$c = \frac{a}{\cos 35°} = a \sec 35°$$

Using the perimeter of the triangle:
$$a + b + c = 30$$
$$a + a \tan 35° + a \sec 35° = 30$$
$$a\left(1 + \tan 35° + \sec 35°\right) = 30$$
$$a = \frac{30}{1 + \tan 35° + \sec 35°}$$
$$a \approx 10.2705$$
$$b = a \tan 35° \approx 10.2705 \tan 35° \approx 7.1915$$
$$c = \frac{a}{\cos 35°} \approx \frac{10.2705}{\cos 35°} \approx 12.5380$$

The sides of the triangle are 7.19 in., 10.27 in. and 12.54 in.

b.   Finding the area: $A = \frac{1}{2}ab \approx \frac{1}{2}(10.2705)(7.1915) \approx 36.93 \text{ in.}^2$

97.   Using the cofunction identities: $\csc\left(90° - \theta\right) = \dfrac{1}{\sin\left(90° - \theta\right)} = \dfrac{1}{\cos\theta} = \sec\theta$

99.   Because $\sin\left(90° - x\right) = \cos x$ and $\cos\left(90° - x\right) = \sin x$ for $0° \leq x \leq 90°$.

5.4 Trigonometric Functions of Any Angle Using Right Triangles

1. A positive angle is $50° + 360° = 410°$, and a negative angle is $50° - 360° = -310°$.

3. A positive angle is $250° + 360° = 610°$, and a negative angle is $250° - 360° = -110°$.

5. Using the Pythagorean theorem:
$$a^2 + b^2 = c^2$$
$$1^2 + 4^2 = c^2$$
$$c^2 = 17$$
$$c = \sqrt{17}$$

7. First find r using the Pythagorean theorem: $r = \sqrt{3^2 + 3^2} = \sqrt{18} = 3\sqrt{2}$
Finding the trigonometric functions:

$$\sin\theta = \frac{y}{r} = \frac{3}{3\sqrt{2}} = \frac{\sqrt{2}}{2} \qquad\qquad \csc\theta = \frac{r}{y} = \frac{3\sqrt{2}}{3} = \sqrt{2}$$

$$\cos\theta = \frac{x}{r} = \frac{3}{3\sqrt{2}} = \frac{\sqrt{2}}{2} \qquad\qquad \sec\theta = \frac{r}{x} = \frac{3\sqrt{2}}{3} = \sqrt{2}$$

$$\tan\theta = \frac{y}{x} = \frac{3}{3} = 1 \qquad\qquad \cot\theta = \frac{x}{y} = \frac{3}{3} = 1$$

9. First find r using the Pythagorean theorem: $r = \sqrt{(-1)^2 + \left(-\sqrt{3}\right)^2} = \sqrt{4} = 2$

Finding the trigonometric functions:

$$\sin\theta = \frac{y}{r} = -\frac{\sqrt{3}}{2} \qquad\qquad \csc\theta = \frac{r}{y} = -\frac{2}{\sqrt{3}} = -\frac{2\sqrt{3}}{3}$$

$$\cos\theta = \frac{x}{r} = -\frac{1}{2} \qquad\qquad \sec\theta = \frac{r}{x} = -2$$

$$\tan\theta = \frac{y}{x} = \frac{-\sqrt{3}}{-1} = \sqrt{3} \qquad\qquad \cot\theta = \frac{x}{y} = \frac{-1}{-\sqrt{3}} = \frac{1}{\sqrt{3}} = \frac{\sqrt{3}}{3}$$

11. First find r using the Pythagorean theorem: $r = \sqrt{(-1)^2 + 2^2} = \sqrt{5}$

Finding the trigonometric functions:

$$\sin\theta = \frac{y}{r} = \frac{2}{\sqrt{5}} = \frac{2\sqrt{5}}{5} \qquad\qquad \csc\theta = \frac{r}{y} = \frac{\sqrt{5}}{2}$$

$$\cos\theta = \frac{x}{r} = -\frac{1}{\sqrt{5}} = -\frac{\sqrt{5}}{5} \qquad\qquad \sec\theta = \frac{r}{x} = -\sqrt{5}$$

$$\tan\theta = \frac{y}{x} = \frac{2}{-1} = -2 \qquad\qquad \cot\theta = \frac{x}{y} = \frac{-1}{2} = -\frac{1}{2}$$

13. First find r using the Pythagorean theorem: $r = \sqrt{1^2 + 4^2} = \sqrt{17}$
Finding the trigonometric functions:

$$\sin\theta = \frac{y}{r} = \frac{4}{\sqrt{17}} = \frac{4\sqrt{17}}{17} \qquad\qquad \csc\theta = \frac{r}{y} = \frac{\sqrt{17}}{4}$$

$$\cos\theta = \frac{x}{r} = \frac{1}{\sqrt{17}} = \frac{\sqrt{17}}{17} \qquad\qquad \sec\theta = \frac{r}{x} = \sqrt{17}$$

$$\tan\theta = \frac{y}{x} = \frac{4}{1} = 4 \qquad\qquad \cot\theta = \frac{x}{y} = \frac{1}{4}$$

15. Since $\cos\theta > 0$ in Quadrants I and IV, and $\sin\theta < 0$ in Quadrants III and IV, then θ is in Quadrant IV.

17. Since $\sec\theta < 0$ in Quadrants II and III, and $\tan\theta > 0$ in Quadrants I and III, then θ is in Quadrant III.

19. Since $\cot\theta > 0$ in Quadrants I and III, and $\csc\theta > 0$ in Quadrants I and II, then θ is in Quadrant I.

21. Since $120°$ is in Quadrant II, the reference angle is $180° - 120° = 60°$.

23. Since $240°$ is in Quadrant III, the reference angle is $240° - 180° = 60°$.

25. Since $-105°$ is in Quadrant III and is coterminal with $-105° + 360° = 255°$, the reference angle is $255° - 180° = 75°$.

27. Since $400°$ is in Quadrant I and is coterminal with $400° - 360° = 40°$, the reference angle is $40°$.

29. Since $\dfrac{7\pi}{4} = \pi + \dfrac{3\pi}{4}$ is in Quadrant IV, the reference angle is $2\pi - \dfrac{7\pi}{4} = \dfrac{\pi}{4}$.

31. Since $-\dfrac{5\pi}{3}$ is in Quadrant I and is coterminal with $-\dfrac{5\pi}{3} + 2\pi = \dfrac{\pi}{3}$, the reference angle is $\dfrac{\pi}{3}$.

33. Here $150°$ is in Quadrant II where sine is positive. The reference angle is $30°$, thus $\sin 150° = \sin 30° = \dfrac{1}{2}$.

35. Here $225°$ is in Quadrant III where sine is negative. The reference angle is $45°$, thus $\sin 225° = -\sin 45° = -\dfrac{\sqrt{2}}{2}$.

37. Here $120°$ is in Quadrant II where cosine is negative. The reference angle is $60°$, thus $\cos 120° = -\cos 60° = -\dfrac{1}{2}$.

39. Here $\dfrac{2\pi}{3}$ is in Quadrant II where sine is positive. The reference angle is $\dfrac{\pi}{3}$, thus $\sin\dfrac{2\pi}{3} = \sin\dfrac{\pi}{3} = \dfrac{\sqrt{3}}{2}$.

41. Here $225°$ is in Quadrant III where tangent is positive. The reference angle is $45°$, thus $\tan 225° = \tan 45° = 1$.

43. Here $330°$ is in Quadrant IV where tangent is negative. The reference angle is $30°$, thus
$$\tan 330° = -\tan 30° = -\dfrac{1}{\sqrt{3}} = -\dfrac{\sqrt{3}}{3}.$$

45. Here $150°$ is in Quadrant II where secant is negative. The reference angle $30°$, thus
$$\sec 150° = -\sec 30° = -\dfrac{2}{\sqrt{3}} = -\dfrac{2\sqrt{3}}{3}.$$

47. Here $\dfrac{3\pi}{2}$ is the quadrant point $(0, -1)$, thus $\cot\dfrac{3\pi}{2} = 0$.

49. Note that $420°$ is coterminal with $420° - 360° = 60°$, therefore it is in Quadrant I where tangent is positive. The reference angle is $60°$, thus $\tan 420° = \tan 60° = \sqrt{3}$.

51. Note that $-210°$ is coterminal with $-210° + 360° = 150°$, therefore it is in Quadrant II where cosine is negative. The reference angle $30°$, thus $\cos\left(-210°\right) = -\cos 30° = -\dfrac{\sqrt{3}}{2}$.

53. Using the negative angle identity: $\tan\left(-45°\right) = -\tan 45° = -1$

55. Note that $-135°$ is coterminal with $-135° + 360° = 225°$, therefore it is in Quadrant III where secant is negative. The reference angle $45°$, thus $\sec\left(-135°\right) = -\sec 45° = -\dfrac{2}{\sqrt{2}} = -\sqrt{2}$.

57. Here $180°$ is the quadrant point $(-1, 0)$, thus $\csc 180°$ is undefined.

59. Here 2π is the quadrant point $(1, 0)$, thus $\sec 2\pi = 1$.

61. Finding the exact value: $\cos 45° + \sin 30° = \dfrac{\sqrt{2}}{2} + \dfrac{1}{2} = \dfrac{\sqrt{2}+1}{2}$

63. Finding the exact value: $\cos 120° - \sin 210° = -\cos 60° - \left(-\sin 30°\right) = -\dfrac{1}{2} + \dfrac{1}{2} = 0$

65. Finding the exact value: $\tan 120° + \cot 135° = -\tan 60° - \cot 45° = -\sqrt{3} - 1$

67. Finding the exact value: $\cot 210° - \tan 330° = \cot 30° - \left(-\tan 30°\right) = \dfrac{1}{\sqrt{3}} + \sqrt{3} = \dfrac{\sqrt{3}}{3} + \dfrac{3\sqrt{3}}{3} = \dfrac{4\sqrt{3}}{3}$

69. Finding the exact value: $\sec 180° + \csc 270° = -1 + \left(-1\right) = -2$

71. Finding the exact value: $\sin\dfrac{\pi}{3} + \cos\dfrac{2\pi}{3} = \sin\dfrac{\pi}{3} - \cos\dfrac{\pi}{3} = \dfrac{\sqrt{3}}{2} - \dfrac{1}{2} = \dfrac{\sqrt{3}-1}{2}$

73. Finding the exact value: $\tan\dfrac{5\pi}{4} - \cot\dfrac{\pi}{4} = \tan\dfrac{\pi}{4} - \cot\dfrac{\pi}{4} = 1 - 1 = 0$

75. Finding the exact value: $\cos 45° \cos 30° + \sin 45° \sin 30° = \dfrac{\sqrt{2}}{2} \cdot \dfrac{\sqrt{3}}{2} + \dfrac{\sqrt{2}}{2} \cdot \dfrac{1}{2} = \dfrac{\sqrt{6}+\sqrt{2}}{4}$

77. Finding the exact value: $\sin 60° \cos 45° - \cos 45° \sin 60° = \dfrac{\sqrt{3}}{2} \cdot \dfrac{\sqrt{2}}{2} - \dfrac{\sqrt{2}}{2} \cdot \dfrac{\sqrt{3}}{2} = \dfrac{\sqrt{6}-\sqrt{6}}{4} = 0$

79. Given $\cos\theta = \dfrac{3}{5} = \dfrac{x}{r}$, we use $x = 3$ and $r = 5$ in the Pythagorean theorem:

$$3^2 + y^2 = 5^2$$
$$9 + y^2 = 25$$
$$y^2 = 16$$
$$y = \pm 4$$

Since θ is in Quadrant IV, choose $y = -4$. Thus: $\sin\theta = \dfrac{y}{r} = -\dfrac{4}{5}$

81. Given $\sin\theta = -\dfrac{5}{13} = \dfrac{y}{r}$, we use $y = -5$ and $r = 13$ in the Pythagorean theorem:

$$x^2 + (-5)^2 = 13^2$$
$$x^2 + 25 = 169$$
$$x^2 = 144$$
$$x = \pm 12$$

Since θ is in Quadrant III, choose $x = -12$. Thus: $\sec\theta = \dfrac{r}{x} = -\dfrac{13}{12}$

83. Given $\cos\theta = -\dfrac{1}{3} = \dfrac{x}{r}$, we use $x = -1$ and $r = 3$ in the Pythagorean theorem:

$$(-1)^2 + y^2 = 3^2$$
$$1 + y^2 = 9$$
$$y^2 = 8$$
$$y = \pm\sqrt{8} = \pm 2\sqrt{2}$$

Since θ is in Quadrant III, choose $y = -2\sqrt{2}$. Thus: $\tan\theta = \dfrac{y}{x} = \dfrac{-2\sqrt{2}}{-1} = 2\sqrt{2}$

85. Given $\sin\theta = -\dfrac{1}{5} = \dfrac{y}{r}$, we use $y = -1$ and $r = 5$ in the Pythagorean theorem:

$$x^2 + (-1)^2 = 5^2$$
$$x^2 + 1 = 25$$
$$x^2 = 24$$
$$x = \pm\sqrt{24} = \pm 2\sqrt{6}$$

Since θ is in Quadrant IV, choose $x = 2\sqrt{6}$. Thus: $\cos\theta = \dfrac{x}{r} = \dfrac{2\sqrt{6}}{5}$

87. Given $\sin\theta = -0.8 = -\dfrac{4}{5} = \dfrac{y}{r}$, we use $y = -4$ and $r = 5$ in the Pythagorean theorem:

$$x^2 + (-4)^2 = 5^2$$
$$x^2 + 16 = 25$$
$$x^2 = 9$$
$$x = \pm 3$$

Since θ is in Quadrant IV, choose $x = 3$. Thus: $\sec\theta = \dfrac{r}{x} = \dfrac{5}{3}$

89. Calculating the value: $\sin 157° \approx 0.3907$

91. Calculating the value: $\cos 435.4° \approx 0.2521$

93. Calculating the value: $\tan 125° \approx -1.4281$

95. Calculating the value: $\cot 214° = \dfrac{1}{\tan 214°} \approx 1.4826$

97. Calculating the value: $\csc 315.4° = \dfrac{1}{\sin 315.4°} \approx -1.4242$

99. Let d represent the distance from the top of the pole to Point A. The supplement of $150°$ is $30°$. The equation is:

$$\tan 30° = \dfrac{d}{20}$$
$$d = 20\tan 30°$$
$$d = 20\left(\dfrac{\sqrt{3}}{3}\right) = \dfrac{20\sqrt{3}}{3} \text{ feet}$$

101. Let d represent the distance from Lakecrest to Woodbrook. Using $210° - 180° = 30°$, the distance can be found from the equation:

$$\sin 30° = \dfrac{d}{100}$$
$$d = 100\tan 30°$$
$$d = 100\left(\dfrac{1}{2}\right) = 50 \text{ miles}$$

103. Note that $\sec 270° = \dfrac{1}{\cos 270°} = \dfrac{1}{0}$, which is undefined.

105. Using the point (x, y): $\cos\theta = \dfrac{x}{r} = \dfrac{x}{\sqrt{x^2 + y^2}}$

Using the point (kx, ky): $\cos\theta = \dfrac{kx}{\sqrt{(kx)^2 + (ky)^2}} = \dfrac{kx}{\sqrt{k^2 x^2 + k^2 y^2}} = \dfrac{kx}{\sqrt{k^2}\sqrt{x^2 + y^2}} = \dfrac{kx}{k\sqrt{x^2 + y^2}} = \dfrac{x}{\sqrt{x^2 + y^2}}$

Note that the two answers are the same.

5.5 Graphs of the Sine and Cosine Functions

1. Upward

3. To the left

5. Vertical

7. Horizontal

9. The graph of $f(x) = \cos x + 3$ is the graph of $y = \cos x$ vertically shifted upward 3 units:

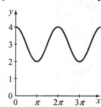

11. The graph of $g(x) = \cos x - \dfrac{1}{2}$ is the graph of $y = \cos x$ vertically shifted downward $\dfrac{1}{2}$ unit:

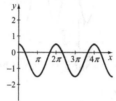

13. The graph of $f(x) = \cos\left(x - \dfrac{\pi}{4}\right)$ is the graph of $y = \cos x$ shifted horizontally $\dfrac{\pi}{4}$ units to the right:

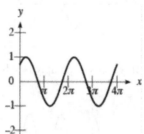

15. The graph of $g(x) = \cos\left(\dfrac{3\pi}{4} + x\right) = \cos\left(x + \dfrac{3\pi}{4}\right)$ is the graph of $y = \cos x$ shifted horizontally $\dfrac{3\pi}{4}$ units to the left:

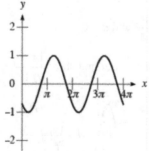

17. The graph of $f(x) = -2\sin x$ is the graph of $y = \sin x$ vertically stretched by a factor of 2 and reflected across the x-axis:

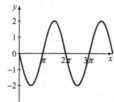

19. The graph of $g(x) = \dfrac{3}{2}\cos x$ is the graph of $y = \cos x$ vertically stretched by a factor of $\dfrac{3}{2}$:

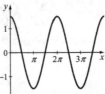

21. The graph of $f(x) = \sin(3x)$ is the graph of $y = \sin x$ compressed horizontally by a factor of $\dfrac{1}{3}$:

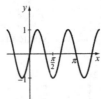

23. The graph of $f(x) = \sin\left(\dfrac{1}{2}x\right)$ is the graph of $y = \sin x$ stretched horizontally by a factor of 2:

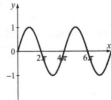

25. The graph of $g(x) = \cos(3x)$ is the graph of $y = \cos x$ compressed horizontally by a factor of $\dfrac{1}{3}$:

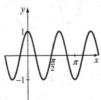

27. $f(x) = -2\sin\left(x - \dfrac{\pi}{4}\right)$: $a = -2, b = 1, c = \dfrac{\pi}{4}$, and $d = 0$

Amplitude: $|-2| = 2$; Period: $p = \dfrac{2\pi}{1} = 2\pi$; Horizontal shift: $\dfrac{|\pi/4|}{1} = \dfrac{\pi}{4}$ units to the right; Reflection across the x-axis

29. $g(x) = \dfrac{1}{2}\sin(2x - \pi)$: $a = \dfrac{1}{2}$, $b = 2$, $c = \pi$, and $d = 0$

Amplitude: $\left|\dfrac{1}{2}\right| = \dfrac{1}{2}$; Period: $p = \dfrac{2\pi}{2} = \pi$; Horizontal shift: $\dfrac{|\pi|}{2} = \dfrac{\pi}{2}$ units to the right

31. $h(x) = -3\sin(4x - \pi) + 2$; $a = -3$, $b = 3$, $c = \pi$, and $d = 2$

Amplitude: $|-3| = 3$; Period: $p = \dfrac{2\pi}{4} = \dfrac{\pi}{2}$; Horizontal shift: $\dfrac{|\pi|}{4} = \dfrac{\pi}{4}$ units to the right

Vertical shift: 2 units upwards; Reflection across the x-axis

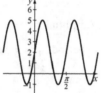

33. $r(x) = -\cos(2\pi x) + 2$; $a = -1$, $b = 2\pi$, $c = 0$, and $d = 2$

Amplitude: $|-1| = 1$; Period: $p = \dfrac{2\pi}{2\pi} = 1$; Horizontal shift: $\dfrac{|0|}{2} = 0$ units

Vertical shift: 2 units upwards; Reflection across the x-axis

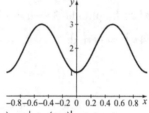

35. Using a graphing device, the graph of $h(x) = 2|\sin(2x)| + 1$ is given:

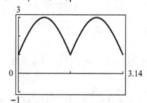

37. No, the graphs are not the same:

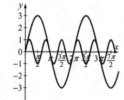

39. No, the graphs are not the same:

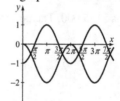

41. No, the graphs are not the same:

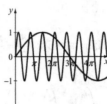

43. Vertical shift: 1 unit upward $\Rightarrow b = 1$; Horizontal shift: $\dfrac{\pi}{2}$ units to the right $\Rightarrow a = \dfrac{\pi}{2}$; Expression: $\sin\left(x - \dfrac{\pi}{2}\right) + 1$

45. Vertical shift: 1 unit downward $\Rightarrow b = -1$; Horizontal shift: π units to the left $\Rightarrow a = -\pi$
Expression: $\sin(x + \pi) - 1$

47. Since a cycle starts at the origin, use $a\sin bx$. Amplitude: $3 \Rightarrow a = \pm 3$; $a = 3$;

One cycle of the curve is complete in $[0, \pi] \Rightarrow$ period: $p = \pi$ so $\dfrac{2\pi}{b} = \pi \Rightarrow b = 2$

Expression: $3\sin(2x)$

49. Since a cycle starts at the origin, use $a\sin bx$. Amplitude: $2 \Rightarrow a = \pm 2$; $a = -2$

One cycle of the curve is complete in $[0, \pi] \Rightarrow$ period: $p = \pi$ so $\dfrac{2\pi}{b} = \pi \Rightarrow b = 2$

Expression: $-2\sin(2x)$

51. Since a cycle does not start at the origin, use $a\cos bx$. Amplitude: $1 \Rightarrow a = \pm 1$; $a = -1$

One cycle of the curve is complete in $[0, 4\pi] \Rightarrow$ period: $p = 4\pi$ so $\dfrac{2\pi}{b} = 4\pi \Rightarrow b = \dfrac{1}{2}$

Expression: $-\cos\left(\dfrac{1}{2}x\right) = -\cos\left(\dfrac{x}{2}\right)$

53. Since a cycle starts at the origin, use $a\sin bx$. Amplitude: $3 \Rightarrow a = \pm 3$; $a = 3$

One cycle of the curve is complete in $[0, 4\pi] \Rightarrow$ period: $p = 4\pi$ so $\dfrac{2\pi}{b} = 4\pi \Rightarrow b = \dfrac{1}{2}$

Expression: $3\sin\left(\dfrac{1}{2}x\right) = 3\sin\left(\dfrac{x}{2}\right)$

55. The correct answer is c.   **57.** The correct answer is a.

59. The correct answer is f.

61. Evaluating when $t = \dfrac{1}{2}$: $d = 7\cos\left[\dfrac{\pi}{2}\left(\dfrac{1}{2}\right)\right] = 7\cos\dfrac{\pi}{4} = \dfrac{7\sqrt{2}}{2}$ units

Evaluating when $t = 4$: $d = 7\cos\left[\dfrac{\pi}{2} \cdot 4\right] = 7\cos 2\pi = 7(1) = 7$ units

63. Evaluating when $t = 4$: $s(4) = 210 + 150\cos\left(\dfrac{\pi}{6} \cdot 4\right) = 210 + 150\cos\dfrac{2\pi}{3} = 210 + 150\left(-\dfrac{1}{2}\right) = 210 - 75 = 135$

Toy sales in April was \$135,000. The period is: $p = \dfrac{2\pi}{b} = \dfrac{2\pi}{\left(\dfrac{\pi}{6}\right)} = 2\pi \cdot \dfrac{6}{\pi} = 12$ months

65. Setting the voltage equal to 0:

$$3t - \frac{\pi}{2} = 0$$

$$3t = \frac{\pi}{2}$$

$$t = \frac{\pi}{6}$$

67. The amplitude is 25, and the period is: $p = \frac{2\pi}{4} = \frac{\pi}{2}$

The frequency is given by: $f = \frac{1}{p} = \frac{2}{\pi}$

69. The amplitude is 80 and the vertical shift is 200, so the maximum distance is $80 + 200 = 280$ miles.

71. **a.** Finding the period: $p = \dfrac{2\pi}{\left(\dfrac{2\pi}{23}\right)} = 2\pi \cdot \dfrac{23}{2\pi} = 23$ days

b. Evaluating the function: $P(1095) = 50\sin\left(\dfrac{2\pi}{23} \cdot 1095\right) + 50 = 50\sin\dfrac{2190\pi}{23} + 50 = 18.4456$

   Their physical potential on their third birthday is approximately 18.4%.

73. The graphs are identical:

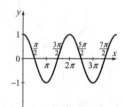

5.6 Graphs of Other Trigonometric Functions

1. The graph of $f(x) = \tan x - 3$ is the graph of $y = \tan x$ shifted vertically downward 3 units:

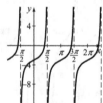

3. The graph of $f(x) = \sec x + 1$ is the graph of $y = \sec x$ shifted vertically upward 1 unit:

5. The graph of $g(x) = \cot x + \dfrac{3}{2}$ is the graph of $y = \cot x$ shifted vertically upward $\dfrac{3}{2}$ units:

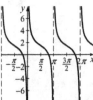

7. The graph of $f(x) = \tan\left(x + \dfrac{\pi}{4}\right)$ is the graph of $y = \tan x$ shifted horizontally $\dfrac{\pi}{4}$ units to the left:

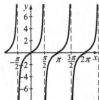

9. The graph of $f(x) = \sec\left(x - \dfrac{\pi}{2}\right)$ is the graph of $y = \sec x$ shifted horizontally $\dfrac{\pi}{2}$ units to the right:

11. The graph of $f(x) = \cot\left(\dfrac{3\pi}{4} + x\right) = \cot\left(x + \dfrac{3\pi}{4}\right)$ is the graph of $y = \cot x$ shifted horizontally $\dfrac{3\pi}{4}$ units to the left:

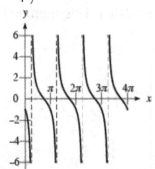

13. The graph of $f(x) = 4\tan x$ is the graph of $y = \tan x$ vertically stretched by a factor of 4:

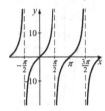

15. The graph of $f(x) = 2\csc x$ is the graph of $y = \csc x$ vertically stretched by a factor of 2:

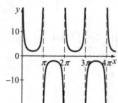

17. The graph of $g(x) = -2\cot x$ is the graph of $y = \cot x$ vertically stretched by a factor of 2 and reflected across the x-axis:

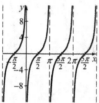

19. The graph of $f(x) = \tan(2x)$ is the graph of $y = \tan x$ compressed horizontally by a factor of $\dfrac{1}{2}$:

21. The graph of $f(x) = \csc(2x)$ is the graph of $y = \csc x$ compressed horizontally by a factor of $\dfrac{1}{2}$:

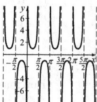

23. The graph of $g(x) = \csc\left(\dfrac{\pi}{3}x\right)$ is the graph of $y = \csc x$ compressed horizontally by a factor of $\dfrac{3}{\pi}$:

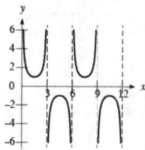

25. $f(x) = \tan\left(x + \dfrac{\pi}{4}\right) + 1$

Period: $p = \pi$; Horizontal shift: $\dfrac{\pi}{4}$ units to the left; Vertical shift: 1 unit upward

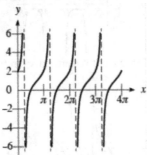

27. $f(x) = 2\sec\left(x + \dfrac{\pi}{4}\right)$

Period: $p = 2\pi$; Horizontal shift: $\dfrac{\pi}{4}$ units to the left; Vertical stretch by a factor of 2

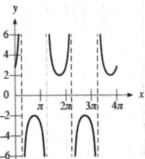

29. $g(x) = \dfrac{1}{2}\cot(2x)$

Period: $p = \dfrac{\pi}{2}$; Certical compression by a factor of $\dfrac{1}{2}$; Horizontal compression by a factor of $\dfrac{1}{2}$

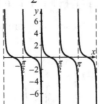

31. $f(x) = -3\csc(x - \pi) + 2$

Period: $p = 2\pi$; Vertical shift: 2 units upward; Horizontal shift: π units to the right

Vertical stretch by a factor of 3; Reflection across the x-axis

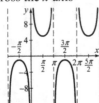

33. $r(x) = -\sec\left(\dfrac{2\pi}{3}x\right) + 2$

Period: $p = \dfrac{2\pi}{\left(\dfrac{2\pi}{3}\right)} = 2\pi \cdot \dfrac{3}{2\pi} = 3$; Horizontal compression by a factor of $\dfrac{3}{2\pi}$

Vertical shift: 2 units downward; Reflection across the x-axis

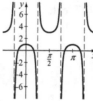

35. Given the direction of the branches, use $a\cot bx$.

$a = 1$; Period: $p = \dfrac{\pi}{2}$ so $\dfrac{\pi}{b} = \dfrac{\pi}{2} \Rightarrow b = 2$.

Expression: $\cot(2x)$

37. Given the direction of the branches, use $a\tan bx$.

$a = 1$; Period: $p = \dfrac{3\pi}{2} - \left(-\dfrac{3\pi}{2}\right) = 3\pi$ so $\dfrac{\pi}{b} = 3\pi \Rightarrow b = \dfrac{1}{3}$.

Expression: $\tan\left(\dfrac{1}{3}x\right) = \tan\left(\dfrac{x}{3}\right)$

39. $f(x) = \tan x$ and $f(x) = -\tan x$ have the same period and asymptotes but are reflections of each other across the x-axis:

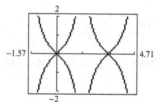

41. $f(x) = 2\sec x$ is a horizontal and vertical stretch of $f(x) = \sec 2x$:

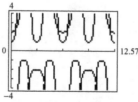

43. $f(x) = \cot(3\pi x)$ is a horizontal compression of $f(x) = \cot\left(\dfrac{\pi}{3}x\right)$:

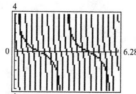

45. Finding the function:

$$\tan x = \frac{5}{d(x)}$$

$$d(x) = \frac{5}{\tan x} = 5\cot x$$

Evaluating: $d(35°) = 5\cot 35° = 7.1407$

The length of the base of the railing is about 7.1407 feet.

47. Let C represent angle SPT. Then we have:

$$\tan(x+C) = \frac{h(x)}{8}$$

$$h(x) = 8\tan(x+C)$$

Since the length of PT is 8 feet, we have:

$$\tan C = \frac{8}{8} = 1$$

$$C = \frac{\pi}{4}$$

Therefore: $h(x) = 8\tan\left(x+\frac{\pi}{4}\right)$

Finding the height when $x = \frac{5\pi}{36}$: $h\left(\frac{5\pi}{36}\right) = 8\tan\left(\frac{5\pi}{36}+\frac{\pi}{4}\right) = 8\tan\frac{7\pi}{18} \approx 21.9798$ ft

49. The domain is all real numbers except $\frac{n\pi}{2}$, where n is any integer.

The range is $(-\infty, 2]\cup[4,\infty)$.

51. Writing the function as: $f(x) = \tan x + \cot x = \frac{\sin x}{\cos x} + \frac{\cos x}{\sin x}$

The denominators are 0 when x is any multiple of $\frac{\pi}{2}$, so the vertical asymptotes are $x = \frac{n\pi}{2}$, where n is any integer.

5.7 Inverse Trigonometric Functions

1. Finding the inverse: $f^{-1}(-2) = 1$

3. Finding the value: $(f \circ f^{-1})(3) = 3$

5. Let $y = \arcsin 1$, therefore:

$$\sin y = 1, y \in \left[-\frac{\pi}{2}, \frac{\pi}{2}\right]$$

$$y = \frac{\pi}{2}$$

Thus $\arcsin 1 = \frac{\pi}{2}$.

7. Let $y = \arccos(-1)$, therefore:

$$\cos y = -1, y \in [0, \pi]$$

$$y = \pi$$

Thus $\arccos(-1) = \pi$.

9. Let $y = \arctan 0$, therefore:

$$\tan y = 0, y \in \left(-\frac{\pi}{2}, \frac{\pi}{2}\right)$$

$$y = 0$$

Thus $\arctan 0 = 0$.

11. Let $y = \arccos \frac{1}{2}$, therefore:

$$\cos y = \frac{1}{2}, y \in [0, \pi]$$

$$y = \frac{\pi}{3}$$

Thus $\arccos \frac{1}{2} = \frac{\pi}{3}$.

13. Let $y = \cos^{-1}\left(-\frac{\sqrt{3}}{2}\right)$, therefore:

$$\cos y = -\frac{\sqrt{3}}{2}, y \in [0, \pi]$$

$$y = \frac{5\pi}{6}$$

Thus $\arccos\left(-\frac{\sqrt{3}}{2}\right) = \frac{5\pi}{6}$.

15. Let $y = \tan^{-1}\left(-\sqrt{3}\right)$, therefore:

$$\tan y = -\sqrt{3}, y \in \left(-\frac{\pi}{2}, \frac{\pi}{2}\right)$$

$$y = -\frac{\pi}{3}$$

Thus $\arctan\left(-\sqrt{3}\right) = -\frac{\pi}{3}$.

17. Calculating the value: $\arcsin\left(-\frac{1}{4}\right) \approx -0.2527$

19. Calculating the value: $\arcsin 0.75 \approx 0.7227$

21. Calculating the value: $\arctan 5 \approx 1.3734$

23. Calculating the value: $\cos^{-1} 0.125 \approx 1.4455$

25. Calculating the value: $\cos^{-1}(-0.95) \approx 2.8240$

27. Calculating the value: $\tan^{-1}(-5) \approx -1.3734$

29. Finding the exact value: $\arccos\left(\cos\left(-\frac{\pi}{3}\right)\right) = \arccos\left(\cos\left(\frac{\pi}{3}\right)\right) = \arccos\frac{1}{2} = \frac{\pi}{3}$

31. Finding the exact value: $\sin\left(\arcsin(0.3)\right) = 0.3$

33. Finding the exact value: $\tan\left(\arctan(4)\right) = 4$

35. Let $t = \arccos \dfrac{12}{13}$. Then $\cos t = \dfrac{12}{13}$. Using the Pythagorean identity:

$$\sin^2 t + \cos^2 t = 1$$

$$\sin^2 t + \left(\frac{12}{13}\right)^2 = 1$$

$$\sin^2 t + \frac{144}{169} = 1$$

$$\sin^2 t = \frac{25}{169}$$

$$\sin t = \pm\frac{5}{13}$$

Since $t \in [0,\pi]$, $\sin t > 0$, so: $\sin\left(\arccos\left(\dfrac{12}{13}\right)\right) = \sin t = \dfrac{5}{13}$

37. Let $t = \arcsin\left(-\dfrac{12}{13}\right)$. Then $\sin t = -\dfrac{12}{13}$. Using the Pythagorean identity:

$$\sin^2 t + \cos^2 t = 1$$

$$\left(-\frac{12}{13}\right)^2 + \cos^2 t = 1$$

$$\frac{144}{169} + \cos^2 t = 1$$

$$\cos^2 t = \frac{25}{169}$$

$$\cos t = \pm\frac{5}{13}$$

Since $t \in \left[-\dfrac{\pi}{2}, \dfrac{\pi}{2}\right]$, $\cos t > 0$, so: $\cos\left(\arcsin\left(-\dfrac{12}{13}\right)\right) = \cos t = \dfrac{5}{13}$

39. The graph of $f(x) = \arctan x - \dfrac{\pi}{2}$ is the graph of $y = \arctan x$ vertically shifted downward $\dfrac{\pi}{2}$ units:

41. The graph of $f(x) = 2\arccos x$ is the graph of $y = \arccos x$ vertically stretched by a factor of 2:

43. The graph of $g(x) = \sin^{-1} 2x - \pi$ is the graph of $y = \arcsin x$ horizontally compressed by a factor of $\frac{1}{2}$ and vertically shifted downward π units:

45. The domain of $y = \arccos x$ is $[-1, 1]$, and 4 is not in this interval.

47. The domain of $y = \arcsin x$ is $[-1, 1]$, and 5 is not in this interval.

49. Finding the exact value: $\csc^{-1} \sqrt{2} = \sin^{-1} \dfrac{1}{\sqrt{2}} = \sin^{-1} \dfrac{\sqrt{2}}{2} = \dfrac{\pi}{4}$

51. Finding the exact value: $\sec^{-1}\left(-\dfrac{2\sqrt{3}}{3}\right) = \cos^{-1}\left(-\dfrac{3}{2\sqrt{3}}\right) = \cos^{-1}\left(-\dfrac{\sqrt{3}}{2}\right) = \dfrac{5\pi}{6}$

53. Finding the exact value: $\csc^{-1}(-2) = \sin^{-1}\left(-\dfrac{1}{2}\right) = -\dfrac{\pi}{6}$

55. Finding the exact value: $\cot^{-1} \sqrt{3} = \tan^{-1} \dfrac{1}{\sqrt{3}} = \dfrac{\pi}{6}$

57. Calculating the value: $\sec^{-1} 2.5 = \cos^{-1}\left(\dfrac{1}{2.5}\right) \approx 1.1593$

59. Calculating the value: $\csc^{-1}(-3.6) = \sin^{-1}\left(-\dfrac{1}{3.6}\right) \approx -0.2815$

61. Calculating the value: $\cot^{-1} 2.4 = \tan^{-1} \dfrac{1}{2.4} \approx 0.3948$

63. Calculating the value: $\cot^{-1}(-3.2) = \tan^{-1}\left(-\dfrac{1}{3.2}\right) \approx -0.3029$

65. Since $\tan\theta = \dfrac{19}{5}$, the angle (in degrees) is: $\theta = \tan^{-1}\left(\dfrac{19}{5}\right) \approx 75.2564°$

67. If a is the length of the wire and h is the height of the pole, then the ratio must be $\dfrac{a}{h} = \dfrac{4}{3}$. Given the description, we have $\sin\theta = \dfrac{3}{4}$, so $\theta = \sin^{-1}\left(\dfrac{3}{4}\right) \approx 48.5904°$. This is a minimum value in order to stay within the necessary ratio.

69. The angle is given by: $\arctan\left(\dfrac{4}{5}\right) \approx 38.6598°$

71. Solving for t:
$$d = 5\sin 2t$$
$$\frac{d}{5} = \sin 2t$$
$$\sin^{-1}\left(\frac{d}{5}\right) = 2t$$
$$t = \frac{1}{2}\sin^{-1}\left(\frac{d}{5}\right)$$

Finding the domain:

$$-1 \le \frac{d}{5} \le 1$$

$$-5 \le d \le 5$$

The domain is $[-5, 5]$.

73. Finding the angle (in degrees):

$$R = \frac{(v_0)^2 \sin 2\theta}{g}$$

$$80 = \frac{(30)^2 \sin 2\theta}{9.8}$$

$$784 = 900 \sin 2\theta$$

$$\frac{196}{225} = \sin 2\theta$$

$$2\theta = \sin^{-1}\left(\frac{196}{225}\right)$$

$$\theta = \frac{1}{2}\sin^{-1}\left(\frac{196}{225}\right) \approx 30.2940°$$

75. Approximating the value: $\arcsin(-0.2) \approx -0.20$ 77. Approximating the value: $\arcsin(-0.8) \approx -0.93$

79. Approximating the value: $\arctan 4 \approx 1.3$ 81. Approximating the value: $\tan^{-1} 6 \approx 1.4$

Chapter 5 Review Exercises

1. Sketching the angle:

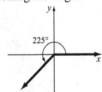

2. Sketching the angle:

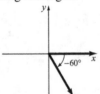

3. Sketching the angle:

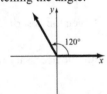

4. Sketching the angle:

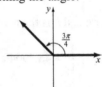

5. Sketching the angle:

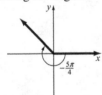

6. Sketching the angle:

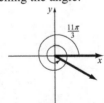

7. The complementary angle is: $90° - 35° = 55°$
   The supplementary angle is: $180° - 35° = 145°$

8. The complementary angle is: $90° - 47° = 43°$
   The supplementary angle is: $180° - 47° = 133°$

9. Converting from degrees to radians: $240° = 240°\left(\dfrac{\pi}{180°}\right) = \dfrac{4\pi}{3}$ radians

10. Converting from degrees to radians: $210° = 210°\left(\dfrac{\pi}{180°}\right) = \dfrac{7\pi}{6}$ radians

11. Converting from degrees to radians: $-150° = -150°\left(\dfrac{\pi}{180°}\right) = -\dfrac{5\pi}{6}$ radians

12. Converting from degrees to radians: $-225° = -225°\left(\dfrac{\pi}{180°}\right) = -\dfrac{5\pi}{4}$ radians

13. Converting from radians to degrees: $\dfrac{5\pi}{6} = \dfrac{5\pi}{6}\left(\dfrac{180°}{\pi}\right) = 150°$

14. Converting from radians to degrees: $-\dfrac{3\pi}{5} = -\dfrac{3\pi}{5}\left(\dfrac{180°}{\pi}\right) = -108°$

15. Converting from radians to degrees: $\dfrac{\pi}{90} = \dfrac{\pi}{90}\left(\dfrac{180°}{\pi}\right) = 2°$

16. Converting from radians to degrees: $\dfrac{7\pi}{5} = \dfrac{7\pi}{5}\left(\dfrac{180°}{\pi}\right) = 252°$

17. Finding the angular speed: $\omega = \dfrac{1\,\text{rev}}{1.5\,\text{min}} \cdot \dfrac{2\pi}{\text{rev}} = \dfrac{4\pi}{3}$ rads / min

    Thus the angle is: $\theta = \dfrac{4\pi}{3}$ or $240°$

18. **a.** Finding the angular speed: $\omega = \dfrac{1\,\text{rev}}{3\,\text{min}} \cdot \dfrac{2\pi}{\text{rev}} = \dfrac{2\pi}{3}$ rads / min

    b. The distance is given by: $s = r\omega t = (2\,\text{ft})\left(\dfrac{2\pi}{3}\dfrac{\text{rad}}{\text{min}}\right)(1\,\text{min}) = \dfrac{4\pi}{3}$ ft

19. Since $t = \dfrac{4\pi}{3} = \pi + \dfrac{\pi}{3}$ is in Quadrant III, its reference angle is $\dfrac{4\pi}{3} - \pi = \dfrac{\pi}{3}$.

20. Since $t = -\dfrac{11\pi}{3} = -\left(3\pi + \dfrac{2\pi}{3}\right) = -3\pi - \dfrac{2\pi}{3}$ is in Quadrant I, its reference angle is $-\dfrac{2\pi}{3} + \pi = \dfrac{\pi}{3}$.

21. Since $t = \dfrac{5\pi}{3} = \pi + \dfrac{2\pi}{3}$ is in Quadrant IV, its reference angle is $2\pi - \dfrac{5\pi}{3} = \dfrac{\pi}{3}$.

22. Since $t = -\dfrac{7\pi}{6} = -\left(\pi + \dfrac{\pi}{6}\right) = -\pi - \dfrac{\pi}{6}$ is in Quadrant II, its reference angle is $\dfrac{\pi}{6}$.

23. Note that $t = -\dfrac{5\pi}{2} = -\dfrac{\pi}{2} - 2\pi$. Finding the trigonometric values:

    $\sin\left(-\dfrac{5\pi}{2}\right) = \sin\left(-\dfrac{\pi}{2}\right) = -\sin\dfrac{\pi}{2} = -1$

    $\cos\left(-\dfrac{5\pi}{2}\right) = \cos\left(-\dfrac{\pi}{2}\right) = \cos\dfrac{\pi}{2} = 0$

    $\tan\left(-\dfrac{5\pi}{2}\right) = \tan\left(-\dfrac{\pi}{2}\right) = -\tan\dfrac{\pi}{2}$ is undefined

24. Note that $t = \dfrac{11\pi}{6} = -\dfrac{\pi}{6} + 2\pi$. Finding the trigonometric values:

$$\sin\left(\frac{11\pi}{6}\right) = \sin\left(-\frac{\pi}{6}\right) = -\sin\frac{\pi}{6} = -\frac{1}{2}$$

$$\cos\left(\frac{11\pi}{6}\right) = \cos\left(-\frac{\pi}{6}\right) = \cos\frac{\pi}{6} = \frac{\sqrt{3}}{2}$$

$$\tan\left(\frac{11\pi}{6}\right) = \tan\left(-\frac{\pi}{6}\right) = -\tan\frac{\pi}{6} = -\frac{1}{\sqrt{3}} = -\frac{\sqrt{3}}{3}$$

25. Note that $t = \dfrac{7\pi}{3} = \dfrac{\pi}{3} + 2\pi$. Finding the trigonometric values:

$$\sin\left(\frac{7\pi}{3}\right) = \sin\left(\frac{\pi}{3}\right) = \frac{\sqrt{3}}{2}$$

$$\cos\left(\frac{7\pi}{3}\right) = \cos\left(\frac{\pi}{3}\right) = \frac{1}{2}$$

$$\tan\left(\frac{7\pi}{3}\right) = \tan\left(\frac{\pi}{3}\right) = \frac{\sqrt{3}}{1} = \sqrt{3}$$

26. Note that $t = -\dfrac{17\pi}{6} = -\dfrac{5\pi}{6} - 2\pi$. Finding the trigonometric values:

$$\sin\left(-\frac{17\pi}{6}\right) = \sin\left(-\frac{5\pi}{6}\right) = -\sin\frac{5\pi}{6} = -\frac{1}{2}$$

$$\cos\left(-\frac{17\pi}{6}\right) = \cos\left(-\frac{5\pi}{6}\right) = \cos\frac{5\pi}{6} = -\frac{\sqrt{3}}{2}$$

$$\tan\left(-\frac{17\pi}{6}\right) = \tan\left(-\frac{5\pi}{6}\right) = -\tan\frac{5\pi}{6} = \frac{1}{\sqrt{3}} = \frac{\sqrt{3}}{3}$$

27. Finding the missing values: $\sin t = \dfrac{1}{2}, \tan t = -\dfrac{\sqrt{3}}{3}$

28. Finding the missing values: $\cos t = \dfrac{\sqrt{2}}{2}, \tan t = -1$

29. Finding the missing values: $\sin t = -\dfrac{\sqrt{2}}{2}, \cos t = \dfrac{\sqrt{2}}{2}$

30. Finding the missing values: $\sin t = -\dfrac{\sqrt{3}}{2}, \tan t = \sqrt{3}$

31. Finding the value: $\tan\left(-\dfrac{\pi}{4}\right) = -\tan\dfrac{\pi}{4} = -1$

32. Finding the value: $\cos\left(-\dfrac{5\pi}{4}\right) = \cos\dfrac{5\pi}{4} = -\dfrac{\sqrt{2}}{2}$

33. The maximum distance is 10 units (the amplitude). Finding the period: $\dfrac{2\pi}{\left(\dfrac{\pi}{3}\right)} = 2\pi \cdot \dfrac{3}{\pi} = 6$ seconds

34. If $\cos\theta = \dfrac{1}{5}$, choose $a = 1$ and $c = 5$ in the Pythagorean theorem:

$$1^2 + b^2 = 5^2$$
$$1 + b^2 = 25$$
$$b^2 = 24$$
$$b = \sqrt{24} = 2\sqrt{6}$$

The six trigonometric values are:

$$\sin\theta = \frac{2\sqrt{6}}{5} \qquad\qquad \cos\theta = \frac{1}{5} \qquad\qquad \tan\theta = \frac{2\sqrt{6}}{1} = 2\sqrt{6}$$

$$\csc\theta = \frac{5}{2\sqrt{6}} = \frac{5\sqrt{6}}{12} \qquad \sec\theta = \frac{5}{1} = 5 \qquad \cot\theta = \frac{1}{2\sqrt{6}} = \frac{\sqrt{6}}{12}$$

35. If $\sin\theta = 0.3 = \dfrac{3}{10}$, choose $b = 3$ and $c = 10$ in the Pythagorean theorem:

$$a^2 + 3^2 = 10^2$$
$$a^2 + 9 = 100$$
$$a^2 = 91$$
$$a = \sqrt{91}$$

The six trigonometric values are:

$$\sin\theta = \frac{3}{10} \qquad\qquad \cos\theta = \frac{\sqrt{91}}{10} \qquad\qquad \tan\theta = \frac{3}{\sqrt{91}} = \frac{3\sqrt{91}}{91}$$

$$\csc\theta = \frac{10}{3} \qquad\qquad \sec\theta = \frac{10}{\sqrt{91}} = \frac{10\sqrt{91}}{91} \qquad \cot\theta = \frac{\sqrt{91}}{3}$$

36. If $\tan\theta = 2 = \dfrac{2}{1}$, choose $a = 1$ and $b = 2$ in the Pythagorean theorem:

$$1^2 + 2^2 = c^2$$
$$1 + 4 = c^2$$
$$5 = c^2$$
$$c = \sqrt{5}$$

The six trigonometric values are:

$$\sin\theta = \frac{2}{\sqrt{5}} = \frac{2\sqrt{5}}{5} \qquad\qquad \cos\theta = \frac{1}{\sqrt{5}} = \frac{\sqrt{5}}{5} \qquad\qquad \tan\theta = \frac{2}{1} = 2$$

$$\csc\theta = \frac{\sqrt{5}}{2} \qquad\qquad \sec\theta = \frac{\sqrt{5}}{1} = \sqrt{5} \qquad\qquad \cot\theta = \frac{1}{2}$$

37. If $\cot\theta = 0.7 = \dfrac{7}{10}$, choose $a = 7$ and $b = 10$ in the Pythagorean theorem:

$$7^2 + 10^2 = c^2$$
$$49 + 100 = c^2$$
$$149 = c^2$$
$$c = \sqrt{149}$$

The six trigonometric values are:

$$\sin\theta = \frac{10}{\sqrt{149}} = \frac{10\sqrt{149}}{149} \qquad \cos\theta = \frac{7}{\sqrt{149}} = \frac{7\sqrt{149}}{149} \qquad \tan\theta = \frac{10}{7}$$

$$\csc\theta = \frac{\sqrt{149}}{10} \qquad\qquad \sec\theta = \frac{\sqrt{149}}{7} \qquad\qquad \cot\theta = \frac{7}{10}$$

38. Finding the other sides:

$$\tan 50° = \frac{7}{a} \qquad\qquad\qquad \sin 50° = \frac{7}{c}$$
$$a\tan 50° = 7 \qquad\qquad\qquad c\sin 50° = 7$$
$$a = \frac{7}{\tan 50°} \approx 5.8737 \qquad\qquad c = \frac{7}{\sin 50°} \approx 9.1379$$

39. Finding the other sides:

$$\tan 62° = \frac{b}{10} \qquad\qquad\qquad \cos 62° = \frac{10}{c}$$
$$b = 10\tan 62° \approx 18.8073 \qquad\qquad c = \frac{10}{\cos 62°} \approx 21.3005$$

40. Let h represent the height of the tower. The equation is:

$$\tan 63° = \frac{h}{150}$$
$$h = 150\tan 63° \approx 294.3916$$

The tower's height is approximately 294 feet.

41. Let y represent the height of the tower and x represent the distance from the second point to the tower. We have the equations:

$$\tan 38° = \frac{y}{x} \qquad\qquad\qquad \tan 35° = \frac{y}{x+12}$$
$$y = x\tan 38° \qquad\qquad\qquad y = (x+12)\tan 35°$$

Setting the equations equal:

$$x\tan 38° = (x+12)\tan 35°$$
$$x\tan 38° = x\tan 35° + 12\tan 35°$$
$$x\tan 38° - x\tan 35° = 12\tan 35°$$
$$x(\tan 38° - \tan 35°) = 12\tan 35°$$
$$x = \frac{12\tan 35°}{\tan 38° - \tan 35°} \approx 103.6345$$

Therefore: $y = x\tan 38° \approx 103.6345\tan 38° \approx 80.9681$

The tower is approximately 81 feet tall.

42. Let c represent the distance traveled by the plane. The equation is:

$$\sin 16° = \frac{5000}{c}$$

$$c = \frac{5000}{\sin 16°} \approx 18{,}139.7764$$

Converting units: $18{,}139.7764 \text{ ft} = 18{,}139.7764 \text{ ft} \cdot \frac{1 \text{ mi}}{5280 \text{ ft}} \approx 3.4356 \text{ mi}$

The plane has traveled approximately 3.44 miles.

43. Let b represent the vertical distance of the incline from its base. The equation is:

$$\sin 22° = \frac{b}{30}$$

$$b = 30 \sin 22° \approx 11.2382$$

The incline is approximately 11.3 feet higher than its base.

44. Let R represent the radius of the path. The equation is:

$$\cos 25° = \frac{R}{3900}$$

$$R = 3900 \cos 25° \approx 3534.6004$$

Since 1 revolution of the Earth is 2π radians, the arc length is: $s = r\theta = 3534.6004(2\pi) = 22{,}208.5493$

The length of the path is approximately 22,209 miles.

45. First find r using the Pythagorean theorem: $r = \sqrt{(-12)^2 + 5^2} = \sqrt{144 + 25} = \sqrt{169} = 13$

Finding the trigonometric value: $\cos\theta = \frac{x}{r} = \frac{-12}{13} = -\frac{12}{13}$

46. First find r using the Pythagorean theorem: $r = \sqrt{(-4)^2 + (-3)^2} = \sqrt{9 + 16} = \sqrt{25} = 5$

Finding the trigonometric value: $\sin\theta = \frac{y}{r} = \frac{-3}{5} = -\frac{3}{5}$

47. Finding the trigonometric value: $\tan\theta = \frac{y}{x} = \frac{-3}{3} = -1$

48. First find r using the Pythagorean theorem: $r = \sqrt{1^2 + (-2)^2} = \sqrt{1 + 4} = \sqrt{5}$

Finding the trigonometric value: $\sec\theta = \frac{r}{x} = \frac{\sqrt{5}}{1} = \sqrt{5}$

49. Since $315°$ is in Quadrant IV, the reference angle is $360° - 315° = 45°$. Thus $\cos 315° = \cos 45° = \frac{\sqrt{2}}{2}$.

50. Since $150°$ is in Quadrant II, the reference angle is $180° - 150° = 30°$. Thus $\tan 315° = -\tan 30° = -\frac{\sqrt{3}}{3}$.

51. Since $-120°$ is coterminal with $-120° + 360° = 240°$, it lies in Quadrant III where secant is negative. The reference angle is $240° - 180° = 60°$. Thus $\sec(-120°) = -\sec 60° = -2$.

52. Since $420°$ is coterminal with $420° - 360° = 60°$, it lies in Quadrant I where sine is positive.

The reference angle is $60°$. Thus $\sin 420° = \sin 60° = \frac{\sqrt{3}}{2}$.

53. The graph of $f(x) = 3\sin x - 1$ is the graph of $y = \sin x$ vertically stretched by a factor of 2 and shifted vertically 1 unit downward:

54. The graph of $f(x) = -2\cos x + 3$ is the graph of $y = \cos x$ vertically stretched by a factor of 2, reflected across the x-axis, and shifted vertically 3 units upward:

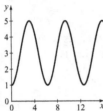

55. The graph of $f(x) = \cos(2x) - 1$ is the graph of $y = \cos x$ compressed horizontally by a factor of $\frac{1}{2}$ and shifted vertically 1 unit downward:

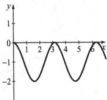

56. The graph of $f(x) = \sin\left(\dfrac{x}{2}\right) + 3$ is the graph of $y = \sin x$ stretched horizontally by a factor of 2 and shifted vertically 3 units upward:

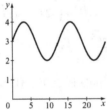

57. $g(x) = 2\sin\left(x + \dfrac{\pi}{4}\right)$: $a = 2, b = 1, c = -\dfrac{\pi}{4}$, and $d = 0$

Amplitude: $|2| = 2$; Period: $p = \dfrac{2\pi}{1} = 2\pi$; Horizontal shift: $\dfrac{|-\pi/4|}{1} = \dfrac{\pi}{4}$ units to the left

58. $g(x) = \cos(2x - \pi) - 3: a = 1, b = 2, c = \pi$, and $d = -3$

Amplitude: $|1| = 1$; Period: $p = \dfrac{2\pi}{2} = \pi$; Horizontal shift: $\dfrac{|\pi|}{2} = \dfrac{\pi}{2}$ units to the left

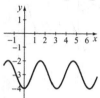

59. The graph of $f(x) = 2\tan x + 1$ is the graph of $y = \tan x$ vertically stretched by a factor of 2 and shifted vertically 1 unit upward:

60. The graph of $f(x) = -\csc x$ is the graph of $y = \csc x$ reflected across the x-axis:

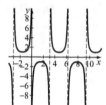

61. $f(x) = -\cot(2x)$

Period: $p = \dfrac{\pi}{2}$; Reflected across the x-axis

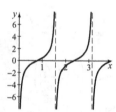

62. $f(x) = \sec\left(x - \dfrac{\pi}{2}\right)$

Period: $p = 2\pi$; Horizontal shift: $\dfrac{\pi}{2}$ units to the right

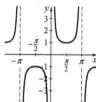

63. $f(x) = 2\tan(x - \pi)$

Period: $p = \pi$; Horizontal shift: π units to the right; Vertically stretched by a factor of 2

64. $f(x) = -\cot\left(x - \dfrac{\pi}{4}\right) + 3$

Period: $p = \pi$; Vertical shift: 3 units upward; Horizontal shift: $\dfrac{\pi}{4}$ units to the right; Reflected across the x-axis

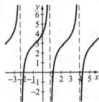

65. Let $y = \arcsin(-1)$, therefore:

$$\sin y = -1, y \in \left[-\dfrac{\pi}{2}, \dfrac{\pi}{2}\right]$$

$$y = -\dfrac{\pi}{2}$$

Thus $\arcsin(-1) = -\dfrac{\pi}{2}$.

66. Let $y = \arccos 0$, therefore:

$$\cos y = 0, y \in [0, \pi]$$

$$y = \dfrac{\pi}{2}$$

Thus $\arccos 0 = \dfrac{\pi}{2}$.

67. Finding the exact value: $\cot^{-1} 0 = \dfrac{\pi}{2} - \tan^{-1} 0 = \dfrac{\pi}{2}$

68. Finding the exact value: $\csc^{-1}(-\sqrt{2}) = \sin^{-1}\left(-\dfrac{1}{\sqrt{2}}\right) = \sin^{-1}\left(-\dfrac{\sqrt{2}}{2}\right) = -\dfrac{\pi}{4}$

69. Finding the exact value: $\arccos\left(\cos\left(-\dfrac{\pi}{4}\right)\right) = \arccos\left(\cos\left(\dfrac{\pi}{4}\right)\right) = \arccos\left(\dfrac{\sqrt{2}}{2}\right) = \dfrac{\pi}{4}$

70. Finding the exact value: $\arcsin(\sin(3\pi)) = \arcsin(0) = 0$

71. Finding the exact value: $\tan(\arctan(7)) = 7$

72. Finding the exact value: $\tan(\arctan(-3)) = -3$

73. Finding the exact value: $\sin(\arcsin(0.4)) = 0.4$

74. Finding the exact value: $\cos(\arccos(0.7)) = 0.7$

75. Let $t = \arccos\left(-\dfrac{12}{13}\right)$. Then $\cos t = -\dfrac{12}{13}$. Using the Pythagorean identity:

$$\sin^2 t + \cos^2 t = 1$$

$$\sin^2 t + \left(-\frac{12}{13}\right)^2 = 1$$

$$\sin^2 t + \frac{144}{169} = 1$$

$$\sin^2 t = \frac{25}{169}$$

$$\sin t = \pm\frac{5}{13}$$

Since $t \in [0, \pi]$, $\sin t > 0$, so: $\sin\left(\arccos\left(-\dfrac{12}{13}\right)\right) = \sin t = \dfrac{5}{13}$

76. Let $t = \arcsin\left(\dfrac{4}{5}\right)$. Then $\sin t = \dfrac{4}{5}$. Using the Pythagorean identity:

$$\sin^2 t + \cos^2 t = 1$$

$$\left(\frac{4}{5}\right)^2 + \cos^2 t = 1$$

$$\frac{16}{25} + \cos^2 t = 1$$

$$\cos^2 t = \frac{9}{25}$$

$$\cos t = \pm\frac{3}{5}$$

Since $t \in \left[-\dfrac{\pi}{2}, \dfrac{\pi}{2}\right]$, $\cos t > 0$, so: $\cos\left(\arcsin\left(\dfrac{4}{5}\right)\right) = \cos t = \dfrac{3}{5}$

77. The graph of $f(x) = -3\arccos x$ is the graph of $y = \arccos x$ vertically stretched by a factor of 3 and reflected across the x-axis:

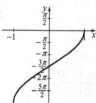

78. The graph of $f(x) = \sin^{-1} x - \dfrac{\pi}{2}$ is the graph of $y = \arcsin x$ vertically shifted downward $\dfrac{\pi}{2}$ units:

79. Since $\tan\theta = \dfrac{1}{6}$, the angle is: $\theta = \tan^{-1}\left(\dfrac{1}{6}\right) \approx 9.4623°$

80. Finding the angle (in degrees):

$$R = \frac{70^2 \sin 2\theta}{g}$$

$$400 = \frac{4900 \sin 2\theta}{9.8}$$

$$3920 = 4900 \sin 2\theta$$

$$\frac{4}{5} = \sin 2\theta$$

$$2\theta = \sin^{-1}\left(\frac{4}{5}\right) \approx 53.1301°$$

$$\theta \approx 26.6°$$

Chapter 5 Test

1. Sketching the angle:

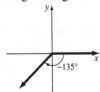

2. Sketching the angle:

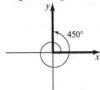

3. Sketching the angle:

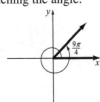

4. Sketching the angle:

5. Converting from degrees to radians: $75° = 75°\left(\frac{\pi}{180°}\right) = \frac{5\pi}{12}$ radians

6. Converting from degrees to radians: $-315° = -315°\left(\frac{\pi}{180°}\right) = -\frac{7\pi}{4}$ radians

7. Converting from radians to degrees: $\frac{\pi}{18} = \frac{\pi}{18}\left(\frac{180°}{\pi}\right) = 10°$

8. Converting from radians to degrees: $-\frac{\pi}{30} = -\frac{\pi}{30}\left(\frac{180°}{\pi}\right) = -6°$

9. Note that $t = -\frac{5\pi}{6}$ is in Quadrant III and has reference angle $\frac{\pi}{6}$. Finding the exact values:

$$\sin\left(-\frac{5\pi}{6}\right) = -\sin\frac{\pi}{6} = -\frac{1}{2} \qquad \cos\left(-\frac{5\pi}{6}\right) = -\cos\frac{\pi}{6} = -\frac{\sqrt{3}}{2}$$

10. Note that $t = \frac{8\pi}{3} = 2\pi + \frac{2\pi}{3}$ so t is in Quadrant II and has reference angle $\frac{\pi}{3}$. Finding the exact values:

$$\sin\left(\frac{8\pi}{3}\right) = \sin\left(\frac{2\pi}{3}\right) = \sin\frac{\pi}{3} = \frac{\sqrt{3}}{2} \qquad \cos\left(\frac{8\pi}{3}\right) = \cos\left(\frac{2\pi}{3}\right) = -\cos\frac{\pi}{3} = -\frac{1}{2}$$

11. Since $\cos t = \dfrac{\sqrt{2}}{2}$, $t = \dfrac{\pi}{4}$ is the reference angle in Quadrant III. Finding the exact values:

$$\sin t = -\sin \frac{\pi}{4} = -\frac{\sqrt{2}}{2} \qquad\qquad \tan t = \tan \frac{\pi}{4} = 1$$

12. If $\sin\theta = \dfrac{2}{5}$, choose $b = 2$ and $c = 5$ in the Pythagorean theorem:

$$a^2 + 2^2 = 5^2$$
$$a^2 + 4 = 25$$
$$a^2 = 21$$
$$a = \sqrt{21}$$

The six trigonometric values are:

$$\sin\theta = \frac{2}{5} \qquad\qquad \cos\theta = \frac{\sqrt{21}}{5} \qquad\qquad \tan\theta = \frac{2}{\sqrt{21}} = \frac{2\sqrt{21}}{21}$$

$$\csc\theta = \frac{5}{2} \qquad\qquad \sec\theta = \frac{5}{\sqrt{21}} = \frac{5\sqrt{21}}{21} \qquad\qquad \cot\theta = \frac{\sqrt{21}}{2}$$

13. If $\tan\theta = 3 = \dfrac{3}{1}$, choose $a = 1$ and $b = 3$ in the Pythagorean theorem:

$$1^2 + 3^2 = c^2$$
$$1 + 9 = c^2$$
$$10 = c^2$$
$$c = \sqrt{10}$$

The six trigonometric values are:

$$\sin\theta = \frac{3}{\sqrt{10}} = \frac{3\sqrt{10}}{10} \qquad \cos\theta = \frac{1}{\sqrt{10}} = \frac{\sqrt{10}}{10} \qquad \tan\theta = \frac{3}{1} = 3$$

$$\csc\theta = \frac{\sqrt{10}}{3} \qquad \sec\theta = \frac{\sqrt{10}}{1} = \sqrt{10} \qquad \cot\theta = \frac{1}{3}$$

14. Finding the other sides:

$$\sin 60° = \frac{a}{3} \qquad\qquad\qquad \cos 60° = \frac{b}{3}$$

$$a = 3\sin 60° = 3\left(\frac{\sqrt{3}}{2}\right) = \frac{3\sqrt{3}}{2} \qquad\qquad b = 3\cos 60° = 3\left(\frac{1}{2}\right) = \frac{3}{2}$$

15. First find r using the Pythagorean theorem: $r = \sqrt{(-1)^2 + 3^3} = \sqrt{1+9} = \sqrt{10}$

Finding the trigonometric values:

$$\cos\theta = \frac{x}{r} = \frac{-1}{\sqrt{10}} = -\frac{\sqrt{10}}{10} \qquad\qquad \csc\theta = \frac{r}{y} = \frac{\sqrt{10}}{3}$$

16. Since $240°$ is in Quadrant III, the reference angle is $240° - 180° = 60°$. Thus:

$$\sin 240° = -\sin 60° = -\frac{\sqrt{3}}{2} \qquad\qquad \sec 240° = -\sec 60° = -2$$

17. $f(x) = -\sin 2x + 1$; $a = -1, b = 2, c = 0$, and $d = 1$

Amplitude: $|-1| = 1$; Period: $p = \dfrac{2\pi}{2} = \pi$; Vertical shift: 1 unit upward; Reflected across the x-axis

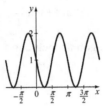

18. $f(x) = 3\sin\left(x - \dfrac{\pi}{4}\right)$; $a = 3, b = 1, c = \dfrac{\pi}{4}$, and $d = 0$

Amplitude: $|3| = 3$; Period: $p = \dfrac{2\pi}{1} = 2\pi$; Horizontal shift: $\dfrac{|\pi/4|}{1} = \dfrac{\pi}{4}$ units to the right

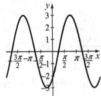

19. $f(x) = 2\cos(2x + \pi)$; $a = 2, b = 2, c = -\pi$, and $d = 0$

Amplitude: $|2| = 2$; Period: $p = \dfrac{2\pi}{2} = \pi$; Horizontal shift: $\dfrac{|-\pi|}{2} = \dfrac{\pi}{2}$ units to the right

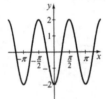

20. $f(x) = \tan 2x + 1$

Period: $p = \dfrac{\pi}{2}$; Vertical shift: 1 unit upward

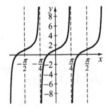

21. $f(x) = \sec\left(x + \dfrac{\pi}{2}\right)$

Period: $p = 2\pi$; Horizontal shift: $\dfrac{\pi}{2}$ units to the left

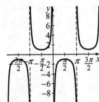

22. $f(x) = -3\cot x$

Period: $p = \pi$; Vertically stretched by a factor of 3; Reflected across the x-axis

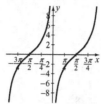

23. Finding the exact value: $\arccos\left(\cos\left(\dfrac{3\pi}{2}\right)\right) = \arccos 0 = \dfrac{\pi}{2}$

24. Finding the exact value: $\tan\left(\arctan(8)\right) = 8$

25. Let $t = \arccos\left(\dfrac{4}{5}\right)$. Then $\cos t = -\dfrac{12}{13}$. Using the Pythagorean identity:

$$\sin^2 t + \cos^2 t = 1$$

$$\sin^2 t + \left(\dfrac{4}{5}\right)^2 = 1$$

$$\sin^2 t + \dfrac{16}{25} = 1$$

$$\sin^2 t = \dfrac{9}{25}$$

$$\sin t = \pm\dfrac{3}{5}$$

Since $t \in [0, \pi]$, $\sin t > 0$, so: $\sin\left(\arccos\left(\dfrac{4}{5}\right)\right) = \sin t = \dfrac{3}{5}$

26. The graph of $f(x) = 2\arcsin x + \pi$ is the graph of $y = \arcsin x$ vertically stretched by a factor of 2 and shifted vertically π units upward:

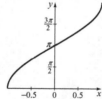

27. The angular speed is: $\omega = \dfrac{1\text{ rev}}{2\min} \cdot \dfrac{2\pi\text{ rads}}{\text{rev}} = \dfrac{\pi\text{ rads}}{\min} = \dfrac{180°}{\min}$

The linear speed is: $v = wt = \dfrac{\pi\text{ rads}}{\min} \cdot 100\text{ ft} = 100\pi\,\dfrac{\text{ft}}{\min} \approx 314\,\dfrac{\text{ft}}{\min}$

28. Since $\sin\theta = \dfrac{10}{30} = \dfrac{1}{3}$, the angle is: $\theta = \sin^{-1}\left(\dfrac{1}{3}\right) \approx 19.4712°$

The wire makes an angle of approximately $19.5°$ with the side of the building.

29. Let a represent the side of the square screen. Using the Pythagorean theorem:

$$a^2 + a^2 = 20^2$$
$$2a^2 = 400$$
$$a^2 = 200$$
$$a = \sqrt{200} = 10\sqrt{2} \approx 14.1$$

The dimensions of the square screen are about $14.1\text{ in.} \times 14.1\text{ in.}$

30. **a.** Finding the period: $p = \dfrac{2\pi}{B} = \dfrac{2\pi}{\left(\dfrac{2\pi}{33}\right)} = 33$ days

b. Evaluating the function: $P(1095) = 50\sin\left[\dfrac{2\pi}{33}(1095)\right] + 50 = 50\sin(208.4875) + 50 = 50(0.9096) + 50 \approx 95.48\%$

Chapter 6
Trigonometric Identities and Equations

6.1 Verifying Identities

1. Factoring the expression: $4x^2 - 9 = (2x+3)(2x-3)$

3. Factoring the expression: $9x^2 - 81 = 9(x^2 - 9) = 9(x+3)(x-3)$

5. Simplifying the expression: $\dfrac{2}{1+x} - \dfrac{1}{1-x} = \dfrac{2(1-x)}{(1+x)(1-x)} - \dfrac{1(1+x)}{(1+x)(1-x)} = \dfrac{2(1-x)-(1+x)}{(1+x)(1-x)} = \dfrac{2-2x-1-x}{(1+x)(1-x)} = \dfrac{1-3x}{1-x^2}$

7. Simplifying the expression: $\dfrac{5}{x-1} + \dfrac{3}{1-x} = \dfrac{5}{x-1} - \dfrac{3}{x-1} = \dfrac{2}{x-1}$

9. For $x = \pi$, $\cos \pi = -1 \neq 0.5$ so $\cos x = 0.5$ is not an identity.

11. For $x = \dfrac{\pi}{2}$, $\sin\left(\dfrac{\pi}{2} + \pi\right) = \sin \dfrac{3\pi}{2} = -1 \neq 1 = \sin \dfrac{\pi}{2} + \sin \pi$ so $\sin(x+\pi) = \sin x + \sin \pi$ is not an identity.

13. For $x = \dfrac{\pi}{2}$, $\sin\left(2\left(\dfrac{\pi}{2}\right)\right) = \sin \pi = 0 \neq 2 = 2\sin \dfrac{\pi}{2}$ so $\sin 2x = 2\sin x$ is not an identity.

15. Writing the expression in terms of sines and cosines: $\cot x \csc x = \dfrac{\cos x}{\sin x} \cdot \dfrac{1}{\sin x} = \dfrac{\cos x}{\sin^2 x}$

17. Writing the expression in terms of sines and cosines: $\dfrac{\tan^2 x}{\sin x} = \tan^2 x \cdot \dfrac{1}{\sin x} = \dfrac{\sin^2 x}{\cos^2 x} \cdot \dfrac{1}{\sin x} = \dfrac{\sin x}{\cos^2 x}$

19. Writing the expression in terms of sines and cosines: $\sec^2 x - 1 = \dfrac{1}{\cos^2 x} - 1 = \dfrac{1}{\cos^2 x} - \dfrac{\cos^2 x}{\cos^2 x} = \dfrac{1 - \cos^2 x}{\cos^2 x} = \dfrac{\sin^2 x}{\cos^2 x}$

21. Factoring the expression: $\sin x + \sin x \cos x = \sin x (1 + \cos x)$

23. Factoring the expression: $1 - \sin^2 x = (1 + \sin x)(1 - \sin x)$

25. Factoring the expression: $\sin^2 x - \cos^2 x = (\sin x + \cos x)(\sin x - \cos x)$

27. Verifying the identity: $\tan x \csc x = \dfrac{\sin x}{\cos x} \cdot \dfrac{1}{\sin x} = \dfrac{1}{\cos x} = \sec x$

29. Verifying the identity: $\sin x + \cos x \cot x = \sin x + \cos x \cdot \dfrac{\cos x}{\sin x} = \sin x + \dfrac{\cos^2 x}{\sin x} = \dfrac{\sin^2 x}{\sin x} + \dfrac{\cos^2 x}{\sin x} = \dfrac{1}{\sin x} = \csc x$

31. Verifying the identity: $\sec^2 x (1 - \sin^2 x) = \dfrac{1}{\cos^2 x}(\cos^2 x) = 1$

33. Verifying the identity: $\sin^2(-x) + \cos^2(-x) = (-\sin x)^2 + \cos^2 x = \sin^2 x + \cos^2 x = 1$

35. Verifying the identity: $(\sec^2 x - 1)\cot^2 x = \tan^2 x \cot^2 x = \dfrac{\sin^2 x}{\cos^2 x} \cdot \dfrac{\cos^2 x}{\sin^2 x} = 1$

37. Verifying the identity: $\dfrac{\cot x}{\csc x} = \dfrac{\frac{\cos x}{\sin x}}{\frac{1}{\sin x}} = \dfrac{\cos x}{\sin x} \cdot \sin x = \cos x$

39. Verifying the identity: $\sin^2 x \sec x = \left(1 - \cos^2 x\right) \cdot \dfrac{1}{\cos x} = \dfrac{1}{\cos x} - \dfrac{\cos^2 x}{\cos x} = \sec x - \cos x$

41. Verifying the identity: $\left(\cos x + \sin x\right)^2 - 2\sin x \cos x = \cos^2 x + 2\cos x \sin x + \sin^2 x - 2\sin x \cos x = \cos^2 x + \sin^2 x = 1$

43. Verifying the identity: $\sec x + \tan x = \dfrac{1}{\cos x} + \dfrac{\sin x}{\cos x} = \dfrac{1 + \sin x}{\cos x}$

45. Verifying the identity: $\cos^3 x = \cos x \cdot \cos^2 x = \cos x \left(1 - \sin^2 x\right) = \cos x - \cos x \sin^2 x$

47. Verifying the identity: $\sec x \cos^3 x = \dfrac{1}{\cos x} \cdot \cos^3 x = \cos^2 x = 1 - \sin^2 x$

49. Verifying the identity: $\dfrac{1}{1 + \cos x} + \dfrac{1}{1 - \cos x} = \dfrac{\left(1 - \cos x\right) + \left(1 + \cos x\right)}{\left(1 + \cos x\right)\left(1 - \cos x\right)} = \dfrac{2}{1 - \cos^2 x} = \dfrac{2}{\sin^2 x} = 2\csc^2 x$

51. Verifying the identity: $\dfrac{\sin x - \sin(-x)}{1 - \cos^2 x} = \dfrac{\sin x + \sin x}{\sin^2 x} = \dfrac{2\sin x}{\sin^2 x} = \dfrac{2}{\sin x} = 2\csc x$

53. Verifying the identity:

$$\dfrac{\sec^2 x}{1 + \sin x} = \dfrac{\sec^2 x}{1 + \sin x} \cdot \dfrac{1 - \sin x}{1 - \sin x}$$

$$= \dfrac{\sec^2 x \left(1 - \sin x\right)}{1 - \sin^2 x}$$

$$= \dfrac{\sec^2 x - \sec^2 x \sin x}{\cos^2 x}$$

$$= \dfrac{\sec^2 x - \sec x \sec x \sin x}{\cos^2 x}$$

$$= \dfrac{\sec^2 x - \sec x \cdot \dfrac{\sin x}{\cos x}}{\cos^2 x}$$

$$= \dfrac{\sec^2 x - \sec x \tan x}{\cos^2 x}$$

55. Verifying the identity: $\cos^2 x - \sin^2 x = \left(1 - \sin^2 x\right) - \sin^2 x = 1 - 2\sin^2 x$

57. Verifying the identity: $\tan x + \cot x = \dfrac{\sin x}{\cos x} + \dfrac{\cos x}{\sin x} = \dfrac{\sin^2 x + \cos^2 x}{\cos x \sin x} = \dfrac{1}{\cos x \sin x} = \dfrac{1}{\cos x} \cdot \dfrac{1}{\sin x} = \sec x \csc x$

59. Verifying the identity: $\cos^4 x - \sin^4 x = \left(\cos^2 x + \sin^2 x\right)\left(\cos^2 x - \sin^2 x\right) = \cos^2 x - \sin^2 x$

61. Verifying the identity: $\dfrac{\tan^2 x - 1}{1 + \tan^2 x} = \dfrac{\tan^2 x - 1}{\sec^2 x} = \cos^2 x \left(\dfrac{\sin^2 x}{\cos^2 x} - 1\right) = \sin^2 x - \cos^2 x = \sin^2 x - \left(1 - \sin^2 x\right) = 2\sin^2 x - 1$

63. Verifying the identity: $\csc^2 x + \sec^2 x = \dfrac{1}{\sin^2 x} + \dfrac{1}{\cos^2 x} = \dfrac{\cos^2 x + \sin^2 x}{\sin^2 x \cos^2 x} = \dfrac{1}{\sin^2 x \cos^2 x} = \csc^2 x \sec^2 x$

65. Verifying the identity: $\sec^4 x - \tan^4 x = \left(\sec^2 x + \tan^2 x\right)\left(\sec^2 x - \tan^2 x\right) = \sec^2 x + \tan^2 x$

67. Verifying the identity:

$$\dfrac{1}{1 + \cos x} = \dfrac{1}{1 + \cos x} \cdot \dfrac{1 - \cos x}{1 - \cos x} = \dfrac{1 - \cos x}{1 - \cos^2 x} = \dfrac{1 - \cos x}{\sin^2 x} = \dfrac{1}{\sin^2 x} - \dfrac{\cos x}{\sin^2 x} = \csc^2 x - \dfrac{\cos x}{\sin x} \cdot \dfrac{1}{\sin x} = \csc^2 x - \cot x \csc x$$

69. Verifying the identity:

$$\left(\csc x - \cot x\right)^2 = \left(\frac{1}{\sin x} - \frac{\cos x}{\sin x}\right)^2 = \left(\frac{1-\cos x}{\sin x}\right)^2 = \frac{\left(1-\cos x\right)^2}{\sin^2 x} = \frac{\left(1-\cos x\right)^2}{1-\cos^2 x} = \frac{\left(1-\cos x\right)^2}{\left(1+\cos x\right)\left(1-\cos x\right)} = \frac{1-\cos x}{1+\cos x}$$

71. Verifying the identity:

$$\cot x + \tan x = \frac{\cos x}{\sin x} + \frac{\sin x}{\cos x}$$
$$= \frac{\cos^2 x + \sin^2 x}{\sin x \cos x}$$
$$= \frac{1}{\sin x \cos x}$$
$$= \frac{1}{\sin x \cos x} \cdot \frac{\cos x}{\cos x}$$
$$= \frac{\cos x}{\sin x \cos^2 x}$$
$$= \frac{1}{\cos^2 x} \cdot \frac{\cos x}{\sin x}$$
$$= \sec^2 x \cot x$$

73. Verifying the identity: $\dfrac{\sec^2 x - 1}{\tan x} = \dfrac{\tan^2 x}{\tan x} = \tan x = \dfrac{\sin x}{\cos x} = \dfrac{\frac{1}{\cos x}}{\frac{1}{\sin x}} = \dfrac{\sec x}{\csc x}$

75. Verifying the identity:

$$\frac{\sin x}{\csc x - \cot x} = \frac{\sin x}{\frac{1}{\sin x} - \frac{\cos x}{\sin x}} = \frac{\sin x}{\frac{1-\cos x}{\sin x}} = \frac{\sin^2 x}{1-\cos x} \cdot \frac{1+\cos x}{1+\cos x} = \frac{\sin^2 x\left(1+\cos x\right)}{1-\cos^2 x} = \frac{\sin^2 x\left(1+\cos x\right)}{\sin^2 x} = 1+\cos x$$

77. Verifying the identity: $a\csc^2 x\left(1+\cos x\right)\left(1-\cos x\right) = a\csc^2 x\left(1-\cos^2 x\right) = a \cdot \dfrac{1}{\sin^2 x} \cdot \sin^2 x = a$

79. Verifying the identity: $\ln\left|\tan x\right| = \ln\left|\dfrac{1}{\cot x}\right| = \ln\left|1\right| - \ln\left|\cot x\right| = 0 - \ln\left|\cot x\right| = -\ln\left|\cot x\right|$

81. No, $\sin\left(x+\pi\right) = \sin x + \sin \pi$ is not an identity since their graphs do not match.

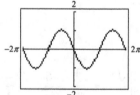 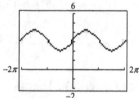

83. Yes, $\cos 2x = 1 - 2\sin^2 x$ is an identity since their graphs are identical.

85. No, $\sin(x-\pi) = \sin x$ is not an identity since their graphs do not match.

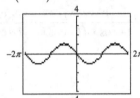 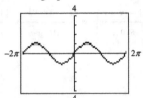

87. It is not an identity since $\sin x$ can take on negative values, whereas the right-hand expression cannot.

89. No. $\cos\dfrac{\pi}{2} = 0$ so $\tan\dfrac{\pi}{2}$ is undefined.

6.2 Sum and Difference Identities

1. Finding the exact value: $\sin\dfrac{\pi}{6} = \dfrac{1}{2}$

3. Finding the exact value: $\cos\left(-\dfrac{5\pi}{4}\right) = \cos\left(\dfrac{5\pi}{4}\right) = -\cos\dfrac{\pi}{4} = -\dfrac{\sqrt{2}}{2}$

5. Finding the exact value: $\cos 330° = \cos 30° = \dfrac{\sqrt{3}}{2}$

7. **a.** Finding the exact value: $\cos\dfrac{\pi}{3} + \cos\dfrac{\pi}{6} = \dfrac{1}{2} + \dfrac{\sqrt{3}}{2} = \dfrac{1+\sqrt{3}}{2}$

    b. Finding the exact value: $\cos\left(\dfrac{\pi}{3} + \dfrac{\pi}{6}\right) = \cos\left(\dfrac{2\pi+\pi}{6}\right) = \cos\dfrac{\pi}{2} = 0$

9. Finding the exact value: $\sin\pi\sin\dfrac{\pi}{3} = 0 \cdot \dfrac{\sqrt{3}}{2} = 0$

11. Finding the exact value: $\sin\left(-\dfrac{\pi}{3}\right)\sin\dfrac{\pi}{3} = -\sin\dfrac{\pi}{3}\sin\dfrac{\pi}{3} = -\dfrac{\sqrt{3}}{2} \cdot \dfrac{\sqrt{3}}{2} = -\dfrac{3}{4}$

13. Finding the exact value: $\sin(45°)\sin(30°) = \dfrac{\sqrt{2}}{2} \cdot \dfrac{1}{2} = \dfrac{\sqrt{2}}{4}$

15. Finding the exact value: $\sin(-45°)\cos(30°) = -\sin(45°)\cos(30°) = -\dfrac{\sqrt{2}}{2} \cdot \dfrac{\sqrt{3}}{2} = -\dfrac{\sqrt{6}}{4}$

17. Finding the exact value: $\cos\pi\cos\dfrac{\pi}{3} + \sin\pi\sin\dfrac{\pi}{3} = (-1)\left(\dfrac{1}{2}\right) + (0)\left(\dfrac{\sqrt{3}}{2}\right) = -\dfrac{1}{2}$

19. Finding the exact value: $\sin(30°)\cos(45°) - \cos(30°)\sin(45°) = \left(\dfrac{1}{2}\right)\left(\dfrac{\sqrt{2}}{2}\right) - \left(\dfrac{\sqrt{3}}{2}\right)\left(\dfrac{\sqrt{2}}{2}\right) = \dfrac{\sqrt{2}}{4} - \dfrac{\sqrt{6}}{4} = \dfrac{\sqrt{2}-\sqrt{6}}{4}$

21. Finding the exact values:

$$\sin\dfrac{11\pi}{12} = \sin\left(\dfrac{2\pi}{3} + \dfrac{\pi}{4}\right) = \sin\dfrac{2\pi}{3}\cos\dfrac{\pi}{4} + \cos\dfrac{2\pi}{3}\sin\dfrac{\pi}{4} = \left(\dfrac{\sqrt{3}}{2}\right)\left(\dfrac{\sqrt{2}}{2}\right) + \left(-\dfrac{1}{2}\right)\left(\dfrac{\sqrt{2}}{2}\right) = \dfrac{\sqrt{6}-\sqrt{2}}{4}$$

$$\cos\dfrac{11\pi}{12} = \cos\left(\dfrac{2\pi}{3} + \dfrac{\pi}{4}\right) = \cos\dfrac{2\pi}{3}\cos\dfrac{\pi}{4} - \sin\dfrac{2\pi}{3}\sin\dfrac{\pi}{4} = \left(-\dfrac{1}{2}\right)\left(\dfrac{\sqrt{2}}{2}\right) - \left(\dfrac{\sqrt{3}}{2}\right)\left(\dfrac{\sqrt{2}}{2}\right) = \dfrac{-\sqrt{2}-\sqrt{6}}{4}$$

$$\tan\dfrac{11\pi}{12} = \tan\left(\dfrac{2\pi}{3} + \dfrac{\pi}{4}\right) = \dfrac{\tan\dfrac{2\pi}{3} + \tan\dfrac{\pi}{4}}{1 - \tan\dfrac{2\pi}{3}\tan\dfrac{\pi}{4}} = \dfrac{-\sqrt{3}+1}{1-\left(-\sqrt{3}\right)(1)} = \dfrac{1-\sqrt{3}}{1+\sqrt{3}} \cdot \dfrac{1-\sqrt{3}}{1-\sqrt{3}} = \dfrac{4-2\sqrt{3}}{-2} = -2+\sqrt{3}$$

23. Finding the exact values:

$$\sin\left(-\frac{\pi}{12}\right) = \sin\left(\frac{\pi}{4} - \frac{\pi}{3}\right) = \sin\frac{\pi}{4}\cos\frac{\pi}{3} - \cos\frac{\pi}{4}\sin\frac{\pi}{3} = \left(\frac{\sqrt{2}}{2}\right)\left(\frac{1}{2}\right) - \left(\frac{\sqrt{2}}{2}\right)\left(\frac{\sqrt{3}}{2}\right) = \frac{\sqrt{2} - \sqrt{6}}{4}$$

$$\cos\left(-\frac{\pi}{12}\right) = \cos\left(\frac{\pi}{4} - \frac{\pi}{3}\right) = \cos\frac{\pi}{4}\cos\frac{\pi}{3} + \sin\frac{\pi}{4}\sin\frac{\pi}{3} = \left(\frac{\sqrt{2}}{2}\right)\left(\frac{1}{2}\right) + \left(\frac{\sqrt{2}}{2}\right)\left(\frac{\sqrt{3}}{2}\right) = \frac{\sqrt{2} + \sqrt{6}}{4}$$

$$\tan\left(-\frac{\pi}{12}\right) = \tan\left(\frac{\pi}{4} - \frac{\pi}{3}\right) = \frac{\tan\frac{\pi}{4} - \tan\frac{\pi}{3}}{1 + \tan\frac{\pi}{4}\tan\frac{\pi}{3}} = \frac{1 - \sqrt{3}}{1 + (1)\left(\sqrt{3}\right)} = \frac{1 - \sqrt{3}}{1 + \sqrt{3}} \cdot \frac{1 - \sqrt{3}}{1 - \sqrt{3}} = \frac{4 - 2\sqrt{3}}{-2} = -2 + \sqrt{3}$$

25. Finding the exact values (note that we could find these without using identities):

$$\sin\frac{3\pi}{4} = \sin\left(\pi - \frac{\pi}{4}\right) = \sin\pi\cos\frac{\pi}{4} - \cos\pi\sin\frac{\pi}{4} = (0)\left(\frac{\sqrt{2}}{2}\right) - (-1)\left(\frac{\sqrt{2}}{2}\right) = \frac{\sqrt{2}}{2}$$

$$\cos\frac{3\pi}{4} = \cos\left(\pi - \frac{\pi}{4}\right) = \cos\pi\cos\frac{\pi}{4} + \sin\pi\sin\frac{\pi}{4} = (-1)\left(\frac{\sqrt{2}}{2}\right) + (0)\left(\frac{\sqrt{2}}{2}\right) = -\frac{\sqrt{2}}{2}$$

$$\tan\frac{3\pi}{4} = \tan\left(\pi - \frac{\pi}{4}\right) = \frac{\tan\pi - \tan\frac{\pi}{4}}{1 + \tan\pi\tan\frac{\pi}{4}} = \frac{0 - 1}{1 + (0)(1)} = -1$$

27. Note that $-\frac{13\pi}{12} = \frac{3\pi}{12} - \frac{16\pi}{12} = \frac{\pi}{4} - \frac{4\pi}{3}$. Finding the exact values:

$$\sin\left(-\frac{13\pi}{12}\right) = \sin\left(\frac{\pi}{4} - \frac{4\pi}{3}\right) = \sin\frac{\pi}{4}\cos\frac{4\pi}{3} - \cos\frac{\pi}{4}\sin\frac{4\pi}{3} = \left(\frac{\sqrt{2}}{2}\right)\left(-\frac{1}{2}\right) - \left(\frac{\sqrt{2}}{2}\right)\left(-\frac{\sqrt{3}}{2}\right) = \frac{-\sqrt{2} + \sqrt{6}}{4}$$

$$\cos\left(-\frac{13\pi}{12}\right) = \cos\left(\frac{\pi}{4} - \frac{4\pi}{3}\right) = \cos\frac{\pi}{4}\cos\frac{4\pi}{3} + \sin\frac{\pi}{4}\sin\frac{4\pi}{3} = \left(\frac{\sqrt{2}}{2}\right)\left(-\frac{1}{2}\right) + \left(\frac{\sqrt{2}}{2}\right)\left(-\frac{\sqrt{3}}{2}\right) = \frac{-\sqrt{2} - \sqrt{6}}{4}$$

$$\tan\left(-\frac{13\pi}{12}\right) = \tan\left(\frac{\pi}{4} - \frac{4\pi}{3}\right) = \frac{\tan\frac{\pi}{4} - \tan\frac{4\pi}{3}}{1 + \tan\frac{\pi}{4}\tan\frac{4\pi}{3}} = \frac{1 - \sqrt{3}}{1 + (1)\left(\sqrt{3}\right)} = \frac{1 - \sqrt{3}}{1 + \sqrt{3}} \cdot \frac{1 - \sqrt{3}}{1 - \sqrt{3}} = \frac{4 - 2\sqrt{3}}{-2} = -2 + \sqrt{3}$$

29. Note that $-\frac{7\pi}{12} = \frac{2\pi}{12} - \frac{9\pi}{12} = \frac{\pi}{6} - \frac{3\pi}{4}$. Finding the exact values:

$$\sin\left(-\frac{7\pi}{12}\right) = \sin\left(\frac{\pi}{6} - \frac{3\pi}{4}\right) = \sin\frac{\pi}{6}\cos\frac{3\pi}{4} - \cos\frac{\pi}{6}\sin\frac{3\pi}{4} = \left(\frac{1}{2}\right)\left(-\frac{\sqrt{2}}{2}\right) - \left(\frac{\sqrt{3}}{2}\right)\left(\frac{\sqrt{2}}{2}\right) = \frac{-\sqrt{2} - \sqrt{6}}{4}$$

$$\cos\left(-\frac{7\pi}{12}\right) = \cos\left(\frac{\pi}{6} - \frac{3\pi}{4}\right) = \cos\frac{\pi}{6}\cos\frac{3\pi}{4} + \sin\frac{\pi}{6}\sin\frac{3\pi}{4} = \left(\frac{\sqrt{3}}{2}\right)\left(-\frac{\sqrt{2}}{2}\right) + \left(\frac{1}{2}\right)\left(\frac{\sqrt{2}}{2}\right) = \frac{-\sqrt{6} + \sqrt{2}}{4}$$

$$\tan\left(-\frac{7\pi}{12}\right) = \tan\left(\frac{\pi}{6} - \frac{3\pi}{4}\right) = \frac{\tan\frac{\pi}{6} - \tan\frac{3\pi}{4}}{1 + \tan\frac{\pi}{6}\tan\frac{3\pi}{4}} = \frac{\frac{1}{\sqrt{3}} - (-1)}{1 + \left(\frac{1}{\sqrt{3}}\right)(-1)} = \frac{1 + \sqrt{3}}{\sqrt{3} - 1} \cdot \frac{\sqrt{3} + 1}{\sqrt{3} + 1} = \frac{4 + 2\sqrt{3}}{2} = 2 + \sqrt{3}$$

31. Finding the exact values (note that we could find these without using identities):

$$\sin 240° = \sin\left(180° + 60°\right) = \sin 180° \cos 60° + \cos 80° \sin 60° = (0)\left(\frac{1}{2}\right) + (-1)\left(\frac{\sqrt{3}}{2}\right) = -\frac{\sqrt{3}}{2}$$

$$\cos 240° = \cos\left(180° + 60°\right) = \cos 180° \cos 60° - \sin 180° \sin 60° = (-1)\left(\frac{1}{2}\right) - (0)\left(\frac{\sqrt{3}}{2}\right) = -\frac{1}{2}$$

$$\tan 240° = \tan\left(180° + 60°\right) = \frac{\tan 180° + \tan 60°}{1 - \tan 180° \tan 60°} = \frac{0 + \sqrt{3}}{1 - 0\left(\sqrt{3}\right)} = \sqrt{3}$$

33. Finding the exact values:

$$\sin 75° = \sin\left(120° - 45°\right) = \sin 120° \cos 45° - \cos 120° \sin 45° = \left(\frac{\sqrt{3}}{2}\right)\left(\frac{\sqrt{2}}{2}\right) - \left(-\frac{1}{2}\right)\left(\frac{\sqrt{2}}{2}\right) = \frac{\sqrt{6} + \sqrt{2}}{4}$$

$$\cos 75° = \cos\left(120° - 45°\right) = \cos 120° \cos 45° + \sin 120° \sin 45° = \left(-\frac{1}{2}\right)\left(\frac{\sqrt{2}}{2}\right) + \left(\frac{\sqrt{3}}{2}\right)\left(\frac{\sqrt{2}}{2}\right) = \frac{-\sqrt{2} + \sqrt{6}}{4}$$

$$\tan 75° = \tan\left(120° - 45°\right) = \frac{\tan 120° - \tan 45°}{1 + \tan 120° \tan 45°} = \frac{-\sqrt{3} - 1}{1 + \left(-\sqrt{3}\right)(1)} = \frac{-1 - \sqrt{3}}{1 - \sqrt{3}} \cdot \frac{1 + \sqrt{3}}{1 + \sqrt{3}} = \frac{-4 - 2\sqrt{3}}{-2} = 2 + \sqrt{3}$$

35. Finding the exact values:

$$\sin 105° = \sin\left(135° - 30°\right) = \sin 135° \cos 30° - \cos 135° \sin 30° = \left(\frac{\sqrt{2}}{2}\right)\left(\frac{\sqrt{3}}{2}\right) - \left(-\frac{\sqrt{2}}{2}\right)\left(\frac{1}{2}\right) = \frac{\sqrt{6} + \sqrt{2}}{4}$$

$$\cos 105° = \cos\left(135° - 30°\right) = \cos 135° \cos 30° + \sin 135° \sin 30° = \left(-\frac{\sqrt{2}}{2}\right)\left(\frac{\sqrt{3}}{2}\right) + \left(\frac{\sqrt{2}}{2}\right)\left(\frac{1}{2}\right) = \frac{-\sqrt{6} + \sqrt{2}}{4}$$

$$\tan 105° = \tan\left(135° - 30°\right) = \frac{\tan 135° - \tan 30°}{1 + \tan 135° \tan 30°} = \frac{-1 - \frac{1}{\sqrt{3}}}{1 + (-1)\left(\frac{1}{\sqrt{3}}\right)} = \frac{-\sqrt{3} - 1}{\sqrt{3} - 1} \cdot \frac{\sqrt{3} + 1}{\sqrt{3} + 1} = \frac{-4 - 2\sqrt{3}}{2} = -2 - \sqrt{3}$$

37. Finding the exact values:

$$\sin\left(-195°\right) = \sin\left(30° - 225°\right) = \sin 30° \cos 225° - \cos 30° \sin 225° = \left(\frac{1}{2}\right)\left(-\frac{\sqrt{2}}{2}\right) - \left(\frac{\sqrt{3}}{2}\right)\left(-\frac{\sqrt{2}}{2}\right) = \frac{-\sqrt{2} + \sqrt{6}}{4}$$

$$\cos\left(-195°\right) = \cos\left(30° - 225°\right) = \cos 30° \cos 225° + \sin 30° \sin 225° = \left(\frac{\sqrt{3}}{2}\right)\left(-\frac{\sqrt{2}}{2}\right) + \left(\frac{1}{2}\right)\left(-\frac{\sqrt{2}}{2}\right) = \frac{-\sqrt{6} - \sqrt{2}}{4}$$

$$\tan\left(-195°\right) = \tan\left(30° - 225°\right) = \frac{\tan 30° - \tan 225°}{1 + \tan 30° \tan 225°} = \frac{\frac{1}{\sqrt{3}} - 1}{1 + \left(\frac{1}{\sqrt{3}}\right)(1)} = \frac{1 - \sqrt{3}}{\sqrt{3} + 1} \cdot \frac{\sqrt{3} - 1}{\sqrt{3} - 1} = \frac{-4 + 2\sqrt{3}}{2} = -2 + \sqrt{3}$$

39. Verifying the identity: $\cos\left(\dfrac{\pi}{2} - a\right) = \cos\dfrac{\pi}{2}\cos a + \sin\dfrac{\pi}{2}\sin a = 0 \cdot \cos a + 1 \cdot \sin a = \sin a$

41. Verifying the identity: $\sec\left(\dfrac{\pi}{2} - a\right) = \dfrac{1}{\cos\left(\dfrac{\pi}{2} - a\right)} = \dfrac{1}{\cos\dfrac{\pi}{2}\cos a + \sin\dfrac{\pi}{2}\sin a} = \dfrac{1}{0 \cdot \cos a + 1 \cdot \sin a} = \dfrac{1}{\sin a} = \csc a$

43. Using the Pythagorean identity:

$$\cos^2 a + \sin^2 a = 1 \qquad\qquad\qquad \cos^2 b + \sin^2 b = 1$$

$$\cos^2 a + \left(-\frac{3}{5}\right)^2 = 1 \qquad\qquad \left(\frac{5}{13}\right)^2 + \sin^2 b = 1$$

$$\cos^2 a + \frac{9}{25} = 1 \qquad\qquad\qquad \frac{25}{169} + \sin^2 b = 1$$

$$\cos^2 a = \frac{16}{25} \qquad\qquad\qquad\qquad \sin^2 b = \frac{144}{169}$$

$$\cos a = \frac{4}{5} \quad (a \text{ in quad. IV}) \qquad\qquad \sin b = -\frac{12}{13} \quad (b \text{ in quad. IV})$$

Now using the sum identity for cosine: $\cos(a+b) = \cos a \cos b - \sin a \sin b = \left(\frac{4}{5}\right)\left(\frac{5}{13}\right) - \left(-\frac{3}{5}\right)\left(-\frac{12}{13}\right) = \frac{20}{65} - \frac{36}{65} = -\frac{16}{65}$

45. Finding the tangent values:

$$\tan a = \frac{\sin a}{\cos a} = \frac{-\dfrac{3}{5}}{\dfrac{4}{5}} = -\frac{3}{4} \qquad\qquad \tan b = \frac{\sin b}{\cos b} = \frac{-\dfrac{12}{13}}{\dfrac{5}{13}} = -\frac{12}{5}$$

Using the sum identity for tangent: $\tan(a+b) = \dfrac{\tan a + \tan b}{1 - \tan a \tan b} = \dfrac{-\dfrac{3}{4} + \left(-\dfrac{12}{5}\right)}{1 - \left(-\dfrac{3}{4}\right)\left(-\dfrac{12}{5}\right)} = \dfrac{-\dfrac{15+48}{20}}{1 - \dfrac{9}{5}} = \dfrac{-\dfrac{63}{20}}{-\dfrac{4}{5}} = \dfrac{-63}{-16} = \dfrac{63}{16}$

47. Finding the value: $\cos\left(a + \dfrac{\pi}{2}\right) = \cos a \cos\dfrac{\pi}{2} - \sin a \sin\dfrac{\pi}{2} = \cos a \cdot 0 - \sin a \cdot 1 = -\sin a = \dfrac{3}{5}$

49. Using the Pythagorean identity:

$$\cos^2 a + \sin^2 a = 1 \qquad\qquad\qquad \cos^2 b + \sin^2 b = 1$$

$$\cos^2 a + \left(\frac{1}{3}\right)^2 = 1 \qquad\qquad \left(-\frac{1}{4}\right)^2 + \sin^2 b = 1$$

$$\cos^2 a + \frac{1}{9} = 1 \qquad\qquad\qquad \frac{1}{16} + \sin^2 b = 1$$

$$\cos^2 a = \frac{8}{9} \qquad\qquad\qquad\qquad \sin^2 b = \frac{15}{16}$$

$$\cos a = -\frac{2\sqrt{2}}{3} \quad (a \text{ in quad. II}) \qquad \sin b = \frac{\sqrt{15}}{4} \quad (b \text{ in quad. II})$$

Now using the difference identity for cosine:

$$\cos(a - b) = \cos a \cos b + \sin a \sin b = \left(-\frac{2\sqrt{2}}{3}\right)\left(-\frac{1}{4}\right) + \left(\frac{1}{3}\right)\left(\frac{\sqrt{15}}{4}\right) = \frac{\sqrt{2}}{6} + \frac{\sqrt{15}}{12} = \frac{2\sqrt{2} + \sqrt{15}}{12}$$

51. Finding the tangent values:

$$\tan a = \frac{\sin a}{\cos a} = \frac{\dfrac{1}{3}}{-\dfrac{2\sqrt{2}}{3}} = -\frac{1}{2\sqrt{2}} = -\frac{\sqrt{2}}{4} \qquad \tan b = \frac{\sin b}{\cos b} = \frac{\dfrac{\sqrt{15}}{4}}{-\dfrac{1}{4}} = -\sqrt{15}$$

Using the difference identity for tangent:

$$\tan(a-b) = \frac{\tan a - \tan b}{1 + \tan a \tan b}$$

$$= \frac{-\dfrac{\sqrt{2}}{4} - \left(-\sqrt{15}\right)}{1 + \left(-\dfrac{\sqrt{2}}{4}\right)\left(-\sqrt{15}\right)}$$

$$= \frac{-\dfrac{\sqrt{2}}{4} + \sqrt{15}}{1 + \dfrac{\sqrt{30}}{4}}$$

$$= \frac{-\sqrt{2} + 4\sqrt{15}}{4 + \sqrt{30}} \cdot \frac{4 - \sqrt{30}}{4 - \sqrt{30}}$$

$$= \frac{-4\sqrt{2} + 2\sqrt{15} + 16\sqrt{15} - 4(15)\sqrt{2}}{16 - 30}$$

$$= \frac{18\sqrt{15} - 64\sqrt{2}}{-14}$$

$$= \frac{32\sqrt{2} - 9\sqrt{15}}{7}$$

53. Finding the value: $\sin\left(a + \dfrac{\pi}{2}\right) = \sin a \cos\dfrac{\pi}{2} + \cos a \sin\dfrac{\pi}{2} = \sin a \cdot 0 + \cos a \cdot 1 = \cos a = -\dfrac{2\sqrt{2}}{3}$

55. Let $f(x) = \dfrac{\sqrt{2}}{2}\sin x + \dfrac{\sqrt{2}}{2}\cos x$. Then $A = B = \dfrac{\sqrt{2}}{2}$, so: $C = \sqrt{A^2 + B^2} = \sqrt{\left(\dfrac{\sqrt{2}}{2}\right)^2 + \left(\dfrac{\sqrt{2}}{2}\right)^2} = \sqrt{\dfrac{2}{4} + \dfrac{2}{4}} = \sqrt{1} = 1$

Therefore $\cos\theta = \dfrac{A}{C} = \dfrac{\left(\dfrac{\sqrt{2}}{2}\right)}{1} = \dfrac{\sqrt{2}}{2}$ and $\sin\theta = \dfrac{B}{C} = \dfrac{\left(\dfrac{\sqrt{2}}{2}\right)}{1} = \dfrac{\sqrt{2}}{2}$, thus $\theta = \dfrac{\pi}{4}$. Therefore $f(x) = \sin\left(x + \dfrac{\pi}{4}\right)$.

57. Let $f(x) = -\sin x + \cos x$. Then $A = -1, B = 1$, so: $C = \sqrt{A^2 + B^2} = \sqrt{(-1)^2 + 1^2} = \sqrt{2}$

Therefore $\cos\theta = \dfrac{A}{C} = \dfrac{-1}{\sqrt{2}} = -\dfrac{\sqrt{2}}{2}$ and $\sin\theta = \dfrac{B}{C} = \dfrac{1}{\sqrt{2}} = \dfrac{\sqrt{2}}{2}$, thus $\theta = \dfrac{3\pi}{4}$. Therefore $f(x) = \sqrt{2}\sin\left(x + \dfrac{3\pi}{4}\right)$.

59. Let $f(x) = \sin x - \sqrt{3}\cos x$. Then $A = 1, B = \sqrt{3}$, so: $C = \sqrt{A^2 + B^2} = \sqrt{1^2 + \left(\sqrt{3}\right)^2} = \sqrt{4} = 2$

Therefore $\cos\theta = \dfrac{A}{C} = \dfrac{1}{2}$ and $\sin\theta = \dfrac{B}{C} = -\dfrac{\sqrt{3}}{2}$, thus $\theta = \dfrac{5\pi}{3}$. Therefore $f(x) = 2\sin\left(x + \dfrac{5\pi}{3}\right)$.

61. Simplifying the expression: $\sin(x - \pi) = \sin x \cos\pi - \cos x \sin\pi = \sin x \cdot (-1) - \cos x \cdot 0 = -\sin x$

63. Simplifying the expression: $\sin(x + n\pi) = \sin x \cos(n\pi) + \cos x \sin(n\pi) = \sin x \cdot (-1) + \cos x \cdot 0 = -\sin x$

65. Simplifying the expression: $\tan\left(x+\dfrac{\pi}{2}\right)=\dfrac{\sin\left(x+\dfrac{\pi}{2}\right)}{\cos\left(x+\dfrac{\pi}{2}\right)}=\dfrac{\sin x\cos\dfrac{\pi}{2}+\cos x\sin\dfrac{\pi}{2}}{\cos x\cos\dfrac{\pi}{2}-\sin x\sin\dfrac{\pi}{2}}=\dfrac{\sin x\bullet 0+\cos x\bullet 1}{\cos x\bullet 0-\sin x\bullet 1}=\dfrac{\cos x}{-\sin x}=-\cot x$

67. Verifying the identity: $\cos(x+x)=\cos x\cos x-\sin x\sin x=\cos^2 x-\sin^2 x$

69. Verifying the identity: $\tan(\pi-x)=\dfrac{\tan\pi-\tan x}{1+\tan\pi\tan x}=\dfrac{0-\tan x}{1+0\bullet\tan x}=\dfrac{-\tan x}{1}=-\tan x$

71. Verifying the identity: $\tan\left(x+\dfrac{\pi}{4}\right)=\dfrac{\tan x+\tan\dfrac{\pi}{4}}{1-\tan x\tan\dfrac{\pi}{4}}=\dfrac{\tan x+1}{1-\tan x}$

73. Verifying the identity: $\cos\left(x-\dfrac{\pi}{2}\right)=\cos\left[-\left(\dfrac{\pi}{2}-x\right)\right]=\cos\left(\dfrac{\pi}{2}-x\right)$

75. Verifying the identity: $\sin\left(\dfrac{\pi}{3}-x\right)=\sin\left[-\left(x-\dfrac{\pi}{3}\right)\right]=-\sin\left(x-\dfrac{\pi}{3}\right)$

77. Verifying the identity: $\cos(x+y)+\cos(x-y)=\cos x\cos y-\sin x\sin y+\cos x\cos y+\sin x\sin y=2\cos x\cos y$

79. Verifying the identity:
$$\sin(x+y)\sin(x-y)=(\sin x\cos y+\cos x\sin y)(\sin x\cos y-\cos x\sin y)$$
$$=(\sin x\cos y)^2-(\cos x\sin y)^2$$
$$=\sin^2 x\cos^2 y-\cos^2 x\sin^2 y$$

81. Let $a=\cos^{-1}0=\dfrac{\pi}{2}$ and $b=\sin^{-1}\dfrac{1}{2}=\dfrac{\pi}{6}$. Therefore:
$$\sin\left(\cos^{-1}0-\sin^{-1}\dfrac{1}{2}\right)=\sin\left(\dfrac{\pi}{2}-\dfrac{\pi}{6}\right)=\sin\dfrac{\pi}{2}\cos\dfrac{\pi}{6}-\cos\dfrac{\pi}{2}\sin\dfrac{\pi}{6}=(1)\left(\dfrac{\sqrt{3}}{2}\right)-(0)\left(\dfrac{1}{2}\right)=\dfrac{\sqrt{3}}{2}$$

83. Let $a=\sin^{-1}\dfrac{3}{5}$, so $\sin a=\dfrac{3}{5}$. Therefore:
$$\cos\left(\sin^{-1}\dfrac{3}{5}+\dfrac{\pi}{2}\right)=\cos\left(a+\dfrac{\pi}{2}\right)=\cos a\cos\dfrac{\pi}{2}-\sin a\sin\dfrac{\pi}{2}=\cos a\bullet 0-\left(\dfrac{3}{5}\right)(1)=-\dfrac{3}{5}$$

85. Let $\theta=\cos^{-1}\dfrac{4}{5}$, so $\cos\theta=\dfrac{4}{5}$. Using the Pythagorean identity:
$$\sin^2\theta+\cos^2\theta=1$$
$$\sin^2\theta+\left(\dfrac{4}{5}\right)^2=1$$
$$\sin^2\theta+\dfrac{16}{25}=1$$
$$\sin^2\theta=\dfrac{9}{25}$$
$$\sin\theta=\dfrac{3}{5}$$

Since $\tan\theta=\dfrac{\sin\theta}{\cos\theta}=\dfrac{3}{4}$, then: $\tan\left(\dfrac{\pi}{4}+\cos^{-1}\dfrac{4}{5}\right)=\tan\left(\dfrac{\pi}{4}+\theta\right)=\dfrac{\tan\dfrac{\pi}{4}+\tan\theta}{1-\tan\dfrac{\pi}{4}\tan\theta}=\dfrac{1+\dfrac{3}{4}}{1-\dfrac{3}{4}}=\dfrac{4+3}{4-3}=7$

87. Let $g(t) = -\dfrac{\sqrt{3}}{2}\sin t + \dfrac{1}{2}\cos t$. Then $A = -\dfrac{\sqrt{3}}{2}, B = \dfrac{1}{2}$, so: $C = \sqrt{A^2 + B^2} = \sqrt{\left(-\dfrac{\sqrt{3}}{2}\right)^2 + \left(\dfrac{1}{2}\right)^2} = \sqrt{\dfrac{3}{4} + \dfrac{1}{4}} = \sqrt{1} = 1$

Therefore $\cos c = \dfrac{A}{C} = \dfrac{\left(-\dfrac{\sqrt{3}}{2}\right)}{1} = -\dfrac{\sqrt{3}}{2}$ and $\sin c = \dfrac{B}{C} = \dfrac{\left(\dfrac{1}{2}\right)}{1} = \dfrac{1}{2}$, thus $c = \dfrac{5\pi}{6}$. Therefore $g(t) = \sin\left(t + \dfrac{5\pi}{6}\right)$.

89. Using the sum identity: $f(x) = \sin\left(300\pi x + \dfrac{\pi}{4}\right) = \sin 300\pi x \cos\dfrac{\pi}{4} + \cos 300\pi x \sin\dfrac{\pi}{4} = \dfrac{\sqrt{2}}{2}\sin 300\pi x + \dfrac{\sqrt{2}}{2}\cos 300\pi x$

Thus $A = \dfrac{\sqrt{2}}{2}$, $B = 300\pi$, $C = \dfrac{\sqrt{2}}{2}$, $D = 300\pi$.

91. Simplifying the expression:
$$\dfrac{f(x+h) - f(x)}{h} = \dfrac{\cos[2(x+h)] - \cos 2x}{h}$$
$$= \dfrac{\cos(2x + 2h) - \cos 2x}{h}$$
$$= \dfrac{\cos 2x \cos 2h - \sin 2x \sin 2h - \cos 2x}{h}$$
$$= \dfrac{\cos 2x(\cos 2h - 1) - \sin 2x \sin 2h}{h}$$

93. Adding the two waves: $y(x) = y_1(x) + y_2(x) = 10\sin(50\pi x) + 10\cos(50\pi x)$

Thus $A = \sqrt{10^2 + 10^2} = \sqrt{200} = 10\sqrt{2}$. Therefore $\cos c = \dfrac{10}{10\sqrt{2}} = \dfrac{\sqrt{2}}{2}$ and $\sin c = \dfrac{10}{10\sqrt{2}} = \dfrac{\sqrt{2}}{2}$, thus $c = \dfrac{\pi}{4}$.

So $A = 10\sqrt{2}, c = \dfrac{\pi}{4}$, therefore $y(x) = 10\sqrt{2}\sin\left(50\pi x + \dfrac{\pi}{4}\right)$.

95. Finding the formula: $\sin 2x = \sin(x + x) = \sin x \cos x + \cos x \sin x = 2\sin x \cos x$

97. Simplifying:
$$\sin(a+b) - \sin(a-b) = (\sin a \cos b + \cos a \sin b) - (\sin a \cos b - \cos a \sin b)$$
$$= \sin a \cos b + \cos a \sin b - \sin a \cos b + \cos a \sin b$$
$$= 2\cos a \sin b$$

99. Verifying the identity: $\sin(a - b) = \sin(a + (-b)) = \sin a \cos(-b) + \cos a \sin(-b) = \sin a \cos b - \cos a \sin b$

6.3 Multiple-Angle Identities; Sum and Product Identities

1. Using the Pythagorean identity:

$$\cos^2 x = 1 - \sin^2 x = 1 - \left(\frac{1}{3}\right)^2 = 1 - \frac{1}{9} = \frac{8}{9}$$

$$\cos x = \pm \frac{2\sqrt{2}}{3}$$

Since $0 < x < \frac{\pi}{2}$, the value is given by: $\cos x = \frac{2\sqrt{2}}{3}$

3. The value is given by: $\sin 2x = 2 \sin x \cos x = 2\left(\frac{1}{3}\right)\left(\frac{2\sqrt{2}}{3}\right) = \frac{4\sqrt{2}}{9}$

5. First find the tangent: $\tan x = \frac{\sin x}{\cos x} = \frac{\left(\frac{1}{3}\right)}{\left(\frac{2\sqrt{2}}{3}\right)} = \frac{1}{2\sqrt{2}} = \frac{\sqrt{2}}{4}$

The value is given by: $\tan 2x = \frac{2 \tan x}{1 - \tan^2 x} = \frac{2\left(\frac{\sqrt{2}}{4}\right)}{1 - \left(\frac{\sqrt{2}}{4}\right)^2} = \frac{\frac{\sqrt{2}}{2}}{1 - \frac{1}{8}} = \frac{\frac{\sqrt{2}}{2}}{\frac{7}{8}} = \frac{\sqrt{2}}{2} \cdot \frac{8}{7} = \frac{4\sqrt{2}}{7}$

7. The value is given by: $\sec 2x = \frac{1}{\cos 2x} = \frac{1}{1 - 2\sin^2 x} = \frac{1}{1 - 2\left(\frac{1}{3}\right)^2} = \frac{1}{1 - \frac{2}{9}} = \frac{1}{\frac{7}{9}} = \frac{9}{7}$

9. Using the Pythagorean identity:

$$\sin^2 x = 1 - \cos^2 x = 1 - \left(-\frac{3}{5}\right)^2 = 1 - \frac{9}{25} = \frac{16}{25}$$

$$\sin x = \pm \frac{4}{5}$$

Since $\pi < x < \frac{3\pi}{2}$, the sine value is $\sin x = -\frac{4}{5}$. The values are given by:

$$\sin 2x = 2 \sin x \cos x = 2\left(-\frac{4}{5}\right)\left(-\frac{3}{5}\right) = \frac{24}{25}$$

$$\cos 2x = 2\cos^2 x - 1 = 2\left(-\frac{3}{5}\right)^2 - 1 = -\frac{7}{25}$$

$$\tan 2x = \frac{\sin 2x}{\cos 2x} = \frac{24/25}{-7/25} = -\frac{24}{7}$$

11. Using the Pythagorean identity:

$$\cos^2 x = 1 - \sin^2 x = 1 - \left(-\frac{1}{2}\right)^2 = \frac{3}{4}$$

$$\cos x = \pm\frac{\sqrt{3}}{2}$$

Since $\pi < x < \frac{3\pi}{2}$, the cosine value is $\cos x = -\frac{\sqrt{3}}{2}$. The values are given by:

$$\sin 2x = 2\sin x \cos x = 2\left(-\frac{1}{2}\right)\left(-\frac{\sqrt{3}}{2}\right) = \frac{\sqrt{3}}{2}$$

$$\cos 2x = 1 - 2\sin^2 x = 1 - 2\left(-\frac{1}{2}\right)^2 = \frac{1}{2}$$

$$\tan 2x = \frac{\sin 2x}{\cos 2x} = \frac{\sqrt{3}/2}{1/2} = \sqrt{3}$$

13. Since $\sec x = 3$, $\cos x = \frac{1}{3}$. Using the Pythagorean identity:

$$\sin^2 x = 1 - \cos^2 x = 1 - \left(\frac{1}{3}\right)^2 = \frac{8}{9}$$

$$\sin x = \pm\frac{2\sqrt{2}}{3}$$

Since $0 < x < \frac{\pi}{2}$, the sine value is $\sin x = \frac{2\sqrt{2}}{3}$. The values are given by:

$$\sin 2x = 2\sin x \cos x = 2\left(\frac{2\sqrt{2}}{3}\right)\left(\frac{1}{3}\right) = \frac{4\sqrt{2}}{9}$$

$$\cos 2x = 2\cos^2 x - 1 = 2\left(\frac{1}{3}\right)^2 - 1 = -\frac{7}{9}$$

$$\tan 2x = \frac{\sin 2x}{\cos 2x} = \frac{4\sqrt{2}/9}{-7/9} = -\frac{4\sqrt{2}}{7}$$

15. Since $\sec x = -\dfrac{6}{5}$, $\cos x = -\dfrac{5}{6}$. Using the Pythagorean identity:

$$\sin^2 x = 1 - \cos^2 x = 1 - \left(-\frac{5}{6}\right)^2 = \frac{11}{36}$$

$$\sin x = \pm\frac{\sqrt{11}}{6}$$

Since $\pi < x < \dfrac{3\pi}{2}$, the sine value is $\sin x = -\dfrac{\sqrt{11}}{6}$. The values are given by:

$$\sin 2x = 2\sin x \cos x = 2\left(-\frac{\sqrt{11}}{6}\right)\left(-\frac{5}{6}\right) = \frac{5\sqrt{11}}{18}$$

$$\cos 2x = 2\cos^2 x - 1 = 2\left(-\frac{5}{6}\right)^2 - 1 = \frac{7}{18}$$

$$\tan 2x = \frac{\sin 2x}{\cos 2x} = \frac{5\sqrt{11}\big/18}{7\big/18} = \frac{5\sqrt{11}}{7}$$

17. Reducing the powers: $\cos^3 x = \cos^2 x \cos x = \left(\dfrac{1+\cos 2x}{2}\right)\cos x = \dfrac{\cos x + \cos x \cos 2x}{2}$

19. Reducing the powers: $\sin x \cos^2 x = \sin x\left(\dfrac{1+\cos 2x}{2}\right) = \dfrac{\sin x + \sin x \cos 2x}{2}$

21. Reducing the powers:

$$\sin^2 x \cos^3 x = \sin^2 x \cos^2 x \cos x$$

$$= \left(\frac{1-\cos 2x}{2}\right)\left(\frac{1+\cos 2x}{2}\right)\cos x$$

$$= \left(\frac{1-\cos^2 2x}{4}\right)\cos x$$

$$= \left(\frac{1-\dfrac{1+\cos 4x}{2}}{4}\right)\cos x$$

$$= \left(\frac{1-\cos 4x}{8}\right)\cos x$$

$$= \frac{\cos x - \cos x \cos 4x}{8}$$

23. Reducing the powers: $\dfrac{\tan^2 x}{\sec^2 x} = \dfrac{\dfrac{\sin^2 x}{\cos^2 x}}{\dfrac{1}{\cos^2 x}} = \sin^2 x = \dfrac{1-\cos 2x}{2}$

25. Using the half-angle identity: $\cos\dfrac{\pi}{12} = \cos\left(\dfrac{1}{2}\cdot\dfrac{\pi}{6}\right) = \sqrt{\dfrac{1+\cos\dfrac{\pi}{6}}{2}} = \sqrt{\dfrac{1+\dfrac{\sqrt{3}}{2}}{2}} = \sqrt{\dfrac{2+\sqrt{3}}{4}} = \dfrac{\sqrt{2+\sqrt{3}}}{2}$

27. Using the half-angle identity:

$$\cos\frac{13\pi}{12} = \cos\left(\frac{1}{2}\cdot\frac{13\pi}{6}\right) = -\sqrt{\frac{1+\cos\dfrac{13\pi}{6}}{2}} = -\sqrt{\frac{1+\cos\dfrac{\pi}{6}}{2}} = -\sqrt{\frac{1+\dfrac{\sqrt{3}}{2}}{2}} = -\sqrt{\frac{2+\sqrt{3}}{4}} = -\frac{\sqrt{2+\sqrt{3}}}{2}$$

29. Using the half-angle identity: $\sin\left(-\dfrac{3\pi}{8}\right) = -\sin\left(\dfrac{1}{2} \cdot \dfrac{3\pi}{4}\right) = -\sqrt{\dfrac{1-\cos\dfrac{3\pi}{4}}{2}} = -\sqrt{\dfrac{1+\dfrac{\sqrt{2}}{2}}{2}} = -\sqrt{\dfrac{2+\sqrt{2}}{4}} = -\dfrac{\sqrt{2+\sqrt{2}}}{2}$

31. Using the half-angle identity: $\tan\dfrac{3\pi}{12} = \tan\left(\dfrac{1}{2} \cdot \dfrac{3\pi}{6}\right) = \tan\left(\dfrac{1}{2} \cdot \dfrac{\pi}{2}\right) = \dfrac{\sin\dfrac{\pi}{2}}{1+\cos\dfrac{\pi}{2}} = \dfrac{1}{1+0} = 1$

33. Using the Pythagorean identity:

$$\cos^2\theta = 1 - \sin^2\theta = 1 - \left(\dfrac{3}{5}\right)^2 = \dfrac{16}{25}$$

$$\cos\theta = \pm\dfrac{4}{5}$$

Since $0 < \theta < \dfrac{\pi}{2}$, the cosine value is $\cos\theta = \dfrac{4}{5}$. Using the half-angle identity:

$$\sin\dfrac{\theta}{2} = \sqrt{\dfrac{1-\cos\theta}{2}} = \sqrt{\dfrac{1-\dfrac{4}{5}}{2}} = \sqrt{\dfrac{1}{10}} = \dfrac{1}{\sqrt{10}} = \dfrac{\sqrt{10}}{10}$$

35. Using the half-angle identity: $\tan\dfrac{\theta}{2} = \dfrac{\sin\theta}{1+\cos\theta} = \dfrac{\dfrac{3}{5}}{1+\dfrac{4}{5}} = \dfrac{\dfrac{3}{5}}{\dfrac{9}{5}} = \dfrac{3}{9} = \dfrac{1}{3}$

37. Using the half-angle identity: $\cot\dfrac{\theta}{2} = \dfrac{1}{\tan\dfrac{\theta}{2}} = \dfrac{1+\cos\theta}{\sin\theta} = \dfrac{1+\dfrac{4}{5}}{\dfrac{3}{5}} = \dfrac{\dfrac{9}{5}}{\dfrac{3}{5}} = \dfrac{9}{3} = 3$

39. Since $\pi < \theta < \dfrac{3\pi}{2}$, $\dfrac{\pi}{2} < \dfrac{\theta}{2} < \dfrac{3\pi}{4}$, so $\dfrac{\theta}{2}$ is in Quadrant II. Using the half-angle identity:

$$\sin\dfrac{\theta}{2} = \sqrt{\dfrac{1-\cos\theta}{2}} = \sqrt{\dfrac{1-\left(-\dfrac{3}{5}\right)}{2}} = \sqrt{\dfrac{8}{10}} = \sqrt{\dfrac{4}{5}} = \dfrac{2}{\sqrt{5}} = \dfrac{2\sqrt{5}}{5}$$

41. Using the Pythagorean identity:

$$\sin^2\theta = 1 - \cos^2\theta = 1 - \left(-\dfrac{3}{5}\right)^2 = \dfrac{16}{25}$$

$$\sin\theta = \pm\dfrac{4}{5}$$

Since $\pi < \theta < \dfrac{3\pi}{2}$, the sine value is $\sin\theta = -\dfrac{4}{5}$. Using the half-angle identity:

$$\tan\dfrac{\theta}{2} = \dfrac{\sin\theta}{1+\cos\theta} = \dfrac{-\dfrac{4}{5}}{1+\left(-\dfrac{3}{5}\right)} = \dfrac{-\dfrac{4}{5}}{\dfrac{2}{5}} = \dfrac{-4}{2} = -2$$

43. Using the half-angle identity: $\cot\dfrac{\theta}{2} = \dfrac{1}{\tan\dfrac{\theta}{2}} = \dfrac{1+\cos\theta}{\sin\theta} = \dfrac{1+\left(-\dfrac{3}{5}\right)}{-\dfrac{4}{5}} = \dfrac{\dfrac{2}{5}}{-\dfrac{4}{5}} = \dfrac{-2}{4} = -\dfrac{1}{2}$

45. Using the product-to-sum identities: $\sin 4x \cos x = \dfrac{1}{2}\left[\sin(4x+3x) + \sin(4x-3x)\right] = \dfrac{1}{2}\left(\sin 7x + \sin x\right)$

47. Using the product-to-sum identities:

$$\sin 2x \sin 6x = \frac{1}{2}\left[\cos(2x-6x)-\cos(2x+6x)\right] = \frac{1}{2}\left[\cos(-4x)-\cos 8x\right] = \frac{1}{2}(\cos 4x - \cos 8x)$$

49. Using the product-to-sum identities:

$$\sin x \sin 3x = \frac{1}{2}\left[\cos(x-3x)-\cos(x+3x)\right] = \frac{1}{2}\left[\cos(-2x)-\cos 4x\right] = \frac{1}{2}(\cos 2x - \cos 4x)$$

51. Using the sum-to-product identities: $\sin 2x - \sin 3x = 2\cos\left(\dfrac{2x+3x}{2}\right)\sin\left(\dfrac{2x-3x}{2}\right) = 2\cos\dfrac{5x}{2}\sin\left(-\dfrac{x}{2}\right) = -2\cos\dfrac{5x}{2}\sin\dfrac{x}{2}$

53. Using the sum-to-product identities:

$$\cos 3x - \cos 5x = -2\sin\left(\frac{3x+5x}{2}\right)\sin\left(\frac{3x-5x}{2}\right) = -2\sin\frac{8x}{2}\sin\left(-\frac{2x}{2}\right) = 2\sin 4x \sin x$$

55. Using the sum-to-product identities: $\cos 5x - \cos 2x = -2\sin\left(\dfrac{5x+2x}{2}\right)\sin\left(\dfrac{5x-2x}{2}\right) = -2\sin\dfrac{7x}{2}\sin\dfrac{3x}{2}$

57. Verifying the identity: $\sec^2 x = \dfrac{1}{\cos^2 x} = \dfrac{1}{\dfrac{1+\cos 2x}{2}} = \dfrac{2}{1+\cos 2x}$

59. Verifying the identity: $2\cos^2 2x = 2\left(\dfrac{1+\cos(2\cdot 2x)}{2}\right) = 1+\cos 4x$

61. Verifying the identity: $\sec^2 2x = \dfrac{1}{\cos^2 2x} = \dfrac{1}{\dfrac{1+\cos(2\cdot 2x)}{2}} = \dfrac{2}{1+\cos 4x}$

63. Verifying the identity: $\cos 6x = \cos(2\cdot 3x) = 1-2\sin^2 3x$

65. Verifying the identity: $\sin 6x = \sin(2\cdot 3x) = 2\sin 3x \cos 3x$

67. Verifying the identity: $\sin(2x+\pi) = \sin 2x \cos\pi + \cos 2x \sin\pi = \sin 2x \cdot (-1) + \cos 2x \cdot (0) = -2\sin x \cos x$

69. Verifying the identity:

$$\cos 4x = \cos(2\cdot 2x)$$
$$= 1-2\sin^2 2x$$
$$= 1-2(\sin 2x)^2$$
$$= 1-2(2\sin x \cos x)^2$$
$$= 1-2(4\sin^2 x \cos^2 x)$$
$$= 1-8\sin^2 x(1-\sin^2 x)$$
$$= 1-8\sin^2 x + 8\sin^4 x$$

71. Verifying the identity:

$$\sin 3x = \sin(2x+x)$$
$$= \sin 2x \cos x + \cos 2x \sin x$$
$$= 2\sin x \cos x \cos x + (2\cos^2 x - 1)\sin x$$
$$= 2\sin x \cos^2 x + (2\cos^2 x - 1)\sin x$$
$$= \sin x(2\cos^2 x + 2\cos^2 x - 1)$$
$$= \sin x(4\cos^2 x - 1)$$

73. Verifying the identity:

$$\cos 3x + \cos x = \cos(2x + x) + \cos x$$
$$= \cos 2x \cos x - \sin 2x \sin x + \cos x$$
$$= \cos 2x \cos x - 2\sin x \cos x \sin x + \cos x$$
$$= \cos 2x \cos x - 2\sin^2 x \cos x + \cos x$$
$$= \cos 2x \cos x + \cos x(1 - 2\sin^2 x)$$
$$= \cos 2x \cos x + \cos x \cos 2x$$
$$= 2\cos 2x \cos x$$
$$= 2\cos x(2\cos^2 x - 1)$$
$$= 4\cos^3 x - 2\cos x$$

75. Verifying the identity: $\tan\left(-\dfrac{x}{2}\right) = -\tan\left(\dfrac{x}{2}\right) = -\left(\dfrac{1 - \cos x}{\sin x}\right) = -\dfrac{1}{\sin x} + \dfrac{\cos x}{\sin x} = -\csc x + \cot x = \cot x - \csc x$

77. Let $\theta = \cos^{-1}\dfrac{3}{5}$, so $\cos\theta = \dfrac{3}{5}$. Therefore: $\cos\left(2\cos^{-1}\dfrac{3}{5}\right) = \cos(2\theta) = 2\cos^2\theta - 1 = 2\left(\dfrac{3}{5}\right)^2 - 1 = -\dfrac{7}{25}$

79. Evaluating: $\sin\left(2\sin^{-1}\dfrac{1}{2}\right) = \sin\left(2 \cdot \dfrac{\pi}{6}\right) = \sin\dfrac{\pi}{3} = \dfrac{\sqrt{3}}{2}$

81. Let $\theta = \cos^{-1}\dfrac{4}{5}$, so $\cos\theta = \dfrac{4}{5}$. Using the Pythagorean identity:

Therefore: $\sin^2\left(\dfrac{1}{2}\cos^{-1}\dfrac{4}{5}\right) = \sin^2\left(\dfrac{1}{2}\theta\right) = \left(\sin\dfrac{\theta}{2}\right)^2 = \left(\sqrt{\dfrac{1 - \cos\theta}{2}}\right)^2 = \dfrac{1 - \dfrac{4}{5}}{2} = \dfrac{1}{10}$

83. Evaluating: $\tan^2\left(\dfrac{1}{2}\sin^{-1}\dfrac{\sqrt{3}}{2}\right) = \tan^2\left(\dfrac{1}{2} \cdot \dfrac{\pi}{3}\right) = \tan^2\dfrac{\pi}{6} = \left(\dfrac{1}{\sqrt{3}}\right)^2 = \dfrac{1}{3}$

85. Using the double-angle identity: $R = \dfrac{40^2 \sin 2\theta}{9.8} = \dfrac{1600(2\sin\theta\cos\theta)}{9.8} = \dfrac{3200\sin\theta\cos\theta}{9.8}$

Now using the Pythagorean identity:
$$\cos^2\theta = 1 - \sin^2\theta = 1 - (0.3)^2 = 0.91$$
$$\cos\theta = \sqrt{0.91}$$

Evaluating: $R = \dfrac{3200\sin\theta\cos\theta}{9.8} = \dfrac{3200(0.3)\sqrt{0.91}}{9.8} = 93.4471$ meters

87. **a.** Solving for b:

$$\sin\left(\dfrac{\alpha}{2}\right) = \dfrac{\dfrac{1}{2}b}{s}$$
$$s\sin\left(\dfrac{\alpha}{2}\right) = \dfrac{1}{2}b$$
$$2s\sin\left(\dfrac{\alpha}{2}\right) = b$$
$$b = 2s\sin\left(\dfrac{\alpha}{2}\right)$$

b. Solving for h:

$$\cos\left(\dfrac{\alpha}{2}\right) = \dfrac{h}{s}$$
$$s\cos\left(\dfrac{\alpha}{2}\right) = h$$
$$h = s\cos\left(\dfrac{\alpha}{2}\right)$$

c. Finding the area: $A = \frac{1}{2}bh = \frac{1}{2} \cdot 2s \sin\left(\frac{\alpha}{2}\right) \cdot s \cos\left(\frac{\alpha}{2}\right) = s^2 \sin\left(\frac{\alpha}{2}\right)\cos\left(\frac{\alpha}{2}\right)$

d. Finding the area: $A = s^2 \sin\left(\frac{\alpha}{2}\right)\cos\left(\frac{\alpha}{2}\right) = s^2 \sqrt{\frac{1-\cos\alpha}{2}}\sqrt{\frac{1+\cos\alpha}{2}} = s^2\sqrt{\frac{1-\cos^2\alpha}{4}} = s^2\frac{\sqrt{\sin^2\alpha}}{2} = \frac{1}{2}s^2\sin\alpha$

e. Since $\tan\alpha = \frac{4}{3} = \frac{b}{a}$, let $b = 4$ and $a = 3$. Finding c: $c = \sqrt{a^2 + b^2} = \sqrt{16+9} = \sqrt{25} = 5$

Therefore $\sin\alpha = \frac{b}{c} = \frac{4}{5}$. Finding the area: $A = \frac{1}{2}s^2\sin\alpha = \frac{1}{2}(6)^2\left(\frac{4}{5}\right) = \frac{72}{5}$

89. Simplifying each expression:
$$\sin(\pi + x) = \sin\pi\cos x + \cos\pi\cos x = -\cos x$$
$$A\sin(\pi - x) = A(\sin\pi\cos x - \cos\pi\cos x) = A\cos x$$
Setting the expressions equal:
$$A\cos x = -\cos x$$
$$A = -1$$

91. Writing the two identities:
$$\cos(a+b) = \cos a\cos b - \sin a\sin b$$
$$\cos(a-b) = \cos a\cos b + \sin a\sin b$$
Adding:
$$\cos(a+b) + \cos(a-b) = \cos a\cos b - \sin a\sin b + \cos a\cos b + \sin a\sin b = 2\cos a\cos b$$
Therefore: $\cos a\cos b = \dfrac{\cos(a+b)+\cos(a-b)}{2} = \dfrac{1}{2}[\cos(a+b) + \cos(a-b)]$

6.4 Trigonometric Equations

1. Completing the identity: $\sin^2 x + \cos^2 x = 1$

3. Completing the identity: $\sec^2 x - \tan^2 x = 1$

5. Solving by factoring:
$$x^2 - 3x - 4 = 0$$
$$(x+1)(x-4) = 0$$
$$x = -1, 4$$

7. **a.** Verifying the identity: $\sin x\cot x = \sin x \cdot \dfrac{\cos x}{\sin x} = \cos x$

b. Solving the equation:
$$\sin x\cot x = 1$$
$$\cos x = 1$$
$$x = 0$$

9. Solving the equation:
$$2\sin x = -1$$
$$\sin x = -\frac{1}{2}$$
$$x = \frac{7\pi}{6}, \frac{11\pi}{6}$$

The general solution is: $x = \dfrac{7\pi}{6} + 2n\pi, \dfrac{11\pi}{6} + 2n\pi$, where n is an integer

11. Solving the equation:

$$\tan x - 1 = 0$$

$$\tan x = 1$$

$$x = \frac{\pi}{4}$$

The general solution is: $x = \frac{\pi}{4} + n\pi$, where n is an integer

13. Solving the equation:

$$\csc x = 2$$

$$\sin x = \frac{1}{2}$$

$$x = \frac{\pi}{6}, \frac{5\pi}{6}$$

The general solution is: $x = \frac{\pi}{6} + 2n\pi, \frac{5\pi}{6} + 2n\pi$, where n is an integer

15. Solving the equation:

$$\sin^2 x = 1$$

$$\sin x = \pm 1$$

$$x = \frac{\pi}{2}, \frac{3\pi}{2}$$

The general solution is: $x = \frac{\pi}{2} + 2n\pi, \frac{3\pi}{2} + 2n\pi$, where n is an integer

Note this could also be written as: $x = \frac{\pi}{2} + n\pi$, where n is an integer

17. Solving the equation:

$$\sin 2x = \frac{1}{2}$$

$$2x = \frac{\pi}{6} + 2n\pi, \frac{5\pi}{6} + 2n\pi$$

$$x = \frac{\pi}{12} + n\pi, \frac{5\pi}{12} + n\pi$$

The general solution is: $x = \frac{\pi}{12} + n\pi, \frac{5\pi}{12} + n\pi$, where n is an integer

19. Solving the equation:

$$\cos 4x + 1 = 0$$

$$\cos 4x = -1$$

$$4x = \pi + 2n\pi$$

$$x = \frac{\pi}{4} + \frac{n\pi}{2}$$

The general solution is: $x = \frac{\pi}{4} + \frac{n\pi}{2}$, where n is an integer

21. Solving the equation:
$$\tan 2x = -1$$
$$2x = \frac{3\pi}{4} + n\pi$$
$$x = \frac{3\pi}{8} + \frac{n\pi}{2}$$

The general solution is: $x = \frac{3\pi}{8} + \frac{n\pi}{2}$, where n is an integer

23. Solving the equation:
$$4\cos x = -3$$
$$\cos x = -\frac{3}{4}$$
$$x = \cos^{-1}\left(-\frac{3}{4}\right), 2\pi - \cos^{-1}\left(-\frac{3}{4}\right)$$
$$x \approx 2.4189, 3.8643$$

The general solution is: $x = 2.4189 + 2n\pi, 3.8643 + 2n\pi$, where n is an integer

25. Solving the equation:
$$2\tan x = \tan x + 3$$
$$\tan x = 3$$
$$x = \tan^{-1} 3 \approx 1.2490$$

The general solution is: $x = 1.2490 + n\pi$, where n is an integer

27. Solving the equation:
$$12 + 3\csc x = 7$$
$$3\csc x = -5$$
$$\csc x = -\frac{5}{3}$$
$$\sin x = -\frac{3}{5}$$
$$x = \pi + \sin^{-1}\left(\frac{3}{5}\right), 2\pi - \sin^{-1}\left(\frac{3}{5}\right)$$
$$x \approx 3.7831, 5.6397$$

The general solution is: $x = 3.7851 + 2n\pi, 5.6397 + 2n\pi$, where n is an integer

29. Solving the equation:
$$4\csc x - 5 = 1$$
$$4\csc x = 6$$
$$\csc x = \frac{3}{2}$$
$$\sin x = \frac{2}{3}$$
$$x = \sin^{-1}\left(\frac{2}{3}\right), \pi - \sin^{-1}\left(\frac{2}{3}\right)$$
$$x \approx 0.7297, 2.4119$$

The general solution is: $x = 0.7297 + 2n\pi, 2.4119 + 2n\pi$, where n is an integer

31. Solving the equation:
$$\sin^2 x - \sin x = 0$$
$$\sin x (\sin x - 1) = 0$$
$$\sin x = 0 \implies x = 0, \pi$$
$$\sin x - 1 = 0 \implies \sin x = 1 \implies x = \frac{\pi}{2}$$

The solutions in the interval $[0, 2\pi)$ are: $x = 0, \dfrac{\pi}{2}, \pi$

33. Solving the equation:
$$\sin^3 x = \sin x$$
$$\sin^3 x - \sin x = 0$$
$$\sin x (\sin^2 x - 1) = 0$$
$$\sin x = 0 \implies x = 0, \pi$$
$$\sin^2 x - 1 = 0 \implies \sin^2 x = 1 \implies \sin x = \pm 1 \implies x = \frac{\pi}{2}, \frac{3\pi}{2}$$

The solutions in the interval $[0, 2\pi)$ are: $x = 0, \dfrac{\pi}{2}, \pi, \dfrac{3\pi}{2}$

35. Solving the equation:
$$\sin^2 x = \cos x + 1$$
$$\sin^2 x - \cos x - 1 = 0$$
$$(1 - \cos^2 x) - \cos x - 1 = 0$$
$$-\cos^2 x - \cos x = 0$$
$$-\cos x (\cos x + 1) = 0$$
$$\cos x = 0 \implies x = \frac{\pi}{2}, \frac{3\pi}{2}$$
$$\cos x + 1 = 0 \implies \cos x = -1 \implies x = \pi$$

The solutions in the interval $[0, 2\pi)$ are: $x = \dfrac{\pi}{2}, \pi, \dfrac{3\pi}{2}$

37. Solving the equation:
$$\cos x - \sec x = 0$$
$$\cos x - \frac{1}{\cos x} = 0$$
$$\cos^2 x - 1 = 0$$
$$\cos^2 x = 1$$
$$\cos x = \pm 1$$
$$x = 0, \pi$$

The solutions in the interval $[0, 2\pi)$ are: $x = 0, \pi$

39. Solving the equation:

$$\sin\left(x - \frac{\pi}{4}\right) = 0$$

$$x - \frac{\pi}{4} = 0 \implies x = \frac{\pi}{4}$$

$$x - \frac{\pi}{4} = \pi \implies x = \pi + \frac{\pi}{4} = \frac{5\pi}{4}$$

The solutions in the interval $[0, 2\pi)$ are: $x = \frac{\pi}{4}, \frac{5\pi}{4}$

41. Solving the equation:

$$\sin\left(2x + \frac{\pi}{2}\right) + 1 = 0$$

$$\sin\left(2x + \frac{\pi}{2}\right) = -1$$

$$2x + \frac{\pi}{2} = \frac{3\pi}{2} + 2n\pi$$

$$2x = \pi + 2n\pi$$

$$x = \frac{\pi}{2} + n\pi$$

The solutions in the interval $[0, 2\pi)$ are: $x = \frac{\pi}{2}, \frac{3\pi}{2}$

43. Solving the equation:

$$\sin^2 x + 2\cos x = 1$$

$$\left(1 - \cos^2 x\right) + 2\cos x = 1$$

$$1 - \cos^2 x + 2\cos x - 1 = 0$$

$$-\cos^2 x + 2\cos x = 0$$

$$-\cos x\left(\cos x - 2\right) = 0$$

$$\cos x = 0 \implies x = \frac{\pi}{2}, \frac{3\pi}{2}$$

$$\cos x - 2 = 0 \implies \cos x = 2 \text{ which has no solution}$$

The solutions in the interval $[0, 2\pi)$ are: $x = \frac{\pi}{2}, \frac{3\pi}{2}$

45. Solving the equation:

$$\cos x = \sec x$$

$$\cos x = \frac{1}{\cos x}$$

$$\cos^2 x = 1$$

$$\cos x = \pm 1$$

$$x = 0, \pi$$

The solutions in the interval $[0, 2\pi)$ are: $x = 0, \pi$

47. Solving the equation:
$$\sin 2x = 2\cos x$$
$$2\sin x\cos x = 2\cos x$$
$$2\sin x\cos x - 2\cos x = 0$$
$$2\cos x(\sin x - 1) = 0$$
$$\cos x = 0 \implies x = \frac{\pi}{2}, \frac{3\pi}{2}$$
$$\sin x - 1 = 0 \implies \sin x = 1 \implies x = \frac{\pi}{2}$$

The solutions in the interval $[0, 2\pi)$ are: $x = \dfrac{\pi}{2}, \dfrac{3\pi}{2}$

49. Solving the equation:
$$\cos 2x + 3\cos x - 1 = 0$$
$$(2\cos^2 x - 1) + 3\cos x - 1 = 0$$
$$2\cos^2 x + 3\cos x - 2 = 0$$
$$(2\cos x - 1)(\cos x + 2) = 0$$
$$2\cos x - 1 = 0 \implies \cos x = \frac{1}{2} \implies x = \frac{\pi}{3}, \frac{5\pi}{3}$$
$$\cos x + 2 = 0 \implies \cos x = -2 \text{ has no solution}$$

The solutions in the interval $[0, 2\pi)$ are: $x = \dfrac{\pi}{3}, \dfrac{5\pi}{3}$

51. Solving the equation:
$$\sec^2 x = 2\tan^2 x$$
$$1 + \tan^2 x = 2\tan^2 x$$
$$1 = \tan^2 x$$
$$\tan x = \pm 1$$
$$x = \frac{\pi}{4}, \frac{3\pi}{4}, \frac{5\pi}{4}, \frac{7\pi}{4}$$

The solutions in the interval $[0, 2\pi)$ are: $x = \dfrac{\pi}{4}, \dfrac{3\pi}{4}, \dfrac{5\pi}{4}, \dfrac{7\pi}{4}$

53. Solving the equation:
$$\tan^2 x + \sec x = -1$$
$$(\sec^2 x - 1) + \sec x = -1$$
$$\sec^2 x + \sec x = 0$$
$$\sec x(\sec x + 1) = 0$$
$$\sec x = 0 \text{ has no solution}$$
$$\sec x + 1 = 0 \implies \sec x = -1 \implies x = \pi$$

The solution in the interval $[0, 2\pi)$ is: $x = \pi$

55. Solving the equation:

$$\cos 2x = -\sin^2 x$$
$$1 - 2\sin^2 x = -\sin^2 x$$
$$1 = \sin^2 x$$
$$\sin x = \pm 1$$
$$x = \frac{\pi}{2}, \frac{3\pi}{2}$$

The solutions in the interval $[0, 2\pi)$ are: $x = \frac{\pi}{2}, \frac{3\pi}{2}$

57. Solving the equation:

$$\tan\left(\frac{x}{2}\right) = \csc x$$
$$\frac{\sin x}{1 + \cos x} = \frac{1}{\sin x}$$
$$\sin^2 x = 1 + \cos x$$
$$1 - \cos^2 x = 1 + \cos x$$
$$-\cos^2 x - \cos x = 0$$
$$-\cos x(\cos x + 1) = 0$$
$$\cos x = 0 \implies x = \frac{\pi}{2}, \frac{3\pi}{2}$$
$$\cos x + 1 = 0 \implies \cos x = -1 \implies x = \pi$$

In the equation, $\csc x$ is undefined for $x = \pi$. The solutions in the interval $[0, 2\pi)$ are: $x = \frac{\pi}{2}, \frac{3\pi}{2}$

59. Solving the equation:

$$2\cos^2 x - 3\cos x + 1 = 0$$
$$(2\cos x - 1)(\cos x - 1) = 0$$
$$2\cos x - 1 = 0 \implies \cos x = \frac{1}{2} \implies x = \frac{\pi}{3}, \frac{5\pi}{3}$$
$$\cos x - 1 = 0 \implies \cos x = 1 \implies x = 0$$

The solutions in the interval $[0, 2\pi)$ are: $x = 0, \frac{\pi}{3}, \frac{5\pi}{3}$

61. Solving the equation:

$$\tan^2 x - 2\tan x + 1 = 0$$
$$(\tan x - 1)^2 = 0$$
$$\tan x - 1 = 0 \implies \tan x = 1 \implies x = \frac{\pi}{4}, \frac{5\pi}{4}$$

The solutions in the interval $[0, 2\pi)$ are: $x = \frac{\pi}{4}, \frac{5\pi}{4}$

63. Solving the equation:

$$\sec^2 x - \sec x = 2$$
$$\sec^2 x - \sec x - 2 = 0$$
$$(\sec x + 1)(\sec x - 2) = 0$$

$$\sec x + 1 = 0 \implies \sec x = -1 \implies \cos x = -1 \implies x = \pi$$

$$\sec x - 2 = 0 \implies \sec x = 2 \implies \cos x = \frac{1}{2} \implies x = \frac{\pi}{3}, \frac{5\pi}{3}$$

The solutions in the interval $[0, 2\pi)$ are: $x = \dfrac{\pi}{3}, \pi, \dfrac{5\pi}{3}$

65. Solving the equation:

$$\cot^2 x + \cot x - \sqrt{3}\cot x - \sqrt{3} = 0$$
$$\cot^2 x + \cot x - \sqrt{3}\cot x - \sqrt{3} = 0$$
$$\left(\cot^2 x + \cot x\right) + \left(-\sqrt{3}\cot x - \sqrt{3}\right) = 0$$
$$\cot x(\cot x + 1) - \sqrt{3}(\cot x + 1) = 0$$
$$(\cot x + 1)\left(\cot x - \sqrt{3}\right) = 0$$

$$\cot x + 1 = 0 \implies \cot x = -1 \implies \tan x = -1 \implies x = \frac{3\pi}{4}, \frac{7\pi}{4}$$

$$\cot x - \sqrt{3} = 0 \implies \cot x = \sqrt{3} \implies \tan x = \frac{1}{\sqrt{3}} \implies x = \frac{\pi}{6}, \frac{7\pi}{6}$$

The solutions in the interval $[0, 2\pi)$ are: $x = \dfrac{3\pi}{4}, \dfrac{7\pi}{4}, \dfrac{\pi}{6}, \dfrac{7\pi}{6}$

67. Solving the equation:

$$4\tan^2 x = 1$$
$$\tan^2 x = \frac{1}{4}$$
$$\tan x = \pm\frac{1}{2}$$

$$x = \tan^{-1}\left(\frac{1}{2}\right), \pi - \tan^{-1}\left(\frac{1}{2}\right), \pi + \tan^{-1}\left(\frac{1}{2}\right), 2\pi - \tan^{-1}\left(\frac{1}{2}\right)$$

$$x \approx 0.4636, 2.6779, 3.6052, 5.8195$$

The solutions in the interval $[0, 2\pi)$ are: $x \approx 0.4636, 2.6779, 3.6052, 5.8195$

69. Solving the equation:

$$3\sin^2 x - 5\sin x - 2 = 0$$
$$(3\sin x + 1)(\sin x - 2) = 0$$

$$\sin x - 2 = 0 \implies \sin x = 2 \text{ gives no solutions}$$

$$3\sin x + 1 = 0 \implies \sin x = -\frac{1}{3}$$

$$x = \pi + \sin^{-1}\left(\frac{1}{3}\right), 2\pi - \pi + \sin^{-1}\left(\frac{1}{3}\right)$$

$$x \approx 3.4814, 5.9433$$

The solutions in the interval $[0, 2\pi)$ are: $x \approx 3.4814, 5.9433$

71. Solving the equation:

$$3\cos^2 x + \cos x - 2 = 0$$

$$(3\cos x - 2)(\cos x + 1) = 0$$

$$\cos x + 1 = 0 \implies \cos x = -1 \implies x = \pi$$

$$3\cos x - 2 = 0 \implies \cos x = \frac{2}{3} \implies x = \cos^{-1}\left(\frac{2}{3}\right) \approx 0.8411, \, 2\pi - \cos^{-1}\left(\frac{2}{3}\right) \approx 5.4421$$

The solutions in the interval $[0, 2\pi)$ are: $x \approx 0.8411, \pi, 5.4421$

73. Solving the equation:

$$2\sin 2x + \cos x = 0$$

$$4\sin x \cos x + \cos x = 0$$

$$\cos x(4\sin x + 1) = 0$$

$$\cos x = 0 \implies x = \frac{\pi}{2}, \frac{3\pi}{2}$$

$$4\sin x + 1 = 0 \implies \sin x = -\frac{1}{4} \implies x = \pi + \sin^{-1}\left(\frac{1}{4}\right) \approx 3.3943, \, 2\pi - \sin^{-1}\left(\frac{1}{4}\right) \approx 6.0305$$

The solutions in the interval $[0, 2\pi)$ are: $x \approx \frac{\pi}{2}, 3.3943, \frac{3\pi}{2}, 6.0305$

75. Solving the equation:

$$\sin 2x = \sin^2 x$$

$$2\sin x \cos x = \sin^2 x$$

$$2\sin x \cos x - \sin^2 x = 0$$

$$\sin x(2\cos x - \sin x) = 0$$

$$\sin x = 0 \implies x = 0, \pi$$

$$2\cos x - \sin x = 0 \implies 2\cos x = \sin x \implies \tan x = 2 \implies x = \tan^{-1} 2 \approx 1.1071, \, \pi + \tan^{-1} 2 \approx 4.2487$$

The solutions in the interval $[0, 2\pi)$ are: $x \approx 0, 1.1071, \pi, 4.2487$

77. Solving the equation:

$$\csc^2 x - \csc x = 20$$

$$\csc^2 x - \csc x - 20 = 0$$

$$(\csc x + 4)(\csc x - 5) = 0$$

$$\csc x + 4 = 0 \implies \csc x = -4 \implies \sin x = -\frac{1}{4} \implies x = \pi + \sin^{-1}\left(\frac{1}{4}\right) \approx 3.3943, \, 2\pi - \sin^{-1}\left(\frac{1}{4}\right) \approx 6.0305$$

$$\csc x - 5 = 0 \implies \csc x = 5 \implies \sin x = \frac{1}{5} \implies x = \sin^{-1}\left(\frac{1}{5}\right) \approx 0.2014, \, \pi - \sin^{-1}\left(\frac{1}{4}\right) \approx 2.9402$$

The solutions in the interval $[0, 2\pi)$ are: $x \approx 0.2014, 2.9402, 3.3943, 6.0305$

79. Solving the equation:

$$4\tan^2 x - 4\tan x = 3$$

$$4\tan^2 x - 4\tan x - 3 = 0$$

$$(2\tan x - 3)(2\tan x + 1) = 0$$

$$2\tan x - 3 = 0 \;\Rightarrow\; \tan x = \frac{3}{2} \;\Rightarrow\; x = \tan^{-1}\left(\frac{3}{2}\right) \approx 0.9828,\; \pi + \tan^{-1}\left(\frac{3}{2}\right) \approx 4.1244$$

$$2\tan x + 1 = 0 \;\Rightarrow\; \tan x = -\frac{1}{2} \;\Rightarrow\; x = \pi - \tan^{-1}\left(\frac{1}{2}\right) \approx 2.6779,\; 2\pi - \tan^{-1}\left(\frac{1}{2}\right) \approx 5.8195$$

The solutions in the interval $[0, 2\pi)$ are: $x \approx 0.9828, 2.6779, 4.1244, 5.8195$

81. Solving the equation:

$$\sin^4 x - \cos^4 x = -\frac{1}{3}$$

$$3\sin^4 x - 3\left(\cos^2 x\right)^2 = -1$$

$$3\sin^4 x - 3\left(1 - \sin^2 x\right)^2 = -1$$

$$3\sin^4 x - 3\left(1 - 2\sin^2 x + \sin^4 x\right) = -\frac{1}{3}$$

$$6\sin^2 x - 3 = -1$$

$$6\sin^2 x = 2$$

$$\sin^2 x = \frac{1}{3}$$

$$\sin x = \pm\frac{1}{\sqrt{3}}$$

$$x = \sin^{-1}\left(\frac{1}{\sqrt{3}}\right) \approx 0.6155,\; \pi - \sin^{-1}\left(\frac{1}{\sqrt{3}}\right) \approx 2.5261,$$

$$x = \pi + \sin^{-1}\left(\frac{1}{\sqrt{3}}\right) \approx 3.7571,\; 2\pi - \sin^{-1}\left(\frac{1}{\sqrt{3}}\right) \approx 5.6677$$

The solutions in the interval $[0, 2\pi)$ are: $x \approx 0.6155, 2.5261, 3.7571, 5.6677$

83. There is no solution:

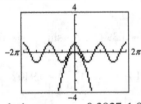

85. The solutions are $x \approx 1.2744, 4.5611$:

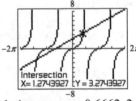

87. The solutions are $x \approx 0.3927, 1.9635, 3.5343, 5.1051$:

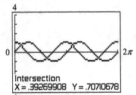

89. The solutions are $x \approx 0.6662, 2.4754$:

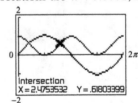

91. Solving for the angle:

$$R = \frac{70^2 \sin\theta \cos\theta}{4.9}$$

$$1470 = 2450\left(2\sin\theta\cos\theta\right)$$

$$\frac{3}{5} = \sin 2\theta$$

$$2\theta = \sin^{-1}\left(\frac{3}{5}\right)$$

$$\theta = \frac{\sin^{-1}\left(\frac{3}{5}\right)}{2} \approx 0.3218$$

The projectile must be fired at an angle of 0.3218 radians, or about $18.43°$.

93. The number of days after the person's 21st birthday is represented by $t - 7670$. Solving the equation:

$$P(t) = 50\sin\left[\frac{2\pi}{23}(t-7670)\right] + 50$$

$$100 = 50\sin\left[\frac{2\pi}{23}(t-7670)\right] + 50$$

$$50 = 50\sin\left[\frac{2\pi}{23}(t-7670)\right]$$

$$1 = \sin\left[\frac{2\pi}{23}(t-7670)\right]$$

$$\frac{2\pi}{23}(t-7670) = \frac{\pi}{2}$$

$$t - 7670 = \frac{23}{4}$$

$$t = \frac{23}{4} + 7670 \approx 7676$$

The day of greatest potential is day 7676, which is 6 days after the person's 21st birthday.

95. Finding when the depth of the river reaches 5 feet:

$$d(t) = 4.5\sin\left(\frac{\pi}{6}t\right) + 7$$

$$5 = 4.5\sin\left(\frac{\pi}{6}t\right) + 7$$

$$-2 = 4.5\sin\left(\frac{\pi}{6}t\right)$$

$$-\frac{4}{9} = \sin\left(\frac{\pi}{6}t\right)$$

$$\frac{\pi}{6}t = \pi + \sin^{-1}\left(\frac{4}{9}\right) \qquad\qquad \frac{\pi}{6}t = 2\pi - \sin^{-1}\left(\frac{4}{9}\right)$$

$$t = \frac{\pi + \sin^{-1}\left(\frac{4}{9}\right)}{\frac{\pi}{6}} \approx 6.8796 \text{ hr} \approx 9 \text{ am} \qquad t = \frac{2\pi - \sin^{-1}\left(\frac{4}{9}\right)}{\frac{\pi}{6}} \approx 11.12 \text{ hr} \approx 1 \text{ pm}$$

It is unsafe to navigate that part of the river between approximately 9 a.m. and 1 p.m.

97. a. Since the side opposite angle θ is the height h, we have:

$$\sin\theta = \frac{h}{6}$$

$$h = 6\sin\theta$$

The side adjacent angle θ is the base b so this gives us:

$$\cos\theta = \frac{b}{6}$$

$$b = 6\cos\theta$$

Finding the area: $A = \frac{1}{2}bh = \frac{1}{2}(6\cos\theta)(6\sin\theta) = 18\sin\theta\cos\theta$

b. Finding the angle:

$$A = 18\sin\theta\cos\theta$$

$$8 = 9(2\sin\theta\cos\theta)$$

$$\frac{8}{9} = \sin 2\theta$$

$$2\theta = \sin^{-1}\left(\frac{8}{9}\right)$$

$$\theta = \frac{\sin^{-1}\left(\frac{8}{9}\right)}{2} \approx 0.5475 \approx 31.3670°$$

c. Writing the area as: $A = 18\sin\theta\cos\theta = 9(2\sin\theta\cos\theta) = 9\sin 2\theta$

The area is maximized when:

$$2\theta = \frac{\pi}{2}$$

$$\theta = \frac{\pi}{4} = 45°$$

99. a. Solving the equation:

$$d(x) = -2.2\cos(0.0175x) + 12.27$$

$$13 = -2.2\cos(0.0175x) + 12.27$$

$$0.73 = -2.2\cos(0.0175x)$$

$$-0.331818 = \cos(0.0175x)$$

$$0.0175x = \pi - \cos^{-1}(0.331818) \qquad\qquad 0.0175x = \pi + \cos^{-1}(0.331818)$$

$$x = \frac{\pi - \cos^{-1}(0.331818)}{0.0175} \approx 109.05 \qquad\qquad x = \frac{\pi + \cos^{-1}(0.331818)}{0.0175} \approx 249.99$$

Miami will have 13 hours of daylight when $x \approx 109, 250$.

b. Since the function is represented by cosine, its maximum is reached half-way between its period.

The period is given by $p = \dfrac{2\pi}{0.0175} \approx 359$ days , so $x = \dfrac{359}{2} \approx 180$ days .

101. No. There is no value of x for which $\sin x$ and $\cos x$ are both equal to 1, since the Pythagorean identity $\sin^2 x + \cos^2 x = 1$ would not be true. This is a misstatement of the rule if $ab = 0$, then $a = 0$ or $b = 0$.

103. The solution is $x \approx 0.7391$:

105. Solving each equation:

$$\cos^2 x - \sin^2 x = -1$$
$$\cos 2x = -1$$
$$2x = \pi, 3\pi$$
$$x = \frac{\pi}{2}, \frac{3\pi}{2}$$

$$\tan\left(\frac{x}{2}\right) = -1$$
$$\frac{x}{2} = \frac{3\pi}{4}, \frac{7\pi}{4}$$
$$x = \frac{3\pi}{2}, \frac{7\pi}{2}$$

Therefore $x = \frac{3\pi}{2} + 2n\pi$, where n is an integer.

Chapter 6 Review Exercises

1. Simplifying the expression: $\sec^2 x \cos x = \dfrac{1}{\cos^2 x} \cdot \cos x = \dfrac{1}{\cos x}$

2. Simplifying the expression: $\tan x \cos x = \dfrac{\sin x}{\cos x} \cdot \cos x = \sin x$

3. Simplifying the expression: $\dfrac{1}{\csc^2 x} = \dfrac{1}{\left(\dfrac{1}{\sin^2 x}\right)} = \sin^2 x$

4. Simplifying the expression: $\cot x \sec x = \dfrac{\cos x}{\sin x} \cdot \dfrac{1}{\cos x} = \dfrac{1}{\sin x}$

5. Verifying the identity: $1 + \cos x = (1 + \cos x) \cdot \dfrac{1 - \cos x}{1 - \cos x} = \dfrac{1 - \cos^2 x}{1 - \cos x} = \dfrac{\sin^2 x}{1 - \cos x}$

6. Verifying the identity: $\sec^4 x - \tan^4 x = \left(\sec^2 x + \tan^2 x\right)\left(\sec^2 x - \tan^2 x\right) = \left(\sec^2 x + \tan^2 x\right) \cdot 1 = \sec^2 x + \tan^2 x$

7. Verifying the identity: $\sin^4 x = \left(\sin^2 x\right)^2 = \left(1 - \cos^2 x\right)^2 = 1 - 2\cos^2 x + \cos^4 x$

8. Verifying the identity: $\sin^2 x \cos^2 x = \sin^2 x\left(1 - \sin^2 x\right) = \sin^2 x - \sin^4 x$

9. Verifying the identity:
$$\cos^4 x - \sin^4 x = \left(\cos^2 x + \sin^2 x\right)\left(\cos^2 x - \sin^2 x\right) = 1 \cdot \left(\cos^2 x - \sin^2 x\right) = \left(1 - \sin^2 x\right) - \sin^2 x = 1 - 2\sin^2 x$$

10. Verifying the identity: $\dfrac{1}{1 + \cos x} + \dfrac{1}{1 - \cos x} = \dfrac{(1 - \cos x) + (1 + \cos x)}{(1 + \cos x)(1 - \cos x)} = \dfrac{2}{1 - \cos^2 x} = \dfrac{2}{\sin^2 x} = 2\csc^2 x$

11. Verifying the identity: $\dfrac{1 + 2\cos x + \cos^2 x}{1 - \cos^2 x} = \dfrac{(1 + \cos x)^2}{(1 + \cos x)(1 - \cos x)} = \dfrac{1 + \cos x}{1 - \cos x}$

12. Verifying the identity: $\csc x + \cot x = \dfrac{1}{\sin x} + \dfrac{\cos x}{\sin x} = \dfrac{1 + \cos x}{\sin x}$

13. Verifying the identity: $\dfrac{\tan^2 x}{\sec x + 1} = \dfrac{\sec^2 x - 1}{\sec x + 1} = \dfrac{(\sec x + 1)(\sec x - 1)}{\sec x + 1} = \sec x - 1$

14. Verifying the identity:

$$\frac{\sec x + \tan x}{\cos x - \tan x - \sec x} = \frac{\dfrac{1 + \sin x}{\cos x}}{\cos x - \dfrac{\sin x + 1}{\cos x}}$$

$$= \frac{1 + \sin x}{\cos^2 x - \sin x - 1}$$

$$= \frac{1 + \sin x}{1 - \sin^2 x - \sin x - 1}$$

$$= \frac{1 + \sin x}{-\sin^2 x - \sin x}$$

$$= \frac{1 + \sin x}{-\sin x(\sin x + 1)}$$

$$= -\csc x$$

15. Writing as a single value: $\sin 45° \cos 30° + \cos 45° \sin 30° = \sin(45° + 30°) = \sin 75°$

16. Writing as a single value: $\cos 150° \cos 45° - \sin 150° \sin 45° = \cos(150° + 45°) = \cos 195°$

17. Writing as a single value: $\cos \dfrac{\pi}{3} \cos \dfrac{\pi}{4} + \sin \dfrac{\pi}{3} \sin \dfrac{\pi}{4} = \cos\left(\dfrac{\pi}{3} - \dfrac{\pi}{4}\right) = \cos \dfrac{\pi}{12}$

18. Writing as a single value: $\sin \dfrac{\pi}{6} \cos \dfrac{\pi}{4} - \cos \dfrac{\pi}{6} \sin \dfrac{\pi}{4} = \sin\left(\dfrac{\pi}{6} - \dfrac{\pi}{4}\right) = \sin\left(-\dfrac{\pi}{12}\right)$

19. Finding the exact values:

$$\sin(-105°) = -\sin 105° = -\sin(60° + 45°) = -(\sin 60° \cos 45° + \cos 60° \sin 45°) = -\left(\frac{\sqrt{3}}{2} \cdot \frac{\sqrt{2}}{2} + \frac{1}{2} \cdot \frac{\sqrt{2}}{2}\right) = \frac{-\sqrt{6} - \sqrt{2}}{4}$$

$$\cos(-105°) = \cos 105° = \cos(60° + 45°) = \cos 60° \cos 45° - \sin 60° \sin 45° = \frac{1}{2} \cdot \frac{\sqrt{2}}{2} - \frac{\sqrt{3}}{2} \cdot \frac{\sqrt{2}}{2} = \frac{\sqrt{2} - \sqrt{6}}{4}$$

$$\tan(-105°) = -\tan 105° = -\tan(60° + 45°) = -\frac{\tan 60° + \tan 45°}{1 - \tan 60° \tan 45°} = \frac{-\sqrt{3} - 1}{1 - \sqrt{3} \cdot 1} = \frac{-1 - \sqrt{3}}{1 - \sqrt{3}} \cdot \frac{1 + \sqrt{3}}{1 + \sqrt{3}} = \frac{-4 - 2\sqrt{3}}{-2} = 2 + \sqrt{3}$$

20. Finding the exact values:

$$\sin 195° = \sin(150° + 45°) = \sin 150° \cos 45° + \cos 150° \sin 45° = \frac{1}{2} \cdot \frac{\sqrt{2}}{2} + \left(-\frac{\sqrt{3}}{2}\right)\left(\frac{\sqrt{2}}{2}\right) = \frac{\sqrt{2} - \sqrt{6}}{4}$$

$$\cos 195° = \cos(150° + 45°) = \cos 150° \cos 45° - \sin 150° \sin 45° = \left(-\frac{\sqrt{3}}{2}\right) \cdot \frac{\sqrt{2}}{2} - \frac{1}{2} \cdot \frac{\sqrt{2}}{2} = \frac{-\sqrt{6} - \sqrt{2}}{4}$$

$$\tan 195° = \tan(150° + 45°) = \frac{\tan 150° + \tan 45°}{1 - \tan 150° \tan 45°} = \frac{-\dfrac{1}{\sqrt{3}} + 1}{1 - \left(-\dfrac{1}{\sqrt{3}}\right) \cdot 1} = \frac{-1 + \sqrt{3}}{1 + \sqrt{3}} \cdot \frac{1 - \sqrt{3}}{1 - \sqrt{3}} = \frac{-4 + 2\sqrt{3}}{-2} = 2 - \sqrt{3}$$

21. Note that $-\dfrac{\pi}{12}=\dfrac{\pi}{6}-\dfrac{\pi}{4}$. Finding the exact values:

$$\sin\left(-\frac{\pi}{12}\right)=\sin\left(\frac{\pi}{6}-\frac{\pi}{4}\right)=\sin\frac{\pi}{6}\cos\frac{\pi}{4}-\cos\frac{\pi}{6}\sin\frac{\pi}{4}=\frac{1}{2}\cdot\frac{\sqrt{2}}{2}-\frac{\sqrt{3}}{2}\cdot\frac{\sqrt{2}}{2}=\frac{\sqrt{2}-\sqrt{6}}{4}$$

$$\cos\left(-\frac{\pi}{12}\right)=\cos\left(\frac{\pi}{6}-\frac{\pi}{4}\right)=\cos\frac{\pi}{6}\cos\frac{\pi}{4}+\sin\frac{\pi}{6}\sin\frac{\pi}{4}=\frac{\sqrt{3}}{2}\cdot\frac{\sqrt{2}}{2}+\frac{1}{2}\cdot\frac{\sqrt{2}}{2}=\frac{\sqrt{6}+\sqrt{2}}{4}$$

$$\tan\left(-\frac{\pi}{12}\right)=\tan\left(\frac{\pi}{6}-\frac{\pi}{4}\right)=\frac{\tan\dfrac{\pi}{6}-\tan\dfrac{\pi}{4}}{1+\tan\dfrac{\pi}{6}\tan\dfrac{\pi}{4}}=\frac{\dfrac{1}{\sqrt{3}}-1}{1+\dfrac{1}{\sqrt{3}}\cdot1}=\frac{1-\sqrt{3}}{1+\sqrt{3}}\cdot\frac{1-\sqrt{3}}{1-\sqrt{3}}=\frac{4-2\sqrt{3}}{-2}=-2+\sqrt{3}$$

22. Note that $\dfrac{13\pi}{12}=\dfrac{3\pi}{4}+\dfrac{\pi}{3}$. Finding the exact values:

$$\sin\frac{13\pi}{12}=\sin\left(\frac{3\pi}{4}+\frac{\pi}{3}\right)=\sin\frac{3\pi}{4}\cos\frac{\pi}{3}+\cos\frac{3\pi}{4}\sin\frac{\pi}{3}=\frac{\sqrt{2}}{2}\cdot\frac{1}{2}+\left(-\frac{\sqrt{2}}{2}\right)\cdot\frac{\sqrt{3}}{2}=\frac{\sqrt{2}-\sqrt{6}}{4}$$

$$\cos\frac{13\pi}{12}=\cos\left(\frac{3\pi}{4}+\frac{\pi}{3}\right)=\cos\frac{3\pi}{4}\cos\frac{\pi}{3}-\sin\frac{3\pi}{4}\sin\frac{\pi}{3}=-\frac{\sqrt{2}}{2}\cdot\frac{1}{2}-\frac{\sqrt{2}}{2}\cdot\frac{\sqrt{3}}{2}=\frac{-\sqrt{2}-\sqrt{6}}{4}$$

$$\tan\frac{13\pi}{12}=\tan\left(\frac{3\pi}{4}+\frac{\pi}{3}\right)=\frac{\tan\dfrac{3\pi}{4}+\tan\dfrac{\pi}{3}}{1-\tan\dfrac{3\pi}{4}\tan\dfrac{\pi}{3}}=\frac{-1+\sqrt{3}}{1-(-1)\cdot\sqrt{3}}=\frac{\sqrt{3}-1}{1+\sqrt{3}}\cdot\frac{1-\sqrt{3}}{1-\sqrt{3}}=\frac{-4+2\sqrt{3}}{-2}=2-\sqrt{3}$$

23. Using the Pythagorean identity:

$$\cos^2 a+\sin^2 a=1 \qquad\qquad\qquad \cos^2 b+\sin^2 b=1$$

$$\left(-\frac{3}{5}\right)^2+\sin^2 a=1 \qquad\qquad\qquad \cos^2 b+\left(-\frac{5}{13}\right)^2=1$$

$$\frac{9}{25}+\sin^2 a=1 \qquad\qquad\qquad \cos^2 b+\frac{25}{169}=1$$

$$\sin^2 a=\frac{16}{25} \qquad\qquad\qquad \cos^2 b=\frac{144}{169}$$

$$\sin a=-\frac{4}{5}\quad(a\text{ in quad. III}) \qquad\qquad \cos b=-\frac{12}{13}\quad(b\text{ in quad. III})$$

Now using the sum identity for cosine: $\cos(a+b)=\cos a\cos b-\sin a\sin b=\left(-\dfrac{3}{5}\right)\left(-\dfrac{12}{13}\right)-\left(-\dfrac{4}{5}\right)\left(-\dfrac{5}{13}\right)=\dfrac{36}{65}-\dfrac{20}{65}=\dfrac{16}{65}$

24. Using the sum identity for sine: $\sin(a+b)=\sin a\cos b+\cos a\sin b=\left(-\dfrac{4}{5}\right)\left(-\dfrac{12}{13}\right)+\left(-\dfrac{3}{5}\right)\left(-\dfrac{5}{13}\right)=\dfrac{48}{65}+\dfrac{15}{65}=\dfrac{63}{65}$

25. Finding the tangent values:

$$\tan a=\frac{\sin a}{\cos a}=\frac{-\dfrac{4}{5}}{-\dfrac{3}{5}}=\frac{4}{3} \qquad\qquad \tan b=\frac{\sin b}{\cos b}=\frac{-\dfrac{5}{13}}{-\dfrac{12}{13}}=\frac{5}{12}$$

Using the sum identity for tangent: $\tan(a+b)=\dfrac{\tan a+\tan b}{1-\tan a\tan b}=\dfrac{\dfrac{4}{3}+\dfrac{5}{12}}{1-\dfrac{4}{3}\cdot\dfrac{5}{12}}=\dfrac{\dfrac{21}{12}}{\dfrac{16}{36}}=\dfrac{63}{16}$

26. Using the sum identity for tangent: $\cot(a+b)=\dfrac{1}{\tan(a+b)}=\dfrac{1}{{}^{63}\!/\!_{16}}=\dfrac{16}{63}$

27. Using the difference identity for sine: $\sin(a-b) = \sin a \cos b - \cos a \sin b = \left(-\dfrac{4}{5}\right)\left(-\dfrac{12}{13}\right) - \left(-\dfrac{3}{5}\right)\left(-\dfrac{5}{13}\right) = \dfrac{48}{65} - \dfrac{15}{65} = \dfrac{33}{65}$

28. Using the difference identity for cosine: $\cos(a-b) = \cos a \cos b + \sin a \sin b = \left(-\dfrac{3}{5}\right)\left(-\dfrac{12}{13}\right) + \left(-\dfrac{4}{5}\right)\left(-\dfrac{5}{13}\right) = \dfrac{36}{65} + \dfrac{20}{65} = \dfrac{56}{65}$

29. Setting the two expressions equal:

$$\sin(2x+c) = \frac{\sqrt{3}}{2}\sin 2x - \frac{1}{2}\cos 2x$$

$$\sin 2x \cos c + \cos 2x \sin c = \frac{\sqrt{3}}{2}\sin 2x - \frac{1}{2}\cos 2x$$

Then $\cos c = \dfrac{\sqrt{3}}{2}$ and $\sin c = -\dfrac{1}{2}$, thus $c = \dfrac{11\pi}{6}$ and $f(x) = \sin\left(2x + \dfrac{11\pi}{6}\right)$.

30. Using the difference identity for sine:

$$f(x) = \sin\left(1000\pi x - \frac{\pi}{6}\right)$$

$$= \sin(1000\pi x)\cos\frac{\pi}{6} - \cos(1000\pi x)\sin\frac{\pi}{6}$$

$$= \sin(1000\pi x) \cdot \frac{\sqrt{3}}{2} - \cos(1000\pi x) \cdot \frac{1}{2}$$

$$= \frac{\sqrt{3}}{2}\sin(1000\pi x) - \frac{1}{2}\cos(1000\pi x)$$

31. Using a Pythagorean identity:

$$\sin^2 x = 1 - \cos^2 x = 1 - \left(\frac{3}{5}\right)^2 = 1 - \frac{9}{25} = \frac{16}{25}$$

$$\sin x = \frac{4}{5}$$

32. Using a Pythagorean identity:

$$1 + \tan^2 x = \sec^2 x$$

$$1 + \tan^2 x = \frac{1}{\cos^2 x}$$

$$1 + \tan^2 x = \frac{1}{\left(\dfrac{3}{5}\right)^2}$$

$$1 + \tan^2 x = \frac{25}{9}$$

$$\tan^2 x = \frac{16}{9}$$

$$\tan x = \frac{4}{3}$$

33. Using a double-angle formula: $\sin 2x = 2\sin x \cos x = 2\left(\dfrac{4}{5}\right)\left(\dfrac{3}{5}\right) = \dfrac{24}{25}$

34. Using a double-angle formula: $\cos 2x = 2\cos^2 x - 1 = 2\left(\dfrac{3}{5}\right)^2 - 1 = \dfrac{18}{25} - 1 = -\dfrac{7}{25}$

35. Reducing the powers: $\sin^2 x \cos^2 x = \dfrac{1-\cos 2x}{2} \cdot \dfrac{1+\cos 2x}{2} = \dfrac{1-\cos^2 2x}{4} = \dfrac{1 - \dfrac{1+\cos 4x}{2}}{4} = \dfrac{2-1-\cos 4x}{8} = \dfrac{1-\cos 4x}{8}$

36. Reducing the powers:

$$\sin^3 x \cos^2 x = \sin x \cdot \sin^2 x \cos^2 x$$

$$= \sin x \cdot \frac{1 - \cos 2x}{2} \cdot \frac{1 + \cos 2x}{2}$$

$$= \sin x \cdot \frac{1 - \cos^2 2x}{4}$$

$$= \sin x \cdot \frac{1 - \dfrac{1 + \cos 4x}{2}}{4}$$

$$= \sin x \cdot \frac{1 - \cos 4x}{8} = \frac{\sin x - \sin x \cos 4x}{8}$$

37. Note that $\dfrac{3\pi}{12} = \dfrac{1}{2} \cdot \dfrac{\pi}{2}$. Using the half-angle identity: $\cos \dfrac{3\pi}{12} = \cos \dfrac{\theta}{2} = \sqrt{\dfrac{1 + \cos \theta}{2}} = \sqrt{\dfrac{1 + \cos \dfrac{\pi}{2}}{2}} = \sqrt{\dfrac{1}{2}} = \dfrac{1}{\sqrt{2}} = \dfrac{\sqrt{2}}{2}$

38. Note that $-\dfrac{\pi}{8} = \dfrac{1}{2} \cdot \left(-\dfrac{\pi}{4} \right)$. Using the half-angle identity:

$$\cos \left(-\frac{\pi}{8} \right) = \cos \frac{\theta}{2} = \sqrt{\frac{1 + \cos \theta}{2}} = \sqrt{\frac{1 + \cos \left(-\dfrac{\pi}{4} \right)}{2}} = \sqrt{\frac{1 + \cos \dfrac{\pi}{4}}{2}} = \sqrt{\frac{1 + \dfrac{\sqrt{2}}{2}}{2}} = \sqrt{\frac{2 + \sqrt{2}}{4}} = \frac{\sqrt{2 + \sqrt{2}}}{2}$$

39. Note that $15° = \dfrac{1}{2} \cdot 30°$. Using the half-angle identity:

$$\cos 15° = \cos \frac{\theta}{2} = \sqrt{\frac{1 + \cos \theta}{2}} = \sqrt{\frac{1 + \cos 30°}{2}} = \sqrt{\frac{1 + \dfrac{\sqrt{3}}{2}}{2}} = \sqrt{\frac{2 + \sqrt{3}}{4}} = \frac{\sqrt{2 + \sqrt{3}}}{2}$$

40. Note that $75° = \dfrac{1}{2} \cdot 150°$. Using the half-angle identity:

$$\sin 75° = \sin \frac{\theta}{2} = \sqrt{\frac{1 - \cos \theta}{2}} = \sqrt{\frac{1 - \cos 150°}{2}} = \sqrt{\frac{1 + \dfrac{\sqrt{3}}{2}}{2}} = \sqrt{\frac{2 + \sqrt{3}}{4}} = \frac{\sqrt{2 + \sqrt{3}}}{2}$$

41. Using the product-to-sum identity: $\sin 4x \cos 2x = \dfrac{1}{2} \left[\sin(4x + 2x) + \sin(4x - 2x) \right] = \dfrac{1}{2} (\sin 6x + \sin 2x)$

42. Using the product-to-sum identity: $\sin x \sin 2x = \dfrac{1}{2} \left[\cos(x - 2x) - \cos(x + 2x) \right] = \dfrac{1}{2} (\cos(-x) - \cos 3x) = \dfrac{1}{2} (\cos x - \cos 3x)$

43. Using the sum-to-product identity:

$$\cos 2x + \cos 3x = 2 \cos \left(\frac{2x + 3x}{2} \right) \cos \left(\frac{2x - 3x}{2} \right) = 2 \cos \left(\frac{5x}{2} \right) \cos \left(\frac{-x}{2} \right) = 2 \cos \left(\frac{5x}{2} \right) \cos \left(\frac{x}{2} \right)$$

44. Using the sum-to-product identity: $\sin 5x + \sin 2x = 2 \sin \left(\dfrac{5x + 2x}{2} \right) \sin \left(\dfrac{5x - 2x}{2} \right) = 2 \sin \left(\dfrac{7x}{2} \right) \sin \left(\dfrac{3x}{2} \right)$

45. Solving the equation:
$$2\cos x - 1 = 0$$
$$2\cos x = 1$$
$$\cos x = \frac{1}{2}$$
$$x = \frac{\pi}{3}, \frac{5\pi}{3}$$

The general solution is: $x = \frac{\pi}{3} + 2\pi n, \frac{5\pi}{3} + 2\pi n$, where n is an integer

46. Solving the equation:
$$\tan^2 x - 1 = 0$$
$$\tan^2 x = 1$$
$$\tan x = \pm 1$$
$$x = \frac{\pi}{4}, \frac{3\pi}{4}$$

The general solution is: $x = \frac{\pi}{4} + n\pi, \frac{3\pi}{4} + n\pi$, where n is an integer

Note this can be written as: $x = \frac{\pi}{4} + \frac{n\pi}{2}$, where n is an integer

47. Solving the equation:
$$\sec x = -2$$
$$\frac{1}{\cos x} = -2$$
$$\cos x = -\frac{1}{2}$$
$$x = \frac{2\pi}{3}, \frac{4\pi}{3}$$

The general solution is: $x = \frac{2\pi}{3} + 2n\pi, \frac{4\pi}{3} + 2n\pi$, where n is an integer

48. Solving the equation:
$$\sin x + \sin^2 x + \cos^2 x = 1$$
$$\sin x + 1 = 1$$
$$\sin x = 0$$
$$x = 0, \pi$$

The general solution is: $x = n\pi$, where n is an integer

49. Solving the equation:
$$3\cos x = -2$$
$$\cos x = -\frac{2}{3}$$
$$x = \pi - \cos^{-1}\left(\frac{2}{3}\right) \approx 2.3005, \pi + \cos^{-1}\left(\frac{2}{3}\right) \approx 3.9827$$

The general solution is: $x \approx 2.3005 + 2n\pi, 3.9827 + 2n\pi$, where n is an integer

50. Solving the equation:

$$5\sin x = 4$$

$$\sin x = \frac{4}{5}$$

$$x = \sin^{-1}\left(\frac{4}{5}\right) \approx 0.9273, \; \pi - \sin^{-1}\left(\frac{4}{5}\right) \approx 2.2143$$

The general solution is: $x \approx 0.9273 + 2n\pi, \, 2.2143 + 2n\pi$, where n is an integer

51. Solving the equation:

$$2\sec x = \sec x + 2.5$$

$$\sec x = 2.5$$

$$\cos x = \frac{1}{2.5}$$

$$x = \cos^{-1}\left(\frac{1}{2.5}\right) \approx 1.1593, \; 2\pi - \cos^{-1}\left(\frac{1}{2.5}\right) \approx 5.1239$$

The general solution is: $x = 1.1593 + 2n\pi, \, 5.1239 + 2n\pi$, where n is an integer

52. Solving the equation:

$$\tan x = \frac{3}{2}$$

$$x = \tan^{-1}\left(\frac{3}{2}\right) \approx 0.9828$$

The general solution is: $x \approx 0.9828 + n\pi$, where n is an integer

53. Solving the equation:

$$2\sin^2 x = 1$$

$$\sin^2 x = \frac{1}{2}$$

$$\sin x = \pm\frac{1}{\sqrt{2}} = \pm\frac{\sqrt{2}}{2}$$

$$x = \frac{\pi}{4}, \frac{3\pi}{4}, \frac{5\pi}{4}, \frac{7\pi}{4}$$

The solutions in the interval $[0, 2\pi)$ are: $x = \frac{\pi}{4}, \frac{3\pi}{4}, \frac{5\pi}{4}, \frac{7\pi}{4}$

54. Solving the equation:

$$\sin^3 x + 2\sin x = 0$$

$$\sin x\left(\sin^2 x + 2\right) = 0$$

$$\sin x = 0 \implies x = 0, \pi$$

$$\sin^2 x + 2 = 0 \implies \sin^2 x = -2 \text{ has no solutions}$$

The solutions in the interval $[0, 2\pi)$ are: $x = 0, \pi$

55. Solving the equation:

$$\cos^3 x - 2\cos x = 0$$

$$\cos x\left(\cos^2 x - 2\right) = 0$$

$$\cos x = 0 \implies x = \frac{\pi}{2}, \frac{3\pi}{2}$$

$$\cos^2 x - 2 = 0 \implies \cos^2 x = 2 \text{ has no solutions}$$

The solutions in the interval $[0, 2\pi)$ are: $x = \frac{\pi}{2}, \frac{3\pi}{2}$

56. Solving the equation:
$$\csc^2 x + 3\csc x + 2 = 0$$
$$(\csc x + 2)(\csc x + 1) = 0$$

$$\csc x + 1 = 0 \implies \csc x = -1 \implies \sin x = -1 \implies x = \frac{3\pi}{2}$$
$$\csc x + 2 = 0 \implies \csc x = -2 \implies \sin x = -\frac{1}{2} \implies x = \frac{7\pi}{6}, \frac{11\pi}{6}$$

The solutions in the interval $[0, 2\pi)$ are: $x = \frac{7\pi}{6}, \frac{3\pi}{2}, \frac{11\pi}{6}$

57. Solving the equation:
$$\sin^2 x = \frac{3}{5}$$

$$\sin x = \pm\sqrt{\frac{3}{5}} = \pm\frac{\sqrt{15}}{5}$$

$$x = \sin^{-1}\left(\frac{\sqrt{15}}{5}\right) \approx 0.8861, \pi - \sin^{-1}\left(\frac{\sqrt{15}}{5}\right) \approx 2.2556, \pi + \sin^{-1}\left(\frac{\sqrt{15}}{5}\right) \approx 4.0277, 2\pi - \sin^{-1}\left(\frac{\sqrt{15}}{5}\right) \approx 5.3971$$

The solutions in the interval $[0, 2\pi)$ are: $x \approx 0.8861, 2.2556, 4.0277, 5.3971$

58. Solving the equation:
$$\tan^2 x - \tan x = 6$$
$$\tan^2 x - \tan x - 6 = 0$$
$$(\tan x + 2)(\tan x - 3) = 0$$

$$\tan x + 2 = 0 \implies \tan x = -2 \implies x = \pi - \tan^{-1} 2 \approx 2.0344, 2\pi - \tan^{-1} 2 \approx 5.1760$$
$$\tan x - 3 = 0 \implies \tan x = 3 \implies x = \tan^{-1} 3 \approx 1.2490, \pi + \tan^{-1} 3 \approx 4.3906$$

The solutions in the interval $[0, 2\pi)$ are: $x \approx 1.2490, 2.0344, 4.3906, 5.1760$

59. The solution is $x \approx -0.4502$:

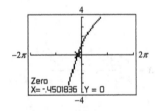

60. The solutions are $x = 0, x \approx 2.3169$:

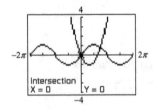

61. Finding the angle:

$$R = \frac{60^2 \sin\theta\cos\theta}{4.9}$$

$$280 = \frac{3600 \sin\theta\cos\theta}{4.9}$$

$$1372 = 1800 \cdot 2\sin\theta\cos\theta$$

$$\frac{343}{450} = \sin 2\theta$$

$$2\theta = \sin^{-1}\left(\frac{343}{450}\right)$$

$$\theta = \frac{\sin^{-1}\left(\frac{343}{450}\right)}{2} \approx 0.4334 \approx 24.83°$$

62. Simplifying the function: $R = \dfrac{75^2 \sin\theta\cos\theta}{4.9} = \dfrac{5625 \cdot \frac{1}{2}\sin 2\theta}{4.9} = \dfrac{5625}{9.8}\sin 2\theta$

Thus R is maximized when $\sin 2\theta$ is largest. This occurs when:

$$\sin 2\theta = 1$$

$$2\theta = 90°$$

$$\theta = 45°$$

63. **a.** Creating a line segment from O perpendicular to the horizontal segment of the triangle yields a right triangle having legs length 3 cm and 4 cm. Thus:

$$r^2 = 3^2 + 4^2 = 25$$

$$r = 5 \text{ cm}$$

b. Since $r = 5$ cm, the triangle with central angle θ is isosceles with base 6 cm. Thus:

$$h^2 + 3^2 = 5^2$$

$$h^2 = 16$$

$$h = 4$$

Therefore $\cos\dfrac{\theta}{2} = \dfrac{4}{5}$.

c. Finding the angle:

$$\cos\frac{\theta}{2} = \frac{4}{5}$$

$$\frac{\theta}{2} = \cos^{-1}\left(\frac{4}{5}\right)$$

$$\theta = 2\cos^{-1}\left(\frac{4}{5}\right) \approx 73.7398°$$

Chapter 6 Test

1. Verifying the identity: $\dfrac{\cot^2 x}{\csc x+1}=\dfrac{\csc^2 x-1}{\csc x+1}=\dfrac{(\csc x+1)(\csc x-1)}{\csc x+1}=\csc x-1$

2. Verifying the identity:

$$\dfrac{\cos x}{1-\sin x}=\dfrac{\cos x}{1-\sin x}\cdot\dfrac{1+\sin x}{1+\sin x}=\dfrac{\cos x(1+\sin x)}{1-\sin^2 x}=\dfrac{\cos x(1+\sin x)}{\cos^2 x}=\dfrac{1+\sin x}{\cos x}=\dfrac{1}{\cos x}+\dfrac{\sin x}{\cos x}=\sec x+\tan x$$

3. Verifying the identity:

$$\dfrac{1}{\sec x+1}+\dfrac{1}{\sec x-1}=\dfrac{(\sec x-1)+(\sec x+1)}{\sec^2 x-1}$$

$$=\dfrac{2\sec x}{\tan^2 x}$$

$$=2\cot^2 x\sec x$$

$$=2\cot x\cdot\cot x\cdot\sec x$$

$$=2\cot x\cdot\dfrac{\cos x}{\sin x}\cdot\dfrac{1}{\cos x}$$

$$=2\cot x\cdot\dfrac{1}{\sin x}$$

$$=2\cot x\csc x$$

4. Verifying the identity: $\sin\left(x+\dfrac{\pi}{2}\right)=\sin x\cos\dfrac{\pi}{2}+\cos x\sin\dfrac{\pi}{2}=\sin x\bullet 0+\cos x\bullet 1=\cos x$

5. Using the sum identity for sine: $\sin\dfrac{\pi}{4}\cos\dfrac{\pi}{6}+\cos\dfrac{\pi}{6}\sin\dfrac{\pi}{4}=\sin\left(\dfrac{\pi}{4}+\dfrac{\pi}{6}\right)=\sin\dfrac{5\pi}{12}$

6. Note that $-\dfrac{11\pi}{12}=-\dfrac{8\pi}{12}-\dfrac{3\pi}{12}=-\dfrac{2\pi}{3}-\dfrac{\pi}{4}$. Using the subtraction identity for cosine:

$$\cos\left(-\dfrac{11\pi}{12}\right)=\cos\left(-\dfrac{2\pi}{3}-\dfrac{\pi}{4}\right)=\cos\left(-\dfrac{2\pi}{3}\right)\cos\dfrac{\pi}{4}+\sin\left(-\dfrac{2\pi}{3}\right)\sin\dfrac{\pi}{4}=\left(-\dfrac{1}{2}\right)\left(\dfrac{\sqrt{2}}{2}\right)+\left(-\dfrac{\sqrt{3}}{2}\right)\left(\dfrac{\sqrt{2}}{2}\right)=\dfrac{-\sqrt{2}-\sqrt{6}}{4}$$

Note this could also be solved using the half-angle identity:

$$\cos\left(-\dfrac{11\pi}{12}\right)=\cos\dfrac{11\pi}{12}=\cos\left(\dfrac{1}{2}\bullet\dfrac{11\pi}{6}\right)=-\sqrt{\dfrac{1+\cos\theta}{2}}=-\sqrt{\dfrac{1+\dfrac{\sqrt{3}}{2}}{2}}=-\sqrt{\dfrac{2+\sqrt{3}}{4}}=-\dfrac{\sqrt{2+\sqrt{3}}}{2}$$

7. Note that $165°=135°+30°$. Using the addition identity for cosine:

$$\cos 165°=\cos\left(135°+30°\right)=\cos 135°\cos 30°-\sin 135°\sin 30°=\left(-\dfrac{\sqrt{2}}{2}\right)\left(\dfrac{\sqrt{3}}{2}\right)-\left(\dfrac{\sqrt{2}}{2}\right)\left(\dfrac{1}{2}\right)=\dfrac{-\sqrt{6}-\sqrt{2}}{4}$$

Note this could also be solved using the half-angle identity:

$$\cos 165°=\cos\dfrac{330°}{2}=-\sqrt{\dfrac{1+\cos 330°}{2}}=-\sqrt{\dfrac{1+\dfrac{\sqrt{3}}{2}}{2}}=-\sqrt{\dfrac{2+\sqrt{3}}{4}}=-\dfrac{\sqrt{2+\sqrt{3}}}{2}$$

8. Using the addition identity for tangent: $\tan 255°=\tan\left(210°+45°\right)=\dfrac{\tan 210°+\tan 45°}{1-\tan 210°\tan 45°}=\dfrac{\dfrac{\sqrt{3}}{3}+1}{1-\left(\dfrac{\sqrt{3}}{3}\right)(1)}=\dfrac{\sqrt{3}+3}{3-\sqrt{3}}=\sqrt{3}+2$

9. Using the Pythagorean identity:

$$\cos^2 a + \sin^2 a = 1 \qquad\qquad \cos^2 b + \sin^2 b = 1$$

$$\left(-\frac{4}{5}\right)^2 + \sin^2 a = 1 \qquad\qquad \cos^2 b + \left(\frac{12}{13}\right)^2 = 1$$

$$\frac{16}{25} + \sin^2 a = 1 \qquad\qquad \cos^2 b + \frac{144}{169} = 1$$

$$\sin^2 a = \frac{9}{25} \qquad\qquad \cos^2 b = \frac{25}{169}$$

$$\sin a = \frac{3}{5} \ (a \text{ in quad. II}) \qquad\qquad \cos b = -\frac{5}{13} \qquad (b \text{ in quad. II})$$

Now using the sum identity for sine: $\sin(a+b) = \sin a \cos b + \cos a \sin b = \left(\frac{3}{5}\right)\left(-\frac{5}{13}\right) + \left(-\frac{4}{5}\right)\left(\frac{12}{13}\right) = -\frac{15}{65} - \frac{48}{65} = -\frac{63}{65}$

10. Finding the tangent values:

$$\tan a = \frac{\sin a}{\cos a} = \frac{\frac{3}{5}}{-\frac{4}{5}} = -\frac{3}{4} \qquad\qquad \tan b = \frac{\sin b}{\cos b} = \frac{\frac{12}{13}}{-\frac{5}{13}} = -\frac{12}{5}$$

Using the difference identity for tangent: $\tan(a-b) = \dfrac{\tan a - \tan b}{1 + \tan a \tan b} = \dfrac{-\frac{3}{4} - \left(-\frac{12}{5}\right)}{1 + \left(-\frac{3}{4}\right) \cdot \left(-\frac{12}{5}\right)} = \dfrac{-\frac{3}{4} + \frac{12}{5}}{1 + \frac{9}{5}} = \dfrac{\frac{33}{20}}{\frac{14}{5}} = \dfrac{33}{56}$

11. Using the sum identity for cosine: $\cos(a+b) = \cos a \cos b - \sin a \sin b = \left(-\frac{4}{5}\right)\left(-\frac{5}{13}\right) - \left(\frac{3}{5}\right)\left(\frac{12}{13}\right) = \frac{20}{65} - \frac{36}{65} = -\frac{16}{65}$

12. Using the Pythagorean identity:

$$\sin^2 x = 1 - \cos^2 x = 1 - \left(-\frac{4}{5}\right)^2 = \frac{9}{25}$$

$$\sin x = \frac{3}{5}$$

Using the double-angle formula: $\sin 2x = 2\sin x \cos x = 2\left(\frac{3}{5}\right)\left(-\frac{4}{5}\right) = -\frac{24}{25}$

13. Using the half-angle formula: $\cos\dfrac{x}{2} = \sqrt{\dfrac{1 + \cos x}{2}} = \sqrt{\dfrac{1 - \frac{4}{5}}{2}} = \sqrt{\dfrac{5-4}{10}} = \dfrac{1}{\sqrt{10}} = \dfrac{\sqrt{10}}{10}$

14. First find the tangent: $\tan x = \dfrac{\frac{3}{5}}{-\frac{4}{5}} = -\frac{3}{4}$

Using the double-angle formula: $\tan 2x = \dfrac{2\tan x}{1 - \tan^2 x} = \dfrac{2\left(-\frac{3}{4}\right)}{1 - \left(-\frac{3}{4}\right)^2} = \dfrac{-\frac{3}{2}}{\frac{7}{16}} = -\frac{24}{7}$

15. Reducing the powers: $\sin^3 x \cos x = \sin^2 x \sin x \cos x = \left(\dfrac{1 - \cos 2x}{2}\right) \cdot \dfrac{1}{2} \cdot 2\sin x \cos x = \dfrac{1}{4}(1 - \cos 2x)\sin 2x$

16. Using a product-to-sum identity: $\sin 3x \cos 2x = \dfrac{1}{2}\left[\sin(3x+2x) + \sin(3x-2x)\right] = \dfrac{1}{2}(\sin 5x + \sin x)$

17. Using a sum-to-product identity: $\cos 3x + \cos 4x = 2\cos\left(\dfrac{3x+4x}{2}\right)\cos\left(\dfrac{3x-4x}{2}\right) = 2\cos\left(\dfrac{7x}{2}\right)\cos\left(\dfrac{-x}{2}\right) = 2\cos\dfrac{7x}{2}\cos\dfrac{x}{2}$

18. Solving the equation:
$$2\sin x - 1 = 0$$
$$2\sin x = 1$$
$$\sin x = \frac{1}{2}$$
$$x = \frac{\pi}{6}, \frac{5\pi}{6}$$

The general solution is: $x = \dfrac{\pi}{6} + 2n\pi, \dfrac{5\pi}{6} + 2n\pi$, where n is an integer

19. Solving the equation:
$$\tan 2x + \sqrt{3} = 0$$
$$\tan 2x = -\sqrt{3}$$
$$2x = \frac{2\pi}{3} + n\pi$$
$$x = \frac{\pi}{3} + \frac{n\pi}{2}$$

The general solution is: $x = \dfrac{\pi}{3} + \dfrac{n\pi}{2}$, where n is an integer

20. Solving the equation:
$$4\cos^2 x - 1 = 0$$
$$4\cos^2 x = 1$$
$$\cos^2 x = \frac{1}{4}$$
$$\cos x = \pm\frac{1}{2}$$
$$x = \frac{\pi}{3}, \frac{2\pi}{3}, \frac{4\pi}{3}, \frac{5\pi}{3}$$

The solutions in the interval $[0, 2\pi)$ are: $x = \dfrac{\pi}{3}, \dfrac{2\pi}{3}, \dfrac{4\pi}{3}, \dfrac{5\pi}{3}$

21. Solving the equation:
$$\sec^2 x - 3\sec x + 2 = 0$$
$$(\sec x - 2)(\sec x - 1) = 0$$
$$\sec x - 2 = 0 \Rightarrow \sec x = 2 \Rightarrow \cos x = \frac{1}{2} \Rightarrow x = \frac{\pi}{3}, \frac{5\pi}{3}$$
$$\sec x - 1 = 0 \Rightarrow \sec x = 1 \Rightarrow \cos x = 1 \Rightarrow x = 0$$

The solutions in the interval $[0, 2\pi)$ are: $x = 0, \dfrac{\pi}{3}, \dfrac{5\pi}{3}$

22. Solving the equation:

$$3\cos x + 1 = 0$$

$$3\cos x = -1$$

$$\cos x = -\frac{1}{3}$$

$$x = \pi - \cos^{-1}\left(\frac{1}{3}\right) \approx 1.911, \pi + \cos^{-1}\left(\frac{1}{3}\right) \approx 4.373$$

The solutions in the interval $[0, 2\pi)$ are: $x \approx 1.911, 4.373$

23. Solving the equation:

$$\tan\left(\frac{x}{2}\right) = 2$$

$$\frac{x}{2} = \tan^{-1}(2) + n\pi$$

$$x = 2\tan^{-1}(2) + 2n\pi \approx 2.214 + 2n\pi$$

The solution in the interval $[0, 2\pi)$ is: $x \approx 2.214$

24. Solving the equation:

$$-3x = 2\cos x$$

$$x \approx -0.564$$

25. Setting the function equal to 1:

$$f(x) = 1$$

$$2\cos\left(3x - \frac{\pi}{2}\right) + 3 = 1$$

$$2\cos\left(3x - \frac{\pi}{2}\right) = -2$$

$$\cos\left(3x - \frac{\pi}{2}\right) = -1$$

$$3x - \frac{\pi}{2} = \pi$$

$$3x = \frac{3\pi}{2}$$

$$x = \frac{\pi}{2}$$

26. The number of days after the person's 21st birthday is represented by $t - 7670$. Solving the equation:

$$P(t) = 50\sin\left[\frac{2\pi}{33}(t - 7670)\right] + 50$$

$$100 = 50\sin\left[\frac{2\pi}{33}(t - 7670)\right] + 50$$

$$50 = 50\sin\left[\frac{2\pi}{33}(t - 7670)\right]$$

$$1 = \sin\left[\frac{2\pi}{33}(t - 7670)\right]$$

$$\frac{2\pi}{33}(t - 7670) = \frac{\pi}{2}$$

$$t - 7670 = \frac{33}{4}$$

$$t = \frac{33}{4} + 7670 \approx 7679 \qquad \text{(rounding up to the next day)}$$

The day of greatest potential is day 7679, which is 9 days after the person's 21st birthday.

Chapter 7
Additional Topics in Trigonometry

7.1 The Law of Sines

1. This is true, since: $\sin 130° = \sin(180° - 50°) = \sin 180° \cos 50° - \cos 180° \sin 50° = 0 \cdot \cos 50° - (-1)\sin 50° = \sin 50°$

3. For $\sin\theta = \dfrac{1}{2}$, there are two angles in the given interval: $\theta = \sin^{-1}\left(\dfrac{1}{2}\right) = 30°, \theta = 180° - 30° = 150°$

5. For $\sin\theta = 0.8$, there are two angles in the given interval: $\theta = \sin^{-1}(0.8) \approx 53.13°, \theta = 180° - 53.13° = 126.87°$

7. Finding angle B: $B = 180° - (44° + 32°) = 104°$

Using the law of sines:

$$\frac{a}{\sin 32°} = \frac{11}{\sin 44°} \qquad\qquad \frac{b}{\sin 104°} = \frac{11}{\sin 44°}$$

$$a = \left(\frac{11}{\sin 44°}\right)\sin 32° \approx 8.3913 \qquad\qquad b = \left(\frac{11}{\sin 44°}\right)\sin 104° \approx 15.3648$$

9. Finding angle C: $C = 180° - (110° + 45°) = 25°$

Using the law of sines:

$$\frac{a}{\sin 110°} = \frac{8}{\sin 25°} \qquad\qquad \frac{b}{\sin 45°} = \frac{8}{\sin 25°}$$

$$a = \left(\frac{8}{\sin 25°}\right)\sin 110° \approx 17.880 \qquad\qquad b = \left(\frac{8}{\sin 25°}\right)\sin 45° \approx 13.3853$$

11. Finding angle C: $C = 180° - (42° + 64°) = 74°$

Using the law of sines:

$$\frac{a}{\sin 42°} = \frac{6}{\sin 64°} \qquad\qquad \frac{c}{\sin 74°} = \frac{6}{\sin 25°}$$

$$a = \left(\frac{6}{\sin 64°}\right)\sin 42° \approx 4.4669 \qquad\qquad c = \left(\frac{6}{\sin 64°}\right)\sin 74° \approx 6.4170$$

13. Finding angle C: $C = 180° - (110° + 20°) = 50°$

Using the law of sines:

$$\frac{a}{\sin 110°} = \frac{15}{\sin 50°} \qquad\qquad \frac{b}{\sin 20°} = \frac{15}{\sin 50°}$$

$$a = \left(\frac{15}{\sin 50°}\right)\sin 110° \approx 18.4002 \qquad\qquad b = \left(\frac{15}{\sin 50°}\right)\sin 20° \approx 6.6971$$

15. Finding angle C: $C = 180° - (80° + 60°) = 40°$

Using the law of sines:

$$\frac{b}{\sin 60°} = \frac{13}{\sin 80°}$$

$$b = \left(\frac{13}{\sin 80°}\right)\sin 60° \approx 11.4320$$

$$\frac{c}{\sin 40°} = \frac{13}{\sin 80°}$$

$$c = \left(\frac{13}{\sin 80°}\right)\sin 40° \approx 8.4851$$

17. Finding angle B: $B = 180° - (40° + 80°) = 60°$

Using the law of sines:

$$\frac{a}{\sin 80°} = \frac{35}{\sin 40°}$$

$$a = \left(\frac{35}{\sin 40°}\right)\sin 80° \approx 53.6231$$

$$\frac{b}{\sin 60°} = \frac{35}{\sin 40°}$$

$$b = \left(\frac{35}{\sin 40°}\right)\sin 60° \approx 47.1554$$

19. Finding angle B: $B = 180° - (130.5° + 20°) = 29.5°$

Using the law of sines:

$$\frac{b}{\sin 29.5°} = \frac{20}{\sin 130.5°}$$

$$b = \left(\frac{20}{\sin 130.5°}\right)\sin 29.5° \approx 12.9516$$

$$\frac{c}{\sin 20°} = \frac{20}{\sin 130.5°}$$

$$c = \left(\frac{20}{\sin 130.5°}\right)\sin 20° \approx 8.9957$$

21. Finding angle B: $B = 180° - (52.1° + 73°) = 54.9°$

Using the law of sines:

$$\frac{b}{\sin 54.9°} = \frac{15}{\sin 130.5°}$$

$$b = \left(\frac{15}{\sin 73°}\right)\sin 54.9° \approx 12.8330$$

$$\frac{b}{\sin 52.1°} = \frac{15}{\sin 130.5°}$$

$$b = \left(\frac{15}{\sin 73°}\right)\sin 52.1° \approx 12.3771$$

23. This is a case of SSA. Using the law of sines:

$$\frac{\sin B}{5} = \frac{\sin 35°}{7}$$

$$\sin B = \frac{5\sin 35°}{7} \approx 0.4097$$

$$B = \sin^{-1}\left(\frac{5\sin 35°}{7}\right) = 24.1858° \text{ or } 155.8142°$$

Since $A + B = 35° + 155.8142° = 190.8142° > 180°$, there is no triangle with $B = 155.8142°$.

Finding angle C: $C = 180° - 35° - 24.1858° = 120.8142°$

Using the law of sines:

$$\frac{c}{\sin 120.8140°} = \frac{7}{\sin 35°}$$

$$c = \left(\frac{7}{\sin 35°}\right)\sin 120.8142° \approx 10.4813$$

The missing sides/angles are: $B = 24.1858°, C = 120.8142°, c \approx 10.4813$

25. This is a case of SSA. Using the law of sines:

$$\frac{\sin B}{5} = \frac{\sin 40°}{6}$$

$$\sin B = \frac{5\sin 40°}{6} \approx 0.5357$$

$$B = \sin^{-1}\left(\frac{5\sin 40°}{6}\right) = 32.3884° \text{ or } 147.6116°$$

Since $A + B = 40° + 147.6116° = 187.6116° > 180°$, there is no triangle with $B = 147.6116°$.
Finding angle C: $C = 180° - 40° - 32.3884° = 107.6116°$
Using the law of sines:

$$\frac{c}{\sin 107.6116°} = \frac{6}{\sin 40°}$$

$$c = \left(\frac{6}{\sin 40°}\right)\sin 107.6116° \approx 8.8968$$

The missing sides/angles are: $B = 32.3884°, C = 107.6116°, c \approx 8.8968$

27. This is a case of SSA. Using the law of sines:

$$\frac{\sin C}{25} = \frac{\sin 70°}{10}$$

$$\sin C = \frac{25\sin 70°}{10} \approx 2.3492$$

The sine of an angle cannot be greater than 1, so there is no triangle with the given information.

29. For $A = 40°$ and $B = 85°$: $C = 180° - 40° - 85° = 55°$
Using the law of sines:

$$\frac{b}{\sin 85°} = \frac{8}{\sin 55°}$$

$$b = \frac{8\sin 85°}{\sin 55°} = 9.7290$$

For $A = 40°$ and $B' = 92°$: $C = 180° - 40° - 92° = 48°$
Using the law of sines:

$$\frac{b+h}{\sin 92°} = \frac{8}{\sin 48°}$$

$$b + h = \frac{8\sin 92°}{\sin 48°} \approx 10.7585$$

$$h = 10.7585 - b \approx 10.7585 - 9.7290 \approx 1.0$$

31. Label the lower triangle counterclockwise from the left corner ABC. Then $A = 12°$, $B = 180° - 20° = 160°$,
and $C = 180° - 12° - 160° = 8°$. Using the law of sines:

$$\frac{h}{\sin 160°} = \frac{7}{\sin 12°}$$

$$h = \frac{7\sin 160°}{\sin 12°} \approx 11.5$$

33. Let C be the top of the tower. Angle $C = 180° - 15° - 60° = 105°$. Using the law of sines:

$$\frac{a}{\sin 15°} = \frac{100}{\sin 105°} \qquad\qquad \frac{h}{a} = \sin 60°$$

$$a = \frac{100\sin 15°}{\sin 105°} \approx 26.7949 \qquad h = 26.7949\sin 60° \approx 23.2051$$

The height of the tower is about 23.2051 feet.

35. This is a SSA case. Using the law of sines:

$$\frac{\sin C}{5} = \frac{\sin 45°}{8}$$

$$\sin C = \frac{5\sin 45°}{8} \approx 0.4419$$

$$C = \sin^{-1}\left(\frac{5\sin 45°}{8}\right) = 26.2278° \text{ or } 153.7722°$$

Since $A + C = 45° + 153.7722° = 198.7722°$, $C = 153.7722°$ is not a possible angle of this triangle.
Finding angle B: $B = 180° - 45° - 26.2278° = 108.7722°$

Using the law of sines:

$$\frac{b}{\sin 108.7722°} = \frac{8}{\sin 45°}$$

$$b = \frac{8\sin 108.7722°}{\sin 45°} \approx 10.7119$$

The distance between flower beds A and C is about 10.7119 feet.

37.   Drawing a figure:

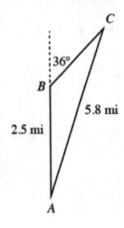

Finding angle B: $B = 180° - 36° = 144°$
Using the law of sines:

$$\frac{\sin C}{2.5} = \frac{\sin 144°}{5.8}$$

$$\sin C = \frac{2.5\sin 144°}{5.8} \approx 0.2534$$

$$C = \sin^{-1}\left(\frac{2.5\sin 144°}{5.8}\right) \approx 14.6762°$$

Finding angle A: $A = 180° - 144° - 14.6762° \approx 21.3238°$
Using the law of sines:

$$\frac{a}{\sin 21.3238°} = \frac{5.8}{\sin 144°}$$

$$a = \frac{5.8\sin 21.3238°}{\sin 144°} \approx 3.5882$$

They traversed a distance of 2.5 + 3.5882 = 6.0882 miles.

39.   Let B represent the target. Drawing the figure:

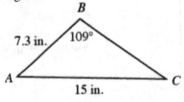

Using the law of sines:

$$\frac{\sin C}{7.3} = \frac{\sin 109°}{15}$$

$$\sin C = \frac{7.3\sin 109°}{15} \approx 0.4602$$

$$C = \sin^{-1}\left(\frac{7.3\sin 109°}{15}\right) \approx 27.3969°$$

Finding angle A: $A = 180° - 109° - 27.3969° = 43.6031°$

Using the law of sines:

$$\frac{a}{\sin 43.6031°} = \frac{15}{\sin 109°}$$

$$a = \frac{15\sin 43.6031°}{\sin 109°} \approx 10.9410$$

The other point is approximately 10.9410 inches from the target.

41. If A is the angle opposite the 7-inch side, then:

$$\frac{\sin A}{7} = \frac{\sin 75°}{10}$$

$$\sin A = \frac{7\sin 75°}{10} \approx 0.6761$$

$$A = \sin^{-1}\left(\frac{7\sin 75°}{10}\right) \approx 42.5434°$$

The remaining angle is given by: $B = 180° - 75° - A = 62.4566°$

The third edge is given by: $b = \frac{10\sin 62.4566°}{\sin 75°} \approx 9.1794$ feet

The third edge is approximately 9.1794 feet long.

43. First find the width of the river:

$$\cos 25° = \frac{w}{250}$$

$$w = 250\cos 25° \approx 226.5769$$

The width of the river is about 227 feet. Considering triangle ABC, angle A is $A = 90° - 25° = 65°$.
Using the law of sines:

$$\frac{\sin C}{250} = \frac{\sin 65°}{230}$$

$$\sin C = \frac{250\sin 65°}{230} \approx 0.9851$$

$$C = \sin^{-1}\left(\frac{250\sin 65°}{230}\right) \approx 80.1026°$$

Angle B is given by: $B = 180° - 65° - 80.1026° = 34.8974°$
Using the law of sines:

$$\frac{d}{\sin 34.8974°} = \frac{230}{\sin 65°}$$

$$d = \frac{230\sin 34.8974°}{\sin 65°} \approx 145.1879$$

The distance between points A and C is about 145 ft.

45. Drawing the figure:

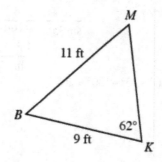

Using the law of sines:

$$\frac{\sin M}{9} = \frac{\sin 62°}{11}$$

$$\sin M = \frac{9 \sin 62°}{11} \approx 0.7224$$

$$M = \sin^{-1}\left(\frac{9 \sin 62°}{11}\right) \approx 46.2340°$$

Finding angle B: $B = 180° - 62° - 46.3540° = 71.7460°$

Using the law of sines:

$$\frac{b}{\sin 71.7460°} = \frac{11}{\sin 62°}$$

$$b = \frac{11 \sin 71.7460°}{\sin 62°} \approx 11.8313$$

Malik and Keisha are approximately 11.8313 feet apart.

47. Drawing the figure:

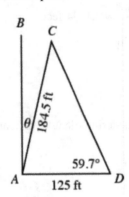

In triangle ACD, using the law of sines:

$$\frac{\sin C}{125} = \frac{\sin 59.7°}{184.5}$$

$$\sin C = \frac{125 \sin 59.7°}{184.5}$$

$$C = \sin^{-1}\left(\frac{125 \sin 59.7°}{184.5}\right) \approx 35.8°$$

Finding angle A: $A = 180° - 59.7° - 35.8° = 84.5°$

Therefore: $\theta = 90° - 84.5° = 5.5°$

49. Finding angle A: $A = 180° - 35° - 50° = 95°$

Using the law of sines:

$$\frac{b}{\sin 50°} = \frac{4}{\sin 95°}$$

$$b = \frac{4 \sin 50°}{\sin 95°} \approx 3.0759 \text{ ft}$$

$$\frac{c}{\sin 35°} = \frac{4}{\sin 95°}$$

$$c = \frac{4 \sin 35°}{\sin 95°} \approx 2.3031 \text{ ft}$$

51. Using triangle BCD, find angle B: $B = 180° - 30° - 130° = 20°$

Using the law of sines:

$$\frac{BC}{\sin 30°} = \frac{15}{\sin 20°}$$

$$BC = \frac{15 \sin 30°}{\sin 20°} \approx 21.9 \text{ yd}$$

Using triangle ABD, find angle B: $B = 70° - 20° = 50°$

Therefore: $D = 100° - 30° = 70°$

Using the law of sines:

$$\frac{AD}{\sin 50°} = \frac{18}{\sin 70°}$$

$$AD = \frac{18\sin 50°}{\sin 70°} \approx 14.7 \text{ yards}$$

53. In the top triangle, the third angle is: $180° - 45° - 30° = 105°$
Using the law of sines:

$$\frac{a}{\sin 30°} = \frac{10}{\sin 105°}$$

$$a = \frac{10\sin 30°}{\sin 105°} \approx 5.1764 \text{ inches}$$

Let d represent the dashed line. Using the law of sines:

$$\frac{d}{\sin 45°} = \frac{10}{\sin 105°}$$

$$d = \frac{10\sin 45°}{\sin 105°} \approx 7.3205$$

In the bottom triangle, the third missing angle is $95°$. Using the law of sines:

$$\frac{b}{\sin 55°} = \frac{7.3205}{\sin 95°} \qquad\qquad \frac{c}{\sin 30°} = \frac{7.3205}{\sin 95°}$$

$$b = \frac{7.3205\sin 55°}{\sin 95°} \approx 6.0195 \text{ inches} \qquad c = \frac{7.3205\sin 30°}{\sin 95°} \approx 3.6742 \text{ inches}$$

The three sides are 5.1764 inches, 6.0195 inches, and 3.6742 inches.

55. The law of sines works for a right triangle as well as for any other, and it is easy to use because $\sin 90° = 1$. The Pythagorean theorem and the trig ratios are more efficient for right triangles, however.

57. There is an infinite number of three angle sets that can solve this equation.

7.2 The Law of Cosines

1. Using the law of cosines:

$$c^2 = a^2 + b^2 - 2ab\cos C$$

$$c^2 = 7^2 + 10^2 - 2(7)(10)\cos 80°$$

$$c^2 = 49 + 100 - 140\cos 80°$$

$$c^2 = 149 - 140\cos 80°$$

$$c^2 \approx 124.6893$$

$$c \approx 11.1664$$

3. Using the law of cosines:

$$b^2 = a^2 + c^2 - 2ac\cos B$$

$$b^2 = 12^2 + 8^2 - 2(12)(8)\cos 56°$$

$$b^2 = 144 + 64 - 192\cos 56°$$

$$b^2 = 208 - 192\cos 56°$$

$$b^2 \approx 100.6350$$

$$b \approx 10.0317$$

5. Using the law of cosines:

$$a^2 = b^2 + c^2 - 2bc\cos A$$

$$a^2 = 8^2 + 4^2 - 2(8)(4)\cos 75°$$

$$a^2 = 64 + 16 - 64\cos 75°$$

$$a^2 = 80 - 64\cos 75°$$

$$a^2 \approx 63.4356$$

$$a \approx 7.9646$$

7. Using the law of cosines:

$$a^2 = b^2 + c^2 - 2bc\cos A$$

$$a^2 = 10^2 + 7^2 - 2(10)(7)\cos 55°$$

$$a^2 = 149 - 140\cos 55°$$

$$a^2 \approx 68.6993$$

$$a \approx 8.2885$$

Now using the law of sines:

$$\frac{\sin B}{10} = \frac{\sin 55°}{8.2885}$$

$$\sin B = \frac{10\sin 55°}{8.2885} \approx 0.9883$$

$$B = \sin^{-1}\left(\frac{10\sin 55°}{8.2885}\right) \approx 81.2265°$$

Finally: $C = 180° - 55° - 81.2265° \approx 43.7735°$

9. Using the law of cosines:

$$c^2 = a^2 + b^2 - 2ab\cos C$$

$$c^2 = 15^2 + 18^2 - 2(15)(18)\cos 37.5°$$

$$c^2 = 549 - 540\cos 37.5°$$

$$c^2 \approx 120.5892$$

$$c \approx 10.9813$$

Now using the law of sines:

$$\frac{\sin A}{15} = \frac{\sin 37.5°}{10.9813}$$

$$\sin A = \frac{15\sin 37.5°}{10.9813} \approx 0.8315$$

$$A = \sin^{-1}\left(\frac{15\sin 37.5°}{10.9813}\right) \approx 56.2575°$$

Finally: $B = 180° - 37.5° - 56.2575° \approx 86.2425°$

11. Using the law of cosines:

$$c^2 = a^2 + b^2 - 2ab\cos C$$

$$10^2 = 5^2 + 7^2 - 2(5)(7)\cos C$$

$$100 = 74 - 70\cos C$$

$$26 = -70\cos C$$

$$\cos C = -\frac{26}{70}$$

$$C = \cos^{-1}\left(-\frac{26}{70}\right) \approx 111.8037°$$

Using the law of cosines:

$$b^2 = a^2 + c^2 - 2ac\cos B$$

$$7^2 = 5^2 + 10^2 - 2(5)(10)\cos B$$

$$49 = 25 + 100 - 2(5)(10)\cos B$$

$$-76 = -100\cos B$$

$$\cos B = \frac{76}{100}$$

$$B = \cos^{-1}\left(\frac{76}{100}\right) \approx 40.5358°$$

Finally: $A = 180° - 111.8037° - 40.5358° \approx 27.6604°$

13.   Using the law of cosines:

$$c^2 = a^2 + b^2 - 2ab \cos C$$
$$29^2 = 13^2 + 17^2 - 2(13)(17) \cos C$$
$$841 = 169 + 289 - 442 \cos C$$
$$383 = -442 \cos C$$
$$\cos C = -\frac{383}{442}$$
$$C = \cos^{-1}\left(-\frac{383}{442}\right) \approx 150.0562°$$

Using the law of cosines:

$$b^2 = a^2 + c^2 - 2ac \cos B$$
$$17^2 = 13^2 + 29^2 - 2(13)(29) \cos B$$
$$289 = 169 + 841 - 2(13)(29) \cos B$$
$$-721 = -754 \cos B$$
$$\cos B = \frac{721}{754}$$
$$B = \cos^{-1}\left(\frac{721}{754}\right) \approx 17.0140°$$

Finally: $A = 180° - 150.0562° - 17.0140° \approx 12.9298°$

15.   Using the law of cosines:

$$b^2 = a^2 + c^2 - 2ac \cos B$$
$$(8.4)^2 = (4.7)^2 + (5.6)^2 - 2(4.7)(5.6) \cos B$$
$$70.56 = 53.45 - 52.64 \cos B$$
$$17.11 = -52.64 \cos B$$
$$\cos B = -\frac{17.11}{52.64}$$
$$B = \cos^{-1}\left(-\frac{17.11}{52.64}\right) \approx 108.9679°$$

Using the law of cosines:

$$a^2 = b^2 + c^2 - 2bc \cos A$$
$$(4.7)^2 = (8.4)^2 + (5.6)^2 - 2(8.4)(5.6) \cos A$$
$$22.09 = 101.92 - 94.08 \cos A$$
$$-79.83 = -94.08 \cos A$$
$$\cos A = \frac{79.83}{94.08}$$
$$A = \cos^{-1}\left(\frac{79.83}{94.08}\right) \approx 31.9475°$$

Finally: $C = 180° - 108.9679° - 31.9475° \approx 39.0846°$

17.   Using the law of cosines:

$$b^2 = a^2 + c^2 - 2ac \cos B$$
$$b^2 = (15)^2 + (21)^2 - 2(15)(21) \cos B$$
$$b^2 = 666 - 630 \cos 100°$$
$$b^2 \approx 775.3984$$
$$b = \sqrt{775.3984} \approx 27.8460$$

Using the law of sines:

$$\frac{\sin A}{15} = \frac{\sin 100°}{27.8460}$$
$$\sin A = \frac{15 \sin 100°}{27.8460} \approx 0.5305$$
$$A = \sin^{-1}\left(\frac{15 \sin 100°}{27.8460}\right) \approx 32.0388°$$

Finally: $C = 180° - 100° - 32.0388° \approx 47.9612°$

19.   Using the law of cosines:

$$a^2 = b^2 + c^2 - 2bc \cos A$$
$$a^2 = (32)^2 + (25)^2 - 2(32)(25) \cos 98°$$
$$a^2 = 1649 - 1600 \cos 98°$$
$$a^2 \approx 1871.6770$$
$$a = \sqrt{1871.6770} \approx 43.2629$$

Using the law of sines:
$$\frac{\sin B}{32} = \frac{\sin 98°}{43.2629}$$

$$\sin B = \frac{32 \sin 98°}{43.2629} \approx 0.7325$$

$$B = \sin^{-1}\left(\frac{32 \sin 98°}{43.2629}\right) \approx 47.0935°$$

Finally: $C = 180° - 98° - 47.0935° \approx 34.9065°$

21. Using the law of cosines:
$$a^2 = b^2 + c^2 - 2bc \cos A$$

$$a^2 = (15.2)^2 + (15.2)^2 - 2(15.2)(15.2)\cos 169°$$

$$a^2 = 462.08 - 462.08 \cos 169°$$

$$a^2 \approx 915.6703$$

$$a = \sqrt{915.6703} \approx 30.2600$$

Using the law of sines:
$$\frac{\sin B}{15.2} = \frac{\sin 169°}{30.2600}$$

$$\sin B = \frac{15.2 \sin 169°}{30.2600} \approx 0.0958$$

$$B = \sin^{-1}\left(\frac{15.2 \sin 169°}{30.2600}\right) = 5.5°$$

Finally: $C = 180° - 169° - 5.5° \approx 5.5°$

23. Finding the area: $A = \frac{1}{2}(35)(16)\sin 77° = 280 \sin 77° \approx 272.8236$

25. Finding the area: $A = \frac{1}{2}(8)(13)\sin 86° = 52 \sin 86° \approx 51.8733$

27. Finding the area using Heron's formula:
$$s = \frac{1}{2}(3+2+4) = \frac{1}{2}(9) = \frac{9}{2}$$

$$A = \sqrt{s(s-a)(s-b)(s-c)} = \sqrt{\frac{9}{2}\left(\frac{9}{2}-3\right)\left(\frac{9}{2}-2\right)\left(\frac{9}{2}-4\right)} = \sqrt{\frac{9}{2}\left(\frac{3}{2}\right)\left(\frac{5}{2}\right)\left(\frac{1}{2}\right)} = \frac{\sqrt{135}}{4} \approx 2.9047$$

29. Finding the area using Heron's formula:
$$s = \frac{1}{2}(3+6+4) = \frac{1}{2}(13) = \frac{13}{2}$$

$$A = \sqrt{s(s-a)(s-b)(s-c)} = \sqrt{\frac{13}{2}\left(\frac{13}{2}-3\right)\left(\frac{13}{2}-6\right)\left(\frac{13}{2}-4\right)} = \sqrt{\frac{13}{2}\left(\frac{7}{2}\right)\left(\frac{1}{2}\right)\left(\frac{5}{2}\right)} = \frac{\sqrt{455}}{4} \approx 5.3327$$

31. Finding the area: $A = \frac{1}{2}(19)(8)\sin 124° = 76 \sin 124° \approx 63.0069$

33. Using the law of cosines:
$$a^2 = b^2 + c^2 - 2ab \cos A$$

$$a^2 = 6^2 + 10^2 - 2(6)(10)\cos 40°$$

$$a^2 = 136 - 120 \cos 40°$$

$$a^2 \approx 44.0747$$

$$a = \sqrt{44.0747} \approx 6.6389$$

You need about 6.64 feet of wood for the third side.

35. Using the law of cosines:

$$c^2 = a^2 + b^2 - 2ab\cos C$$

$$c^2 = 10^2 + 10^2 - 2(10)(10)\cos 110°$$

$$c^2 = 200 - 200\cos 110°$$

$$c^2 \approx 268.4040$$

$$c = \sqrt{268.4040} \approx 16.3830 \text{ inches}$$

37. a. It would use the law of cosines.

b. Using the law of cosines:

$$a^2 = m^2 + z^2 - 2mz\cos A$$

$$a^2 = 62^2 + 44^2 - 2(44)(62)\cos 95°$$

$$a^2 \approx 6255.5217$$

$$a = \sqrt{6255.5217} \approx 79.09 \text{ m}$$

39. Using the law of cosines:

$$a^2 = b^2 + c^2 - 2bc\cos A$$

$$26^2 = 24^2 + 21^2 - 2(24)(21)\cos A$$

$$676 = 1017 - 1008\cos A$$

$$-341 = -1008\cos A$$

$$\cos A = \frac{341}{1008}$$

$$A = \cos^{-1}\left(\frac{341}{1008}\right) \approx 70.2271°$$

41. Using the law of cosines:

$$a^2 = b^2 + c^2 - 2bc\cos A$$

$$a^2 = 8^2 + 5^2 - 2(8)(5)\cos 85°$$

$$a^2 = 64 + 25 - 80\cos 85°$$

$$a^2 = 82.0275$$

$$a = 9.0569$$

Finding the area: $A = \dfrac{1}{2}(8)(5)\sin 85° = 20\sin 85° \approx 19.9239$

The third edge is approximately 9.0569 inches, and the area is approximately 19.9239 in².

43. Let h = depth of the wreckage below the water's surface. The distance d between the boats can be found using the law of cosines:

$$d^2 = 500^2 + 700^2 - 2(500)(700)\cos 100°$$

$$d^2 = 861,553.7244$$

$$d \approx 928.1992 \text{ ft}$$

Finding the area: $A = \dfrac{1}{2}(500)(700)\sin 100° \approx 172,341.3568$

Since $A = \frac{1}{2}bh$, we have:

$$\frac{1}{2}bh = 172,341.3568$$

$$\frac{1}{2}(928.1992)h = 172,341.3568$$

$$464.0996h = 172,341.3568$$

$$h = 371.3456 \text{ feet}$$

The wreckage is about 371.3456 feet below the water's surface.

45. Using the law of cosines:

$$b^2 = 16^2 + 14^2 - 2(16)(14)\cos 25°$$

$$b^2 \approx 45.9741$$

$$b \approx 6.7804$$

Using the law of cosines again:

$$16^2 = 14^2 + (6.7804)^2 - 2(14)(6.7804)\cos A$$

$$256 = 241.9741 - 189.8518\cos A$$

$$14.0259 = -189.8518\cos A$$

$$\cos A = -\frac{14.0259}{189.8518}$$

$$A = \cos^{-1}\left(-\frac{14.0259}{189.8518}\right) \approx 94.2368°$$

She should input 6.7804 cm for the length and 94.2368° for the angle.

47. The supplement of 38° is $180° - 38° = 142°$. Drawing the figure:

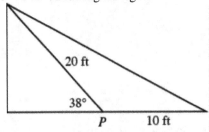

Using the law of cosines:

$$p^2 = 20^2 + 10^2 - 2(20)(10)\cos 142°$$

$$p^2 \approx 815.2043$$

$$p \approx 28.5518$$

The distance is approximately 28.5518 ft.

49. The side s of the square is the side opposite the angle formed by the radii to the corners of the square. The triangle formed has sides of length 15 inches. Using the law of cosines:

$$A = s^2 = 15^2 + 15^2 - 2(15)(15)\cos 90° = 450 \text{ in}^2$$

51. For the right triangle with hypotenuse BE, the leg marked with the dashed line is length $1 \cdot \tan 45° = 1 \cdot 1 = 1$.

Using the Pythagorean theorem:

$$(BE)^2 = 1^2 + 1^2 = 2$$

$$BE = \sqrt{2} \approx 1.41 \text{ in.}$$

Using the law of cosines:

$$(AE)^2 = 3^2 + \left(\sqrt{2}\right)^2 - 2(3)\left(\sqrt{2}\right)\cos 45°$$

$$(AE)^2 = 5$$

$$AE = \sqrt{5} \approx 2.24 \text{ in.}$$

Using right triangle DAB:

$$\cos 45° = \frac{3}{DB}$$

$$DB = \frac{3}{\cos 45°} = \frac{3}{\left(\frac{1}{\sqrt{2}}\right)} = 3\sqrt{2}$$

Therefore:

$$DB = DE + \sqrt{2}$$

$$DE + \sqrt{2} = 3\sqrt{2}$$

$$DE = 2\sqrt{2} \approx 2.83 \text{ in}$$

53. Drawing the figure:

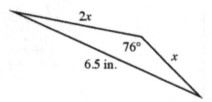

Using the law of cosines:

$$(6.5)^2 = x^2 + (2x)^2 - 2(x)(2x)\cos 76°$$

$$42.25 = 5x^2 - 4x^2 \cos 76°$$

$$42.25 = x^2 \left(5 - 4\cos 76°\right)$$

$$x^2 = \frac{42.25}{5 - 4\cos 76°}$$

$$x = \sqrt{\frac{42.25}{5 - 4\cos 76°}} \approx 3.2370 \text{ in.}$$

$$2x = 2(3.2370) \approx 6.4739 \text{ in.}$$

The arrows are about 3.2370 inches and 6.4739 inches from the target.

55. Using the law of cosines:

$$c^2 = a^2 + b^2 - 2ab\cos C$$

$$c^2 = a^2 + b^2 - 2ab\cos 90°$$

$$c^2 = a^2 + b^2 - 2ab(0)$$

$$c^2 = a^2 + b^2$$

Therefore $a^2 + b^2 = c^2$, which is the Pythagorean theorem.

57. A direct application of the law of cosines results in a single equation with an unknown side and an unknown angle, and cannot be solved uniquely.

59. If the sum of the squares of the two smaller sides is equal to the square of the largest side (Pythagorean theorem), then the triangle has a right angle.

61. If the quotient of the side lengths is equal to the cosine of the acute angle, then the triangle has a right angle.

63. If C is a right angle, then the area formula yields: $A = \frac{1}{2}ab\sin 90° = \frac{1}{2}ab(1) = \frac{1}{2}ab$

7.3 Polar Coordinates

1. Quadrant II
5. This corresponds to point E.
9. This corresponds to point B.

3. Quadrant III
7. This corresponds to point F.

11. **a.** Plotting $(2, \pi)$ on a rectangular grid:

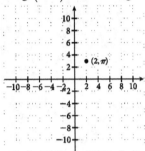

b. Plotting $(2, \pi)$ on a polar grid:

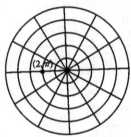

13. Plotting the point $\left(1, \dfrac{\pi}{2}\right)$:

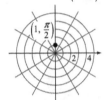

15. Plotting the point $\left(-3, \dfrac{\pi}{3}\right)$:

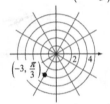

17. Plotting the point $\left(\dfrac{1}{2}, -\pi\right)$:

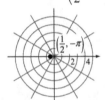

19. Plotting the point $\left(0, \dfrac{3\pi}{2}\right)$:

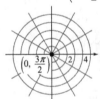

21. Converting to rectangular coordinates:

$$x = 3\cos\frac{\pi}{4} = 3\left(\frac{\sqrt{2}}{2}\right) = \frac{3\sqrt{2}}{2} \qquad y = 3\sin\frac{\pi}{4} = 3\left(\frac{\sqrt{2}}{2}\right) = \frac{3\sqrt{2}}{2}$$

The rectangular point is $\left(\dfrac{3\sqrt{2}}{2}, \dfrac{3\sqrt{2}}{2}\right)$.

23. Converting to rectangular coordinates:

$$x = -1\cos\frac{\pi}{6} = -\frac{\sqrt{3}}{2} \qquad y = -1\sin\frac{\pi}{6} = -\frac{1}{2}$$

The rectangular point is $\left(-\dfrac{\sqrt{3}}{2}, -\dfrac{1}{2}\right)$.

25. Converting to rectangular coordinates:

$$x = -4\cos\frac{7\pi}{6} = -4\left(-\frac{\sqrt{3}}{2}\right) = 2\sqrt{3} \qquad y = -4\sin\frac{7\pi}{6} = -4\left(-\frac{1}{2}\right) = 2$$

The rectangular point is $\left(2\sqrt{3}, 2\right)$.

27. Converting to rectangular coordinates:
$$x = \frac{3}{2}\cos\frac{\pi}{2} = \frac{3}{2}(0) = 0 \qquad\qquad y = \frac{3}{2}\sin\frac{\pi}{2} = \frac{3}{2}(1) = \frac{3}{2}$$
The rectangular point is $\left(0, \frac{3}{2}\right)$.

29. Finding r: $r = \sqrt{1^2 + \left(\sqrt{3}\right)^2} = \sqrt{1+3} = \sqrt{4} = 2$

Finding θ:
$$\tan\theta = \frac{\sqrt{3}}{1} = \sqrt{3}$$
$$\theta = \frac{\pi}{3} \text{ or } \frac{4\pi}{3}$$

Since the point is in quadrant I, $\theta = \frac{\pi}{3}$. The polar point is $(r, \theta) = \left(2, \frac{\pi}{3}\right)$.

31. Finding r: $r = \sqrt{\left(-\sqrt{3}\right)^2 + (-1)^2} = \sqrt{3+1} = \sqrt{4} = 2$

Finding θ:
$$\tan\theta = \frac{-1}{-\sqrt{3}} = \frac{1}{\sqrt{3}}$$
$$\theta = \frac{\pi}{6} \text{ or } \frac{7\pi}{6}$$

Since the point is in quadrant III, $\theta = \frac{7\pi}{6}$. The polar point is $(r, \theta) = \left(2, \frac{7\pi}{6}\right)$.

33. Finding r: $r = \sqrt{0^2 + 1^2} = \sqrt{1} = 1$

Finding θ:
$$\tan\theta = \frac{1}{0} \text{ is undefined}$$
$$\theta = \frac{\pi}{2} \text{ or } \frac{3\pi}{2}$$

Since the point is on the positive y-axis, $\theta = \frac{\pi}{2}$. The polar point is $(r, \theta) = \left(1, \frac{\pi}{2}\right)$.

35. For $r < 0$, a point is: $(-2, \pi - \pi) = (-2, 0)$ \qquad For $r > 0$, a point is: $(2, \pi - 2\pi) = (2, -\pi)$

37. For $r < 0$, a point is: $\left(-4, \frac{3\pi}{2} - \pi\right) = \left(-4, \frac{\pi}{2}\right)$ \qquad For $r > 0$, a point is: $\left(4, \frac{3\pi}{2} + 2\pi\right) = \left(4, \frac{7\pi}{2}\right)$

39. For $r < 0$, a point is: $\left(-\frac{3}{4}, \frac{\pi}{6} + \pi\right) = \left(-\frac{3}{4}, \frac{7\pi}{6}\right)$ \qquad For $r > 0$, a point is: $\left(\frac{3}{4}, \frac{\pi}{6} + 2\pi\right) = \left(\frac{3}{4}, \frac{13\pi}{6}\right)$

41. For $r < 0$, a point is: $\left(-\frac{11}{7}, -5\pi + 6\pi\right) = \left(-\frac{11}{7}, \pi\right)$ \qquad For $r > 0$, a point is: $\left(\frac{11}{7}, -5\pi + 5\pi\right) = \left(\frac{11}{7}, 0\right)$

43. For $r < 0$, a point is: $\left(-1.3, \frac{3\pi}{4} + \pi\right) = \left(-1.3, \frac{7\pi}{4}\right)$ \qquad For $r > 0$, a point is: $\left(1.3, \frac{3\pi}{4} + 2\pi\right) = \left(1.3, \frac{11\pi}{4}\right)$

45. Converting to polar form:
$$x = 2$$
$$r\cos\theta = 2$$

47. Converting to polar form:
$$x + 2y = 4$$
$$r\cos\theta + 2(r\sin\theta) = 4$$
$$r\cos\theta + 2r\sin\theta = 4$$

49. Converting to polar form:

$$x^2 + y^2 = 25$$
$$r^2 = 25$$
$$r = 5$$

51. Converting to polar form:

$$(x+1)^2 + y^2 = 1$$
$$x^2 + 2x + 1 + y^2 = 1$$
$$x^2 + y^2 + 2x = 0$$
$$r^2 + 2r\cos\theta = 0$$
$$r(r + 2\cos\theta) = 0$$
$$r + 2\cos\theta = 0$$
$$r = -2\cos\theta$$

53. Converting to polar form:

$$y = x^2$$
$$r\sin\theta = (r\cos\theta)^2$$
$$r\sin\theta = r^2\cos^2\theta$$
$$\sin\theta = r\cos^2\theta$$

55. Converting to polar form:

$$y = 2x^2 + x$$
$$r\sin\theta = 2(r\cos\theta)^2 + r\cos\theta$$
$$r\sin\theta = 2r^2\cos^2\theta + r\cos\theta$$
$$\sin\theta = 2r\cos^2\theta + \cos\theta$$

57. Converting to rectangular form:

$$r = 3$$
$$\sqrt{x^2 + y^2} = 3$$
$$\left(\sqrt{x^2 + y^2}\right)^2 = 3^2$$
$$x^2 + y^2 = 9$$

59. Converting to rectangular form:

$$\theta = \frac{\pi}{4}$$
$$\tan\theta = \tan\frac{\pi}{4}$$
$$\frac{y}{x} = 1$$
$$y = x$$

61. Converting to rectangular form:

$$r\cos\theta = 4$$
$$x = 4$$

63. Converting to rectangular form:

$$2r\cos\theta + r\sin\theta = 4$$
$$2x + y = 4$$

65. Converting to rectangular form:

$$r = 2\cos\theta$$
$$r^2 = 2r\cos\theta$$
$$x^2 + y^2 = 2x$$
$$x^2 - 2x + y^2 = 0$$
$$x^2 - 2x + 1 + y^2 = 1$$
$$(x-1)^2 + y^2 = 1$$

67. Converting to rectangular form:

$$r^2\cos 2\theta = 4$$
$$r^2\left(\cos^2\theta - \sin^2\theta\right) = 4$$
$$r^2\cos^2\theta - r^2\sin^2\theta = 4$$
$$(r\cos\theta)^2 - (r\sin\theta)^2 = 4$$
$$x^2 - y^2 = 4$$

69. Converting to rectangular coordinates:

$$x = 3\cos\left(-\frac{2\pi}{3}\right) = 3\cos\frac{2\pi}{3} = 3\left(-\frac{1}{2}\right) = -\frac{3}{2}$$

$$y = 3\sin\left(-\frac{2\pi}{3}\right) = -3\sin\frac{2\pi}{3} = -3\left(\frac{\sqrt{3}}{2}\right) = -\frac{3\sqrt{3}}{2}$$

The rectangular point is $\left(-\dfrac{3}{2}, -\dfrac{3\sqrt{3}}{2}\right)$.

71. The coordinates (r, θ) and $(r, \theta + 2\pi)$ are equivalent in the polar coordinate system, since the terminal side of $\theta + 2\pi$ is the same as the terminal side of θ.

73. Two features of the polar coordinate system that are different from those of the rectangular system:

(1) The coordinates of a point in the polar coordinate system are expressed in terms of real number and measures of angles, whereas in the rectangular coordinate system, the coordinates are expressed in terms of real numbers only.

(2) The rectangular coordinate of a point are unique, whereas the polar coordinate of a point are not.

7.4 Graphs of Polar Equations

1. The maximum occurs when $\sin\theta = 1$, thus $\theta = \dfrac{\pi}{2}$.

3. Solving the equation:
$$\cos 2\theta = -1$$
$$2\theta = \pi, 3\pi, \ldots$$
$$\theta = \frac{\pi}{2}, \frac{3\pi}{2}$$
In the interval $[0, \pi]$, the solution is $\theta = \dfrac{\pi}{2}$.

5. Solving the equation:
$$\cos 2\theta = 0$$
$$2\theta = \frac{\pi}{2}, \frac{3\pi}{2}, \frac{5\pi}{2}, \frac{7\pi}{2}, \ldots$$
$$\theta = \frac{\pi}{4}, \frac{3\pi}{4}, \frac{5\pi}{4}, \frac{7\pi}{4}$$
In the interval $[0, \pi]$, the solutions are $\theta = \dfrac{\pi}{4}, \dfrac{3\pi}{4}$.

7. $r = 4$ is a circle centered at the origin with radius 4.

Sketching the graph of $r = 4$:

9. $\theta = \dfrac{\pi}{4}$ is a line angled $\dfrac{\pi}{4}$ from the polar axis.

Sketching the graph of $\theta = \dfrac{\pi}{4}$:

11. Converting to rectangular coordinates:
$$r = 2\sec\theta$$
$$r = \frac{2}{\cos\theta}$$
$$r\cos\theta = 2$$
$$x = 2$$
$r = 2\sec\theta$ is a vertical line 2 units right of the origin.
Sketching the graph of $r = 2\sec\theta$:

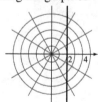

13. Converting to rectangular coordinates:
$$r = -4\csc\theta$$
$$r = \frac{-4}{\sin\theta}$$
$$r\sin\theta = -4$$
$$y = -4$$
$r = -4\csc\theta$ is a horizontal line 4 units below the origin.
Sketching the graph of $r = -4\csc\theta$:

15. Note the table of values:

θ	0	$\dfrac{\pi}{4}$	$\dfrac{\pi}{2}$	$\dfrac{3\pi}{4}$	π
$r = 2\cos\theta$	2	$\sqrt{2} \approx 1.4$	0	$-\sqrt{2} \approx -1.4$	-2

$r = 2\cos\theta$ is a circle with radius 1 and center on the x-axis. Sketching the graph of $r = 2\cos\theta$:

17. Note the table of values:

θ	0	$\dfrac{\pi}{4}$	$\dfrac{\pi}{2}$	$\dfrac{3\pi}{4}$	π
$r = -4\cos\theta$	-4	$-2\sqrt{2} \approx -2.8$	0	$2\sqrt{2} \approx 2.8$	4

$r = -4\cos\theta$ is a circle with radius 2 and center on the x-axis. Sketching the graph of $r = -4\cos\theta$:

19. Note the table of values:

θ	0	$\dfrac{\pi}{4}$	$\dfrac{\pi}{2}$	$\dfrac{3\pi}{4}$	π
$r = -\sin\theta$	0	$-\dfrac{\sqrt{2}}{2} \approx -0.7$	-1	$-\dfrac{\sqrt{2}}{2} \approx -0.7$	0

$r = -\sin\theta$ is a circle with radius $\dfrac{1}{2}$ and center on the y-axis. Sketching the graph of $r = -\sin\theta$:

21. Note the table of values:

θ	0	$\dfrac{\pi}{4}$	$\dfrac{\pi}{2}$	$\dfrac{3\pi}{4}$	π
$r = \dfrac{3}{2}\cos\theta$	$\dfrac{3}{2}$	$\dfrac{3\sqrt{2}}{4} \approx 1.1$	0	$-\dfrac{3\sqrt{2}}{4} \approx -1.1$	$-\dfrac{3}{2}$

$r = \dfrac{3}{2}\cos\theta$ is a circle with radius $\dfrac{3}{4}$ and center on the x-axis. Sketching the graph of $r = \dfrac{3}{2}\cos\theta$:

23. The graph is to the right of the line $\theta = \dfrac{\pi}{2}$ so $r = a\cos\theta$. Since the center is $\left(\dfrac{3}{2}, 0\right)$, $\dfrac{a}{2} = \dfrac{3}{2}$, so $a = 3$.

The equation is $r = 3\cos\theta$.

25. The graph is to the left of the line $\theta = \dfrac{\pi}{2}$ so $r = a\cos\theta$. Since the center is $(-2, 0)$, $\dfrac{a}{2} = -2$, so $a = -4$.

The equation is $r = -4\cos\theta$.

27. The graph is horizontal and 3 units above the x-axis so:

$$r\sin\theta = 3$$

$$r = \frac{3}{\sin\theta}$$

$$r = 3\csc\theta$$

29. The graph is vertical and 4 units to the right of the y-axis so:

$$r\cos\theta = 4$$

$$r = \frac{4}{\cos\theta}$$

$$r = 4\sec\theta$$

31. Note the table of values:

θ	0	$\dfrac{\pi}{6}$	$\dfrac{\pi}{4}$	$\dfrac{\pi}{3}$	$\dfrac{\pi}{2}$	π
$r = 2\cos 2\theta$	2	1	0	−1	−2	2

The graph of $r = 2\cos 2\theta$ is a four-petaled rose:

33. Note the table of values:

θ	0	$\dfrac{\pi}{6}$	$\dfrac{\pi}{4}$	$\dfrac{\pi}{3}$	$\dfrac{\pi}{2}$	π
$r = 1 + \cos\theta$	2	$\dfrac{2+\sqrt{3}}{2} \approx 1.9$	$\dfrac{2+\sqrt{2}}{2} \approx 1.7$	$\dfrac{3}{2}$	1	0

The graph of $r = 1 + \cos\theta$ is a cardiod:

35. Note the table of values:

θ	0	$\dfrac{\pi}{6}$	$\dfrac{\pi}{4}$	$\dfrac{\pi}{3}$	$\dfrac{\pi}{2}$	π
$r = 2 - 2\sin\theta$	2	1	$2 - \sqrt{2} \approx 0.6$	$2 - \sqrt{3} \approx 0.3$	0	2

The graph of $r = 2 - 2\sin\theta$ is a cardiod:

37. Note the table of values:

θ	0	$\dfrac{\pi}{6}$	$\dfrac{\pi}{4}$	$\dfrac{\pi}{3}$	$\dfrac{\pi}{2}$	π
$r = 3\sin(3\theta)$	0	3	$\dfrac{3\sqrt{2}}{2} \approx 2.1$	0	-3	0

The graph of $r = 3\sin(3\theta)$ is a three-petaled rose:

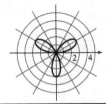

39. Note the table of values:

θ	0	$\dfrac{\pi}{12}$	$\dfrac{\pi}{8}$	$\dfrac{\pi}{6}$	$\dfrac{\pi}{4}$
$r = \pm\sqrt{4\cos(2\theta)}$	± 2	$\pm\sqrt{2\sqrt{3}} \approx \pm 1.9$	$\pm\sqrt{2\sqrt{2}} \approx \pm 1.7$	$\pm\sqrt{2} \approx \pm 1.4$	0

The graph of $r^2 = 4\cos(2\theta)$ is a lemniscate:

41. Note the table of values:

θ	0	$\dfrac{\pi}{6}$	$\dfrac{\pi}{4}$	$\dfrac{\pi}{3}$	$\dfrac{\pi}{2}$	π
$r = 4 - 3\cos\theta$	1	$\dfrac{3\sqrt{3}}{2} \approx 1.4$	$\dfrac{8 - 3\sqrt{2}}{2} \approx 1.8$	$\dfrac{5}{2}$	4	7

The graph of $r = 4 - 3\cos\theta$ is a limacon with no inner loop:

43. Note the table of values:

θ	0	$\dfrac{\pi}{6}$	$\dfrac{\pi}{4}$	$\dfrac{\pi}{3}$	$\dfrac{\pi}{2}$	π	$\dfrac{3\pi}{2}$
$r = 2 + \sin\theta$	2	$\dfrac{5}{2}$	$\dfrac{4 + \sqrt{2}}{2} \approx 2.7$	$\dfrac{4 + \sqrt{3}}{2} \approx 2.9$	3	2	1

The graph of $r = 2 + \sin\theta$ is a limacon with no inner loop:

45. Note the table of values:

θ	0	$\dfrac{\pi}{6}$	$\dfrac{\pi}{4}$	$\dfrac{\pi}{3}$	$\dfrac{\pi}{2}$	π	$\dfrac{3\pi}{2}$
$r = 2 + 3\cos\theta$	5	$\dfrac{4+3\sqrt{3}}{2} \approx 4.6$	$\dfrac{4+3\sqrt{2}}{2} \approx 4.1$	$\dfrac{7}{2}$	2	-1	2

The graph of $r = 2 + 3\cos\theta$ is a limacon with an inner loop:

47. Sketching the polar graph of $r = 5 - 4\sin\theta$:

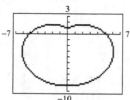

49. Sketching the polar graph of $r = \cos\left(\pi - \dfrac{\pi}{4}\right)$:

51. Sketching the polar graph of $r = 3\sin 4\theta$:

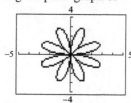

53. Sketching the polar graph of $r = 2\theta,\ 0 \le \theta \le 4\pi$:

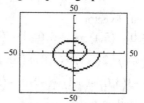

55. The maximum value is: $\theta_{max} = \pi$

57. The maximum value is: $\theta_{max} = 2\pi$

59. Using the sum identity for cosine:

$$r = 2 - 2\cos\left(\theta + \frac{\pi}{2}\right) = 2 - 2\left(\cos\theta\cos\frac{\pi}{2} - \sin\theta\sin\frac{\pi}{2}\right) = 2 - 2\left(\cos\theta \cdot 0 - \sin\theta \cdot 1\right) = 2 + 2\sin\theta$$

61. The graph of r_2 is obtained by rotating the graph of r_1 by $\dfrac{\pi}{3}$ units clockwise.

$r_1 = 2\sin(3\theta)$

$r_2 = 2\sin\left(3\left(\theta + \dfrac{\pi}{3}\right)\right)$

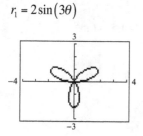

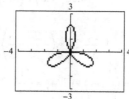

7.5 Vectors

1. Graphing the vector $\langle 1,0 \rangle$ in standard position:

3. Graphing the vector $\langle -5,-3 \rangle$ in standard position:

    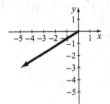

5. Graphing the vector $\left\langle \dfrac{4}{3},-6 \right\rangle$ in standard position:

7. Writing in terms of **i** and **j**: $\mathbf{u} = \langle -4,6 \rangle = -4\mathbf{i} + 6\mathbf{j}$

9. Writing in terms of **i** and **j**: $\mathbf{w} = \langle -2,-1.5 \rangle = -2\mathbf{i} - 1.5\mathbf{j}$

11. Writing in terms of **i** and **j**: $\mathbf{u} = \left\langle \dfrac{1}{3},\dfrac{3}{4} \right\rangle = \dfrac{1}{3}\mathbf{i} + \dfrac{3}{4}\mathbf{j}$

13. Finding the indicated vectors:
    $$\mathbf{u} - \mathbf{v} = \langle 3,0 \rangle - \langle 5,1 \rangle = \langle 3-5,0-1 \rangle = \langle -2,-1 \rangle$$
    $$\mathbf{u} + 2\mathbf{v} = \langle 3,0 \rangle + 2\langle 5,1 \rangle = \langle 3,0 \rangle + \langle 10,2 \rangle = \langle 3+10,0+2 \rangle = \langle 13,2 \rangle$$
    $$-3\mathbf{u} + \mathbf{v} = -3\langle 3,0 \rangle + \langle 5,1 \rangle = \langle -9,0 \rangle + \langle 5,1 \rangle = \langle -9+5,0+1 \rangle = \langle -4,1 \rangle$$

15. Finding the indicated vectors:
    $$\mathbf{u} - \mathbf{v} = \langle -4,5 \rangle - \langle 3,-7 \rangle = \langle -4-3,5-(-7) \rangle = \langle -7,12 \rangle$$
    $$\mathbf{u} + 2\mathbf{v} = \langle -4,5 \rangle + 2\langle 3,-7 \rangle = \langle -4,5 \rangle + \langle 6,-14 \rangle = \langle -4+6,5-14 \rangle = \langle 2,-9 \rangle$$
    $$-3\mathbf{u} + \mathbf{v} = -3\langle -4,5 \rangle + \langle 3,-7 \rangle = \langle 12,-15 \rangle + \langle 3,-7 \rangle = \langle 12+3,-15-7 \rangle = \langle 15,-22 \rangle$$

17. Finding the indicated vectors:
    $$\mathbf{u} - \mathbf{v} = \langle 1.5,2.5 \rangle - \langle 0,1 \rangle = \langle 1.5+0,2.5-1 \rangle = \langle 1.5,1.5 \rangle$$
    $$\mathbf{u} + 2\mathbf{v} = \langle 1.5,2.5 \rangle + 2\langle 0,1 \rangle = \langle 1.5,2.5 \rangle + \langle 0,2 \rangle = \langle 1.5+0,2.5+2 \rangle = \langle 1.5,4.5 \rangle$$
    $$-3\mathbf{u} + \mathbf{v} = -3\langle 1.5,2.5 \rangle + \langle 0,1 \rangle = \langle -4.5,-7.5 \rangle + \langle 0,1 \rangle = \langle -4.5+0,-7.5+1 \rangle = \langle -4.5,-6.5 \rangle$$

19. Finding the indicated vectors:
    $$\mathbf{u} - \mathbf{v} = \left\langle \dfrac{1}{3},\dfrac{2}{5} \right\rangle - \langle 1,2 \rangle = \left\langle \dfrac{1}{3}-1,\dfrac{2}{5}-2 \right\rangle = \left\langle -\dfrac{2}{3},-\dfrac{8}{5} \right\rangle$$
    $$\mathbf{u} + 2\mathbf{v} = \left\langle \dfrac{1}{3},\dfrac{2}{5} \right\rangle + 2\langle 1,2 \rangle = \left\langle \dfrac{1}{3},\dfrac{2}{5} \right\rangle + \langle 2,4 \rangle = \left\langle \dfrac{1}{3}+2,\dfrac{2}{5}+4 \right\rangle = \left\langle \dfrac{7}{3},\dfrac{22}{5} \right\rangle$$
    $$-3\mathbf{u} + \mathbf{v} = -3\left\langle \dfrac{1}{3},\dfrac{2}{5} \right\rangle + \langle 1,2 \rangle = \left\langle -1,-\dfrac{6}{5} \right\rangle + \langle 1,2 \rangle = \left\langle -1+1,-\dfrac{6}{5}+2 \right\rangle = \left\langle 0,\dfrac{4}{5} \right\rangle$$

21. Finding the indicated vectors:
    $$\mathbf{u} - \mathbf{v} = (-2\mathbf{i} + 3\mathbf{j}) - (4\mathbf{i} - \mathbf{j}) = -2\mathbf{i} + 3\mathbf{j} - 4\mathbf{i} + \mathbf{j} = -6\mathbf{i} + 4\mathbf{j}$$
    $$\mathbf{u} + 2\mathbf{v} = -2\mathbf{i} + 3\mathbf{j} + 2(4\mathbf{i} - \mathbf{j}) = -2\mathbf{i} + 3\mathbf{j} + 8\mathbf{i} - 2\mathbf{j} = 6\mathbf{i} + \mathbf{j}$$
    $$-3\mathbf{u} + \mathbf{v} = -3(-2\mathbf{i} + 3\mathbf{j}) + (4\mathbf{i} - \mathbf{j}) = 6\mathbf{i} - 9\mathbf{j} + 4\mathbf{i} - \mathbf{j} = 10\mathbf{i} - 10\mathbf{j}$$

23. Finding the indicated vectors:

$$\mathbf{u} - \mathbf{v} = (-1.1\mathbf{i} + 4\mathbf{j}) - (4\mathbf{i} + 2.4\mathbf{j}) = -1.1\mathbf{i} + 4\mathbf{j} - 4\mathbf{i} - 2.4\mathbf{j} = -5.1\mathbf{i} + 1.6\mathbf{j}$$

$$\mathbf{u} + 2\mathbf{v} = -1.1\mathbf{i} + 4\mathbf{j} + 2(4\mathbf{i} + 2.4\mathbf{j}) = -1.1\mathbf{i} + 4\mathbf{j} + 8\mathbf{i} + 4.8\mathbf{j} = 6.9\mathbf{i} + 8.8\mathbf{j}$$

$$-3\mathbf{u} + \mathbf{v} = -3(-1.1\mathbf{i} + 4\mathbf{j}) + (4\mathbf{i} + 2.4\mathbf{j}) = 3.3\mathbf{i} - 12\mathbf{j} + 4\mathbf{i} + 2.4\mathbf{j} = 7.3\mathbf{i} - 9.6\mathbf{j}$$

25. Finding the magnitude: $\|\mathbf{u}\| = \sqrt{(-1)^2 + 2^2} = \sqrt{1+4} = \sqrt{5}$

Finding the direction angle in Quadrant II:

$$\sin\theta = \frac{2}{\sqrt{5}}$$

$$\theta = 180° - \arcsin\left(\frac{2}{\sqrt{5}}\right) \approx 180° - 63.43° \approx 116.57°$$

27. Finding the magnitude: $\|\mathbf{v}\| = \sqrt{1^2 + (1.5)^2} = \sqrt{1+2.25} = \sqrt{3.25}$

Finding the direction angle in Quadrant I:

$$\cos\theta = \frac{1}{\sqrt{3.25}}$$

$$\theta = \arccos\left(\frac{1}{\sqrt{3.25}}\right) = 56.31°$$

29. Finding the magnitude: $\|\mathbf{v}\| = \sqrt{\left(\frac{4}{3}\right)^2 + \left(\frac{2}{5}\right)^2} = \sqrt{\frac{16}{9} + \frac{4}{25}} = \sqrt{\frac{436}{225}} = \frac{2\sqrt{109}}{15}$

Finding the direction angle in Quadrant I:

$$\cos\theta = \frac{\left(\frac{4}{3}\right)}{\left(\frac{2\sqrt{109}}{15}\right)} = \frac{10}{\sqrt{109}}$$

$$\theta = \arccos\left(\frac{15}{\sqrt{109}}\right) = 16.70°$$

31. Finding the magnitude: $\|\mathbf{v}\| = \sqrt{4^2 + (-2)^2} = \sqrt{16+4} = \sqrt{20} = 2\sqrt{5}$

Finding the direction angle in Quadrant IV:

$$\cos\theta = \frac{4}{2\sqrt{5}} = \frac{2}{\sqrt{5}}$$

$$\theta = 360° - \arccos\left(\frac{2}{\sqrt{5}}\right) \approx 360° - 26.57° \approx 333.43°$$

33. Finding the magnitude: $\|\mathbf{v}\| = \sqrt{1^2 + (2.5)^2} = \sqrt{1+6.25} = \sqrt{7.25}$

Finding the direction angle in Quadrant I:

$$\cos\theta = \frac{1}{\sqrt{7.25}}$$

$$\theta = \arccos\left(\frac{1}{\sqrt{7.25}}\right) = 68.20°$$

35. Finding the magnitude: $\|\mathbf{u}\| = \sqrt{3^2 + 4^2} = \sqrt{9+16} = \sqrt{25} = 5$

The unit vector is: $\mathbf{w} = \dfrac{\mathbf{u}}{\|\mathbf{u}\|} = \dfrac{\langle 3, 4 \rangle}{5} = \left\langle \dfrac{3}{5}, \dfrac{4}{5} \right\rangle$

37. Finding the magnitude: $\|\mathbf{w}\| = \sqrt{1^2 + 1^2} = \sqrt{1+1} = \sqrt{2}$

The unit vector is: $\mathbf{u} = \dfrac{\mathbf{w}}{\|\mathbf{w}\|} = \dfrac{\langle 1,1 \rangle}{\sqrt{2}} = \left\langle \dfrac{1}{\sqrt{2}}, \dfrac{1}{\sqrt{2}} \right\rangle = \left\langle \dfrac{\sqrt{2}}{2}, \dfrac{\sqrt{2}}{2} \right\rangle$

39. Finding the magnitude: $\|\mathbf{v}\| = \sqrt{(-2)^2 + 1^2} = \sqrt{4+1} = \sqrt{5}$

The unit vector is: $\mathbf{w} = \dfrac{\mathbf{v}}{\|\mathbf{v}\|} = \dfrac{\langle -2,1 \rangle}{\sqrt{5}} = \left\langle -\dfrac{2}{\sqrt{5}}, \dfrac{1}{\sqrt{5}} \right\rangle = \left\langle -\dfrac{2\sqrt{5}}{5}, \dfrac{\sqrt{5}}{5} \right\rangle = -\dfrac{2\sqrt{5}}{5}\mathbf{i} + \dfrac{\sqrt{5}}{5}\mathbf{j}$

41. Finding each component:

$u_x = \|\mathbf{u}\|\cos\theta = 19\cos 34° \approx 15.7517$ $\qquad$ $u_y = \|\mathbf{u}\|\sin\theta = 19\sin 34° \approx 10.6247$

The component form is $\mathbf{u} = \langle 15.7517, 10.6247 \rangle$.

43. Finding each component:

$u_x = \|\mathbf{u}\|\cos\theta = 10\cos 190° \approx -9.8481$ $\qquad$ $u_y = \|\mathbf{u}\|\sin\theta = 10\sin 190° \approx -1.7365$

The component form is $\mathbf{u} = \langle -9.8481, -1.7365 \rangle$.

45. Finding each component:

$u_x = \|\mathbf{u}\|\cos\theta = 4.6\cos 180° = -4.6$ $\qquad$ $u_y = \|\mathbf{u}\|\sin\theta = 4.6\sin 180° = 0$

The component form is $\mathbf{u} = \langle -4.6, 0 \rangle$.

47. Note that pointed northwest corresponds to the angle $\theta = 180° - 45° = 135°$. Finding each component:

$u_x = \|\mathbf{u}\|\cos\theta = 22\cos 135° \approx -15.5563$ $\qquad$ $u_y = \|\mathbf{u}\|\sin\theta = 22\sin 135° \approx 15.5563$

The component form is $\mathbf{u} = \langle -15.5563, 15.5563 \rangle$.

49. Note that S30°E corresponds to the angle $\theta = 300°$. Finding each component:

$u_x = \|\mathbf{u}\|\cos\theta = 15\cos 300° = 7.5$ $\qquad$ $u_y = \|\mathbf{u}\|\sin\theta = 15\sin 300° \approx -12.99$

The wind velocity vector is $\mathbf{u} = \langle 7.5, -12.99 \rangle$.

51. **a.** Note that S60°W corresponds to the angle $\theta = 210°$. Finding each component:

$v_x = \|\mathbf{v}\|\cos\theta = 20\cos 210° \approx -17.32$ $\qquad$ $v_y = \|\mathbf{v}\|\sin\theta = 20\sin 210° = -10$

The wind velocity vector is $\mathbf{v} = \langle -17.32, -10 \rangle$.

b. Converting knots to miles per hour: 20 knots = 20(1.15 mph) = 23 mph

Finding each component:

$v_x = \|\mathbf{v}\|\cos\theta = 23\cos 210° \approx -19.92$ $\qquad$ $v_y = \|\mathbf{v}\|\sin\theta = 23\sin 210° = -11.5$

The wind velocity vector is $\mathbf{v} = \langle -19.92, -11.50 \rangle$.

53. **a.** Note that S17°E corresponds to $\theta_1 = 270° + 17° = 287°$, and S38°E corresponds to $\theta_2 = 270° + 38° = 308°$.

Finding the vectors:

$\mathbf{u} = \langle 2.4\cos 287°, 2.4\sin 287° \rangle = \langle 0.7017, -2.2951 \rangle$

$\mathbf{v} = \langle 1.8\cos 308°, 1.8\sin 308° \rangle = \langle 1.1082, -1.4184 \rangle$

The east-west distance is given by the sum of the x-components: $u_x + v_x = 0.7017 + 1.1082 \approx 1.81$ miles

b. The north-south distance is given by the magnitude of the sum of the y-components:

$|u_y + v_y| = |-2.2951 - 1.4184| = |-3.7135| \approx 3.71$ miles

c. Her final location is given by the sum vector $\mathbf{u} + \mathbf{v} = \langle 1.8099, -3.7135 \rangle$. Thus, her distance from the starting

point is: $\|\mathbf{u} + \mathbf{v}\| = \|\langle 1.8099, -3.7135 \rangle\| = \sqrt{(1.8099)^2 + (-3.7135)^2} = \sqrt{17.0658} \approx 4.13$ miles

d. Finding the angle:

$$\cos\theta = \frac{u_x + v_x}{\|\mathbf{u}+\mathbf{v}\|} = \frac{1.8099}{4.1311}$$

$$\theta = \arccos\left(\frac{1.8099}{4.1311}\right) = 64.0163°$$

$90° - 64.0163° = 25.9837°$

She walks in the direction S26°E.

55. If $\mathbf{v}$ is the velocity of the boat, than $\|\mathbf{v}\| = 5$ mph. Using $\theta = 90° - 45° = 45°$, we have the components of the boat velocity:

$$v_x = \|\mathbf{v}\|\cos 45° = \frac{5\sqrt{2}}{2} \approx 3.53553 \qquad v_y = \|\mathbf{v}\|\sin 45° = \frac{5\sqrt{2}}{2} \approx 3.53553$$

Thus, $\mathbf{v} = \left\langle \frac{5\sqrt{2}}{2}, \frac{5\sqrt{2}}{2} \right\rangle = \langle 3.53553, 3.53553 \rangle$.

For the wind, $\|\mathbf{w}\| = 12$ mph and $\theta = 90°$ gives $\mathbf{w} = \langle \|\mathbf{w}\|\cos 90°, \|\mathbf{w}\|\sin 90° \rangle = \langle 0, 12 \rangle$.

The resultant velocity vector is: $\mathbf{u} = \mathbf{v} + \mathbf{w} = \langle 3.53553, 3.53553 \rangle + \langle 0, 12 \rangle = \langle 3.53553, 15.53553 \rangle$

Finding the speed: $\|\mathbf{u}\| = \sqrt{(3.53553)^2 + (15.53553)^2} \approx \sqrt{253.8527} \approx 15.93$ mph

Finding the direction:

$$\theta = \arccos\left(\frac{3.53553}{15.53553}\right) \approx 77.18°$$

$90° - 77.18° = 12.82°$

The resulting direction is N12.82°E.

57. If $\|\mathbf{v}\| = 0$, then $v_x^2 + v_y^2 = 0$. If either v_x or v_y are nonzero, then $v_x^2 + v_y^2 > 0$, which can't happen. Therefore $v_x = v_y = 0$ and hence $\mathbf{v} = \langle 0, 0 \rangle$.

59. Let $\mathbf{u} = \langle a, b \rangle$. Setting the two expressions equal:

$$\|k\mathbf{u}\| = k\|\mathbf{u}\|$$

$$\sqrt{(ka)^2 + (kb)^2} = k\sqrt{a^2 + b^2}$$

$$\sqrt{k^2 a^2 + k^2 b^2} = k\sqrt{a^2 + b^2}$$

$$\sqrt{k^2(a^2 + b^2)} = k\sqrt{a^2 + b^2}$$

$$|k|\sqrt{a^2 + b^2} = k\sqrt{a^2 + b^2}$$

$$|k| = k$$

This will occur whenever $k \geq 0$.

7.6 Dot Product of Vectors

1.   Finding the dot product: $\mathbf{v} \cdot \mathbf{w} = (-3)(2) + (4)(-3) = -6 - 12 = -18$

3.   Finding the dot product: $\mathbf{v} \cdot \mathbf{w} = (5)(-2) + (-8)\left(\dfrac{1}{2}\right) = -10 - 4 = -14$

5.   Finding the dot product: $\mathbf{v} \cdot \mathbf{w} = (3)(1) + (-1)(3) = 3 - 3 = 0$

7.   Finding the dot product: $\mathbf{v} \cdot \mathbf{w} = \left(-\dfrac{5}{3}\right)\left(\dfrac{2}{5}\right) + \left(\dfrac{4}{5}\right)\left(\dfrac{1}{3}\right) = -\dfrac{2}{3} + \dfrac{4}{15} = -\dfrac{6}{15} = -\dfrac{2}{5}$

9.   Finding the values:

$$\mathbf{v} \cdot \mathbf{w} = (1)(-2) + (3)(0) = -2$$

$$\|\mathbf{v}\| = \sqrt{1^2 + 3^2} = \sqrt{10}$$

$$\|\mathbf{w}\| = \sqrt{(-2)^2 + 0^2} = 2$$

Using the dot product theorem:

$$\mathbf{v} \cdot \mathbf{w} = \|\mathbf{v}\|\|\mathbf{w}\|\cos\theta$$

$$-2 = \sqrt{10} \cdot 2\cos\theta$$

$$\cos\theta = \dfrac{-2}{2\sqrt{10}} = \dfrac{-1}{\sqrt{10}} \approx -0.3162$$

$$\theta \approx 108.4°$$

11.   Finding the angle:

$$\mathbf{v} \cdot \mathbf{w} = (-2)(0) + (0)(3) = 0$$

$$\theta = \cos^{-1}(0) = 90°$$

13.   Finding the values:

$$\mathbf{v} \cdot \mathbf{w} = (4)(2) + (3)(-1) = 5$$

$$\|\mathbf{v}\| = \sqrt{4^2 + 3^2} = 5$$

$$\|\mathbf{w}\| = \sqrt{2^2 + (-1)^2} = \sqrt{5}$$

Using the dot product theorem:

$$\mathbf{v} \cdot \mathbf{w} = \|\mathbf{v}\|\|\mathbf{w}\|\cos\theta$$

$$5 = 5 \cdot \sqrt{5}\cos\theta$$

$$\cos\theta = \dfrac{5}{5\sqrt{5}} = \dfrac{1}{\sqrt{5}} \approx 0.4472$$

$$\theta \approx 63.4°$$

15.   Finding the values:

$$\mathbf{v} \cdot \mathbf{w} = \left(\dfrac{1}{3}\right)(6) + (1)(-1) = 1$$

$$\|\mathbf{v}\| = \sqrt{\left(\dfrac{1}{3}\right)^2 + 1^2} = \sqrt{\dfrac{10}{9}} = \dfrac{\sqrt{10}}{3}$$

$$\|\mathbf{w}\| = \sqrt{6^2 + (-1)^2} = \sqrt{37}$$

Using the dot product theorem:

$$\mathbf{v} \cdot \mathbf{w} = \|\mathbf{v}\|\|\mathbf{w}\|\cos\theta$$

$$1 = \dfrac{\sqrt{10}}{3} \cdot \sqrt{37}\cos\theta$$

$$\cos\theta = \dfrac{3}{\sqrt{10}\sqrt{37}} = \dfrac{3}{\sqrt{370}} \approx 0.1560$$

$$\theta \approx 81.0°$$

17.   Finding the values:

$$\mathbf{v} \cdot \mathbf{w} = (2)(2) + (-4)(6) = -20$$

$$\|\mathbf{w}\|^2 = 2^2 + 6^2 = 40$$

$$\text{proj}_w\mathbf{v} = \left(\dfrac{\mathbf{v} \cdot \mathbf{w}}{\|\mathbf{w}\|^2}\right)\mathbf{w} = \dfrac{-20}{40}\langle 2, 6 \rangle = \langle -1, -3 \rangle$$

Finding $\mathbf{v}_1$ and $\mathbf{v}_2$:

$$\mathbf{v}_1 = \text{proj}_w\mathbf{v} = \langle -1, -3 \rangle \qquad \mathbf{v}_2 = \mathbf{v} - \mathbf{v}_1 = \langle 2, -4 \rangle - \langle -1, -3 \rangle = \langle 3, -1 \rangle$$

19. Finding the values:

$$\mathbf{v} \cdot \mathbf{w} = (10)(2) + (5)(-1) = 15$$

$$\|\mathbf{w}\|^2 = 2^2 + (-1)^2 = 5$$

$$\text{proj}_w \mathbf{v} = \left(\frac{\mathbf{v} \cdot \mathbf{w}}{\|\mathbf{w}\|^2}\right)\mathbf{w} = \frac{15}{5}\langle 2, -1 \rangle = \langle 6, -3 \rangle$$

Finding $\mathbf{v}_1$ and $\mathbf{v}_2$:

$$\mathbf{v}_1 = \text{proj}_w \mathbf{v} = \langle 6, -3 \rangle \qquad \mathbf{v}_2 = \mathbf{v} - \mathbf{v}_1 = \langle 10, 5 \rangle - \langle 6, -3 \rangle = \langle 4, 8 \rangle$$

21. Finding the values:

$$\mathbf{v} \cdot \mathbf{w} = (6)(3) + (12)(1) = 30$$

$$\|\mathbf{w}\|^2 = 3^2 + 1^2 = 10$$

$$\text{proj}_w \mathbf{v} = \left(\frac{\mathbf{v} \cdot \mathbf{w}}{\|\mathbf{w}\|^2}\right)\mathbf{w} = \frac{30}{10}\langle 3, 1 \rangle = \langle 9, 3 \rangle$$

Finding $\mathbf{v}_1$ and $\mathbf{v}_2$:

$$\mathbf{v}_1 = \text{proj}_w \mathbf{v} = \langle 9, 3 \rangle \qquad \mathbf{v}_2 = \mathbf{v} - \mathbf{v}_1 = \langle 6, 12 \rangle - \langle 9, 3 \rangle = \langle -3, 9 \rangle$$

23. Finding the values:

$$\mathbf{v} \cdot \mathbf{w} = (4)(-3) + (5)(4) = 8$$

$$\|\mathbf{w}\|^2 = (-3)^2 + 4^2 = 25$$

$$\text{proj}_w \mathbf{v} = \left(\frac{\mathbf{v} \cdot \mathbf{w}}{\|\mathbf{w}\|^2}\right)\mathbf{w} = \frac{8}{25}\langle -3, 4 \rangle = \left\langle -\frac{24}{25}, \frac{32}{25} \right\rangle$$

Finding $\mathbf{v}_1$ and $\mathbf{v}_2$:

$$\mathbf{v}_1 = \text{proj}_w \mathbf{v} = \left\langle -\frac{24}{25}, \frac{32}{25} \right\rangle \qquad \mathbf{v}_2 = \mathbf{v} - \mathbf{v}_1 = \langle 4, 5 \rangle - \left\langle -\frac{24}{25}, \frac{32}{25} \right\rangle = \left\langle \frac{124}{25}, \frac{93}{25} \right\rangle$$

25. Finding the dot product: $\mathbf{v} \cdot \mathbf{w} = (1)(-4) + (2)(1) = -2 \neq 0$. No, the vectors are not orthogonal.

27. Finding the dot product: $\mathbf{v} \cdot \mathbf{w} = (2)(-6) + (-3)(4) = -24 \neq 0$. No, the vectors are not orthogonal.

29. Finding the dot product: $\mathbf{v} \cdot \mathbf{w} = \left(\frac{1}{3}\right)(6) + (2)\left(\frac{5}{2}\right) = 7 \neq 0$. No, the vectors are not orthogonal.

31. Finding the dot product: $\mathbf{v} \cdot \mathbf{w} = (1)(0) + (0)(3) = 0$. Yes, the vectors are orthogonal.

33. Performing the operations: $2\mathbf{u} + 3\mathbf{w} = 2\langle 3, 2 \rangle + 3\langle -2, -1 \rangle = \langle 6, 4 \rangle + \langle -6, -3 \rangle = \langle 0, 1 \rangle$

35. Performing the operations: $-\mathbf{u} \cdot (\mathbf{v} + \mathbf{w}) = -\langle 3, 2 \rangle \cdot (\langle -1, 4 \rangle + \langle -2, -1 \rangle) = \langle -3, -2 \rangle \cdot \langle -3, 3 \rangle = (-3)(-3) + (-2)(3) = 3$

37. Performing the operations: $3\mathbf{u} + \mathbf{v} - 2\mathbf{w} = 3\langle 3, 2 \rangle + \langle -1, 4 \rangle - 2\langle -2, -1 \rangle = \langle 9, 6 \rangle + \langle -1, 4 \rangle + \langle 4, 2 \rangle = \langle 12, 12 \rangle$

39. Performing the operations:

$$\mathbf{u} - \mathbf{v} = \langle 3, 2 \rangle - \langle -1, 4 \rangle = \langle 4, -2 \rangle$$

$$(\mathbf{u} - \mathbf{v}) \cdot \mathbf{w} = \langle 4, -2 \rangle \cdot \langle -2, -1 \rangle = -8 + 2 = -6$$

$$\|\mathbf{w}\|^2 = (-2)^2 + (-1)^2 = 5$$

$$\text{proj}_w (\mathbf{u} - \mathbf{v}) = \left(\frac{(\mathbf{u} - \mathbf{v}) \cdot \mathbf{w}}{\|\mathbf{w}\|^2}\right)\mathbf{w} = \frac{-6}{5}\langle -2, -1 \rangle = \left\langle \frac{12}{5}, \frac{6}{5} \right\rangle$$

41. Finding the work: $W = \|\mathbf{F}\| d \cos\theta = 20(100)\cos 45° \approx 1{,}414$ ft-lbs

43. Setting the dot product equal to 0:
$$\langle 10, 3 \rangle \cdot \langle x, 15 \rangle = 0$$
$$(10)(x) + (3)(15) = 0$$
$$10x + 45 = 0$$
$$10x = -45$$
$$x = -4.5$$

45. Let $\mathbf{v} = \langle 1, 2 \rangle$ and $\mathbf{w} = \langle 5, 3 \rangle$ be the position vectors for the *Swan* and *Dolphin*, respectively. Finding the values:
$$\mathbf{v} \cdot \mathbf{w} = 5 + 6 = 11$$
$$\|\mathbf{w}\|^2 = 5^2 + 3^2 = 34$$
$$\text{proj}_w \mathbf{v} = \left(\frac{\mathbf{v} \cdot \mathbf{w}}{\|\mathbf{w}\|^2} \right) \mathbf{w} = \frac{11}{34} \langle 5, 3 \rangle = \left\langle \frac{55}{34}, \frac{33}{34} \right\rangle$$
$$\mathbf{v}_2 = \mathbf{v} - \mathbf{v}_1 = \langle 1, 2 \rangle - \left\langle \frac{55}{34}, \frac{33}{34} \right\rangle = \left\langle -\frac{21}{34}, \frac{35}{34} \right\rangle$$
$$\|\mathbf{v}_2\| = \left\| \left\langle -\frac{21}{34}, \frac{35}{34} \right\rangle \right\| = \sqrt{\left(-\frac{21}{34} \right)^2 + \left(\frac{35}{34} \right)^2} \approx 1.20 \text{ miles}$$

Swan must travel approximately 1.20 miles.

47. The $10°$ incline reduces the angle of the force to $20°$.
Finding the work: $W = \|\mathbf{F}\| d \cos \theta = 20(100) \cos 20° \approx 1{,}879$ ft-lbs

49. Finding the horsepower: $P = \dfrac{1}{550}(F \cdot v) = \dfrac{1}{550}(\|\mathbf{F}\| \cos 30° \cdot 10) = \dfrac{1}{550}(1500 \cos 30° \cdot 10) \approx 23.6$ horsepower

51. Setting the dot product equal to 0:
$$\langle 4, a \rangle \cdot \langle -3, 2 \rangle = 0$$
$$(4)(-3) + (a)(2) = 0$$
$$-12 + 2a = 0$$
$$2a = 12$$
$$a = 6$$

53. Starting with the left side:
$$\mathbf{u} \cdot (\mathbf{v} + \mathbf{w}) = \langle u_x, u_y \rangle \cdot \langle v_x + w_x, v_y + w_y \rangle$$
$$= u_x(v_x + w_x) + u_y(v_y + w_y)$$
$$= u_x v_x + u_x w_x + u_y v_y + u_y w_y$$
$$= (u_x v_x + u_y v_y) + (u_x w_x + u_y w_y)$$
$$= \mathbf{u} \cdot \mathbf{v} + \mathbf{u} \cdot \mathbf{w}$$

55. Starting with the left side: $\mathbf{v} \cdot \mathbf{v} = \langle v_x, v_y \rangle \cdot \langle v_x, v_y \rangle = v_x \cdot v_x + v_y \cdot v_y = v_x^2 + v_y^2 = \|\mathbf{v}\|^2$

7.7 Trigonometric Form of a Complex Number

1. Evaluating the expression: $i^3 = i^2 \cdot i = -1 \cdot i = -i$

3. Evaluating the expression: $-i^4 = -(1) = -1$

5. Evaluating the expression: $(3+2i) - (4+i) = 3 + 2i - 4 - i = -1 + i$

7. Finding r: $r = \sqrt{2^2 + (-1)^2} = \sqrt{4+1} = \sqrt{5}$

9. Finding r: $r = \sqrt{1^2 + (-2)^2} = \sqrt{1+4} = \sqrt{5}$

11. Finding r: $r = \sqrt{\left(\frac{1}{2}\right)^2 + \left(\frac{3}{4}\right)^2} = \sqrt{\frac{1}{4} + \frac{9}{16}} = \sqrt{\frac{13}{16}} = \frac{\sqrt{13}}{4}$

13. Finding r: $r = \sqrt{0^2 + 2^2} = 2$

    Since $\theta = \frac{\pi}{2}$, the trigonometric form is: $2i = 2\left(\cos\frac{\pi}{2} + i\sin\frac{\pi}{2}\right)$

15. Finding r: $r = \sqrt{(-4)^2 + 0^2} = 4$

    Since $\theta = \pi$, the trigonometric form is: $-4 = 4\left(\cos\pi + i\sin\pi\right)$

17. Finding r: $r = \sqrt{1^2 + \left(\sqrt{3}\right)^2} = \sqrt{1+3} = \sqrt{4} = 2$

    The number $1 - \sqrt{3}i$ corresponds to the point $\left(1, -\sqrt{3}\right)$, a point in Quadrant IV. Therefore:

    $$\cos\theta = \frac{1}{2}$$

    $$\theta = 2\pi - \frac{\pi}{3} = \frac{5\pi}{3}$$

    The trigonometric form is: $1 - \sqrt{3}i = 2\left(\cos\frac{5\pi}{3} + i\sin\frac{5\pi}{3}\right)$

19. Finding r: $r = \sqrt{4^2 + (-4)^2} = \sqrt{32} = 4\sqrt{2}$

    The number $4 - 4i$ corresponds to the point $\left(4, -4\right)$, a point in Quadrant IV. Therefore:

    $$\cos\theta = \frac{4}{4\sqrt{2}} = \frac{1}{\sqrt{2}} = \frac{\sqrt{2}}{2}$$

    $$\theta = 2\pi - \frac{\pi}{4} = \frac{7\pi}{4}$$

    The trigonometric form is: $4 - 4i = 4\sqrt{2}\left(\cos\frac{7\pi}{4} + i\sin\frac{7\pi}{4}\right)$

21. Finding r: $r = \sqrt{\left(2\sqrt{3}\right)^2 + (-2)^2} = \sqrt{12+4} = 4$

    The number $2\sqrt{3} - 2i$ corresponds to the point $\left(2\sqrt{3}, -2\right)$, a point in Quadrant IV. Therefore:

    $$\cos\theta = \frac{2\sqrt{3}}{4} = \frac{\sqrt{3}}{2}$$

    $$\theta = 2\pi - \frac{\pi}{6} = \frac{11\pi}{6}$$

    The trigonometric form is: $2\sqrt{3} - 2i = 4\left(\cos\frac{11\pi}{6} + i\sin\frac{11\pi}{6}\right)$

23. Computing in trigonometric form:

$$2\left(\cos\frac{\pi}{4}+i\sin\frac{\pi}{4}\right)\cdot 4\left(\cos\frac{\pi}{3}+i\sin\frac{\pi}{3}\right)=(2)(4)\left[\cos\left(\frac{\pi}{4}+\frac{\pi}{3}\right)+i\sin\left(\frac{\pi}{4}+\frac{\pi}{3}\right)\right]=8\left(\cos\frac{7\pi}{12}+i\sin\frac{7\pi}{12}\right)$$

25. Computing in trigonometric form:

$$\frac{1}{2}\left(\cos\frac{5\pi}{4}+i\sin\frac{5\pi}{4}\right)\cdot 3\left(\cos\frac{4\pi}{3}+i\sin\frac{4\pi}{3}\right)=\left(\frac{1}{2}\right)(3)\left[\cos\left(\frac{5\pi}{4}+\frac{4\pi}{3}\right)+i\sin\left(\frac{5\pi}{4}+\frac{4\pi}{3}\right)\right]$$

$$=\frac{3}{2}\left(\cos\frac{31\pi}{12}+i\sin\frac{31\pi}{12}\right)$$

$$=\frac{3}{2}\left(\cos\frac{7\pi}{12}+i\sin\frac{7\pi}{12}\right)$$

27. Computing in trigonometric form:

$$\frac{5\left(\cos\frac{\pi}{4}+i\sin\frac{\pi}{4}\right)}{2\left(\cos\frac{\pi}{6}+i\sin\frac{\pi}{6}\right)}=\frac{5}{2}\left[\cos\left(\frac{\pi}{4}-\frac{\pi}{6}\right)+i\sin\left(\frac{\pi}{4}-\frac{\pi}{6}\right)\right]=\frac{5}{2}\left(\cos\frac{\pi}{12}+i\sin\frac{\pi}{12}\right)$$

29. Finding r: $r=\sqrt{1^2+1^2}=\sqrt{2}$

The number $1+i$ corresponds to the point $(1,1)$, a point in Quadrant I. Therefore:

$$\cos\theta=\frac{1}{\sqrt{2}}$$

$$\theta=\frac{\pi}{4}$$

The trigonometric form is: $1+i=\sqrt{2}\left(\cos\frac{\pi}{4}+i\sin\frac{\pi}{4}\right)$

Using De Moivre's Theorem:

$$(1+i)^4=\left[\sqrt{2}\left(\cos\frac{\pi}{4}+i\sin\frac{\pi}{4}\right)\right]^4=\left(\sqrt{2}\right)^4\left[\cos\left(4\cdot\frac{\pi}{4}\right)+i\sin\left(4\cdot\frac{\pi}{4}\right)\right]=4\left(\cos\pi+i\sin\pi\right)=4\left(-1+i\cdot 0\right)=-4$$

31. Finding r: $r=\sqrt{\left(\sqrt{3}\right)^2+1^2}=\sqrt{3+1}=2$

The number $\sqrt{3}+i$ corresponds to the point $\left(\sqrt{3},1\right)$, a point in Quadrant I. Therefore:

$$\cos\theta=\frac{\sqrt{3}}{2}$$

$$\theta=\frac{\pi}{6}$$

The trigonometric form is: $\sqrt{3}+i=2\left(\cos\frac{\pi}{6}+i\sin\frac{\pi}{6}\right)$

Using De Moivre's Theorem:

$$\left(\sqrt{3}+i\right)^3=\left[2\left(\cos\frac{\pi}{6}+i\sin\frac{\pi}{6}\right)\right]^3$$

$$=(2)^3\left[\cos\left(3\cdot\frac{\pi}{6}\right)+i\sin\left(3\cdot\frac{\pi}{6}\right)\right]$$

$$=8\left(\cos\frac{\pi}{2}+i\sin\frac{\pi}{2}\right)$$

$$=8\left(0+i\cdot 1\right)$$

$$=8i$$

33. Finding r: $r = \sqrt{(-3)^2 + \left(-3\sqrt{3}\right)^2} = \sqrt{9 + 27} = 6$

The number $-3 - 3i\sqrt{3}$ corresponds to the point $\left(-3, -\sqrt{3}\right)$, a point in Quadrant III. Therefore:

$$\cos\theta = \frac{-3}{6} = -\frac{1}{2}$$

$$\theta = \pi + \frac{\pi}{3} = \frac{4\pi}{3}$$

The trigonometric form is: $-3 - 3i\sqrt{3} = 6\left(\cos\frac{4\pi}{3} + i\sin\frac{4\pi}{3}\right)$

Using De Moivre's Theorem:

$$\left(-3 - 3i\sqrt{3}\right)^3 = \left[6\left(\cos\frac{\pi}{6} + i\sin\frac{\pi}{6}\right)\right]^3$$

$$= (6)^3\left[\cos\left(3 \cdot \frac{4\pi}{3}\right) + i\sin\left(3 \cdot \frac{4\pi}{3}\right)\right]$$

$$= 216(\cos 4\pi + i\sin 4\pi)$$

$$= 216(1 + i \cdot 0)$$

$$= 216$$

35. Finding r: $r = \sqrt{0^2 + 1^2} = \sqrt{1} = 1$

The number i corresponds to the point $(0,1)$, so $\theta = \frac{\pi}{2}$.

The trigonometric form is: $i = 1\left(\cos\frac{\pi}{2} + i\sin\frac{\pi}{2}\right) = \cos\frac{\pi}{2} + i\sin\frac{\pi}{2}$

The square roots of i are: $\sqrt{1}\left[\cos\left(\dfrac{\frac{\pi}{2} + 2k\pi}{2}\right) + i\sin\left(\dfrac{\frac{\pi}{2} + 2k\pi}{2}\right)\right]$ (for $k = 0, 1$)

For $k = 0$: $\cos\frac{\pi}{4} + i\sin\frac{\pi}{4} = \frac{\sqrt{2}}{2} + \frac{\sqrt{2}}{2}i \approx 0.707 + 0.707i$

For $k = 1$: $\cos\left(\dfrac{\frac{\pi}{2} + 2\pi}{2}\right) + i\sin\left(\dfrac{\frac{\pi}{2} + 2\pi}{2}\right) = \cos\frac{5\pi}{4} + i\sin\frac{5\pi}{4} = -\frac{\sqrt{2}}{2} - \frac{\sqrt{2}}{2}i \approx -0.707 - 0.707i$

37. Finding r: $r = \sqrt{1^2 + \left(\sqrt{3}\right)^2} = \sqrt{4} = 2$

The number $1 + i\sqrt{3}$ corresponds to the point $\left(1, \sqrt{3}\right)$ in Quadrant I, so:

$$\cos\theta = \frac{1}{2}$$

$$\theta = \frac{\pi}{3}$$

The trigonometric form is: $1 + \sqrt{3}i = 2\left(\cos\frac{\pi}{3} + i\sin\frac{\pi}{3}\right)$

The square roots of $1 + i\sqrt{3}$ are: $\sqrt{2}\left[\cos\left(\dfrac{\frac{\pi}{3} + 2k\pi}{2}\right) + i\sin\left(\dfrac{\frac{\pi}{3} + 2k\pi}{2}\right)\right]$ (for $k = 0, 1$)

For $k = 0$: $\sqrt{2}\left(\cos\dfrac{\pi}{6} + i\sin\dfrac{\pi}{6}\right) = \sqrt{2}\left(\dfrac{\sqrt{3}}{2} + \dfrac{1}{2}i\right) = \dfrac{\sqrt{6}}{2} + \dfrac{\sqrt{2}}{2}i \approx 1.225 + 0.707i$

For $k = 1$:

$$\sqrt{2}\left[\cos\left(\dfrac{\dfrac{\pi}{3} + 2\pi}{2}\right) + i\sin\left(\dfrac{\dfrac{\pi}{3} + 2\pi}{2}\right)\right] = \sqrt{2}\left(\cos\dfrac{7\pi}{6} + i\sin\dfrac{7\pi}{6}\right) = \sqrt{2}\left(-\dfrac{\sqrt{3}}{2} - \dfrac{1}{2}i\right) = -\dfrac{\sqrt{6}}{2} - \dfrac{\sqrt{2}}{2}i \approx -1.225 - 0.707i$$

39. Finding r: $r = \sqrt{(-1)^2 + 0^2} = 1$

The number -1 corresponds to the point $(-1, 0)$, so $\theta = \pi$.

The trigonometric form is: $-1 = 1(\cos\pi + i\sin\pi)$

Since $\sqrt[5]{1} = 1$, the fifth roots of -1 are: $\cos\left(\dfrac{\pi + 2k\pi}{5}\right) + i\sin\left(\dfrac{\pi + 2k\pi}{5}\right)$, $k = 0, 1, 2, 3, 4$

For $k = 0$: $\cos\dfrac{\pi}{5} + i\sin\dfrac{\pi}{5} \approx 0.809 + 0.588i$

For $k = 1$: $\cos\dfrac{3\pi}{5} + i\sin\dfrac{3\pi}{5} \approx -0.309 + 0.951i$

For $k = 2$: $\cos\dfrac{5\pi}{5} + i\sin\dfrac{5\pi}{5} = \cos\pi + i\sin\pi = -1$

For $k = 3$: $\cos\dfrac{7\pi}{5} + i\sin\dfrac{7\pi}{5} \approx -0.309 - 0.951i$

For $k = 4$: $\cos\dfrac{9\pi}{5} + i\sin\dfrac{9\pi}{5} \approx 0.809 - 0.588i$

41. Finding r: $r = \sqrt{(-16)^2 + 0^2} = 16$

The number -16 corresponds to the point $(-16, 0)$, so $\theta = \pi$.

The trigonometric form is: $-16 = 16(\cos\pi + i\sin\pi)$

Since $\sqrt[4]{16} = 2$, the fourth roots of -16 are: $2\left[\cos\left(\dfrac{\pi + 2k\pi}{4}\right) + i\sin\left(\dfrac{\pi + 2k\pi}{4}\right)\right]$, $k = 0, 1, 2, 3$

For $k = 0$: $2\left(\cos\dfrac{\pi}{4} + i\sin\dfrac{\pi}{4}\right) \approx \sqrt{2} + i\sqrt{2} \approx 1.414 + 1.414i$

For $k = 1$: $2\left(\cos\dfrac{3\pi}{4} + i\sin\dfrac{3\pi}{4}\right) = -\sqrt{2} + i\sqrt{2} \approx -1.414 + 1.414i$

For $k = 2$: $2\left(\cos\dfrac{5\pi}{4} + i\sin\dfrac{5\pi}{4}\right) = -\sqrt{2} - i\sqrt{2} \approx -1.414 - 1.414i$

For $k = 3$: $2\left(\cos\dfrac{7\pi}{4} + i\sin\dfrac{7\pi}{4}\right) = \sqrt{2} - i\sqrt{2} \approx 1.414 - 1.414i$

43. Finding r: $r = \sqrt{0^2 + (-8)^2} = 8$

The number $-8i$ corresponds to the point $(0,-8)$, so $\theta = \dfrac{3\pi}{2}$.

The trigonometric form is: $-8i = 8\left(\cos\dfrac{3\pi}{2} + i\sin\dfrac{3\pi}{2}\right)$

The fourth roots of $-8i$ are:

$$\sqrt[4]{8}\left[\cos\left(\dfrac{\dfrac{3\pi}{2}+2k\pi}{4}\right) + i\sin\left(\dfrac{\dfrac{3\pi}{2}+2k\pi}{4}\right)\right] = \sqrt[4]{8}\left[\cos\left(\dfrac{3\pi+4k\pi}{8}\right) + i\sin\left(\dfrac{3\pi+4k\pi}{8}\right)\right], k = 0,1,2,3$$

For $k = 0$: $\sqrt[4]{8}\left(\cos\dfrac{3\pi}{8} + i\sin\dfrac{3\pi}{8}\right) \approx 0.644 + 1.554i$

For $k = 1$: $\sqrt[4]{8}\left(\cos\dfrac{7\pi}{8} + i\sin\dfrac{7\pi}{8}\right) \approx -1.554 + 0.644i$

For $k = 2$: $\sqrt[4]{8}\left(\cos\dfrac{11\pi}{8} + i\sin\dfrac{11\pi}{8}\right) \approx -0.644 - 1.554i$

For $k = 3$: $\sqrt[4]{8}\left(\cos\dfrac{15\pi}{8} + i\sin\dfrac{15\pi}{8}\right) \approx 1.554 - 0.644i$

45. Solving the equation:
$$z^3 + 1 = 0$$
$$z^3 = -1$$
$$z = \sqrt[3]{-1} \text{ so we need the cube roots of } -1$$

Finding r: $r = \sqrt{(-1)^2 + 0^2} = 1$

The number -1 corresponds to the point $(-1,0)$, so $\theta = \pi$.

The trigonometric form is: $-1 = 1(\cos\pi + i\sin\pi)$

Since $\sqrt[3]{1} = 1$, the cube roots of -1 are: $\cos\left(\dfrac{\pi + 2k\pi}{3}\right) + i\sin\left(\dfrac{\pi + 2k\pi}{3}\right), k = 0,1,2$

For $k = 0$: $\cos\dfrac{\pi}{3} + i\sin\dfrac{\pi}{3} = \dfrac{1}{2} + \dfrac{\sqrt{3}}{2}i \approx 0.5 + 0.866i$

For $k = 1$: $\cos\pi + i\sin\pi = -1$

For $k = 2$: $\cos\dfrac{5\pi}{3} + i\sin\dfrac{5\pi}{3} = \dfrac{1}{2} - \dfrac{\sqrt{3}}{2}i \approx 0.5 - 0.866i$

47. Solving the equation:
$$iz^3 = 1$$
$$z^3 = \dfrac{1}{i}$$
$$z^3 = \dfrac{1}{i} \cdot \dfrac{i}{i} = \dfrac{i}{i^2} = -i$$
$$z = \sqrt[3]{-i} \text{ so we need the cube roots of } -i$$

Finding r: $r = \sqrt{0^2 + (-1)^2} = 1$

The number $-i$ corresponds to the point $(0,-1)$, so $\theta = \dfrac{3\pi}{2}$.

The trigonometric form is: $-i = 1\left(\cos\dfrac{3\pi}{2} + i\sin\dfrac{3\pi}{2}\right)$

Since $\sqrt[3]{1} = 1$, the cube roots of $-i$ are:

$$\cos\left(\dfrac{\dfrac{3\pi}{2}+2k\pi}{3}\right) + i\sin\left(\dfrac{\dfrac{3\pi}{2}+2k\pi}{3}\right) = \cos\left(\dfrac{3\pi+4k\pi}{6}\right) + i\sin\left(\dfrac{3\pi+4k\pi}{6}\right),\ k = 0, 1, 2$$

For $k = 0$: $\cos\dfrac{\pi}{2} + i\sin\dfrac{\pi}{2} \approx i$

For $k = 1$: $\cos\dfrac{7\pi}{6} + i\sin\dfrac{7\pi}{6} = -\dfrac{\sqrt{3}}{2} - \dfrac{1}{2}i \approx -0.866 - 0.5i$

For $k = 2$: $\cos\dfrac{11\pi}{6} + i\sin\dfrac{11\pi}{6} = \dfrac{\sqrt{3}}{2} - \dfrac{1}{2} \approx 0.866 - 0.5i$

49. Let $z = r(\cos\theta + i\sin\theta)$. Using De Moivre's Theorem:

$$\left(\sqrt[n]{r}\left[\cos\left(\dfrac{\theta+2k\pi}{n}\right) + i\sin\left(\dfrac{\theta+2k\pi}{n}\right)\right]\right)^n = r\left[\cos(\theta+2k\pi) + i\sin(\theta+2k\pi)\right] = r(\cos\theta + i\sin\theta) = z$$

51. There is one solution.

Chapter 7 Review Exercises

1. Finding angle B: $B = 180° - (68° + 40°) = 72°$

Using the law of sines:

$$\dfrac{b}{\sin 72°} = \dfrac{25}{\sin 68°}$$
$$b = \dfrac{25\sin 72°}{\sin 68°} \approx 25.6437$$

$$\dfrac{c}{\sin 40°} = \dfrac{25}{\sin 68°}$$
$$c = \dfrac{25\sin 40°}{\sin 68°} \approx 17.3317$$

2. Finding angle A: $A = 180° - (55.7° + 67°) = 57.3°$

Using the law of sines:

$$\dfrac{a}{\sin 57.3°} = \dfrac{43}{\sin 55.7°}$$
$$a = \dfrac{43\sin 57.3°}{\sin 55.7°} \approx 43.8022$$

$$\dfrac{c}{\sin 67°} = \dfrac{43}{\sin 55.7°}$$
$$c = \dfrac{43\sin 67°}{\sin 55.7°} \approx 47.9140$$

3. Finding angle B: $B = 180° - (52.1° + 73°) = 54.9°$

Using the law of sines:

$$\dfrac{b}{\sin 54.9°} = \dfrac{15}{\sin 73°}$$
$$b = \dfrac{15\sin 54.9°}{\sin 73°} \approx 12.8330$$

$$\dfrac{c}{\sin 52.1°} = \dfrac{15}{\sin 73°}$$
$$c = \dfrac{15\sin 52.1°}{\sin 73°} \approx 12.3771$$

4. Finding angle C: $C = 180° - (78.4° + 61°) = 40.6°$

Using the law of sines:

$$\dfrac{a}{\sin 78.4°} = \dfrac{19}{\sin 61°}$$
$$a = \dfrac{19\sin 78.4°}{\sin 61°} \approx 21.2800$$

$$\dfrac{c}{\sin 40.6°} = \dfrac{19}{\sin 61°}$$
$$c = \dfrac{19\sin 40.6°}{\sin 61°} \approx 14.1372$$

5. Using the law of sines:

$$\frac{\sin B}{8} = \frac{\sin 65°}{10}$$

$$\sin B = \frac{8 \sin 65°}{10} \approx 0.7250$$

$$B = \arcsin\left(\frac{8 \sin 65°}{10}\right) \approx 46.4727° \quad (B \neq 133.5273°)$$

Finding angle C: $C = 180° - 65° - 46.4727° = 68.5273°$
Using the law of sines:

$$\frac{c}{\sin 68.5273°} = \frac{10}{\sin 65°}$$

$$c = \frac{10 \sin 68.5273°}{\sin 65°} \approx 10.2679$$

6. Using the law of sines:

$$\frac{\sin B}{12} = \frac{\sin 125°}{15}$$

$$\sin B = \frac{12 \sin 125°}{15} \approx 0.6553$$

$$B = \arcsin\left(\frac{12 \sin 125°}{15}\right) \approx 40.9440° \quad (B \neq 139.0560°)$$

Finding angle C: $C = 180° - 125° - 40.9440° = 14.0560°$
Using the law of sines:

$$\frac{c}{\sin 14.0560°} = \frac{15}{\sin 125°}$$

$$c = \frac{15 \sin 14.0560°}{\sin 125°} \approx 4.4473$$

7. Using the law of sines:

$$\frac{\sin B}{15} = \frac{\sin 35°}{13}$$

$$\sin B = \frac{15 \sin 35°}{13} \approx 0.6618$$

$$B = \arcsin\left(\frac{15 \sin 35°}{13}\right) \approx 41.4387° \text{ or } 138.5613°$$

Finding angle C: $C = 180° - 35° - 41.4387° = 103.5613°$
Using the law of sines:

$$\frac{c}{\sin 103.5613°} = \frac{13}{\sin 35°}$$

$$c = \frac{13 \sin 103.5613°}{\sin 35°} \approx 22.0329$$

Using $B' = 138.5613°$, finding angle C': $C' = 180° - 35° - 138.5613° = 6.4387°$
Using the law of sines:

$$\frac{c'}{\sin 6.4387°} = \frac{13}{\sin 35°}$$

$$c' = \frac{13 \sin 6.4387°}{\sin 35°} \approx 2.5416$$

8. Using the law of sines:

$$\frac{\sin B}{7} = \frac{\sin 56°}{12}$$

$$\sin B = \frac{7 \sin 56°}{12} \approx 0.4836$$

$$B = \arcsin\left(\frac{7 \sin 56°}{12}\right) \approx 28.9211° \quad (B \neq 151.0789°)$$

Finding angle C: $C = 180° - 56° - 28.9211° = 95.0789°$

Using the law of sines:

$$\frac{c}{\sin 95.0789°} = \frac{12}{\sin 56°}$$

$$c = \frac{12 \sin 95.0789°}{\sin 56°} \approx 14.4178$$

9. Let h represent the height of the pole. If R is the point at the top of the pole, then angle R is $180° - 32° - 40° = 108°$. Using the law of sines to find p:

$$\frac{p}{\sin P} = \frac{r}{\sin R}$$

$$\frac{p}{\sin 32°} = \frac{300}{\sin 108°}$$

$$p = \frac{300 \sin 32°}{\sin 108°} \approx 167.1570$$

Now finding h:

$$\sin 40° = \frac{h}{p}$$

$$h = 167.1570 \sin 40° \approx 107.4465$$

The height of the building is 107.4465 feet.

10. Finding angle B: $B = 180° - 110° - 35° = 35°$

Using the law of sines:

$$\frac{a}{\sin 35°} = \frac{10}{\sin 110°}$$

$$a = \frac{10 \sin 35°}{\sin 110°} \approx 6.1039$$

Finding angle C: $C = 180° - 70° - 70° = 40°$

Using the law of sines:

$$\frac{c}{\sin 40°} = \frac{a}{\sin 70°}$$

$$c = \frac{6.1039 \sin 40°}{\sin 70°} \approx 4.1753$$

Therefore: $a = b \approx 6.1039, c \approx 4.1753$

11. Finding angle B: $B = 180° - 88° - 85° = 7°$

Using the law of sines:

$$\frac{x}{\sin 85°} = \frac{309.5}{\sin 7°}$$

$$x = \frac{309.5 \sin 85°}{\sin 7°} \approx 2{,}530 \text{ ft}$$

The distance from A to B is approximately 2,530 feet.

12. Finding angle B: $B = 180° - 29.7° - 53.1° = 97.2°$
Using the law of sines:

$$\frac{x}{\sin 29.7°} = \frac{50}{\sin 97.2°}$$

$$x = \frac{50 \sin 29.7°}{\sin 97.2°} \approx 25 \text{ ft}$$

The distance from Carl to the tree is approximately 25 feet.

13. Using the law of cosines:

$$a^2 = 9^2 + 5^2 - 2(9)(5)\cos 35°$$

$$a^2 \approx 32.2763$$

$$a \approx 5.6812$$

Using the law of cosines again:

$$9^2 = (5.6812)^2 + 5^2 - 2(5.6812)(5)\cos B$$

$$81 = 57.2763 - 56.8122 \cos B$$

$$23.7237 = -56.8122 \cos B$$

$$\cos B = -\frac{23.7237}{56.8122} \approx -0.4176$$

$$B = \arccos(-0.4176) \approx 114.6819°$$

Finding angle C: $C \approx 180° - 35° - 114.6819° = 30.3181°$

14. Using the law of cosines:

$$b^2 = 13^2 + 16^2 - 2(13)(16)\cos 68°$$

$$b^2 \approx 269.1637$$

$$b \approx 16.4062$$

Using the law of cosines again:

$$16^2 = 13^2 + (16.4062)^2 - 2(13)(16.4062)\cos C$$

$$256 = 438.1634 - 426.5612 \cos C$$

$$-182.1634 = -426.5612 \cos C$$

$$\cos C = -\frac{-182.1634}{-426.5612} \approx 0.4271$$

$$C = \arccos\left(\frac{182.1634}{426.5612}\right) \approx 64.7194°$$

Finding angle C: $C \approx 180° - 68° - 64.7194° = 47.2806°$

15. Using the law of cosines:

$$c^2 = 30^2 + 20^2 - 2(30)(20)\cos 107°$$

$$c^2 = 1300 - 1200\cos 107°$$

$$c^2 \approx 1650.85$$

$$c \approx 40.6306$$

Using the law of cosines again:

$$30^2 = 20^2 + (40.6306)^2 - 2(20)(40.6306)\cos A$$

$$900 = 2050.8457 - 1625.2240\cos A$$

$$-1150.8457 = -1625.2240\cos A$$

$$\cos A = \frac{-1150.8457}{-1625.2240} = 0.7081$$

$$A = \arccos\left(\frac{1150.8457}{1625.2240}\right) \approx 44.9182°$$

Finding angle B: $B \approx 180° - 107° - 44.9182° = 28.0818°$

16. Using the law of cosines:

$$a^2 = 18^2 + 14^2 - 2(18)(14)\cos 63.4°$$

$$a^2 \approx 294.3294$$

$$a \approx 17.1560$$

Using the law of cosines again:

$$18^2 = (17.1560)^2 + 14^2 - 2(17.1560)(14)\cos B$$

$$324 = 490.3283 - 480.3680\cos B$$

$$-166.3283 = -480.3680\cos B$$

$$\cos B = \frac{166.3283}{480.3680} = 0.3463$$

$$B = \arccos\left(\frac{166.3283}{480.3680}\right) \approx 69.7417°$$

Finding angle C: $C \approx 180° - 63.4° - 69.7417° = 46.8583°$

17. Using the law of cosines:

$$c^2 = 35^2 + 25^2 - 2(35)(25)\cos 95°$$

$$c^2 = 1850 - 1750\cos 95°$$

$$c^2 \approx 2002.5225$$

$$c \approx 44.7496$$

Using the law of cosines again:

$$35^2 = 25^2 + (44.7496)^2 - 2(25)(44.7496)\cos A$$

$$1225 = 2627.5267 - 2237.48\cos A$$

$$-1402.5267 = -2237.48\cos A$$

$$\cos A = \frac{1402.5267}{2237.48} = 0.6268$$

$$A = \arccos\left(\frac{1402.5267}{2237.48}\right) \approx 51.1832°$$

Finding angle B: $B \approx 180° - 95° - 51.1832° = 33.8168°$

18. Using the law of cosines:
$$a^2 = 10^2 + 16^2 - 2(10)(16)\cos 120°$$
$$a^2 \approx 516$$
$$a \approx 22.7156$$

Using the law of cosines again:
$$10^2 = (22.7156)^2 + 16^2 - 2(22.7156)(16)\cos B$$
$$100 = 771.9985 - 726.8992\cos B$$
$$-671.9985 = -726.8992\cos B$$
$$\cos B = \frac{671.9985}{726.8992} = 0.9245$$
$$B = \arccos\left(\frac{671.9985}{726.8992}\right) \approx 22.4110°$$

Finding angle C: $C \approx 180° - 120° - 22.4110° = 37.5890°$

19. Using the law of cosines:
$$8^2 = 4^2 + 6^2 - 2(4)(6)\cos C$$
$$64 = 52 - 48\cos C$$
$$12 = -48\cos C$$
$$\cos C = -\frac{1}{4}$$
$$C = \arccos\left(-\frac{1}{4}\right) \approx 104.4775°$$

Using the law of sines:
$$\frac{\sin B}{6} = \frac{\sin 104.4775°}{8}$$
$$\sin B = \frac{6\sin 104.4775°}{8} \approx 0.7262$$
$$B = \arcsin\left(\frac{6\sin 104.4775°}{8}\right) \approx 46.5675°$$

Finding angle A: $A \approx 180° - 104.4775° - 46.5675° = 28.9550°$

20. Using the law of cosines:
$$11^2 = 7^2 + 9^2 - 2(7)(9)\cos C$$
$$121 = 130 - 126\cos C$$
$$-9 = -126\cos C$$
$$\cos C = \frac{1}{14}$$
$$C = \arccos\left(\frac{1}{14}\right) \approx 85.9040°$$

Using the law of sines:
$$\frac{\sin B}{9} = \frac{\sin 85.9040°}{11}$$
$$\sin B = \frac{9\sin 85.9040°}{11} \approx 0.8161$$
$$B = \arcsin\left(\frac{9\sin 85.9040°}{11}\right) \approx 54.6955°$$

Finding angle A: $A \approx 180° - 85.9040° - 54.6955° = 39.4005°$

21. Finding the area: $A = \dfrac{1}{2}ab\sin C = \dfrac{1}{2}(35)(25)\sin 95° \approx 435.84$

22. Finding the area: $A = \dfrac{1}{2}bc\sin A = \dfrac{1}{2}(10)(16)\sin 120° = 80\left(\dfrac{\sqrt{3}}{2}\right) = 40\sqrt{3} \approx 69.28$

23. Plotting the polar point $\left(4, \dfrac{\pi}{6}\right)$:

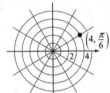

24. Plotting the polar point $\left(-2, \dfrac{\pi}{4}\right)$:

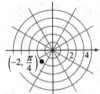

25. Converting to rectangular coordinates:
$$x = r\cos\theta = 4\cos\dfrac{11\pi}{6} = 4\left(\dfrac{\sqrt{3}}{2}\right) = 2\sqrt{3} \qquad y = r\sin\theta = 4\sin\dfrac{11\pi}{6} = 4\left(-\dfrac{1}{2}\right) = -2$$

The rectangular point is $\left(2\sqrt{3}, -2\right)$.

26. Converting to rectangular coordinates:
$$x = r\cos\theta = \dfrac{1}{3}\cos\dfrac{3\pi}{4} = \dfrac{1}{3}\left(-\dfrac{\sqrt{2}}{2}\right) = -\dfrac{\sqrt{2}}{6} \qquad y = r\sin\theta = \dfrac{1}{3}\sin\dfrac{3\pi}{4} = \dfrac{1}{3}\left(\dfrac{\sqrt{2}}{2}\right) = \dfrac{\sqrt{2}}{6}$$

The rectangular point is $\left(-\dfrac{\sqrt{2}}{6}, \dfrac{\sqrt{2}}{6}\right)$.

27. Converting to rectangular coordinates:
$$x = r\cos\theta = -2\cos\dfrac{3\pi}{2} = -2(0) = 0 \qquad y = r\sin\theta = -2\sin\dfrac{3\pi}{2} = -2(-1) = 2$$

The rectangular point is $(0, 2)$.

28. Converting to rectangular coordinates:
$$x = r\cos\theta = 3\cos\dfrac{5\pi}{3} = 3\left(\dfrac{1}{2}\right) = \dfrac{3}{2} \qquad y = r\sin\theta = 3\sin\dfrac{5\pi}{3} = 3\left(-\dfrac{\sqrt{3}}{2}\right) = -\dfrac{3\sqrt{3}}{2}$$

The rectangular point is $\left(\dfrac{3}{2}, -\dfrac{3\sqrt{2}}{2}\right)$.

29. Finding r: $r = \sqrt{(-1)^2 + \left(\sqrt{3}\right)^2} = \sqrt{1+3} = \sqrt{4} = 2$

Finding θ:
$$\tan\theta = \dfrac{\sqrt{3}}{-1} = -\sqrt{3}$$
$$\theta = \dfrac{2\pi}{3} \text{ or } \dfrac{5\pi}{3}$$

Since the point is in quadrant II, $\theta = \dfrac{2\pi}{3}$. The polar point is $(r, \theta) = \left(2, \dfrac{2\pi}{3}\right)$.

30. Finding r: $r = \sqrt{(-5)^2 + 5^2} = \sqrt{50} = 5\sqrt{2}$

Finding θ:

$$\tan\theta = \frac{5}{-5} = -1$$

$$\theta = \frac{3\pi}{4} \text{ or } \frac{7\pi}{4}$$

Since the point is in quadrant II, $\theta = \frac{3\pi}{4}$. The polar point is $(r, \theta) = \left(5\sqrt{2}, \frac{3\pi}{4}\right)$.

31. Finding r: $r = \sqrt{0^2 + 3^2} = 3$

Since the point is on the y-axis, $\theta = \frac{\pi}{2}$. The polar point is $(r, \theta) = \left(3, \frac{\pi}{2}\right)$.

32. Finding r: $r = \sqrt{\left(-2\sqrt{3}\right)^2 + 2^2} = \sqrt{12 + 4} = \sqrt{16} = 4$

Finding θ:

$$\tan\theta = \frac{2}{-2\sqrt{3}} = -\frac{1}{\sqrt{3}}$$

$$\theta = \frac{5\pi}{6} \text{ or } \frac{11\pi}{6}$$

Since the point is in quadrant II, $\theta = \frac{5\pi}{6}$. The polar point is $(r, \theta) = \left(4, \frac{5\pi}{6}\right)$.

33. Converting to polar form:

$$(x-1)^2 + y^2 = \frac{9}{4}$$

$$x^2 - 2x + 1 + y^2 = \frac{9}{4}$$

$$x^2 + y^2 - 2x = \frac{5}{4}$$

$$r^2 - 2r\cos\theta = \frac{5}{4}$$

34. Converting to rectangular form:

$$r\cos\theta = \frac{5}{2}$$

$$x = \frac{5}{2}$$

35. $r = \frac{3}{2}$ is a circle centered at the origin with radius $\frac{3}{2}$.

36. $\theta = -\frac{\pi}{6}$ is a line angled $-\frac{\pi}{6}$ from the x-axis.

37. Note the table of values:

θ	0	$\frac{\pi}{4}$	$\frac{\pi}{2}$	π
$r = 2\cos\theta$	2	$\sqrt{2} \approx 1.4$	0	-2

The graph of $r = 2\cos\theta$ is a circle with radius 1 and center on the x-axis:

38. Note the table of values:

θ	0	$\dfrac{\pi}{4}$	$\dfrac{\pi}{2}$	π
$r = 4\sin\theta$	0	$2\sqrt{2} \approx 2.8$	4	0

The graph of $r = 4\sin\theta$ is a circle with radius 2 and center on the y-axis.

39. Note the table of values:

θ	0	$\dfrac{\pi}{6}$	$\dfrac{\pi}{4}$	$\dfrac{\pi}{3}$	$\dfrac{\pi}{2}$	π
$r = 3(1-\cos\theta)$	0	$\dfrac{3(2-\sqrt{3})}{2} \approx 0.4$	$\dfrac{3(2-\sqrt{2})}{2} \approx 0.9$	$\dfrac{3}{2}$	3	6

The graph of $r = 3(1-\cos\theta)$ is a cardiod:

40. Note the table of values:

θ	0	$\dfrac{\pi}{6}$	$\dfrac{\pi}{4}$	$\dfrac{\pi}{3}$	$\dfrac{\pi}{2}$	π
$r = 2(1+\sin\theta)$	2	3	$2+\sqrt{2} \approx 3.4$	$2+\sqrt{3} \approx 3.7$	4	2

The graph of $r = 2(1+\sin\theta)$ is a cardiod:

41. Finding the magnitude: $\|\langle 3,6\rangle\| = \sqrt{3^2+6^2} = \sqrt{9+36} = \sqrt{45} = 3\sqrt{5} \approx 6.71$

Finding the direction angle in Quadrant I:

$$\cos\theta = \frac{3}{3\sqrt{5}} = \frac{1}{\sqrt{5}}$$

$$\theta = \arccos\left(\frac{1}{\sqrt{5}}\right) \approx 63.43°$$

42. Finding the magnitude: $\|\langle 7,-2\rangle\| = \sqrt{7^2+(-2)^2} = \sqrt{49+4} = \sqrt{53} \approx 7.28$

Finding the direction angle in Quadrant IV:

$$\cos\theta = \frac{7}{\sqrt{53}}$$

$$\theta = 360° - \arccos\left(\frac{7}{\sqrt{53}}\right) = 360° - 15.9454° = 344.05°$$

43. Finding the magnitude: $\left\|\langle -5, 7\rangle\right\| = \sqrt{(-5)^2 + 7^2} = \sqrt{25 + 49} = \sqrt{74} \approx 8.60$

Finding the direction angle in Quadrant II:

$$\sin\theta = \frac{7}{\sqrt{74}}$$

$$\theta = 180° - \arcsin\left(\frac{7}{\sqrt{74}}\right) \approx 180° - 54.4623° \approx 125.54°$$

44. Finding the magnitude: $\left\|\left\langle \frac{1}{3}, -\frac{4}{3}\right\rangle\right\| = \sqrt{\left(\frac{1}{3}\right)^2 + \left(-\frac{4}{3}\right)^2} = \sqrt{\frac{1}{9} + \frac{16}{9}} = \frac{\sqrt{17}}{3} \approx 1.37$

Finding the direction angle in Quadrant IV:

$$\cos\theta = \frac{\left(\frac{1}{3}\right)}{\left(\frac{\sqrt{17}}{3}\right)} = \frac{1}{\sqrt{17}}$$

$$\theta = 360° - \cos^{-1}\left(\frac{1}{\sqrt{17}}\right) = 360° - 75.9638° = 284.04°$$

45. Finding the indicated vectors:

$$\mathbf{u} - \mathbf{v} = \langle 0, 4\rangle - \langle -2, 4\rangle = \langle 2, 0\rangle$$

$$\mathbf{u} + 2\mathbf{v} = \langle 0, 4\rangle + 2\langle -2, 4\rangle = \langle 0, 4\rangle + \langle -4, 8\rangle = \langle -4, 12\rangle$$

$$-3\mathbf{u} + \mathbf{v} = -3\langle 0, 4\rangle + \langle -2, 4\rangle = \langle 0, -12\rangle + \langle -2, 4\rangle = \langle -2, -8\rangle$$

46. Finding the indicated vectors:

$$\mathbf{u} - \mathbf{v} = \langle 7, -3\rangle - \langle 2, 9\rangle = \langle 5, -12\rangle$$

$$\mathbf{u} + 2\mathbf{v} = \langle 7, -3\rangle + 2\langle 2, 9\rangle = \langle 7, -3\rangle + \langle 4, 18\rangle = \langle 11, 15\rangle$$

$$-3\mathbf{u} + \mathbf{v} = -3\langle 7, -3\rangle + \langle 2, 9\rangle = \langle -21, 9\rangle + \langle 2, 9\rangle = \langle -19, 18\rangle$$

47. Finding the indicated vectors:

$$\mathbf{u} - \mathbf{v} = \langle -2.5, 5.5\rangle - \langle 3, 0\rangle = \langle -5.5, 5.5\rangle$$

$$\mathbf{u} + 2\mathbf{v} = \langle -2.5, 5.5\rangle + 2\langle 3, 0\rangle = \langle -2.5, 5.5\rangle + \langle 6, 0\rangle = \langle 3.5, 5.5\rangle$$

$$-3\mathbf{u} + \mathbf{v} = -3\langle -2.5, 5.5\rangle + \langle 3, 0\rangle = \langle 7.5, -16.5\rangle + \langle 3, 0\rangle = \langle 10.5, -16.5\rangle$$

48. Finding the indicated vectors:

$$\mathbf{u} - \mathbf{v} = \langle 5.2, 6.3\rangle - \langle 2, -1\rangle = \langle 3.2, 7.3\rangle$$

$$\mathbf{u} + 2\mathbf{v} = \langle 5.2, 6.3\rangle + 2\langle 2, -1\rangle = \langle 5.2, 6.3\rangle + \langle 4, -2\rangle = \langle 9.2, 4.3\rangle$$

$$-3\mathbf{u} + \mathbf{v} = -3\langle 5.2, 6.3\rangle + \langle 2, -1\rangle = \langle -15.6, -18.9\rangle + \langle 2, -1\rangle = \langle -13.6, -19.9\rangle$$

49. Finding the magnitude: $\left\|\langle -12, 5\rangle\right\| = \sqrt{(-12)^2 + 5^2} = \sqrt{144 + 25} = \sqrt{169} = 13$

The unit vector is: $\mathbf{u} = \dfrac{\langle -12, 5\rangle}{\left\|\langle -12, 5\rangle\right\|} = \dfrac{\langle -12, 5\rangle}{13} = \left\langle -\dfrac{12}{13}, \dfrac{5}{13}\right\rangle$

50. Finding the magnitude: $\left\|\langle 3, -2\rangle\right\| = \sqrt{3^2 + (-2)^2} = \sqrt{9 + 4} = \sqrt{13}$

The unit vector is: $\mathbf{u} = \dfrac{\langle 3, -2\rangle}{\sqrt{13}} = \left\langle \dfrac{3}{\sqrt{13}}, \dfrac{-2}{\sqrt{13}}\right\rangle = \left\langle \dfrac{3\sqrt{13}}{13}, -\dfrac{2\sqrt{13}}{13}\right\rangle$

51. Writing in terms of $\mathbf{i}$ and $\mathbf{j}$: $\langle 6, -3\rangle = 6\mathbf{i} - 3\mathbf{j}$

52. Writing in terms of $\mathbf{i}$ and $\mathbf{j}$: $\langle -9, -5\rangle = -9\mathbf{i} - 5\mathbf{j}$

53. Finding the values:

$$\mathbf{u} \cdot \mathbf{v} = \langle 4, -2 \rangle \cdot \langle 3, 7 \rangle = 4(3) + (-2)(7) = 12 - 14 = -2$$

$$\|\mathbf{u}\| = \sqrt{4^2 + (-2)^2} = \sqrt{16 + 4} = \sqrt{20} = 2\sqrt{5}$$

$$\|\mathbf{v}\| = \sqrt{3^2 + 7^2} = \sqrt{9 + 49} = \sqrt{58}$$

Now finding the angle:

$$\mathbf{u} \cdot \mathbf{v} = \|\mathbf{u}\| \|\mathbf{v}\| \cos\theta$$

$$-2 = \left(2\sqrt{5}\right)\left(\sqrt{58}\right)\cos\theta$$

$$\cos\theta = \frac{-2}{2\sqrt{290}} = -0.587$$

$$\theta = \arccos\left(\frac{-1}{\sqrt{290}}\right) \approx 93.4°$$

54. Finding the values:

$$\mathbf{u} \cdot \mathbf{v} = \langle -3, 2 \rangle \cdot \langle 0, -1 \rangle = -3(0) + (2)(-1) = -2$$

$$\|\mathbf{u}\| = \sqrt{9 + 4} = \sqrt{13}$$

$$\|\mathbf{v}\| = \sqrt{0 + 1} = 1$$

Now finding the angle:

$$\mathbf{u} \cdot \mathbf{v} = \|\mathbf{u}\| \|\mathbf{v}\| \cos\theta$$

$$-2 = \sqrt{13}(1)\cos\theta$$

$$\cos\theta = \frac{-2}{\sqrt{13}}$$

$$\theta = \arccos\left(\frac{-2}{\sqrt{13}}\right) \approx 123.7°$$

55. Finding the values:

$$\mathbf{u} \cdot \mathbf{v} = \langle -4, 2 \rangle \cdot \left\langle 3, \frac{2}{3} \right\rangle = -4(3) + 2\left(\frac{2}{3}\right) = -12 + \frac{4}{3} = -\frac{32}{3}$$

$$\|\mathbf{u}\| = \sqrt{(-4)^2 + 2^2} = \sqrt{16 + 4} = \sqrt{20} = 2\sqrt{5}$$

$$\|\mathbf{v}\| = \sqrt{3^2 + \left(\frac{2}{3}\right)^2} = \sqrt{9 + \frac{4}{9}} = \frac{\sqrt{85}}{3}$$

Now finding the angle:

$$\mathbf{u} \cdot \mathbf{v} = \|\mathbf{u}\| \|\mathbf{v}\| \cos\theta$$

$$-\frac{32}{3} = \left(2\sqrt{5}\right)\left(\frac{\sqrt{85}}{3}\right)\cos\theta$$

$$-\frac{32}{3} = \frac{10\sqrt{17}}{3}\cos\theta$$

$$\cos\theta = \frac{-32}{10\sqrt{17}}$$

$$\theta = \arccos\left(\frac{-16}{5\sqrt{17}}\right) \approx 140.9°$$

56. Finding the values:

$$\mathbf{u} \cdot \mathbf{v} = \left\langle -\frac{1}{2}, -1 \right\rangle \cdot \left\langle -3, -2 \right\rangle = \frac{3}{2} + 2 = \frac{7}{2}$$

$$\|\mathbf{u}\| = \sqrt{\frac{1}{4} + 1} = \sqrt{\frac{5}{4}} = \frac{\sqrt{5}}{2}$$

$$\|\mathbf{v}\| = \sqrt{9 + 4} = \sqrt{13}$$

Now finding the angle:

$$\mathbf{u} \cdot \mathbf{v} = \|\mathbf{u}\| \|\mathbf{v}\| \cos\theta$$

$$\frac{7}{2} = \left(\frac{\sqrt{5}}{2} \right) \left(\sqrt{13} \right) \cos\theta$$

$$\cos\theta = \frac{7}{\sqrt{65}}$$

$$\theta = \arccos\left(\frac{7}{\sqrt{65}} \right) \approx 29.7°$$

57. Finding the values:

$$\mathbf{v} \cdot \mathbf{w} = 2(2) + (-2)(4) = 4 - 8 = -4$$

$$\|\mathbf{w}\|^2 = 2^2 + 4^2 = 4 + 16 = 20$$

$$\text{proj}_w \mathbf{v} = \left(\frac{\mathbf{v} \cdot \mathbf{w}}{\|\mathbf{w}\|^2} \right) \mathbf{w} = \left(\frac{-4}{20} \right) \langle 2, 4 \rangle = \left\langle -\frac{2}{5}, -\frac{4}{5} \right\rangle$$

Finding $\mathbf{v}_1$ and $\mathbf{v}_2$:

$$\mathbf{v}_1 = \text{proj}_w \mathbf{v} = \left\langle -\frac{2}{5}, -\frac{4}{5} \right\rangle \qquad \mathbf{v}_2 = \mathbf{v} - \mathbf{v}_1 = \langle 2, -2 \rangle - \left\langle -\frac{2}{5}, -\frac{4}{5} \right\rangle = \left\langle \frac{12}{5}, -\frac{6}{5} \right\rangle$$

58. Finding the values:

$$\mathbf{v} \cdot \mathbf{w} = -4(3) + 2(3) = -6$$

$$\|\mathbf{w}\|^2 = 3^2 + 3^2 = 18$$

$$\text{proj}_w \mathbf{v} = \left(\frac{\mathbf{v} \cdot \mathbf{w}}{\|\mathbf{w}\|^2} \right) \mathbf{w} = \left(\frac{-6}{18} \right) \langle 3, 3 \rangle = \langle -1, -1 \rangle$$

Finding $\mathbf{v}_1$ and $\mathbf{v}_2$:

$$\mathbf{v}_1 = \text{proj}_w \mathbf{v} = \langle -1, -1 \rangle \qquad \mathbf{v}_2 = \mathbf{v} - \mathbf{v}_1 = \langle -4, 2 \rangle - \langle -1, -1 \rangle = \langle -3, 3 \rangle$$

59. Finding the values:

$$\mathbf{v} \cdot \mathbf{w} = -1(5) + 5(1) = 0$$

$$\|\mathbf{w}\|^2 = 5^2 + 1^2 = 25 + 1 = 26$$

$$\text{proj}_w \mathbf{v} = \left(\frac{\mathbf{v} \cdot \mathbf{w}}{\|\mathbf{w}\|^2} \right) \mathbf{w} = \left(\frac{0}{26} \right) \langle 5, 1 \rangle = \langle 0, 0 \rangle$$

Finding $\mathbf{v}_1$ and $\mathbf{v}_2$:

$$\mathbf{v}_1 = \text{proj}_w \mathbf{v} = \langle 0, 0 \rangle \qquad \mathbf{v}_2 = \mathbf{v} - \mathbf{v}_1 = \langle -1, 5 \rangle - \langle 0, 0 \rangle = \langle -1, 5 \rangle$$

60. Finding the values:

$$\mathbf{v} \cdot \mathbf{w} = 1(-3) + 2(3) = 3$$

$$\|\mathbf{w}\|^2 = 9 + 9 = 18$$

$$\text{proj}_w \mathbf{v} = \left(\frac{\mathbf{v} \cdot \mathbf{w}}{\|\mathbf{w}\|^2} \right) \mathbf{w} = \left(\frac{3}{18} \right) \langle -3, 3 \rangle = \left\langle -\frac{1}{2}, \frac{1}{2} \right\rangle$$

Finding $\mathbf{v}_1$ and $\mathbf{v}_2$:

$$\mathbf{v}_1 = \text{proj}_w \mathbf{v} = \left\langle -\frac{1}{2}, \frac{1}{2} \right\rangle \qquad \mathbf{v}_2 = \mathbf{v} - \mathbf{v}_1 = \langle 1, 2 \rangle - \left\langle -\frac{1}{2}, \frac{1}{2} \right\rangle = \left\langle \frac{3}{2}, \frac{3}{2} \right\rangle$$

61. Finding r: $r = \sqrt{0^2 + (-6)^2} = \sqrt{36} = 6$

Since $\theta = \frac{3\pi}{2}$, the trigonometric form is: $-6i = 6 \left(\cos \frac{3\pi}{2} + i \sin \frac{3\pi}{2} \right)$

62. Finding r: $r = \sqrt{10^2 + 0^2} = 10$

Since $\theta = 0$, the trigonometric form is: $10 = 10 \left(\cos 0 + i \sin 0 \right)$

63. Finding r: $r = \sqrt{(-1)^2 + \left(\sqrt{3} \right)^2} = \sqrt{1 + 3} = \sqrt{4} = 2$

The number $-1 + i\sqrt{3}$ corresponds to the point $\left(-1, \sqrt{3} \right)$, a point in Quadrant II. Therefore:

$$\cos \theta = -\frac{1}{2}$$

$$\theta = \pi - \frac{\pi}{3} = \frac{2\pi}{3}$$

The trigonometric form is: $-1 + i\sqrt{3} = 2 \left(\cos \frac{2\pi}{3} + i \sin \frac{2\pi}{3} \right)$

64. Finding r: $r = \sqrt{(-3)^2 + \left(-3\sqrt{3} \right)^2} = \sqrt{9 + 27} = \sqrt{36} = 6$

The number $-3 - 3i\sqrt{3}$ corresponds to the point $\left(-3, -3\sqrt{3} \right)$, a point in Quadrant III. Therefore:

$$\cos \theta = -\frac{3}{6} = -\frac{1}{2}$$

$$\theta = \pi + \frac{\pi}{3} = \frac{4\pi}{3}$$

The trigonometric form is: $-3 - 3i\sqrt{3} = 6 \left(\cos \frac{4\pi}{3} + i \sin \frac{4\pi}{3} \right)$

65. Finding r: $r = \sqrt{\left(-2\sqrt{3} \right)^2 + 2^2} = \sqrt{12 + 4} = \sqrt{16} = 4$

The number $-2\sqrt{3} + 2i$ corresponds to the point $\left(-2\sqrt{3}, 2 \right)$, a point in Quadrant II. Therefore:

$$\sin \theta = \frac{2}{4} = \frac{1}{2}$$

$$\theta = \pi - \frac{\pi}{6} = \frac{5\pi}{6}$$

The trigonometric form is: $-2\sqrt{3} + 2i = 4 \left(\cos \frac{5\pi}{6} + i \sin \frac{5\pi}{6} \right)$

66. Finding r: $r = \sqrt{\left(-3\sqrt{3}\right)^2 + (-3)^2} = \sqrt{27+9} = \sqrt{36} = 6$

The number $-3\sqrt{3} - 3i$ corresponds to the point $\left(-3\sqrt{3}, -3\right)$, a point in Quadrant III. Therefore:

$$\sin\theta = \frac{-3}{6} = -\frac{1}{2}$$

$$\theta = \pi + \frac{\pi}{6} = \frac{7\pi}{6}$$

The trigonometric form is: $-3 - 3i\sqrt{3} = 6\left(\cos\frac{7\pi}{6} + i\sin\frac{7\pi}{6}\right)$

67. First write each number in trigonometric form:

$$r_1 = \sqrt{1^2 + 1^2} = \sqrt{2} \qquad\qquad r_2 = \sqrt{2^2 + (-2)^2} = \sqrt{8} = 2\sqrt{2}$$

$$\theta_1 = \cos^{-1}\left(\frac{1}{\sqrt{2}}\right) = \frac{\pi}{4} \qquad \theta_2 = 2\pi - \cos^{-1}\left(\frac{2}{2\sqrt{2}}\right) = 2\pi - \cos^{-1}\left(\frac{1}{\sqrt{2}}\right) = \frac{7\pi}{4}$$

Now finding the values:

$$z_1 z_2 = \left(\sqrt{2}\right)\left(2\sqrt{2}\right)\left[\cos\left(\frac{\pi}{4} + \frac{7\pi}{4}\right) + i\sin\left(\frac{\pi}{4} + \frac{7\pi}{4}\right)\right] = 4\left(\cos 2\pi + i\sin 2\pi\right) = 4\left(\cos 0 + i\sin 0\right)$$

$$\frac{z_1}{z_2} = \frac{\sqrt{2}}{2\sqrt{2}}\left[\cos\left(\frac{\pi}{4} - \frac{7\pi}{4}\right) + i\sin\left(\frac{\pi}{4} - \frac{7\pi}{4}\right)\right] = \frac{1}{2}\left[\cos\left(-\frac{3\pi}{2}\right) + i\sin\left(-\frac{3\pi}{2}\right)\right] = \frac{1}{2}\left(\cos\frac{\pi}{2} + i\sin\frac{\pi}{2}\right)$$

68. First write each number in trigonometric form:

$$r_1 = \sqrt{\left(\sqrt{3}\right)^2 + 1^2} = 2 \qquad\qquad r_2 = \sqrt{\left(\sqrt{3}\right)^2 + (-1)^2} = 2$$

$$\theta_1 = \sin^{-1}\left(\frac{1}{2}\right) = \frac{\pi}{6} \qquad\qquad \theta_2 = \sin^{-1}\left(\frac{-1}{2}\right) = \frac{11\pi}{6}$$

Now finding the values:

$$z_1 z_2 = (2)(2)\left[\cos\left(\frac{\pi}{6} + \frac{11\pi}{6}\right) + i\sin\left(\frac{\pi}{6} + \frac{11\pi}{6}\right)\right] = 4\left(\cos 2\pi + i\sin 2\pi\right) = 4\left(\cos 0 + i\sin 0\right)$$

$$\frac{z_1}{z_2} = \frac{2}{2}\left[\cos\left(\frac{\pi}{6} - \frac{11\pi}{6}\right) + i\sin\left(\frac{\pi}{6} - \frac{11\pi}{6}\right)\right] = \cos\left(\frac{-5\pi}{3}\right) + i\sin\left(\frac{-5\pi}{3}\right) = \cos\frac{\pi}{3} + i\sin\frac{\pi}{3}$$

69. First write each number in trigonometric form:

$$r_1 = \sqrt{(-1)^2 + \left(\sqrt{3}\right)^2} = \sqrt{4} = 2 \qquad\qquad r_2 = \sqrt{1^2 + (-1)^2} = \sqrt{2}$$

$$\theta_1 = \cos^{-1}\left(\frac{-1}{2}\right) = \frac{2\pi}{3} \qquad\qquad \theta_2 = 2\pi - \cos^{-1}\left(\frac{1}{\sqrt{2}}\right) = \frac{7\pi}{4}$$

Now finding the values:

$$z_1 z_2 = (2)\left(\sqrt{2}\right)\left[\cos\left(\frac{2\pi}{3} + \frac{7\pi}{4}\right) + i\sin\left(\frac{2\pi}{3} + \frac{7\pi}{4}\right)\right] = 2\sqrt{2}\left(\cos\frac{29\pi}{12} + i\sin\frac{29\pi}{12}\right) = 2\sqrt{2}\left(\cos\frac{5\pi}{12} + i\sin\frac{5\pi}{12}\right)$$

$$\frac{z_1}{z_2} = \frac{2}{\sqrt{2}}\left[\cos\left(\frac{2\pi}{3} - \frac{7\pi}{4}\right) + i\sin\left(\frac{2\pi}{3} - \frac{7\pi}{4}\right)\right] = \sqrt{2}\left[\cos\left(-\frac{13\pi}{12}\right) + i\sin\left(-\frac{13\pi}{12}\right)\right] = \sqrt{2}\left(\cos\frac{11\pi}{12} + i\sin\frac{11\pi}{12}\right)$$

70. First write each number in trigonometric form:

$$r_1 = \sqrt{1^2 + \left(-\sqrt{3}\right)^2} = 2 \qquad\qquad r_2 = \sqrt{1^2 + \left(\sqrt{3}\right)^2} = 2$$

$$\theta_1 = 2\pi - \cos^{-1}\left(\frac{1}{2}\right) = \frac{5\pi}{3} \qquad\qquad \theta_2 = \cos^{-1}\left(\frac{1}{2}\right) = \frac{\pi}{3}$$

Now finding the values:

$$z_1 z_2 = (2)(2)\left[\cos\left(\frac{5\pi}{3} + \frac{\pi}{3}\right) + i\sin\left(\frac{5\pi}{3} + \frac{\pi}{3}\right)\right] = 4\left(\cos 2\pi + i\sin 2\pi\right) = 4\left(\cos 0 + i\sin 0\right)$$

$$\frac{z_1}{z_2} = \frac{2}{2}\left[\cos\left(\frac{5\pi}{3} - \frac{\pi}{3}\right) + i\sin\left(\frac{5\pi}{3} - \frac{\pi}{3}\right)\right] = \cos\frac{4\pi}{3} + i\sin\frac{4\pi}{3}$$

71. Finding r: $\sqrt{1^2 + (-1)^2} = \sqrt{2}$

The number $1 - i$ corresponds to the point $(1, -1)$, a point in Quadrant IV. Therefore:

$$\cos\theta = \frac{1}{\sqrt{2}}$$

$$\theta = 2\pi - \frac{\pi}{4} = \frac{7\pi}{4}$$

The trigonometric form is: $1 - i = \sqrt{2}\left(\cos\frac{7\pi}{4} + i\sin\frac{7\pi}{4}\right)$

Using De Moivre's Theorem: $(1-i)^4 = \left(\sqrt{2}\right)^4\left[\cos\left(4 \cdot \frac{7\pi}{4}\right) + i\sin\left(4 \cdot \frac{7\pi}{4}\right)\right] = 4\left(\cos 7\pi + i\sin 7\pi\right) = 4\left(-1 + 0i\right) = -4$

72. Finding r: $\sqrt{(-2)^2 + 2^2} = \sqrt{8} = 2\sqrt{2}$

The number $-2 + 2i$ corresponds to the point $(-2, 2)$, a point in Quadrant II. Therefore:

$$\cos\theta = \frac{-2}{2\sqrt{2}} = -\frac{1}{\sqrt{2}}$$

$$\theta = \pi - \frac{\pi}{4} = \frac{3\pi}{4}$$

The trigonometric form is: $-2 + 2i = 2\sqrt{2}\left(\cos\frac{3\pi}{4} + i\sin\frac{3\pi}{4}\right)$

Using De Moivre's Theorem:

$$(-2+2i)^4 = \left(2\sqrt{2}\right)^4\left[\cos\left(4 \cdot \frac{3\pi}{4}\right) + i\sin\left(4 \cdot \frac{3\pi}{4}\right)\right] = 64\left(\cos 3\pi + i\sin 3\pi\right) = 64\left(-1 + 0i\right) = -64$$

73. Finding r: $\sqrt{\left(\sqrt{3}\right)^2 + (-1)^2} = \sqrt{4} = 2$

The number $\sqrt{3} - i$ corresponds to the point $\left(\sqrt{3}, -1\right)$, a point in Quadrant IV. Therefore:

$$\cos\theta = \frac{\sqrt{3}}{2}$$

$$\theta = 2\pi - \frac{\pi}{6} = \frac{11\pi}{6}$$

The trigonometric form is: $\sqrt{3} - i = 2\left(\cos\frac{11\pi}{6} + i\sin\frac{11\pi}{6}\right)$

Using De Moivre's Theorem: $\left(\sqrt{3} - i\right)^3 = (2)^3\left[\cos\left(3 \cdot \frac{11\pi}{6}\right) + i\sin\left(3 \cdot \frac{11\pi}{6}\right)\right] = 8\left(\cos\frac{11\pi}{2} + i\sin\frac{11\pi}{2}\right) = 8\left(0 - 1i\right) = -8i$

74. Finding r: $\sqrt{(-1)^2 + \left(-\sqrt{3}\right)^2} = \sqrt{4} = 2$

The number $-1 - i\sqrt{3}$ corresponds to the point $\left(-1, -\sqrt{3}\right)$, a point in Quadrant III. Therefore:

$$\cos\theta = -\frac{1}{2}$$

$$\theta = \pi + \frac{\pi}{3} = \frac{4\pi}{3}$$

The trigonometric form is: $-1 - i\sqrt{3} = 2\left(\cos\frac{4\pi}{3} + i\sin\frac{4\pi}{3}\right)$

Using De Moivre's Theorem: $\left(-1 - i\sqrt{3}\right)^3 = (2)^3\left[\cos\left(3\cdot\frac{4\pi}{3}\right) + i\sin\left(3\cdot\frac{4\pi}{3}\right)\right] = 8\left(\cos 4\pi + i\sin 4\pi\right) = 8\left(1 + 0i\right) = 8$

75. Finding r: $r = \sqrt{0^2 + (-1)^2} = 1$

The number $-i$ corresponds to the point $(0, -1)$, so $\theta = \frac{3\pi}{2}$.

The trigonometric form is: $-i = \cos\frac{3\pi}{2} + i\sin\frac{3\pi}{2}$

The square roots of $-i$ are: $\sqrt{1}\left[\cos\left(\dfrac{\frac{3\pi}{2} + 2k\pi}{2}\right) + i\sin\left(\dfrac{\frac{3\pi}{2} + 2k\pi}{2}\right)\right] = \cos\frac{3\pi + 4k\pi}{4} + i\sin\frac{3\pi + 4k\pi}{4}$ (for $k = 0, 1$)

For $k = 0$: $\cos\frac{3\pi}{4} + i\sin\frac{3\pi}{4} = -\frac{\sqrt{2}}{2} + \frac{\sqrt{2}}{2}i \approx -0.707 + 0.707i$

For $k = 1$: $\cos\frac{7\pi}{4} + i\sin\frac{7\pi}{4} = \frac{\sqrt{2}}{2} - \frac{\sqrt{2}}{2}i \approx 0.707 - 0.707i$

76. Finding r: $r = \sqrt{0^2 + 3^2} = 3$

The number $3i$ corresponds to the point $(0, 3)$, so $\theta = \frac{\pi}{2}$.

The trigonometric form is: $3i = 3\left(\cos\frac{\pi}{2} + i\sin\frac{\pi}{2}\right)$

The square roots of $3i$ are: $\sqrt{3}\left[\cos\left(\dfrac{\frac{\pi}{2} + 2k\pi}{2}\right) + i\sin\left(\dfrac{\frac{\pi}{2} + 2k\pi}{2}\right)\right] = \sqrt{3}\left(\cos\frac{\pi + 4k\pi}{4} + i\sin\frac{\pi + 4k\pi}{4}\right)$ (for $k = 0, 1$)

For $k = 0$: $\sqrt{3}\left(\cos\frac{\pi}{4} + i\sin\frac{\pi}{4}\right) = \sqrt{3}\left(\frac{\sqrt{2}}{2} + \frac{\sqrt{2}}{2}i\right) \approx 1.225 + 1.225i$

For $k = 1$: $\sqrt{3}\left(\cos\frac{5\pi}{4} + i\sin\frac{5\pi}{4}\right) = \sqrt{3}\left(-\frac{\sqrt{2}}{2} - \frac{\sqrt{2}}{2}i\right) \approx -1.225 - 1.225i$

77. Finding r: $r = \sqrt{2^2 + \left(-2\sqrt{3}\right)^2} = \sqrt{4+12} = \sqrt{16} = 4$

The number $2 - 2i\sqrt{3}$ corresponds to the point $\left(2, -2\sqrt{3}\right)$ in Quadrant IV, so:

$$\cos\theta = \frac{2}{4} = \frac{1}{2}$$

$$\theta = 2\pi - \frac{\pi}{3} = \frac{5\pi}{3}$$

The trigonometric form is: $2 - 2i\sqrt{3} = 4\left(\cos\frac{5\pi}{3} + i\sin\frac{5\pi}{3}\right)$

The square roots of $2 - 2i\sqrt{3}$ are:

$$\sqrt{4}\left[\cos\left(\frac{\frac{5\pi}{3} + 2k\pi}{2}\right) + i\sin\left(\frac{\frac{5\pi}{3} + 2k\pi}{2}\right)\right] = 2\left(\cos\frac{5\pi + 6k\pi}{6} + i\sin\frac{5\pi + 6k\pi}{6}\right) \text{ (for } k = 0, 1)$$

For $k = 0$: $2\left(\cos\frac{5\pi}{6} + i\sin\frac{5\pi}{6}\right) = 2\left(-\frac{\sqrt{3}}{2} + \frac{1}{2}i\right) = -\sqrt{3} + i \approx -1.732 + i$

For $k = 1$: $2\left(\cos\frac{11\pi}{6} + i\sin\frac{11\pi}{6}\right) = 2\left(\frac{\sqrt{3}}{2} - \frac{1}{2}i\right) = \sqrt{3} - i \approx 1.732 - i$

78. Finding r: $r = \sqrt{(-1)^2 + (-1)^2} = \sqrt{1+1} = \sqrt{2}$

The number $-1 - i$ corresponds to the point $(-1, -1)$ in Quadrant III, so:

$$\cos\theta = -\frac{1}{\sqrt{2}}$$

$$\theta = \pi + \frac{\pi}{4} = \frac{5\pi}{4}$$

The trigonometric form is: $-1 - i = \sqrt{2}\left(\cos\frac{5\pi}{4} + i\sin\frac{5\pi}{4}\right)$

The square roots of $-1 - i$ are:

$$\sqrt{\sqrt{2}}\left[\cos\left(\frac{\frac{5\pi}{4} + 2k\pi}{2}\right) + i\sin\left(\frac{\frac{5\pi}{4} + 2k\pi}{2}\right)\right] = \sqrt[4]{2}\left(\cos\frac{5\pi + 8k\pi}{8} + i\sin\frac{5\pi + 8k\pi}{8}\right) \text{ (for } k = 0, 1)$$

For $k = 0$: $\sqrt[4]{2}\left(\cos\frac{5\pi}{8} + i\sin\frac{5\pi}{8}\right) \approx -0.455 + 1.099i$

For $k = 1$: $\sqrt[4]{2}\left(\cos\frac{13\pi}{8} + i\sin\frac{13\pi}{8}\right) \approx 0.455 - 1.099i$

Chapter 7 Test

1. Finding angle C: $C = 180° - (65° + 30°) = 85°$

   Using the law of sines:
   $$\frac{b}{\sin 30°} = \frac{20}{\sin 65°}$$
   $$b = \frac{20 \sin 30°}{\sin 65°} \approx 11.03$$

   $$\frac{c}{\sin 85°} = \frac{20}{\sin 65°}$$
   $$c = \frac{20 \sin 85°}{\sin 65°} \approx 21.98$$

2. Using the law of cosines:
   $$a^2 = 5^2 + 12^2 - 2(5)(12)\cos 60°$$
   $$a^2 = 169 - 120\left(\frac{1}{2}\right)$$
   $$a^2 = 109$$
   $$a \approx 10.44$$

   Using the law of sines:
   $$\frac{\sin B}{5} = \frac{\sin 60°}{10.44}$$
   $$\sin B = \frac{5 \sin 60°}{10.44} \approx 0.4148$$
   $$B = \arcsin\left(\frac{5 \sin 60°}{10.44}\right) \approx 24.50°$$

   Finding angle C: $C = 180° - 60° - 24.50° \approx 95.50°$

3. Using the law of cosines:
   $$c^2 = a^2 + b^2 - 2ab\cos C$$
   $$15^2 = 10^2 + 8^2 - 2(10)(8)\cos C$$
   $$61 = -160\cos C$$
   $$\cos C = -\frac{61}{160}$$
   $$C = \arccos\left(-\frac{61}{160}\right) \approx 112.41°$$

   Using the law of cosines again:
   $$b^2 = a^2 + c^2 - 2ac\cos B$$
   $$64 = 100 + 225 - 300\cos B$$
   $$-261 = -300\cos B$$
   $$\cos B = \frac{261}{300}$$
   $$B = \arccos\left(\frac{261}{300}\right) \approx 29.54°$$

   Finding angle C: $C = 180° - 112.41° - 29.54° = 38.05°$

4.   Using the law of sines:
$$\frac{\sin B}{7} = \frac{\sin 45°}{12}$$
$$\sin B = \frac{7\sin 45°}{12}$$
$$B = \arcsin\left(\frac{7\sin 45°}{12}\right) \approx 24.36°$$

Finding angle A: $A = 180° - 45° - 24.36° \approx 110.64°$
Using the law of sines:
$$\frac{a}{\sin 110.64°} = \frac{12}{\sin 45°}$$
$$a = \frac{12\sin 110.64°}{\sin 45°} \approx 15.88$$

5.   Finding the area: $A = \frac{1}{2}bc\sin A = \frac{1}{2}(10)(20)\sin 30° = 100\left(\frac{1}{2}\right) = 50 \text{ in}^2$

6.   Finding r: $r = \sqrt{\left(-4\sqrt{3}\right)^2 + (-4)^2} = \sqrt{48+16} = \sqrt{64} = 8$

Finding θ:
$$\tan\theta = \frac{-4}{-4\sqrt{3}} = \frac{1}{\sqrt{3}}$$
$$\theta = \frac{\pi}{6} \text{ or } \frac{7\pi}{6}$$

Since the point is in quadrant III, $\theta = \frac{7\pi}{6}$. The polar point is $(r, \theta) = \left(8, \frac{7\pi}{6}\right)$.

7.   Converting to rectangular coordinates:
$$x = r\cos\theta = 5\cos\left(-\frac{3\pi}{4}\right) = 5\left(-\frac{\sqrt{2}}{2}\right) = -\frac{5\sqrt{2}}{2} \qquad y = r\sin\theta = 5\sin\left(-\frac{3\pi}{4}\right) = -5\left(\frac{\sqrt{2}}{2}\right) = -\frac{5\sqrt{2}}{2}$$

The rectangular point is $\left(-\frac{5\sqrt{2}}{2}, -\frac{5\sqrt{2}}{2}\right)$.

8.   Converting to polar form:
$$x^2 + (y-1)^2 = 1$$
$$x^2 + \left(y^2 - 2y + 1\right) = 1$$
$$x^2 + y^2 - 2y = 0$$
$$r^2 - 2r\sin\theta = 0$$
$$r(r - 2\sin\theta) = 0$$
$$r = 2\sin\theta$$

9.   **a.**   Converting to rectangular form:
$$r = 2.5$$
$$\sqrt{x^2 + y^2} = 2.5$$
$$x^2 + y^2 = 6.25$$

   b.   Converting to rectangular form:
$$\theta = -\frac{2\pi}{3}$$
$$\frac{y}{x} = \tan\left(-\frac{2\pi}{3}\right)$$
$$\frac{y}{x} = \sqrt{3}$$
$$y = \sqrt{3}x$$

10. The graph of $r = \dfrac{9}{2}$ is a circle centered at the origin with radius $\dfrac{9}{2}$.

11. The graph of $r = 4(1 - \sin\theta)$ is a cardiod:

12. Finding the magnitude: $\|\langle 4, -3 \rangle\| = \sqrt{4^2 + (-3)^2} = \sqrt{25} = 5$

Finding the direction angle in Quadrant IV:

$$\cos\theta = \frac{4}{5}$$

$$\theta = 360° - \arccos\left(\frac{4}{5}\right) \approx 360° - 36.8699° \approx 323.1°$$

13. Finding the horizontal and vertical components:

$$v_1 = 8\cos 140° \approx -6.13 \qquad\qquad v_2 = 8\sin 140° \approx 5.14$$

The vector is $\mathbf{v} = \langle -6.13, 5.14 \rangle$.

14. Finding the dot product: $\mathbf{u} \cdot \mathbf{v} = (-3)(2) + (1)(4) = -6 + 4 = -2$

15. Evaluating the quantity: $3\mathbf{u} - \mathbf{v} = 3\langle -3, 1 \rangle - \langle 2, 4 \rangle = \langle -9, 3 \rangle - \langle 2, 4 \rangle = \langle -11, -1 \rangle$

16. Finding the magnitudes:

$$\|\mathbf{u}\| = \|\langle -3, 1 \rangle\| = \sqrt{(-3)^2 + 1^2} = \sqrt{9 + 1} = \sqrt{10}$$

$$\|\mathbf{v}\| = \|\langle 2, 4 \rangle\| = \sqrt{2^2 + 4^2} = \sqrt{4 + 16} = \sqrt{20} = 2\sqrt{5}$$

17. Finding the projection: $\operatorname{proj}_v \mathbf{u} = \left(\dfrac{\mathbf{u} \cdot \mathbf{v}}{\|\mathbf{v}\|^2}\right)\mathbf{v} = \left(\dfrac{-2}{2^2 + 4^2}\right)\langle 2, 4 \rangle = -\dfrac{2}{20}\langle 2, 4 \rangle = \left\langle -\dfrac{1}{5}, -\dfrac{2}{5} \right\rangle$

18. Multiplying the complex numbers:

$$3\left(\cos\frac{\pi}{6} + i\sin\frac{\pi}{6}\right) \cdot 2\left(\cos\frac{\pi}{4} + i\sin\frac{\pi}{4}\right) = 3 \cdot 2\left[\cos\left(\frac{\pi}{6} + \frac{\pi}{4}\right) + i\sin\left(\frac{\pi}{6} + \frac{\pi}{4}\right)\right] = 6\left(\cos\frac{5\pi}{12} + i\sin\frac{5\pi}{12}\right)$$

19. Dividing the complex numbers: $\dfrac{6\left(\cos\dfrac{\pi}{4} + i\sin\dfrac{\pi}{4}\right)}{3\left(\cos\dfrac{\pi}{6} + i\sin\dfrac{\pi}{6}\right)} = \dfrac{6}{2}\left[\cos\left(\dfrac{\pi}{4} - \dfrac{\pi}{6}\right) + i\sin\left(\dfrac{\pi}{4} - \dfrac{\pi}{6}\right)\right] = 2\left(\cos\dfrac{\pi}{12} + i\sin\dfrac{\pi}{12}\right)$

20. Using the law of cosines:

$$a^2 = b^2 + c^2 - 2bc \cos A$$

$$a^2 = 3^2 + 5^2 - 2(3)(5) \cos 50°$$

$$a^2 = 34 - 30 \cos 50°$$

$$a^2 = 14.7164$$

$$a \approx 3.8362$$

The perimeter is: $3 + 5 + 3.8362 \approx 11.84$ ft

21. The angle from the x-axis is $130°$. Finding the horizontal and vertical components:

$$v_1 = 10 \cos 130° \approx -6.4279 \qquad v_2 = 10 \sin 130° \approx 7.6604$$

The position vector is $\mathbf{v} = \langle -6.43, 7.66 \rangle$.

22. Finding the work: $W = \|\mathbf{F}\| d \cos\theta = 20(50) \cos 25° \approx 906.31$ ft-lbs

Chapter 8
Systems of Equations and Inequalities

8.1 Systems of Linear Equations and Inequalities in Two Variables

1. The intersection point is $(-1, 2)$.

3. Substituting $x = 3$: $y = 2x - 1 = 2(3) - 1 = 5$

The intersection point is $(3, 5)$.

5. Solving the second equation for x:
$$x + 2y = 8$$
$$x = -2y + 8$$
Substituting into the first equation:
$$2x - y = 6$$
$$2(-2y + 8) - y = 6$$
$$-4y + 16 - y = 6$$
$$-5y = -10$$
$$y = 2$$
$$x = -2(2) + 8 = 4$$

The intersection point is $(4, 2)$.

7. Substituting the point $(4, -2)$:
$$4 + 5(-2) = 4 - 10 = -6 \qquad -4 + 2(-2) = -4 - 4 = -8$$

9. Substituting the point $(0, 2)$:
$$2(0) - 3(2) = 0 - 6 = -6 \qquad -0 + 2(2) = 0 + 4 = 4$$

11. Substituting the point $(a, a - 5)$:
$$a - (a - 5) = a - a + 5 = 5 \qquad -2a + 2(a - 5) = -2a + 2a - 10 = -10$$

13. Multiply the first equation by 2 and add to the second equation:
$$2x + 4y = 14$$
$$-2x + y = 1$$
Adding yields:
$$5y = 15$$
$$y = 3$$

Substituting into the first equation:
$$x + 2y = 7$$
$$x + 2(3) = 7$$
$$x + 6 = 7$$
$$x = 1$$
The solution is: $x = 1, y = 3$

15. Adding the two equations yields:
$$3x = -3$$
$$x = -1$$
Substituting into the first equation:
$$-3x + y = 5$$
$$-3(-1) + y = 5$$
$$3 + y = 5$$
$$y = 2$$
The solution is: $x = -1, y = 2$

17. Multiply the first equation by -1 and add it to the second equation:
$$-4x - 2y = -10$$
$$4x + 2y = 3$$
Adding yields $0 = -7$, which is false. There is no solution to the system.

19. Adding the two equations yields:
$$4x = 8$$
$$x = 2$$
Substituting into the second equation:
$$x + y = -1$$
$$2 + y = -1$$
$$y = -3$$
The solution is: $x = 2, y = -3$

21. Multiply the first equation by 2 and add it to the second equation:
$$2x + 2y = 10$$
$$-2x - 2y = -10$$
Adding yields $0 = 0$, which is true. This is a dependent system.

23. Substituting $y = -3$ into the first equation:
$$3x - 6y = 2$$
$$3x - 6(-3) = 2$$
$$3x + 18 = 2$$
$$3x = -16$$
$$x = -\frac{16}{3}$$
The solution is: $x = -\frac{16}{3}, y = -3$

25. Multiply the first equation by 3 and the second equation by 2:
$$-6x - 9y = 0$$
$$6x + 10y = -4$$

Adding yields: $y = -4$

Substituting into the second equation:
$$3x + 5y = -2$$
$$3x + 5(-4) = -2$$
$$3x - 20 = -2$$
$$3x = 18$$
$$x = 6$$

The solution is: $x = 6, y = -4$

27. Multiply the second equation by -2 and add it to the first equation:
$$-3x + 2y = \frac{1}{2}$$
$$-8x - 2y = -6$$

Adding yields:
$$-11x = -\frac{11}{2}$$
$$x = \frac{1}{2}$$

Substituting into the second equation:
$$4x + y = 3$$
$$4\left(\frac{1}{2}\right) + y = 3$$
$$2 + y = 3$$
$$y = 1$$

The solution is: $x = \frac{1}{2}, y = 1$

29. Multiply the first equation by 6 and the second equation by 12 to clear fractions:
$$3x + 2y = -12$$
$$3x + 8y = -30$$

Multiply the first equation by -1 and add it to the second equation:
$$-3x - 2y = 12$$
$$3x + 8y = -30$$

Adding yields:
$$6y = -18$$
$$y = -3$$

Substituting into the first equation:
$$3x + 2y = -12$$
$$3x + 2(-3) = -12$$
$$3x - 6 = -12$$
$$3x = -6$$
$$x = -2$$

The solution is: $x = -2, y = -3$

31. The system is equivalent to:

$$3x + 3y = 1$$
$$-2x + y = 2$$

Multiply the second equation by –3 and add it to the first equation:

$$3x + 3y = 1$$
$$6x - 3y = -6$$

Adding yields:

$$9x = -5$$
$$x = -\frac{5}{9}$$

Substituting into the second equation:

$$-2x + y = 2$$
$$-2\left(-\frac{5}{9}\right) + y = 2$$
$$\frac{10}{9} + y = 2$$
$$y = \frac{8}{9}$$

The solution is: $x = -\frac{5}{9}, y = \frac{8}{9}$

33. Multiply the second equation by 6 to clear fractions:

$$x + 4y = -5$$
$$2x + 3y = 6$$

Multiply the first equation by –2 and add it to the second equation:

$$-2x - 8y = 10$$
$$2x + 3y = 6$$

Adding yields:

$$-5y = 16$$
$$y = -\frac{16}{5}$$

Substituting into the first equation:

$$x + 4y = -5$$
$$x + 4\left(-\frac{16}{5}\right) = -5$$
$$x - \frac{64}{5} = -5$$
$$x = \frac{39}{5}$$

The solution is: $x = \frac{39}{5}, y = -\frac{16}{5}$

35. Multiply the first equation by 6 to clear fractions:

$$3(x+1) + 2(y-1) = 6$$
$$3x + y = 7$$

Simplifying the first equation results in the system:

$$3x + 2y = 5$$
$$3x + y = 7$$

Multiply the second equation by –2 and add it to the first equation:
$$3x + 2y = 5$$
$$-6x - 2y = -14$$
Adding yields:
$$-3x = -9$$
$$x = 3$$
Substituting into the second equation:
$$3x + y = 7$$
$$3(3) + y = 7$$
$$9 + y = 7$$
$$y = -2$$
The solution is: $x = 3, y = -2$

37. The solution is: $x = -3.75, y = 2.875$

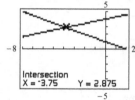

39. The solution is: $x = -0.75, y = 2.75$

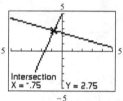

41. The red line is the equation $y = x$, and the blue line is the equation $y = -2x + 3$. The system is:
$$x - y = 0$$
$$2x + y = 3$$

43. Graphing the inequality $x < -2$:

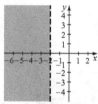

45. Graphing the inequality $-2x + y \geq -4$:

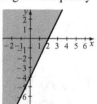

47. Graphing the inequality $x > y + 6$:

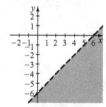

49. Graphing the inequality $3x - 4y > 12$:

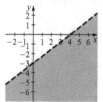

51. Graphing the inequality $3x + 5y > 10$:

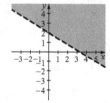

53. Graphing the system $\begin{cases} -2x + y \leq 8 \\ -x + y \geq 2 \end{cases}$:

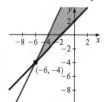

55. Graphing the system $\begin{cases} y \geq -2 \\ 5x + 2y \leq 10 \end{cases}$:

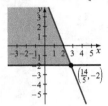

57. Graphing the system $\begin{cases} -x + y < 3 \\ x + y > -5 \end{cases}$:

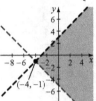

59. Graphing the system $\begin{cases} x + y \leq 4 \\ -4x + 2y \geq -1 \end{cases}$:

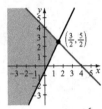

61. Graphing the system $\begin{cases} y \leq -2 \\ y \geq -5 \\ x \leq -1 \end{cases}$:

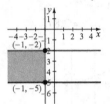

63. Graphing the system $\begin{cases} x + y \leq 4 \\ -x + y \leq 4 \\ x + 5y \geq 8 \end{cases}$:

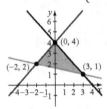

65. Graphing the system $\begin{cases} -3x + y \leq -1 \\ 4x + y \leq 6 \end{cases}$:

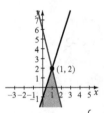

67. Graphing the system $\begin{cases} x \leq 0 \\ -5x + 4y \leq 20 \\ 3x + 4y \geq -12 \end{cases}$:

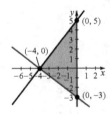

69. Graphing the system $\begin{cases} -\dfrac{4}{3}x + y \geq -5 \\ -4x + 3y \leq 13 \\ x + y \geq 2 \end{cases}$:

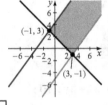

71. Evaluating the function at the corner points:

(x,y)	$P = 10x + 8y$
$(5,2)$	66
$(5,10)$	130
$(9,10)$	170
$(9,2)$	106

The maximum value is $P = 170$ when $x = 9$ and $y = 10$.

(x, y)	$P = 16x + 10y$
$(0, 0)$	0
$(5, 10)$	180

73. Evaluating the function at the corner points:

The minimum value is $P = 0$ when $x = 0$ and $y = 0$.

75. Let x represent the ticket sales and y represent the merchandise sales. The system of equations (in billions) is:

$$y = 4x$$
$$x + y = 3$$

Substituting into the second equation:

$$x + 4x = 3$$
$$5x = 3$$
$$x = 0.6$$
$$y = 4(0.6) = 2.4$$

The revenue from ticket sales was $0.6 billion = $600 million and the revenue from merchandise sales was $2.4 billion.

77. **a.** Let r represent the time spent running and w represent the time spent walking. The total number of calories is $330 + 450 + 220 = 1000$, so $\dfrac{1000}{4} = 250$ calories need to be burned. The system of equations is:

$$8r + 3w = 250$$
$$r + w = 40$$

Multiply the second equation by -3 and add to the first equation:

$$8r + 3w = 250$$
$$-3r - 3w = -120$$

Adding yields:

$$5r = 130$$
$$r = 26$$

Substituting into the second equation:

$$r + w = 40$$
$$26 + w = 40$$
$$w = 14$$

You should spend 26 minutes running and 14 minutes walking.

b. The system of equations is:

$$8r + 3w = 250$$
$$r + w = 20$$

Multiply the second equation by -3 and add to the first equation:

$$8r + 3w = 250$$
$$-3r - 3w = -60$$

Adding yields:

$$5r = 190$$
$$r = 38$$

Substituting into the second equation:

$$r + w = 20$$
$$38 + w = 20$$
$$w = -18$$

No, this solution isn't realistic, since the walking time cannot be negative.

79. Let x represent the number of advance tickets sold and y represent the number of other tickets sold.
The system of equations is:
$$x + y = 80$$
$$380x + 700y = 39{,}040$$
Multiply the first equation by -700 and add to the second equation:
$$-700x - 700y = -56{,}000$$
$$380x + 700y = 39{,}040$$
Adding yields:
$$-320x = -16{,}960$$
$$x = 53$$
Substituting into the first equation:
$$x + y = 80$$
$$53 + y = 80$$
$$y = 27$$
There were 53 advance tickets sold at \$380 and 27 other tickets sold at \$700.

81.   **a.**   The total volume can be written as: $x + y = 10$

      b.   The volume of acid can be written as:
$$0.10x + 0.25y = .15(10)$$
$$0.10x + 0.25y = 1.5$$

      c.   Multiply the first equation by -0.10 and add to the second equation:
$$-0.10x - 0.10y = -1$$
$$0.10x + 0.25y = 1.5$$
Adding yields:
$$0.15y = 0.5$$
$$y = \frac{10}{3} = 3\frac{1}{3}$$
Substituting into the first equation:
$$x + y = 10$$
$$x + \frac{10}{3} = 10$$
$$x = \frac{20}{3} = 6\frac{2}{3}$$
You need $6\frac{2}{3}$ gallons of 10% solution and $3\frac{1}{3}$ gallons of 25% solution for a 15% solution.

      d.   No. The acidity of the less acidic of the two solutions used to make the mixture is greater than the acidity desired.

83.   **a.**   The system of inequalities is: $\begin{cases} x + y \le 10{,}000 \\ x \ge 6000 \\ y \le 4000 \\ y \ge 0 \end{cases}$

      b.   Graphing the system of inequalities:

85. a. The system of inequalities is: $\begin{cases} x+y \le 200 \\ 6x+8y \ge 960 \\ x \ge 40 \\ y \ge 0 \end{cases}$

b. Graphing the system of inequalities:

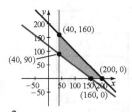

87. a. The system of inequalities is: $\begin{cases} x \ge 3y \\ y \ge 5 \\ x+y \le 30 \\ x \ge 0 \end{cases}$

b. Graphing the system of inequalities:

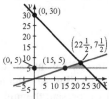

89. Let x represent the number of model 120 and y represent the number of model 140. The profit is given by: $P = 12x + 10y$

The constraints are given by: $\begin{cases} x+1.5y \le 1{,}000 \\ x \ge 300 \\ y \ge 0 \end{cases}$

Evaluating P at the corner points:

(x,y)	$P = 12x + 10y$
$(300,0)$	\$3,600
$(1000,0)$	\$12,000
$(300,467)$	\$8,270

They should make 1,000 of model 120 and none of model 140.

91. Let x represent the days driving and y represent the days busing. The time is given by: $T = \dfrac{4}{3}x + 2.5y$

The constraints are given by: $\begin{cases} 6x+3y \le 90 \\ x+y \ge 20 \\ x, y \ge 0 \end{cases}$

Evaluating T at the corner points:

(x,y)	$T = \dfrac{4}{3}x + 2.5y$
$(0,20)$	50
$(0,30)$	75
$(10,10)$	38.3

She should drive 10 days and bus 10 days to minimize her commuting time.

93. Let x represent the number of drivers and y represent the number of putters.
The profit is given by: $P = 3x + 2y$

The constraints are given by: $\begin{cases} 20 \le x \le 50 \\ 30 \le y \le 50 \\ x + y \le 80 \end{cases}$

Evaluating P at the corner points:

(x, y)	$P = 3x + 2y$
$(20, 30)$	\$120
$(20, 50)$	\$160
$(30, 50)$	\$190
$(50, 50)$	\$210

They should produce 50 drivers and 30 putters.

95. a. Graphing the system:

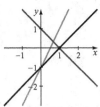

b. No, there is not a single point where all three lines intersect.
c. No, there is not an ordered pair that satisfies all three equations.

97. Let x represent the number of adult tickets and y represent the number of children tickets. The system of equations is:
$$x + y = 1{,}000$$
$$8x + 8y = 8{,}000$$

Since these equations are multiples of each other, there is no unique solution. The system is dependent.

8.2 Systems of Linear Equations in Three Variables

1. Substituting $x = 1, y = -2, z = 0$:
$$3(1) - 0 = 3$$
$$2(1) + (-2) - 2(0) = 0$$
$$3(1) - 2(-2) + 0 = 7$$

3. Substituting $x = 0, y = 1, z = -4$:
$$5(0) - 1 + 3(-4) = -13$$
$$0 - 1 + 2(-4) = -9$$
$$4(0) - 1 + (-4) = -5$$

5. Substituting $x = -9 - 11z, y = 5 + 7z$:
$$(-9 - 11z) + 2(5 + 7z) - 3z = -9 - 11z + 10 + 14z - 3z = 1$$
$$2(-9 - 11z) + 3(5 + 7z) + z = -18 - 22z + 15 + 21z + z = -3$$

7. Substituting $z = -2$ into the second equation:
$$-2y - z = 0$$
$$-2y - (-2) = 0$$
$$-2y + 2 = 0$$
$$-2y = -2$$
$$y = 1$$

Substituting $z = -2, y = 1$ into the first equation:
$$x - y + z = 1$$
$$x - 1 + (-2) = 1$$
$$x - 3 = 1$$
$$x = 4$$

The solution is: $x = 4, y = 1, z = -2$

9. Solving the third equation for w:
$$3w = 9$$
$$w = 3$$

Substituting $w = 3$ into the second equation:
$$v - w = 1$$
$$v - 3 = 1$$
$$v = 4$$

Substituting $w = 3$, $v = 4$ into the first equation:
$$-2u + v + 3w = -1$$
$$-2u + 4 + 3(3) = -1$$
$$-2u + 13 = -1$$
$$-2u = -14$$
$$u = 7$$

The solution is: $u = 7, v = 4, w = 3$

11. Adding the first two equations results in the system:
$$x + 2y \quad\;\; = 2$$
$$3y + 3z = 6$$
$$3y - 3z = -6$$

Multiplying the second equation by -1 and adding to the third equation results in the system:
$$x + 2y \quad\;\; = 2$$
$$3y + 3z = 6$$
$$-6z = -12$$

Solving the third equation for z:
$$-6z = -12$$
$$z = 2$$

Substituting $z = 2$ into the second equation:
$$3y + 3z = 6$$
$$3y + 3(2) = 6$$
$$3y + 6 = 6$$
$$3y = 0$$
$$y = 0$$

Substituting $z = 2$, $y = 0$ into the first equation:
$$x + 2y = 2$$
$$x + 2(0) = 2$$
$$x = 2$$

The solution is: $x = 2, y = 0, z = 2$

13. Adding twice the first equation to the second equation, and -3 times the first equation to the third equation results in the system:
$$x + 2y \quad\;\; = 0$$
$$8y + 8z = 8$$
$$-6y - 3z = -9$$

Dividing the second equation by 8 results in the system:
$$x + 2y \quad\;\; = 0$$
$$y + z = 1$$
$$-6y - 3z = -9$$

Adding 6 times the second equation to the third equation results in the system:
$$x + 2y \quad\;\; = 0$$
$$y + z = 1$$
$$3z = -3$$

Solving the third equation for z:
$$3z = -3$$
$$z = -1$$

Substituting $z = -1$ into the second equation:
$$y + z = 1$$
$$y + (-1) = 1$$
$$y = 2$$

Substituting $z = -1, y = 2$ into the first equation:
$$x + 2y = 0$$
$$x + 2(2) = 0$$
$$x = -4$$

The solution is: $x = -4, y = 2, z = -1$

15. Reversing the first and second equations results in the system:
$$x \quad - z = 2$$
$$5x + y \quad = 0$$
$$4y + z = -2$$

Adding -5 times the first equation to the second equation results in the system:
$$x \quad - z = 2$$
$$y + 5z = -10$$
$$4y + z = -2$$

Adding -4 times the second equation to the third equation results in the system:
$$x \quad - z = 2$$
$$y + 5z = -10$$
$$-19z = 38$$

Solving the third equation for z:
$$-19z = 38$$
$$z = -2$$

Substituting $z = -2$ into the second equation:
$$y + 5z = -10$$
$$y + 5(-2) = -10$$
$$y - 10 = -10$$
$$y = 0$$

Substituting $z = -2, y = 0$ into the first equation:
$$x - z = 2$$
$$x - (-2) = 2$$
$$x + 2 = 2$$
$$x = 0$$

The solution is: $x = 0, y = 0, z = -2$

17. Adding -1 times the first equation to the third equation results in the system:
$$x - 4y - 3z = -3$$
$$y + z = 2$$
$$7y + 6z = 3$$

Adding -7 times the second equation to the third equation results in the system:
$$x - 4y - 3z = -3$$
$$y + z = 2$$
$$-z = -11$$

Solving the third equation for z:
$$-z = -11$$
$$z = 11$$

Substituting $z = 11$ into the second equation:
$$y + z = 2$$
$$y + 11 = 2$$
$$y = -9$$

Substituting $z = 11, y = -9$ into the first equation:
$$x - 4y - 3z = -3$$
$$x - 4(-9) - 3(11) = -3$$
$$x + 3 = -3$$
$$x = -6$$

The solution is: $x = -6, y = -9, z = 11$

19. Reversing the first and second equations results in the system:
$$x - y - z = 1$$
$$3x + 2y + 3z = 1$$
$$x + 4y + 5z = -1$$

Adding –3 times the first equation to the second equation, and –1 times the first equation to the third equation results in the system:
$$x - y - z = 1$$
$$5y + 6z = -2$$
$$5y + 6z = -2$$

Adding –1 times the second equation to the third equation results in the system:
$$x - y - z = 1$$
$$5y + 6z = -2$$
$$0 = 0$$

Solving the second equation for z:

$$5y + 6z = -2$$
$$6z = -2 - 5y$$
$$z = -\frac{1}{3} - \frac{5}{6}y$$

Substituting into the first equation:

$$x - y - z = 1$$
$$x = y + z + 1$$
$$x = y + \left(-\frac{1}{3} - \frac{5}{6}y \right) + 1$$
$$x = \frac{2}{3} + \frac{1}{6}y$$

The system is dependent. The solution is: $x = \dfrac{2}{3} + \dfrac{1}{6}y,\ z = -\dfrac{1}{3} - \dfrac{5}{6}y$

21. Adding –1 times the first equation to the third equation results in the system:
$$x \quad\ + 2z = 0$$
$$y + z = -1$$
$$8y + 2z = 1$$

Adding –8 times the second equation to the third equation results in the system:
$$x \quad\ + 2z = 0$$
$$y + z = -1$$
$$-6z = 9$$

Solving the third equation for z:

$$-6z = 9$$
$$z = -\frac{3}{2}$$

Substituting $z = -\dfrac{3}{2}$ into the second equation:

$$y + z = -1$$
$$y - \frac{3}{2} = -1$$
$$y = \frac{1}{2}$$

Substituting $z = -\dfrac{3}{2}$, $y = \dfrac{1}{2}$ into the first equation:

$$x + 2z = 0$$
$$x + 2\left(-\frac{3}{2} \right) = 0$$
$$x - 3 = 0$$
$$x = 3$$

The solution is: $x = 3, y = \dfrac{1}{2}, z = -\dfrac{3}{2}$

23. Reversing the first and second equations results in the system:

$$x - 4y + z = 6$$
$$5x \quad\;\; + 3z = 2$$
$$x + 8y + z = -10$$

Adding -5 times the first equation to the second equation, and -1 times the first equation to the third equation results in the system:

$$x - 4y + \;\; z = 6$$
$$20y - 2z = -28$$
$$12y = -16$$

Solving the third equation for y:

$$12y = -16$$
$$y = -\frac{4}{3}$$

Substituting $y = -\dfrac{4}{3}$ into the second equation:

$$20y - 2z = -28$$
$$10y - z = -14$$
$$10\left(-\frac{4}{3}\right) - z = -14$$
$$-\frac{40}{3} - z = -14$$
$$-z = -\frac{2}{3}$$
$$z = \frac{2}{3}$$

Substituting $y = -\dfrac{4}{3}, z = \dfrac{2}{3}$ into the first equation:

$$x - 4y + z = 6$$
$$x - 4\left(-\frac{4}{3}\right) + \frac{2}{3} = 6$$
$$x + 6 = 6$$
$$x = 0$$

The solution is: $x = 0, y = -\dfrac{4}{3}, z = \dfrac{2}{3}$

25. Reversing the first and third equations results in the system:

$$x + 4y - 2z = 0$$
$$2x - y + \;\; z = 2$$
$$5x + 6y - 2z = 2$$

Adding -2 times the first equation to the second equation, and -5 times the first equation to the third equation results in the system:

$$x + 4y - 2z = 0$$
$$-9y + 5z = 2$$
$$-14y + 8z = 2$$

Adding $-\dfrac{14}{9}$ times the second equation to the third equation results in the system:

$$x + 4y - 2z = 0$$
$$-9y + 5z = 2$$
$$\frac{2}{9}z = -\frac{10}{9}$$

Solving the third equation for z:

$$\frac{2}{9}z = -\frac{10}{9}$$
$$z = -5$$

Substituting $z = -5$ into the second equation:
$$-9y + 5z = 2$$
$$-9y + 5(-5) = 2$$
$$-9y - 25 = 2$$
$$-9y = 27$$
$$y = -3$$

Substituting $z = -5, y = -3$ into the first equation:
$$x + 4y - 2z = 0$$
$$x + 4(-3) - 2(-5) = 0$$
$$x - 12 + 10 = 0$$
$$x - 2 = 0$$
$$x = 2$$

The solution is: $x = 2, y = -3, z = -5$

27. Reversing the first and second equations results in the system:
$$-u + 4v + w = -1$$
$$3u - 2v + 2w = -2$$
$$5u + 3v + 5w = 1$$

Adding 3 times the first equation to the second equation, and 5 times the first equation to the third equation results in the system:
$$-u + 4v + \quad w = -1$$
$$10v + \quad 5w = -5$$
$$23v + 10w = -4$$

Adding $-\dfrac{23}{10}$ times the second equation to the third equation results in the system:
$$-u + 4v + \quad w = -1$$
$$10v + 5w = -5$$
$$-\dfrac{3}{2}w = \dfrac{15}{2}$$

Solving the third equation for w:
$$-\dfrac{3}{2}w = \dfrac{15}{2}$$
$$w = -5$$

Substituting $w = -5$ into the second equation:
$$10v + 5w = -5$$
$$10v + 5(-5) = -5$$
$$10v - 25 = -5$$
$$10v = 20$$
$$v = 2$$

Substituting $w = -5, v = 2$ into the first equation:
$$-u + 4v + w = -1$$
$$-u + 4(2) - 5 = -1$$
$$-u + 3 = -1$$
$$-u = -4$$
$$u = 4$$

The solution is: $u = 4, v = 2, w = -5$

29. Adding -1 times the second equation to the first equation results in the system:
$$r + \quad 2s - 3t = 1$$
$$3r - \quad s + \quad t = 6$$
$$-6r + 3s - 2t = -1$$

Adding -3 times the first equation to the second equation, and 6 times the first equation to the third equation results in the system:
$$r + \quad 2s - 3t = 1$$
$$-7s + 10t = 3$$
$$15s - 20t = 5$$

Adding 2 times the second equation to the third equation results in the system:
$$r + \quad 2s - 3t = 1$$
$$-7s + 10t = 3$$
$$s \quad\quad = 11$$

Substituting $s = 11$ into the second equation:
$$-7s + 10t = 3$$
$$-7(11) + 10t = 3$$
$$-77 + 10t = 3$$
$$10t = 80$$
$$t = 8$$

Substituting $s = 11, t = 8$ into the first equation:
$$r + 2s - 3t = 1$$
$$r + 2(11) - 3(8) = 1$$
$$r + 22 - 24 = 1$$
$$r - 2 = 1$$
$$r = 3$$

The solution is: $r = 3, s = 11, t = 8$

31. Adding -2 times the first equation to the second equation results in the system:
$$x - 2y - z = 7$$
$$y + 3z = -4$$

Solving the second equation for y:
$$y + 3z = -4$$
$$y = -4 - 3z$$

Substituting $y = -4 - 3z$ into the first equation:
$$x - 2y - z = 7$$
$$x - 2(-4 - 3z) - z = 7$$
$$x + 8 + 5z = 7$$
$$x = -1 - 5z$$

The solution is: $x = -1 - 5z, \; y = -4 - 3z$

33. Adding -3 times the first equation to the second equation results in the system:
$$r + 2s = 1$$
$$-s + 4t = 4$$

Solving the second equation for s:
$$-s + 4t = 4$$
$$-s = 4 - 4t$$
$$s = -4 + 4t$$

Substituting $s = -4 + 4t$ into the first equation:
$$r + 2s = 1$$
$$r + 2(-4 + 4t) = 1$$
$$r - 8 + 8t = 1$$
$$r = 9 - 8t$$

The solution is: $r = 9 - 8t, \; s = -4 + 4t$

35. Adding the first and second equations results in the system:
$$-3x - 2y - z = 7$$
$$y = 4$$

Substituting $y = 4$ into the first equation:
$$-3x - 2y - z = 7$$
$$-3x - 2(4) - z = 7$$
$$-3x - 8 - z = 7$$
$$-z = 15 + 3x$$
$$z = -15 - 3x$$

The solution is: $y = 4, \; z = -15 - 3x$

37. Adding -3 times the first equation to the second equation, and 2 times the first equation to the third equation results in the system:
$$x - 2y - 5z = -3$$
$$8z = 10$$
$$2z = -10$$

Dividing the second equation by 8 and the third equation by 2 results in the system:
$$x - 2y - 5z = -3$$
$$z = \frac{5}{4}$$
$$z = -5$$

Since this produces two different values for z, there is no solution. The system is inconsistent.

39. Let x represent the percentage invested in mutual funds, y the percentage invested in high-yield bonds, and z the percentage invested in the CD. The system of equations is:

$$x+y+z=1 \qquad\qquad x+y+z=1$$
$$2x+y+5z=2.7 \quad \text{or} \quad 2x+y+5z=2.7$$
$$x=y+z \qquad\qquad x-y-z=0$$

Adding -2 times the first equation to the second equation, and -1 times the first equation to the third equation yields the system:

$$x+y+z=1$$
$$-y+3z=0.7$$
$$-2y-2z=-1$$

Adding -2 times the second equation to the third equation yields the system:

$$x+y+z=1$$
$$-y+3z=0.7$$
$$-8z=-2.4$$

Solving the third equation for z:

$$-8z=-2.4$$
$$z=0.3$$

Substituting $z=0.3$ into the second equation:

$$-y+3z=0.7$$
$$y-3(0.3)=-0.7$$
$$y-0.9=-0.7$$
$$y=0.2$$

Substituting $z=0.3$, $y=0.2$ into the first equation:

$$x+y+z=1$$
$$x+0.2+0.3=1$$
$$x+0.5=1$$
$$x=0.5$$

The investor should allocate 50% to the mutual fund, 20% to the high-yield bond, and 30% to the CD.

41. The system of equations is:

$$A+B\quad=55 \qquad\qquad A+B\quad=55$$
$$B+C=80 \quad \text{or} \quad B+C=80$$
$$B+C=4A \qquad -4A+B+C=0$$

Adding 4 times the first equation to the third equation yields the system:

$$A+B\quad=55$$
$$B+C=80$$
$$5B+C=220$$

Adding -5 times the second equation to the third equation yields the system:

$$A+B\quad=55$$
$$B+C=80$$
$$-4C=-180$$

Solving the third equation for C:

$$-4C=-180$$
$$C=45$$

Substituting $C=45$ into the second equation:

$$B+C=80$$
$$B+45=80$$
$$B=35$$

Substituting $C=45$, $B=35$ into the first equation:

$$A+B=55$$
$$A+35=55$$
$$A=20$$

The amperages are 20 ohms for A, 35 ohms for B, and 45 ohms for C.

43. The system of equations is:
$$A + B + 2C = 140$$
$$2A + B \quad = 125$$
$$B + 2C = 95$$

Adding −2 times the first equation to the second equation yields the system:
$$A + B + 2C = 140$$
$$-B - 4C = -155$$
$$B + 2C = 95$$

Adding the second equation to the third equation yields the system:
$$A + B + 2C = 140$$
$$-B - 4C = -155$$
$$-2C = -60$$

Solving the third equation for C:
$$-2C = -60$$
$$C = 30$$

Substituting $C = 30$ into the second equation:
$$-B - 4C = -155$$
$$B + 4(30) = 155$$
$$B + 120 = 155$$
$$B = 35$$

Substituting $C = 30, B = 45$ into the first equation:
$$A + B + 2C = 140$$
$$A + 35 + 2(30) = 140$$
$$A + 95 = 140$$
$$A = 45$$

Level A is $45 per day, level B is $35 per day, and level C is $30 per day.

45. Let x represent the Florida market share, y represent the New York market share, and z represent the California market share. The system of equations is:
$$x + y + z = 68.7 \qquad x + y + z = 68.7$$
$$x = y \qquad \text{or} \qquad x - y \quad = 0$$
$$z = x - 1.2 \qquad -x \quad + z = -1.2$$

Adding −1 times the first equation to the second equation, and the first equation to the third equation yields the system:
$$x + y + z = 68.7$$
$$-2y - z = -68.7$$
$$y + 2z = 67.5$$

Reversing the second and third equations results in the system:
$$x + y + z = 68.7$$
$$y + 2z = 67.5$$
$$-2y - z = -68.7$$

Adding 2 times the second equation to the third equation yields the system:
$$x + y + z = 68.7$$
$$y + 2z = 67.5$$
$$3z = 66.3$$

Solving the third equation for z:
$$3z = 66.3$$
$$z = 22.1$$

Substituting $z = 22.1$ into the second equation:
$$y + 2z = 67.5$$
$$y + 2(22.1) = 67.5$$
$$y + 44.2 = 67.5$$
$$y = 23.3$$

Substituting $z = 22.1, y = 23.3$ into the first equation:
$$x + y + z = 68.7$$
$$x + 23.3 + 22.1 = 68.7$$
$$x + 45.4 = 68.7$$
$$x = 23.3$$

Florida's and New York's market shares were both 23.3% and California's market share was 22.1%.

47. **a.** The ordered pair $(1,1)$ yields:
$$f(1) = 1$$
$$a(1)^2 + b(1) + c = 1$$
$$a + b + c = 1$$
The ordered pair $(-2,-8)$ yields:
$$f(-2) = -8$$
$$a(-2)^2 + b(-2) + c = -8$$
$$4a - 2b + c = -8$$

b. The system of equations is:
$$a - b + c = -3$$
$$a + b + c = 1$$
$$4a - 2b + c = -8$$
Adding -1 times the first equation to the second equation, and -4 times the first equation to the third equation yields the system:
$$a - b + c = -3$$
$$2b = 4$$
$$2b - 3c = 4$$
Adding -1 times the second equation to the third equation yields the system:
$$a - b + c = -3$$
$$2b = 4$$
$$-3c = 0$$
Solving the third equation for c:
$$-3c = 0$$
$$c = 0$$

Substituting $c = 0$ into the second equation:
$$2b = 4$$
$$b = 2$$

Substituting $c = 0, b = 2$ into the first equation:
$$a - b + c = -3$$
$$a - 2 + 0 = -3$$
$$a = -1$$

The solution is: $a = -1, b = 2, c = 0$

c. The function is: $f(x) = -x^2 + 2x$

49. Using the point $(2,6)$:
$$f(2) = 6$$
$$4a + 2b + c = 6$$
Using the point $(1,1)$:
$$f(1) = 1$$
$$a + b + c = 1$$
The vertex of $(1,1)$ yields:
$$\frac{-b}{2a} = 1$$
$$-b = 2a$$
$$2a + b = 0$$

The system of equations is:
$$a+b+c=1$$
$$4a+2b+c=6$$
$$2a+b=0$$

Adding -4 times the first equation to the second equation, and -2 times the first equation to the third equation yields the system:
$$a+b+c=1$$
$$-2b-3c=2$$
$$-b-2c=-2$$

Reversing the second and third equations results in the system:
$$a+b+c=1$$
$$-b-2c=-2$$
$$-2b-3c=2$$

Adding -2 times the second equation to the third equation yields the system:
$$a+b+c=1$$
$$-b-2c=-2$$
$$c=6$$

Substituting $c=6$ into the second equation:
$$-b-2c=-2$$
$$b+2(6)=2$$
$$b+12=2$$
$$b=-10$$

Substituting $c=6$, $b=-10$ into the first equation:
$$a+b+c=1$$
$$a-10+6=1$$
$$a-4=1$$
$$a=5$$

The function is: $f(x)=5x^2-10x+6$

8.3 Solving Systems of Equations Using Matrices

1. The augmented matrix is: $\begin{bmatrix} 4 & 1 & -2 & | & 6 \\ -1 & -1 & 1 & | & -2 \\ 3 & 0 & -1 & | & 4 \end{bmatrix}$

3. The augmented matrix is: $\begin{bmatrix} 3 & -2 & 1 & | & -1 \\ 1 & 1 & -4 & | & 3 \\ -2 & -1 & 3 & | & 0 \end{bmatrix}$

5. The augmented matrix is: $\begin{bmatrix} 6 & -2 & 1 & | & 0 \\ -5 & 1 & -3 & | & -2 \\ 2 & -3 & 5 & | & 7 \end{bmatrix}$

7. The augmented matrix is: $\begin{bmatrix} 1 & 1 & 2 & | & -3 \\ -3 & 2 & 1 & | & 1 \end{bmatrix}$

9. Multiplying the second row by $\dfrac{1}{2}$: $\begin{bmatrix} 1 & -2 & 0 & | & -1 \\ 1 & -4 & -1 & | & \dfrac{1}{2} \\ 3 & 5 & 1 & | & 2 \end{bmatrix}$

11. Switching row 1 and row 2: $\begin{bmatrix} 2 & -8 & -2 & | & 1 \\ 1 & -2 & 0 & | & -1 \\ 3 & 5 & 1 & | & 2 \end{bmatrix}$

13. Multiplying the first row by 2 and adding to the second row: $\begin{bmatrix} 1 & -2 & 0 & | & -1 \\ 4 & -12 & -2 & | & -1 \\ 3 & 5 & 1 & | & 2 \end{bmatrix}$

15. The system of equations is: $\begin{cases} 1x + 0y = -7 \\ 0x + 1y = 3 \end{cases}$

It is consistent, with a solution of: $x = -7, y = 3$

17. The system of equations is: $\begin{cases} 2x + 0y = 6 \\ 0x + 1y = 5 \end{cases}$

It is consistent, with a solution of: $x = 3, y = 5$

19. The system of equations is: $\begin{cases} x & +\, 3z = 5 \\ & y - 2z = -2 \\ & 0 = 0 \end{cases}$

It is consistent. Solving in terms of z:

$$y - 2z = -2 \qquad\qquad x + 3z = 5$$
$$y = -2 + 2z \qquad\qquad x = 5 - 3z$$

The solution is: $x = 5 - 3z, \ y = -2 + 2z$

21. The system of equations is: $\begin{cases} x & -\, 5u = 2 \\ & y - 2u = -3 \\ & z + 3u = 5 \end{cases}$

It is consistent. Solving in terms of u:

$$z + 3u = 5 \qquad y - 2u = -3 \qquad x - 5u = 2$$
$$z = 5 - 3u \qquad y = -3 + 2u \qquad x = 2 + 5u$$

The solution is: $x = 2 + 5u, \ y = -3 + 2u, \ z = 5 - 3u$

23. Form the augmented matrix: $\left[\begin{array}{cc|c} 1 & 3 & 10 \\ -2 & -5 & -12 \end{array}\right]$

Adding 2 times the first row to the second row: $\left[\begin{array}{cc|c} 1 & 3 & 10 \\ 0 & 1 & 8 \end{array}\right]$

Substituting $y = 8$ into the first equation:

$$x + 3y = 10$$
$$x + 3(8) = 10$$
$$x + 24 = 10$$
$$x = -14$$

The solution is: $x = -14, y = 8$

25. Form the augmented matrix: $\left[\begin{array}{cc|c} -2 & 1 & -5 \\ 4 & -1 & 6 \end{array}\right]$

Adding 2 times the first row to the second row: $\left[\begin{array}{cc|c} -2 & 1 & -5 \\ 0 & 1 & -4 \end{array}\right]$

Substituting $y = -4$ into the first equation:

$$-2x + y = -5$$
$$-2x - 4 = -5$$
$$-2x = -1$$
$$x = \frac{1}{2}$$

The solution is: $x = \frac{1}{2}, y = -4$

27. Form the augmented matrix: $\begin{bmatrix} -1 & 1 & | & 2 \\ 7 & -4 & | & -2 \end{bmatrix}$

Adding 7 times the first row to the second row: $\begin{bmatrix} -1 & 1 & | & 2 \\ 0 & 3 & | & 12 \end{bmatrix}$

Solving the second equation for y:
$$3y = 12$$
$$y = 4$$

Substituting $y = 4$ into the first equation:
$$-x + y = 2$$
$$-x + 4 = 2$$
$$-x = -2$$
$$x = 2$$

The solution is: $x = 2, y = 4$

29. Form the augmented matrix: $\begin{bmatrix} 1 & 2 & | & 1 \\ 1 & 5 & | & -2 \end{bmatrix}$

Adding -1 times the first row to the second row: $\begin{bmatrix} 1 & 2 & | & 1 \\ 0 & 3 & | & -3 \end{bmatrix}$

Solving the second equation for y:
$$3y = -3$$
$$y = -1$$

Substituting $y = -1$ into the first equation:
$$x + 2y = 1$$
$$x + 2(-1) = 1$$
$$x - 2 = 1$$
$$x = 3$$

The solution is: $x = 3, y = -1$

31. Form the augmented matrix: $\begin{bmatrix} 5 & 3 & | & -1 \\ -10 & -6 & | & 2 \end{bmatrix}$

Adding 2 times the first row to the second row: $\begin{bmatrix} 5 & 3 & | & -1 \\ 0 & 0 & | & 0 \end{bmatrix}$

The system is dependent. Solving the first equation for y:
$$5x + 3y = -1$$
$$3y = -1 - 5x$$
$$y = -\frac{5}{3}x - \frac{1}{3}$$

The solution is: $y = -\dfrac{1}{3} - \dfrac{5}{3}x$

33. Form the augmented matrix: $\begin{bmatrix} 2 & -3 & | & 7 \\ 4 & -6 & | & 9 \end{bmatrix}$

Adding -2 times the first row to the second row: $\begin{bmatrix} 2 & -3 & | & 7 \\ 0 & 0 & | & -5 \end{bmatrix}$

The system is inconsistent. There is no solution.

35. Form the augmented matrix: $\begin{bmatrix} 1 & 1 & 1 & | & 3 \\ 1 & 2 & 1 & | & 5 \\ -2 & 1 & -1 & | & 4 \end{bmatrix}$

Adding −1 times the first row to the second row and 2 times the first row to the third row: $\begin{bmatrix} 1 & 1 & 1 & | & 3 \\ 0 & 1 & 0 & | & 2 \\ 0 & 3 & 1 & | & 10 \end{bmatrix}$

Adding −3 times the second row to the third row: $\begin{bmatrix} 1 & 1 & 1 & | & 3 \\ 0 & 1 & 0 & | & 2 \\ 0 & 0 & 1 & | & 4 \end{bmatrix}$

Substituting $y = 2$, $z = 4$ into the first equation:

$x + y + z = 3$

$x + 2 + 4 = 3$

$x + 6 = 3$

$x = -3$

The solution is: $x = -3, y = 2, z = 4$

37. Form the augmented matrix: $\begin{bmatrix} 1 & 3 & -2 & | & 4 \\ -5 & -3 & -2 & | & -8 \\ 1 & -1 & -1 & | & 0 \end{bmatrix}$

Adding 5 times the first row to the second row and −1 times the first row to the third row: $\begin{bmatrix} 1 & 3 & -2 & | & 4 \\ 0 & 12 & -12 & | & 12 \\ 0 & -4 & 1 & | & -4 \end{bmatrix}$

Dividing the second row by 12: $\begin{bmatrix} 1 & 3 & -2 & | & 4 \\ 0 & 1 & -1 & | & 1 \\ 0 & -4 & 1 & | & -4 \end{bmatrix}$

Adding 4 times the second row to the third row: $\begin{bmatrix} 1 & 3 & -2 & | & 4 \\ 0 & 1 & -1 & | & 1 \\ 0 & 0 & -3 & | & 0 \end{bmatrix}$

Solving the third equation for z:

$-3z = 0$

$z = 0$

Substituting $z = 0$ into the second equation:

$y - z = 1$

$y - 0 = 1$

$y = 1$

Substituting $z = 0$, $y = 1$ into the first equation:

$x + 3y - 2z = 4$

$x + 3(1) - 2(0) = 4$

$x + 3 = 4$

$x = 1$

The solution is: $x = 1, y = 1, z = 0$

39. Form the augmented matrix: $\begin{bmatrix} 3 & -4 & 0 & | & 14 \\ 1 & -1 & 2 & | & 14 \\ -1 & 0 & 4 & | & 18 \end{bmatrix}$

Switching the first and second rows: $\begin{bmatrix} 1 & -1 & 2 & | & 14 \\ 3 & -4 & 0 & | & 14 \\ -1 & 0 & 4 & | & 18 \end{bmatrix}$

Adding –3 times the first row to the second row and the first row to the third row: $\begin{bmatrix} 1 & -1 & 2 & | & 14 \\ 0 & -1 & -6 & | & -28 \\ 0 & -1 & 6 & | & 32 \end{bmatrix}$

Adding –1 times the second row to the third row: $\begin{bmatrix} 1 & -1 & 2 & | & 14 \\ 0 & -1 & -6 & | & -28 \\ 0 & 0 & 12 & | & 60 \end{bmatrix}$

Solving the third equation for z:

$12z = 60$

$z = 5$

Substituting $z = 5$ into the second equation:

$-y - 6z = -28$

$y + 6(5) = 28$

$y + 30 = 28$

$y = -2$

Substituting $z = 5$, $y = -2$ into the first equation:

$x - y + 2z = 14$

$x - (-2) + 2(5) = 14$

$x + 12 = 14$

$x = 2$

The solution is: $x = 2, y = -2, z = 5$

41. Form the augmented matrix: $\begin{bmatrix} 1 & 2 & -1 & | & 2 \\ -2 & 1 & -3 & | & 6 \\ -1 & 3 & -4 & | & 8 \end{bmatrix}$

Adding 2 times the first row to the second row and the first row to the third row: $\begin{bmatrix} 1 & 2 & -1 & | & 2 \\ 0 & 5 & -5 & | & 10 \\ 0 & 5 & -5 & | & 10 \end{bmatrix}$

Adding –1 times the second row to the third row: $\begin{bmatrix} 1 & 2 & -1 & | & 2 \\ 0 & 5 & -5 & | & 10 \\ 0 & 0 & 0 & | & 0 \end{bmatrix}$

Solving the second equation equation for y:

$5y - 5z = 10$

$y - z = 2$

$y = 2 + z$

Substituting $y = 2 + z$ into the first equation:

$x + 2y - z = 2$

$x + 2(2 + z) - z = 2$

$x + 4 + z = 2$

$x = -2 - z$

The solution is: $x = -2 - z, \ y = 2 + z$

An alternate form of the solution is: $x = -y, \ z = y - 2$

43. Form the augmented matrix: $\begin{bmatrix} -1 & 2 & -3 & | & 2 \\ 2 & 3 & 2 & | & 1 \\ 3 & 1 & 5 & | & 1 \end{bmatrix}$

Adding 2 times the first row to the second row and 3 times the first row to the third row: $\begin{bmatrix} -1 & 2 & -3 & | & 2 \\ 0 & 7 & -4 & | & 5 \\ 0 & 7 & -4 & | & 7 \end{bmatrix}$

Adding –1 times the second row to the third row: $\begin{bmatrix} -1 & 2 & -3 & | & 2 \\ 0 & 7 & -4 & | & 5 \\ 0 & 0 & 0 & | & 2 \end{bmatrix}$

The system is inconsistent. There is no solution.

45. Form the augmented matrix: $\begin{bmatrix} -1 & 4 & 3 & | & 6 \\ 2 & -8 & -4 & | & 8 \end{bmatrix}$

Adding 2 times the first row to the second row: $\begin{bmatrix} -1 & 4 & 3 & | & 6 \\ 0 & 0 & 2 & | & 20 \end{bmatrix}$

Solving the second equation for z:
$$2z = 20$$
$$z = 10$$

Substituting $z = 10$ into the first equation:
$$-x + 4y + 3z = 6$$
$$-x + 4y + 3(10) = 6$$
$$-x + 4y + 30 = 6$$
$$-x = -24 - 4y$$
$$x = 4y + 24$$

The solution is: $x = 4y + 24$, $z = 10$

47. Form the augmented matrix: $\begin{bmatrix} 3 & 4 & -8 & | & 14 \\ 2 & -2 & 4 & | & 28 \end{bmatrix}$

Switching the first and second rows: $\begin{bmatrix} 2 & -2 & 4 & | & 28 \\ 3 & 4 & -8 & | & 14 \end{bmatrix}$

Dividing the first row by 2: $\begin{bmatrix} 1 & -1 & 2 & | & 14 \\ 3 & 4 & -8 & | & 14 \end{bmatrix}$

Adding -3 times the first row to the second row: $\begin{bmatrix} 1 & -1 & 2 & | & 14 \\ 0 & 7 & -14 & | & -28 \end{bmatrix}$

Solving the second equation for s:
$$7s - 14t = -28$$
$$7s = 14t - 28$$
$$s = 2t - 4$$

Substituting $s = 2t - 4$ into the first equation:
$$r - s + 2t = 14$$
$$r - (2t - 4) + 2t = 14$$
$$r - 2t + 4 + 2t = 14$$
$$r + 4 = 14$$
$$r = 10$$

The solution is: $r = 10$, $s = 2t - 4$

49. Form the augmented matrix: $\begin{bmatrix} 3 & 4 & -8 & | & 10 \\ -6 & -8 & 16 & | & 20 \end{bmatrix}$

Adding 2 times the first row to the second row: $\begin{bmatrix} 3 & 4 & -8 & | & 10 \\ 0 & 0 & 0 & | & 40 \end{bmatrix}$

The system is inconsistent. There is no solution.

51. First re-write the system as: $\begin{cases} z + 2y & = 0 \\ z & - 5x = -1 \\ 2y + 3x = 3 \end{cases}$

Form the augmented matrix: $\begin{bmatrix} 1 & 2 & 0 & | & 0 \\ 1 & 0 & -5 & | & -1 \\ 0 & 2 & 3 & | & 3 \end{bmatrix}$

Adding -1 times the first row to the second row: $\begin{bmatrix} 1 & 2 & 0 & | & 0 \\ 0 & -2 & -5 & | & -1 \\ 0 & 2 & 3 & | & 3 \end{bmatrix}$

Adding the second row to the third row: $\begin{bmatrix} 1 & 2 & 0 & | & 0 \\ 0 & -2 & -5 & | & -1 \\ 0 & 0 & -2 & | & 2 \end{bmatrix}$

Solving the third equation for x:
$$-2x = 2$$
$$x = -1$$

Substituting $x = -1$ into the second equation:
$$-2y - 5x = -1$$
$$2y + 5(-1) = 1$$
$$2y - 5 = 1$$
$$2y = 6$$
$$y = 3$$

Substituting $x = -1$, $y = 3$ into the first equation:
$$z + 2y = 0$$
$$z + 2(3) = 0$$
$$z = -6$$

The solution is: $x = -1, y = 3, z = -6$

53. Let c represent the pounds of Columbian, j represent the pounds of Java, and k represent the pounds of Kona in the mixture. The system of equations is:

$$c + j + k = 10$$
$$c = 2(j + k)$$
$$k = \frac{1}{2}j$$

which can be written as

$$c + j + k = 10$$
$$c - 2j - 2k = 0$$
$$j - 2k = 0$$

Form the augmented matrix: $\begin{bmatrix} 1 & 1 & 1 & | & 10 \\ 1 & -2 & -2 & | & 0 \\ 0 & 1 & -2 & | & 0 \end{bmatrix}$

Adding -1 times the first row to the second row: $\begin{bmatrix} 1 & 1 & 1 & | & 10 \\ 0 & -3 & -3 & | & -10 \\ 0 & 1 & -2 & | & 0 \end{bmatrix}$

Switching the second and third rows: $\begin{bmatrix} 1 & 1 & 1 & | & 10 \\ 0 & 1 & -2 & | & 0 \\ 0 & -3 & -3 & | & -10 \end{bmatrix}$

Adding 3 times the second row to the third row: $\begin{bmatrix} 1 & 1 & 1 & | & 10 \\ 0 & 1 & -2 & | & 0 \\ 0 & 0 & -9 & | & -10 \end{bmatrix}$

Solving the third equation for k:
$$-9k = -10$$
$$k = \frac{10}{9} = 1\frac{1}{9}$$

Substituting $k = \frac{10}{9}$ into the second equation:
$$j - 2k = 0$$
$$j - 2\left(\frac{10}{9}\right) = 0$$
$$j = \frac{20}{9} = 2\frac{2}{9}$$

Substituting $k = \frac{10}{9}$, $j = \frac{20}{9}$ into the first equation:
$$c + j + k = 10$$
$$c + \frac{20}{9} + \frac{10}{9} = 10$$
$$c + \frac{30}{9} = 10$$
$$c = \frac{20}{3} = 6\frac{2}{3}$$

The blend should have $6\frac{2}{3}$ pounds of Colombian, $2\frac{2}{9}$ pounds of Java, and $1\frac{1}{9}$ pounds of Kona.

55. Let x represent the number of cheese pizzas ordered and y the number of pepperoni pizzas ordered.
The system of equations is:
$$x + y = 8$$
$$5x + 6y = 43$$

Form the augmented matrix: $\begin{bmatrix} 1 & 1 & | & 8 \\ 5 & 6 & | & 43 \end{bmatrix}$

Adding -5 times the first row to the second row: $\begin{bmatrix} 1 & 1 & | & 8 \\ 0 & 1 & | & 3 \end{bmatrix}$

Substituting $y = 3$ into the first equation:
$$x + y = 8$$
$$x + 3 = 8$$
$$x = 5$$
The scout leader ordered 5 cheese pizzas and 3 pepperoni pizzas.

57. Let a represent the number of Brand A boxes and b the number of Brand B boxes. The system of equations is:
$$\begin{array}{cc} a = b + 4 & a - b = 4 \\ \quad\quad \text{or} & \\ 10a + 12b = 172 & 10a + 12b = 172 \end{array}$$

Form the augmented matrix: $\begin{bmatrix} 1 & -1 & | & 4 \\ 10 & 12 & | & 172 \end{bmatrix}$

Adding -10 times the first row to the second row: $\begin{bmatrix} 1 & -1 & | & 4 \\ 0 & 22 & | & 132 \end{bmatrix}$

Solving the second equation for b: $\quad\quad\quad\quad$ Substituting $b = 6$ into the first equation:
$$22b = 132 \quad\quad\quad\quad\quad\quad\quad\quad\quad\quad a - b = 4$$
$$b = 6 \quad\quad\quad\quad\quad\quad\quad\quad\quad\quad\quad a - 6 = 4$$
$$a = 10$$
There were 10 boxes of Brand A and 6 boxes of Brand B diapers sold.

59. Let x represent the percentage in the mutual fund, y represent the percentage in the high-yield bond, and z represent the percentage in the CD. The system of equations is:
$$\begin{array}{cc} x + y + z = 1 & x + y + z = 1 \\ 3x + y + 5z = 3.5 & \quad\text{or}\quad 3x + y + 5z = 3.5 \\ x = y + z & x - y - z = 0 \end{array}$$

Form the augmented matrix: $\begin{bmatrix} 1 & 1 & 1 & | & 1 \\ 3 & 1 & 5 & | & 3.5 \\ 1 & -1 & -1 & | & 0 \end{bmatrix}$

Adding -3 times the first row to the second row and -1 times the first row to the third row: $\begin{bmatrix} 1 & 1 & 1 & | & 1 \\ 0 & -2 & 2 & | & 0.5 \\ 0 & -2 & -2 & | & -1 \end{bmatrix}$

Adding -1 times the second row to the third row: $\begin{bmatrix} 1 & 1 & 1 & | & 1 \\ 0 & -2 & 2 & | & 0.5 \\ 0 & 0 & -4 & | & -1.5 \end{bmatrix}$

Solving the third equation for z:
$$-4z = -1.5$$
$$z = 0.375$$

Substituting $z = 0.375$ into the second equation:

$$-2y + 2z = 0.5$$
$$2y - 2(0.375) = -0.5$$
$$2y - 0.75 = -0.5$$
$$2y = .25$$
$$y = 0.125$$

Substituting $z = 0.375, y = 0.125$ into the first equation:

$$x + y + z = 1$$
$$x + 0.125 + 0.375 = 1$$
$$x + 0.5 = 1$$
$$x = 0.5$$

They should allocate 50% to mutual funds, 12.5% to high-yield bonds, and 37.5% to CDs.

61. The system of equations is:

$$A + B = 60 \qquad\qquad A + B \quad\;\; = 60$$
$$B + C = 100 \qquad \text{or} \qquad B + C = 100$$
$$B + C = 2.5A \qquad\qquad -2.5A + B + C = 0$$

Form the augmented matrix: $\begin{bmatrix} 1 & 1 & 0 & 60 \\ 0 & 1 & 1 & 100 \\ -2.5 & 1 & 1 & 0 \end{bmatrix}$

Adding 2.5 times the first row to the third row: $\begin{bmatrix} 1 & 1 & 0 & 60 \\ 0 & 1 & 1 & 100 \\ 0 & 3.5 & 1 & 150 \end{bmatrix}$

Adding –3.5 times the second row to the third row: $\begin{bmatrix} 1 & 1 & 0 & 60 \\ 0 & 1 & 1 & 100 \\ 0 & 0 & -2.5 & -200 \end{bmatrix}$

Solving the third equation for C:

$$-2.5C = -200$$
$$C = 80$$

Substituting $C = 80$ into the second equation:

$$B + C = 100$$
$$B + 80 = 100$$
$$B = 20$$

Substituting $C = 80, B = 20$ into the first equation:

$$A + B = 60$$
$$A + 20 = 60$$
$$A = 40$$

The resistances of $A, B,$ and C are 40 ohms, 20 ohms, and 80 ohms, respectively.

63. Form the augmented matrix: $\begin{bmatrix} 1 & 1 & 3 \\ -1 & 1 & 1 \\ 2 & 1 & 6 \end{bmatrix}$

Adding the first row to the second row and –2 times the first row to the third row: $\begin{bmatrix} 1 & 1 & 3 \\ 0 & 2 & 4 \\ 0 & -1 & 0 \end{bmatrix}$

Solving the third equation for y:

$$-y = 0$$
$$y = 0$$

Solving the second equation for y:

$$2y = 4$$
$$y = 2$$

Thus the system is inconsistent. There is no intersection point for the three lines. Note the graphs:

65. a. The first equation is the second equation multiplied by 3. The second equation is the first equation multiplied by $\frac{1}{3}$.

b. Because the equations are multiplies of each other, the values that satisfy one will satisfy the other.

c. Solving the second equation for w:
$$2u + 2v - w = -1$$
$$-w = -2u - 2v - 1$$
$$w = 2u + 2v + 1$$

d. Using $u = 1, v = 1$: $w = 2(1) + 2(1) + 1 = 5$

Using $u = -1, v = 1$: $w = 2(-1) + 2(1) + 1 = 1$

Two points are $(1,1,5)$ and $(-1,1,1)$.

8.4 Operations with Matrices

1. $a_{11} = -1$

3. The dimensions are 3×4.

5. $a_{34} = \pi$

7. False. For addition, matrices must have the same dimensions so that corresponding entries can be added.

9. True. The product of an $m \times n$ matrix and $n \times p$ matrix is an $m \times p$ matrix.

11. Performing the operations: $B + C = \begin{bmatrix} 8 + (-4) & 0 + 5 \\ 3 + 0 & -2 + 1 \\ 2 + (-2) & -6 + 7 \end{bmatrix} = \begin{bmatrix} 4 & 5 \\ 3 & -1 \\ 0 & 1 \end{bmatrix}$

13. Performing the operations: $2B + C = \begin{bmatrix} 16 & 0 \\ 6 & -4 \\ 4 & -12 \end{bmatrix} + \begin{bmatrix} -4 & 5 \\ 0 & 1 \\ -2 & 7 \end{bmatrix} = \begin{bmatrix} 12 & 5 \\ 6 & -3 \\ 2 & -5 \end{bmatrix}$

15. Performing the operations: $-3C + B = \begin{bmatrix} 12 & -15 \\ 0 & -3 \\ 6 & -21 \end{bmatrix} + \begin{bmatrix} 8 & 0 \\ 3 & -2 \\ 2 & -6 \end{bmatrix} = \begin{bmatrix} 20 & -15 \\ 3 & -5 \\ 8 & -27 \end{bmatrix}$

17. $A + 2B$ is not defined. The dimensions do not allow for addition.

19. Performing the operations: $AB = \begin{bmatrix} 1(8) - 3(3) + \frac{1}{3}(2) & 1(0) - 3(-2) + \frac{1}{3}(-6) \\ 5(8) + 0(3) - 2(2) & 5(0) + 0(-2) - 2(-6) \end{bmatrix} = \begin{bmatrix} -\frac{1}{3} & 4 \\ 36 & 12 \end{bmatrix}$

21. BC is not defined. The number of columns of matrix B does not match the number of rows of the second matrix.

23. Performing the operations: $\frac{1}{2}A = \frac{1}{2}\begin{bmatrix} 1 & -3 & \frac{1}{3} \\ 5 & 0 & -2 \end{bmatrix} = \begin{bmatrix} \frac{1}{2} & -\frac{3}{2} & \frac{1}{6} \\ \frac{5}{2} & 0 & -1 \end{bmatrix}$

25. Performing the operations:

$$A(B+C) = A\left(\begin{bmatrix} 8 & 0 \\ 3 & -2 \\ 2 & -6 \end{bmatrix} + \begin{bmatrix} -4 & 5 \\ 0 & 1 \\ -2 & 7 \end{bmatrix}\right)$$

$$= \begin{bmatrix} 1 & -3 & \dfrac{1}{3} \\ 5 & 0 & -2 \end{bmatrix}\begin{bmatrix} 4 & 5 \\ 3 & -1 \\ 0 & 1 \end{bmatrix}$$

$$= \begin{bmatrix} 1(4)-3(3)+\dfrac{1}{3}(0) & 1(5)-3(-1)+\dfrac{1}{3}(1) \\ 5(4)+0(-1)-2(1) & 5(5)+0(-1)-2(1) \end{bmatrix}$$

$$= \begin{bmatrix} -5 & \dfrac{25}{3} \\ 20 & 23 \end{bmatrix}$$

27. Performing the operations: $C(AB) = \begin{bmatrix} -4 & 5 \\ 0 & 1 \\ -2 & 7 \end{bmatrix}\begin{bmatrix} -\dfrac{1}{3} & 4 \\ 36 & 12 \end{bmatrix} = \begin{bmatrix} -4\left(-\dfrac{1}{3}\right)+5(36) & -4(4)+5(12) \\ 0\left(-\dfrac{1}{3}\right)+1(36) & 0(4)+1(12) \\ -2\left(-\dfrac{1}{3}\right)+7(36) & -2(4)+7(12) \end{bmatrix} = \begin{bmatrix} \dfrac{544}{3} & 44 \\ 36 & 12 \\ \dfrac{758}{3} & 76 \end{bmatrix}$

29. **a.** Performing the operations: $AB = \begin{bmatrix} -4(1)+2(-3) \\ -1(1)+0(-3) \end{bmatrix} = \begin{bmatrix} -10 \\ -1 \end{bmatrix}$

b. The dimensions do not allow for subtraction.

c. The dimensions do not allow for multiplication in the given order.

31. **a.** Performing the operations: $AB = \begin{bmatrix} 0(3)+4(2) & 0(-7)+4(-1) \\ -6(3)+7(2) & -6(-7)+7(-1) \end{bmatrix} = \begin{bmatrix} 8 & -4 \\ -4 & 35 \end{bmatrix}$

b. Performing the operations: $3B-2A = \begin{bmatrix} 9 & -21 \\ 6 & -3 \end{bmatrix} - \begin{bmatrix} 0 & 8 \\ -12 & 14 \end{bmatrix} = \begin{bmatrix} 9 & -29 \\ 18 & -17 \end{bmatrix}$

c. Performing the operations: $BA = \begin{bmatrix} 3(0)-7(-6) & 3(4)-7(7) \\ 2(0)-1(-6) & 2(4)-1(7) \end{bmatrix} = \begin{bmatrix} 42 & -37 \\ 6 & 1 \end{bmatrix}$

33. **a.** Performing the operations: $AB = \begin{bmatrix} 3(4)-2(9) & 3(-2)-2(3) \\ 7(4)-6(1)-1(9) & 7(-2)-1(3) \\ 5(4)+2(1)-1(9) & 5(-2)-1(3) \end{bmatrix} = \begin{bmatrix} -6 & -12 \\ 13 & -17 \\ 13 & -13 \end{bmatrix}$

b. The dimensions do not allow for subtraction.

c. The dimensions do not allow for multiplication in the given order.

35. Performing the operations: $AB+AC = \begin{bmatrix} 6 & -1 \\ 5 & 1 \end{bmatrix}\begin{bmatrix} 2 \\ 4 \end{bmatrix} + \begin{bmatrix} 6 & -1 \\ 5 & 1 \end{bmatrix}\begin{bmatrix} 3 \\ -2 \end{bmatrix} = \begin{bmatrix} 8 \\ 14 \end{bmatrix} + \begin{bmatrix} 20 \\ 13 \end{bmatrix} = \begin{bmatrix} 28 \\ 27 \end{bmatrix}$

37. Performing the operations: $CA-B = \left(\begin{bmatrix} 2 & 1 \\ 0 & -9 \end{bmatrix}\begin{bmatrix} 1 & 2 \\ 0 & -5 \end{bmatrix}\right) - \begin{bmatrix} 7 & -4 \\ -4 & -7 \end{bmatrix} = \begin{bmatrix} 2 & -1 \\ 0 & 45 \end{bmatrix} - \begin{bmatrix} 7 & -4 \\ -4 & -7 \end{bmatrix} = \begin{bmatrix} -5 & 3 \\ 4 & 52 \end{bmatrix}$

39. Performing the operations: $2C + BA = \begin{bmatrix} -8 & 2 \\ 10 & -14 \end{bmatrix} + \begin{bmatrix} 18 & -4 \\ 13 & 7 \end{bmatrix} = \begin{bmatrix} 10 & -2 \\ 23 & -7 \end{bmatrix}$

41. Performing the operations:

$$C(B-A) = \begin{bmatrix} 1 & 2 & 3 \\ -2 & -3 & -1 \\ 3 & 1 & 2 \end{bmatrix} \left(\begin{bmatrix} 4 & 3 \\ -6 & 2 \\ 3 & -1 \end{bmatrix} - \begin{bmatrix} 4 & 1 \\ 0 & 2 \\ 5 & 1 \end{bmatrix} \right) = \begin{bmatrix} 1 & 2 & 3 \\ -2 & -3 & -1 \\ 3 & 1 & 2 \end{bmatrix} \begin{bmatrix} 0 & 2 \\ -6 & 0 \\ -2 & -2 \end{bmatrix} = \begin{bmatrix} -18 & -4 \\ 20 & -2 \\ -10 & 2 \end{bmatrix}$$

43. Finding the values: **45.** Finding the values:

$p_{11} = ag + bj$ $p_{32} = eh + fk$

$p_{33} = ei + fl$ $p_{23} = ci + dl$

47. Performing the operations:

$$A^2 = \begin{bmatrix} 2 & -1 \\ 1 & 0 \end{bmatrix} \begin{bmatrix} 2 & -1 \\ 1 & 0 \end{bmatrix} = \begin{bmatrix} 4-1 & -2+0 \\ 2+0 & -1+0 \end{bmatrix} = \begin{bmatrix} 3 & -2 \\ 2 & -1 \end{bmatrix}$$

$$A^3 = A^2 A = \begin{bmatrix} 3 & -2 \\ 2 & -1 \end{bmatrix} \begin{bmatrix} 2 & -1 \\ 1 & 0 \end{bmatrix} = \begin{bmatrix} 4 & -3 \\ 3 & -2 \end{bmatrix}$$

49. Performing the operations:

$$A^2 = \begin{bmatrix} -4 & 0 \\ 0 & 3 \end{bmatrix} \begin{bmatrix} -4 & 0 \\ 0 & 3 \end{bmatrix} = \begin{bmatrix} 16 & 0 \\ 0 & 9 \end{bmatrix}$$

$$A^3 = A^2 A = \begin{bmatrix} 16 & 0 \\ 0 & 9 \end{bmatrix} \begin{bmatrix} -4 & 0 \\ 0 & 3 \end{bmatrix} = \begin{bmatrix} -64 & 0 \\ 0 & 27 \end{bmatrix}$$

51. Performing the operations:

$$A^2 = \begin{bmatrix} 3 & 0 & 0 \\ 0 & 1 & 1 \\ -4 & 1 & 0 \end{bmatrix} \begin{bmatrix} 3 & 0 & 0 \\ 0 & 1 & 1 \\ -4 & 1 & 0 \end{bmatrix} = \begin{bmatrix} 9 & 0 & 0 \\ -4 & 2 & 1 \\ -12 & 1 & 1 \end{bmatrix}$$

$$A^3 = A^2 A = \begin{bmatrix} 9 & 0 & 0 \\ -4 & 2 & 1 \\ -12 & 1 & 1 \end{bmatrix} \begin{bmatrix} 3 & 0 & 0 \\ 0 & 1 & 1 \\ -4 & 1 & 0 \end{bmatrix} = \begin{bmatrix} 27 & 0 & 0 \\ -16 & 3 & 2 \\ -40 & 2 & 1 \end{bmatrix}$$

53. Finding the product: $AB = \begin{bmatrix} 0 & 1 \\ a & 0 \end{bmatrix} \begin{bmatrix} 0 & a \\ 1 & 0 \end{bmatrix} = \begin{bmatrix} 1 & 0 \\ 0 & a^2 \end{bmatrix} = \begin{bmatrix} 1 & 0 \\ 0 & 1 \end{bmatrix}$

For these to be equal, we must have:

$a^2 = 1$

$a = \pm 1$

55. Finding the products:

$$AB = \begin{bmatrix} 2 & 1 \\ 1 & 3 \end{bmatrix} \begin{bmatrix} 2 & 2a+b \\ b-a & 6 \end{bmatrix} = \begin{bmatrix} b-a+4 & 4a+2b+6 \\ 3b-3a+2 & 2a+b+18 \end{bmatrix}$$

$$BA = \begin{bmatrix} 2 & 2a+b \\ b-a & 6 \end{bmatrix} \begin{bmatrix} 2 & 1 \\ 1 & 3 \end{bmatrix} = \begin{bmatrix} 2a+b+4 & 6a+3b+2 \\ 2b-2a+6 & b-a+18 \end{bmatrix}$$

For these to be equal, the first row entries must be equal:

$b-a+4 = 2a+b+4$ $4a+2b+6 = 6a+3b+2$

$3a = 0$ $-2a-b = -4$

$a = 0$ $2a+b = 4$

Substituting $a = 0$ into the second equation:
$$2a + b = 4$$
$$2(0) + b = 4$$
$$b = 4$$
Note that these two values check for the second row entries also.

57. Finding the product: $AB = \begin{bmatrix} a^2 - 3a + 3 & 1 \\ 0 & 2b + 5 \end{bmatrix}\begin{bmatrix} 0 & 1 \\ 1 & 0 \end{bmatrix} = \begin{bmatrix} 1 & a^2 - 3a + 3 \\ 2b + 5 & 0 \end{bmatrix} = \begin{bmatrix} 1 & 1 \\ 1 & 0 \end{bmatrix}$

For these to be equal, the two equations must be true:

$$a^2 - 3a + 3 = 1 \qquad\qquad 2b + 5 = 1$$
$$a^2 - 3a + 2 = 0 \qquad\qquad 2b = -4$$
$$(a - 2)(a - 1) = 0 \qquad\qquad b = -2$$
$$a = 1, 2$$

The values are: $a = 1, 2; \ b = -2$

59. The cost matrix for 12 gallons would be: $12\begin{bmatrix} \$2.40 \\ \$2.65 \end{bmatrix} = \begin{bmatrix} 12(2.40) \\ 12(2.65) \end{bmatrix} = \begin{bmatrix} \$28.80 \\ \$31.80 \end{bmatrix}$

It will cost \$28.80 for regular and \$31.80 for the high-octane fuel.

61. a. Finding the product: $GP = \begin{bmatrix} 9274.3 \\ 9824.6 \\ 10{,}082.2 \end{bmatrix}\begin{bmatrix} 0.2 & 0.09 & 0.014 \end{bmatrix} = \begin{bmatrix} 1854.86 & 834.687 & 129.8402 \\ 1964.92 & 884.214 & 137.5444 \\ 2016.44 & 907.398 & 141.1508 \end{bmatrix}$

b. This represents the breakdown of the contribution from each of these three sectors per year.

c. Yes. It will be a 1×1 matrix representing the total contribution of these three sectors over the given years.

63. Finding the product: $FC = \begin{bmatrix} 10.5 & 2 & 1 \\ 8 & 1.5 & 1 \\ 4 & 1 & 0.5 \end{bmatrix}\begin{bmatrix} 10 \\ 6 \\ 5 \end{bmatrix} = \begin{bmatrix} 122 \\ 94 \\ 48.50 \end{bmatrix}$

The cost for a sofa is \$122, for a loveseat is \$94, and for a chair is \$48.50.

65. The product is $AB = \begin{bmatrix} 0 & 0 \\ 0 & 0 \end{bmatrix}$. No, since neither A nor B was the zero matrix.

67. Finding the products:

$AI = \begin{bmatrix} 2 & -1 \\ 1 & 0 \end{bmatrix}\begin{bmatrix} 1 & 0 \\ 0 & 1 \end{bmatrix} = \begin{bmatrix} 2 & -1 \\ 1 & 0 \end{bmatrix}$ \qquad $IA = \begin{bmatrix} 1 & 0 \\ 0 & 1 \end{bmatrix}\begin{bmatrix} 2 & -1 \\ 1 & 0 \end{bmatrix} = \begin{bmatrix} 2 & -1 \\ 1 & 0 \end{bmatrix}$

Note that $AI = IA = A$.

69. Finding the products:

$AB = \begin{bmatrix} 1 & 2 \\ 3 & 4 \end{bmatrix}\begin{bmatrix} 0 & 1 \\ 1 & 1 \end{bmatrix} = \begin{bmatrix} 2 & 3 \\ 4 & 7 \end{bmatrix}$ \qquad $BA = \begin{bmatrix} 0 & 1 \\ 1 & 1 \end{bmatrix}\begin{bmatrix} 1 & 2 \\ 3 & 4 \end{bmatrix} = \begin{bmatrix} 3 & 4 \\ 4 & 6 \end{bmatrix}$

Note that $AB \neq BA$. The corresponding entries of the resulting matrices are computed using different rows and columns.

8.5 Matrices and Inverses

1. Yes, they are inverses of each other: $\begin{bmatrix} 5 & 2 \\ -3 & -1 \end{bmatrix}\begin{bmatrix} -1 & -2 \\ 3 & 5 \end{bmatrix} = \begin{bmatrix} 1 & 0 \\ 0 & 1 \end{bmatrix}$

3. Yes, they are inverses of each other: $\begin{bmatrix} -6 & 5 \\ 4 & -3 \end{bmatrix}\begin{bmatrix} \frac{3}{2} & \frac{5}{2} \\ 2 & 3 \end{bmatrix} = \begin{bmatrix} 1 & 0 \\ 0 & 1 \end{bmatrix}$

5. Yes, they are inverses of each other: $\begin{bmatrix} -1 & 3 & -1 \\ 0 & -5 & 2 \\ 1 & 0 & 0 \end{bmatrix}\begin{bmatrix} 0 & 0 & 1 \\ 2 & 1 & 2 \\ 5 & 3 & 5 \end{bmatrix} = \begin{bmatrix} 1 & 0 & 0 \\ 0 & 1 & 0 \\ 0 & 0 & 1 \end{bmatrix}$

7. Form the augmented matrix: $\left[\begin{array}{cc|cc} 2 & 3 & 1 & 0 \\ 1 & 1 & 0 & 1 \end{array}\right]$

   Switching the first and second rows: $\left[\begin{array}{cc|cc} 1 & 1 & 0 & 1 \\ 2 & 3 & 1 & 0 \end{array}\right]$

   Adding -2 times the first row to the second row: $\left[\begin{array}{cc|cc} 1 & 1 & 0 & 1 \\ 0 & 1 & 1 & -2 \end{array}\right]$

   Adding -1 times the second row to the first row: $\left[\begin{array}{cc|cc} 1 & 0 & -1 & 3 \\ 0 & 1 & 1 & -2 \end{array}\right]$

   The inverse is: $\begin{bmatrix} -1 & 3 \\ 1 & -2 \end{bmatrix}$

9. Form the augmented matrix: $\left[\begin{array}{cc|cc} -1 & 3 & 1 & 0 \\ -1 & 4 & 0 & 1 \end{array}\right]$

   Multiplying the first row by -1: $\left[\begin{array}{cc|cc} 1 & -3 & -1 & 0 \\ -1 & 4 & 0 & 1 \end{array}\right]$

   Adding the first row to the second row: $\left[\begin{array}{cc|cc} 1 & -3 & -1 & 0 \\ 0 & 1 & -1 & 1 \end{array}\right]$

   Adding 3 times the second row to the first row: $\left[\begin{array}{cc|cc} 1 & 0 & -4 & 3 \\ 0 & 1 & -1 & 1 \end{array}\right]$

   The inverse is: $\begin{bmatrix} -4 & 3 \\ -1 & 1 \end{bmatrix}$

11. Form the augmented matrix: $\left[\begin{array}{cc|cc} 5 & 3 & 1 & 0 \\ 3 & 2 & 0 & 1 \end{array}\right]$

    Multiplying the first row by $\frac{1}{5}$: $\left[\begin{array}{cc|cc} 1 & \frac{3}{5} & \frac{1}{5} & 0 \\ 3 & 2 & 0 & 1 \end{array}\right]$

    Adding -3 times the first row to the second row: $\left[\begin{array}{cc|cc} 1 & \frac{3}{5} & \frac{1}{5} & 0 \\ 0 & \frac{1}{5} & -\frac{3}{5} & 1 \end{array}\right]$

Multiplying the second row by 5: $\begin{bmatrix} 1 & \dfrac{3}{5} & \bigm| & \dfrac{1}{5} & 0 \\ 0 & 1 & \bigm| & -3 & 5 \end{bmatrix}$

Adding $-\dfrac{3}{5}$ times the second row to the first row: $\begin{bmatrix} 1 & 0 & \bigm| & 2 & -3 \\ 0 & 1 & \bigm| & -3 & 5 \end{bmatrix}$

The inverse is: $\begin{bmatrix} 2 & -3 \\ -3 & 5 \end{bmatrix}$

13. Form the augmented matrix: $\begin{bmatrix} 4 & 0 & 5 & \bigm| & 1 & 0 & 0 \\ 0 & 1 & -6 & \bigm| & 0 & 1 & 0 \\ 3 & 0 & 4 & \bigm| & 0 & 0 & 1 \end{bmatrix}$

Multiplying the first row by $\dfrac{1}{4}$: $\begin{bmatrix} 1 & 0 & \dfrac{5}{4} & \bigm| & \dfrac{1}{4} & 0 & 0 \\ 0 & 1 & -6 & \bigm| & 0 & 1 & 0 \\ 3 & 0 & 4 & \bigm| & 0 & 0 & 1 \end{bmatrix}$

Adding -3 times the first row to the third row: $\begin{bmatrix} 1 & 0 & \dfrac{5}{4} & \bigm| & \dfrac{1}{4} & 0 & 0 \\ 0 & 1 & -6 & \bigm| & 0 & 1 & 0 \\ 0 & 0 & \dfrac{1}{4} & \bigm| & -\dfrac{3}{4} & 0 & 1 \end{bmatrix}$

Multiplying the third row by 4: $\begin{bmatrix} 1 & 0 & \dfrac{5}{4} & \bigm| & \dfrac{1}{4} & 0 & 0 \\ 0 & 1 & -6 & \bigm| & 0 & 1 & 0 \\ 0 & 0 & 1 & \bigm| & -3 & 0 & 4 \end{bmatrix}$

Adding $-\dfrac{5}{4}$ times the third row to the first row and 6 times the third row to the second row:

$\begin{bmatrix} 1 & 0 & 0 & \bigm| & 4 & 0 & -5 \\ 0 & 1 & 0 & \bigm| & -18 & 1 & 24 \\ 0 & 0 & 1 & \bigm| & -3 & 0 & 4 \end{bmatrix}$

The inverse is: $\begin{bmatrix} 4 & 0 & -5 \\ -18 & 1 & 24 \\ -3 & 0 & 4 \end{bmatrix}$

15. Form the augmented matrix: $\begin{bmatrix} -1 & -1 & -1 & \bigm| & 1 & 0 & 0 \\ 3 & 3 & 4 & \bigm| & 0 & 1 & 0 \\ 0 & 1 & 0 & \bigm| & 0 & 0 & 1 \end{bmatrix}$

Multiplying the first row by -1: $\begin{bmatrix} 1 & 1 & 1 & \bigm| & -1 & 0 & 0 \\ 3 & 3 & 4 & \bigm| & 0 & 1 & 0 \\ 0 & 1 & 0 & \bigm| & 0 & 0 & 1 \end{bmatrix}$

Adding -3 times the first row to the second row: $\begin{bmatrix} 1 & 1 & 1 & \bigm| & -1 & 0 & 0 \\ 0 & 0 & 1 & \bigm| & 3 & 1 & 0 \\ 0 & 1 & 0 & \bigm| & 0 & 0 & 1 \end{bmatrix}$

Switching the second row and the third row: $\begin{bmatrix} 1 & 1 & 1 & -1 & 0 & 0 \\ 0 & 1 & 0 & 0 & 0 & 1 \\ 0 & 0 & 1 & 3 & 1 & 0 \end{bmatrix}$

Adding –1 times the second row to the first row and –1 time the third row to the first row: $\begin{bmatrix} 1 & 0 & 0 & -4 & -1 & -1 \\ 0 & 1 & 0 & 0 & 0 & 1 \\ 0 & 0 & 1 & 3 & 1 & 0 \end{bmatrix}$

The inverse is: $\begin{bmatrix} -4 & -1 & -1 \\ 0 & 0 & 1 \\ 3 & 1 & 0 \end{bmatrix}$

17. Form the augmented matrix: $\begin{bmatrix} 4 & -2 & 1 & 1 & 0 & 0 \\ -2 & 1 & 2 & 0 & 1 & 0 \\ 1 & 2 & 4 & 0 & 0 & 1 \end{bmatrix}$

Switching the first row and the third row: $\begin{bmatrix} 1 & 2 & 4 & 0 & 0 & 1 \\ -2 & 1 & 2 & 0 & 1 & 0 \\ 4 & -2 & 1 & 1 & 0 & 0 \end{bmatrix}$

Adding 2 times the first row to the second row and –4 times the first row to the third row:
$\begin{bmatrix} 1 & 2 & 4 & 0 & 0 & 1 \\ 0 & 5 & 10 & 0 & 1 & 2 \\ 0 & -10 & -15 & 1 & 0 & -4 \end{bmatrix}$

Multiplying the second row by $\dfrac{1}{5}$: $\begin{bmatrix} 1 & 2 & 4 & 0 & 0 & 1 \\ 0 & 1 & 2 & 0 & \dfrac{1}{5} & \dfrac{2}{5} \\ 0 & -10 & -15 & 1 & 0 & -4 \end{bmatrix}$

Adding –2 times the second row to the first row and 10 times the second row to the third row:
$\begin{bmatrix} 1 & 0 & 0 & 0 & -\dfrac{2}{5} & \dfrac{1}{5} \\ 0 & 1 & 2 & 0 & \dfrac{1}{5} & \dfrac{2}{5} \\ 0 & 0 & 5 & 1 & 2 & 0 \end{bmatrix}$

Multiplying the third row by $\dfrac{1}{5}$: $\begin{bmatrix} 1 & 0 & 0 & 0 & -\dfrac{2}{5} & \dfrac{1}{5} \\ 0 & 1 & 2 & 0 & \dfrac{1}{5} & \dfrac{2}{5} \\ 0 & 0 & 1 & \dfrac{1}{5} & \dfrac{2}{5} & 0 \end{bmatrix}$

Adding −2 times the third row to the second row: $\begin{bmatrix} 1 & 0 & 0 & \bigg| & 0 & -\dfrac{2}{5} & \dfrac{1}{5} \\[2mm] 0 & 1 & 0 & \bigg| & -\dfrac{2}{5} & -\dfrac{3}{5} & \dfrac{2}{5} \\[2mm] 0 & 0 & 1 & \bigg| & \dfrac{1}{5} & \dfrac{2}{5} & 0 \end{bmatrix}$

The inverse is: $\begin{bmatrix} 0 & -\dfrac{2}{5} & \dfrac{1}{5} \\[2mm] -\dfrac{2}{5} & -\dfrac{3}{5} & \dfrac{2}{5} \\[2mm] \dfrac{1}{5} & \dfrac{2}{5} & 0 \end{bmatrix}$

19. Form the augmented matrix: $\begin{bmatrix} 0 & \dfrac{1}{2} & \dfrac{1}{2} & \bigg| & 1 & 0 & 1 \\[2mm] \dfrac{1}{2} & 0 & \dfrac{1}{2} & \bigg| & 0 & 1 & 0 \\[2mm] \dfrac{1}{2} & \dfrac{1}{2} & 0 & \bigg| & 0 & 0 & 1 \end{bmatrix}$

Multiplying all three rows by 2 to clear fractions: $\begin{bmatrix} 0 & 1 & 1 & | & 2 & 0 & 0 \\ 1 & 0 & 1 & | & 0 & 2 & 0 \\ 1 & 1 & 0 & | & 0 & 0 & 2 \end{bmatrix}$

Switching the first row and the second row: $\begin{bmatrix} 1 & 0 & 1 & | & 0 & 2 & 0 \\ 0 & 1 & 1 & | & 2 & 0 & 0 \\ 1 & 1 & 0 & | & 0 & 0 & 2 \end{bmatrix}$

Adding −1 times the first row to the third row: $\begin{bmatrix} 1 & 0 & 1 & | & 0 & 2 & 0 \\ 0 & 1 & 1 & | & 2 & 0 & 0 \\ 0 & 1 & -1 & | & 0 & -2 & 2 \end{bmatrix}$

Adding −1 times the second row to the third row: $\begin{bmatrix} 1 & 0 & 1 & | & 0 & 2 & 0 \\ 0 & 1 & 1 & | & 2 & 0 & 0 \\ 0 & 0 & -2 & | & -2 & -2 & 2 \end{bmatrix}$

Multiplying the third row by $-\dfrac{1}{2}$: $\begin{bmatrix} 1 & 0 & 1 & | & 0 & 2 & 0 \\ 0 & 1 & 1 & | & 2 & 0 & 0 \\ 0 & 0 & 1 & | & 1 & 1 & -1 \end{bmatrix}$

Adding −1 times the third row to the second row and the first row: $\begin{bmatrix} 1 & 0 & 0 & | & -1 & 1 & 1 \\ 0 & 1 & 0 & | & 1 & -1 & 1 \\ 0 & 0 & 1 & | & 1 & 1 & -1 \end{bmatrix}$

The inverse is: $\begin{bmatrix} -1 & 1 & 1 \\ 1 & -1 & 1 \\ 1 & 1 & -1 \end{bmatrix}$

21. Form the augmented matrix: $\begin{bmatrix} 1 & -1 & 0 & 3 & | & 1 & 0 & 0 & 0 \\ 0 & 1 & -2 & 0 & | & 0 & 1 & 0 & 0 \\ -3 & 3 & 1 & -10 & | & 0 & 0 & 1 & 0 \\ 0 & -1 & 2 & 1 & | & 0 & 0 & 0 & 1 \end{bmatrix}$

Adding 3 times the first row to the third row: $\begin{bmatrix} 1 & -1 & 0 & 3 & | & 1 & 0 & 0 & 0 \\ 0 & 1 & -2 & 0 & | & 0 & 1 & 0 & 0 \\ 0 & 0 & 1 & -1 & | & 3 & 0 & 1 & 0 \\ 0 & -1 & 2 & 1 & | & 0 & 0 & 0 & 1 \end{bmatrix}$

Adding the second row to the first row and the fourth row: $\begin{bmatrix} 1 & 0 & -2 & 3 & | & 1 & 1 & 0 & 0 \\ 0 & 1 & -2 & 0 & | & 0 & 1 & 0 & 0 \\ 0 & 0 & 1 & -1 & | & 3 & 0 & 1 & 0 \\ 0 & 0 & 0 & 1 & | & 0 & 1 & 0 & 1 \end{bmatrix}$

Adding 2 times the third row to the first row and the second row: $\begin{bmatrix} 1 & 0 & 0 & 1 & | & 7 & 1 & 2 & 0 \\ 0 & 1 & 0 & -2 & | & 6 & 1 & 2 & 0 \\ 0 & 0 & 1 & -1 & | & 3 & 0 & 1 & 0 \\ 0 & 0 & 0 & 1 & | & 0 & 1 & 0 & 1 \end{bmatrix}$

Adding the fourth row to the third row, 2 times the fourth row to the second row, and -1 times the fourth row to the first row: $\begin{bmatrix} 1 & 0 & 0 & 0 & | & 7 & 0 & 2 & -1 \\ 0 & 1 & 0 & 0 & | & 6 & 3 & 2 & 2 \\ 0 & 0 & 1 & 0 & | & 3 & 1 & 1 & 1 \\ 0 & 0 & 0 & 1 & | & 0 & 1 & 0 & 1 \end{bmatrix}$

The inverse is: $\begin{bmatrix} 7 & 0 & 2 & -1 \\ 6 & 3 & 2 & 2 \\ 3 & 1 & 1 & 1 \\ 0 & 1 & 0 & 1 \end{bmatrix}$

23. Solving using the inverse: $\begin{bmatrix} x \\ y \\ z \end{bmatrix} = \begin{bmatrix} 0 & 0 & 1 \\ 2 & 1 & 2 \\ 5 & 3 & 5 \end{bmatrix} \begin{bmatrix} 6 \\ -2 \\ 4 \end{bmatrix} = \begin{bmatrix} 4 \\ 18 \\ 44 \end{bmatrix}$

The solution is: $x = 4, y = 18, z = 44$

25. Solving using the inverse: $\begin{bmatrix} x \\ y \\ z \end{bmatrix} = \begin{bmatrix} \frac{1}{2} & -\frac{1}{2} & 0 \\ \frac{1}{2} & \frac{1}{2} & 0 \\ -\frac{1}{2} & \frac{1}{2} & 1 \end{bmatrix} \begin{bmatrix} -2 \\ 1 \\ -1 \end{bmatrix} = \begin{bmatrix} -\frac{3}{2} \\ -\frac{1}{2} \\ \frac{1}{2} \end{bmatrix}$

The solution is: $x = -\frac{3}{2}, y = -\frac{1}{2}, z = \frac{1}{2}$

27. First finding the inverse: $A = \begin{bmatrix} 1 & -1 \\ -3 & 4 \end{bmatrix} \Rightarrow A^{-1} = \begin{bmatrix} 4 & 1 \\ 3 & 1 \end{bmatrix}$

Solving the equation: $X = A^{-1}B = \begin{bmatrix} 4 & 1 \\ 3 & 1 \end{bmatrix} \begin{bmatrix} -2 \\ 5 \end{bmatrix} = \begin{bmatrix} -3 \\ -1 \end{bmatrix}$

The solution is: $x = -3, y = -1$

29. First finding the inverse: $A = \begin{bmatrix} 2 & 4 \\ 1 & 1 \end{bmatrix} \Rightarrow A^{-1} = \begin{bmatrix} -\dfrac{1}{2} & 2 \\ \dfrac{1}{2} & -1 \end{bmatrix}$

Solving the equation: $X = A^{-1}B = \begin{bmatrix} -\dfrac{1}{2} & 2 \\ \dfrac{1}{2} & -1 \end{bmatrix} \begin{bmatrix} 1 \\ -2 \end{bmatrix} = \begin{bmatrix} -\dfrac{9}{2} \\ \dfrac{5}{2} \end{bmatrix}$

The solution is: $x = -\dfrac{9}{2}, y = \dfrac{5}{2}$

31. First finding the inverse: $A = \begin{bmatrix} 3 & 7 \\ 1 & 2 \end{bmatrix} \Rightarrow A^{-1} = \begin{bmatrix} -2 & 7 \\ 1 & -3 \end{bmatrix}$

Solving the equation: $X = A^{-1}B = \begin{bmatrix} -2 & 7 \\ 1 & -3 \end{bmatrix} \begin{bmatrix} -11 \\ -3 \end{bmatrix} = \begin{bmatrix} 1 \\ -2 \end{bmatrix}$

The solution is: $x = 1, y = -2$

33. First finding the inverse: $A = \begin{bmatrix} 2 & -5 \\ -3 & 2 \end{bmatrix} \Rightarrow A^{-1} = \begin{bmatrix} -\dfrac{2}{11} & -\dfrac{5}{11} \\ -\dfrac{3}{11} & -\dfrac{2}{11} \end{bmatrix}$

Solving the equation: $X = A^{-1}B = \begin{bmatrix} -\dfrac{2}{11} & -\dfrac{5}{11} \\ -\dfrac{3}{11} & -\dfrac{2}{11} \end{bmatrix} \begin{bmatrix} -7 \\ -6 \end{bmatrix} = \begin{bmatrix} 4 \\ 3 \end{bmatrix}$

The solution is: $x = 4, y = 3$

35. First finding the inverse: $A = \begin{bmatrix} 1 & 2 \\ 3 & 4 \end{bmatrix} \Rightarrow A^{-1} = \begin{bmatrix} -2 & 1 \\ \dfrac{3}{2} & -\dfrac{1}{2} \end{bmatrix}$

Solving the equation: $X = A^{-1}B = \begin{bmatrix} -2 & 1 \\ \dfrac{3}{2} & -\dfrac{1}{2} \end{bmatrix} \begin{bmatrix} 3 \\ 3 \end{bmatrix} = \begin{bmatrix} -3 \\ 3 \end{bmatrix}$

The solution is: $x = -3, y = 3$

37. First finding the inverse: $A = \begin{bmatrix} 1 & -3 & 2 \\ 0 & 1 & 1 \\ 2 & -6 & 3 \end{bmatrix} \Rightarrow A^{-1} = \begin{bmatrix} -9 & 3 & 5 \\ -2 & 1 & 1 \\ 2 & 0 & -1 \end{bmatrix}$

Solving the equation: $X = A^{-1}B = \begin{bmatrix} -9 & 3 & 5 \\ -2 & 1 & 1 \\ 2 & 0 & -1 \end{bmatrix} \begin{bmatrix} -1 \\ 4 \\ 3 \end{bmatrix} = \begin{bmatrix} 36 \\ 9 \\ -5 \end{bmatrix}$

The solution is: $x = 36, y = 9, z = -5$

39. First finding the inverse: $A = \begin{bmatrix} 1 & -1 & 1 \\ 0 & 1 & 2 \\ -2 & 3 & 1 \end{bmatrix} \Rightarrow A^{-1} = \begin{bmatrix} -5 & 4 & -3 \\ -4 & 3 & -2 \\ 2 & -1 & 1 \end{bmatrix}$

Solving the equation: $X = A^{-1}B = \begin{bmatrix} -5 & 4 & -3 \\ -4 & 3 & -2 \\ 2 & -1 & 1 \end{bmatrix} \begin{bmatrix} 5 \\ -1 \\ 6 \end{bmatrix} = \begin{bmatrix} -47 \\ -35 \\ 17 \end{bmatrix}$

The solution is: $x = -47, y = -35, z = 17$

41. First finding the inverse: $A = \begin{bmatrix} 3 & -6 & 2 \\ 1 & 2 & 3 \\ 0 & 1 & -1 \end{bmatrix} \Rightarrow A^{-1} = \begin{bmatrix} \dfrac{5}{19} & \dfrac{4}{19} & \dfrac{22}{19} \\ -\dfrac{1}{19} & \dfrac{3}{19} & \dfrac{7}{19} \\ -\dfrac{1}{19} & \dfrac{3}{19} & -\dfrac{12}{19} \end{bmatrix}$

Solving the equation: $X = A^{-1}B = \begin{bmatrix} \dfrac{5}{19} & \dfrac{4}{19} & \dfrac{22}{19} \\ -\dfrac{1}{19} & \dfrac{3}{19} & \dfrac{7}{19} \\ -\dfrac{1}{19} & \dfrac{3}{19} & -\dfrac{12}{19} \end{bmatrix} \begin{bmatrix} -6 \\ -1 \\ 5 \end{bmatrix} = \begin{bmatrix} 4 \\ 2 \\ -3 \end{bmatrix}$

The solution is: $x = 4, y = 2, z = -3$

43. First finding the inverse: $A = \begin{bmatrix} 1 & -2 & -1 \\ 2 & -3 & 2 \\ -3 & 6 & 4 \end{bmatrix} \Rightarrow A^{-1} = \begin{bmatrix} -24 & 2 & -7 \\ -14 & 1 & -4 \\ 3 & 0 & 1 \end{bmatrix}$

Solving the equation: $X = A^{-1}B = \begin{bmatrix} -24 & 2 & -7 \\ -14 & 1 & -4 \\ 3 & 0 & 1 \end{bmatrix} \begin{bmatrix} \dfrac{3}{2} \\ -3 \\ 1 \end{bmatrix} = \begin{bmatrix} -49 \\ -28 \\ \dfrac{11}{2} \end{bmatrix}$

The solution is: $x = -49, y = -28, z = \dfrac{11}{2}$

45. First finding the inverse: $A = \begin{bmatrix} 1 & -1 & 0 & 1 \\ 0 & 1 & 0 & -2 \\ -2 & 2 & 1 & -3 \\ 0 & -1 & 0 & 3 \end{bmatrix} \Rightarrow A^{-1} = \begin{bmatrix} 1 & 2 & 0 & 1 \\ 0 & 3 & 0 & 2 \\ 2 & 1 & 1 & 1 \\ 0 & 1 & 0 & 1 \end{bmatrix}$

Solving the equation: $X = A^{-1}B = \begin{bmatrix} 1 & 2 & 0 & 1 \\ 0 & 3 & 0 & 2 \\ 2 & 1 & 1 & 1 \\ 0 & 1 & 0 & 1 \end{bmatrix} \begin{bmatrix} -3 \\ 0 \\ 1 \\ 0 \end{bmatrix} = \begin{bmatrix} -3 \\ 0 \\ -5 \\ 0 \end{bmatrix}$

The solution is: $x = -3, y = 0, z = -5, w = 0$

47. Finding the power: $A^2 = \begin{bmatrix} 1 & 1 \\ 0 & 1 \end{bmatrix} \begin{bmatrix} 1 & 1 \\ 0 & 1 \end{bmatrix} = \begin{bmatrix} 1 & 2 \\ 0 & 1 \end{bmatrix}$

Form the augmented matrix: $\left[\begin{array}{cc|cc} 1 & 2 & 1 & 0 \\ 0 & 1 & 0 & 1 \end{array} \right]$

Adding -2 times the second row to the first row: $\left[\begin{array}{cc|cc} 1 & 0 & 1 & -2 \\ 0 & 1 & 0 & 1 \end{array} \right]$

Inverse of A^2: $\begin{bmatrix} 1 & -2 \\ 0 & 1 \end{bmatrix}$

Finding the power: $A^3 = A^2 A = \begin{bmatrix} 1 & 2 \\ 0 & 1 \end{bmatrix} \begin{bmatrix} 1 & 1 \\ 0 & 1 \end{bmatrix} = \begin{bmatrix} 1 & 3 \\ 0 & 1 \end{bmatrix}$

Form the augmented matrix: $\left[\begin{array}{cc|cc} 1 & 3 & 1 & 0 \\ 0 & 1 & 0 & 1 \end{array} \right]$

Adding -3 times the second row to the first row: $\left[\begin{array}{cc|cc} 1 & 0 & 1 & -3 \\ 0 & 1 & 0 & 1 \end{array} \right]$

Inverse of A^3: $\begin{bmatrix} 1 & -3 \\ 0 & 1 \end{bmatrix}$

49. Finding the power: $A^2 = \begin{bmatrix} 2 & 1 \\ 0 & -1 \end{bmatrix} \begin{bmatrix} 2 & 1 \\ 0 & -1 \end{bmatrix} = \begin{bmatrix} 4 & 1 \\ 0 & 1 \end{bmatrix}$

Form the augmented matrix: $\left[\begin{array}{cc|cc} 4 & 1 & 1 & 0 \\ 0 & 1 & 0 & 1 \end{array} \right]$

Adding -1 times the second row to the first row: $\left[\begin{array}{cc|cc} 4 & 0 & 1 & -1 \\ 0 & 1 & 0 & 1 \end{array} \right]$

Multiplying the first row by $\dfrac{1}{4}$: $\left[\begin{array}{cc|cc} 1 & 0 & \dfrac{1}{4} & -\dfrac{1}{4} \\ 0 & 1 & 0 & 1 \end{array} \right]$

Inverse of A^2: $\begin{bmatrix} \dfrac{1}{4} & -\dfrac{1}{4} \\ 0 & 1 \end{bmatrix}$

Finding the power: $A^3 = A^2 A = \begin{bmatrix} 4 & 1 \\ 0 & 1 \end{bmatrix} \begin{bmatrix} 2 & 1 \\ 0 & -1 \end{bmatrix} = \begin{bmatrix} 8 & 3 \\ 0 & -1 \end{bmatrix}$

Form the augmented matrix: $\left[\begin{array}{cc|cc} 8 & 3 & 1 & 0 \\ 0 & -1 & 0 & 1 \end{array} \right]$

Adding 3 times the second row to the first row: $\left[\begin{array}{cc|cc} 8 & 0 & 1 & 3 \\ 0 & -1 & 0 & 1 \end{array} \right]$

Multiplying the first row by $\dfrac{1}{8}$ and the second row by -1: $\begin{bmatrix} 1 & 0 & \bigm| & \dfrac{1}{8} & \dfrac{3}{8} \\ 0 & 1 & \bigm| & 0 & -1 \end{bmatrix}$

Inverse of A^3: $\begin{bmatrix} \dfrac{1}{8} & \dfrac{3}{8} \\ 0 & -1 \end{bmatrix}$

51. Finding the power: $A^2 = \begin{bmatrix} 2 & 0 & 0 \\ 0 & 1 & 2 \\ 0 & 0 & 1 \end{bmatrix} \begin{bmatrix} 2 & 0 & 0 \\ 0 & 1 & 2 \\ 0 & 0 & 1 \end{bmatrix} = \begin{bmatrix} 4 & 0 & 0 \\ 0 & 1 & 4 \\ 0 & 0 & 1 \end{bmatrix}$

Form the augmented matrix: $\begin{bmatrix} 4 & 0 & 0 & \bigm| & 1 & 0 & 0 \\ 0 & 1 & 4 & \bigm| & 0 & 1 & 0 \\ 0 & 0 & 1 & \bigm| & 0 & 0 & 1 \end{bmatrix}$

Adding -4 times the third row to the second row: $\begin{bmatrix} 4 & 0 & 0 & \bigm| & 1 & 0 & 0 \\ 0 & 1 & 0 & \bigm| & 0 & 1 & -4 \\ 0 & 0 & 1 & \bigm| & 0 & 0 & 1 \end{bmatrix}$

Multiplying the first row by $\dfrac{1}{4}$: $\begin{bmatrix} 1 & 0 & 0 & \bigm| & \dfrac{1}{4} & 0 & 0 \\ 0 & 1 & 0 & \bigm| & 0 & 1 & -4 \\ 0 & 0 & 1 & \bigm| & 0 & 0 & 1 \end{bmatrix}$

Inverse of A^2: $\begin{bmatrix} \dfrac{1}{4} & 0 & 0 \\ 0 & 1 & -4 \\ 0 & 0 & 1 \end{bmatrix}$

Finding the power: $A^3 = A^2 A = \begin{bmatrix} 4 & 0 & 0 \\ 0 & 1 & 4 \\ 0 & 0 & 1 \end{bmatrix} \begin{bmatrix} 2 & 0 & 0 \\ 0 & 1 & 2 \\ 0 & 0 & 1 \end{bmatrix} = \begin{bmatrix} 8 & 0 & 0 \\ 0 & 1 & 6 \\ 0 & 0 & 1 \end{bmatrix}$

Form the augmented matrix: $\begin{bmatrix} 8 & 0 & 0 & \bigm| & 1 & 0 & 0 \\ 0 & 1 & 6 & \bigm| & 0 & 1 & 0 \\ 0 & 0 & 1 & \bigm| & 0 & 0 & 1 \end{bmatrix}$

Adding -6 times the third row to the second row: $\begin{bmatrix} 8 & 0 & 0 & \bigm| & 1 & 0 & 0 \\ 0 & 1 & 0 & \bigm| & 0 & 1 & -6 \\ 0 & 0 & 1 & \bigm| & 0 & 0 & 1 \end{bmatrix}$

Multiplying the first row by $\dfrac{1}{8}$: $\begin{bmatrix} 1 & 0 & 0 & \bigm| & \dfrac{1}{8} & 0 & 0 \\ 0 & 1 & 0 & \bigm| & 0 & 1 & -6 \\ 0 & 0 & 1 & \bigm| & 0 & 0 & 1 \end{bmatrix}$

Inverse of A^3: $\begin{bmatrix} \dfrac{1}{8} & 0 & 0 \\ 0 & 1 & -6 \\ 0 & 0 & 1 \end{bmatrix}$

53. Let x represent the price of adult tickets and y represent the price of child tickets. The system of equations is:

$$12x + 6y = 174$$
$$8x + 3y = 111$$

First finding the inverse: $A = \begin{bmatrix} 12 & 6 \\ 8 & 3 \end{bmatrix} \Rightarrow A^{-1} = \begin{bmatrix} -\dfrac{1}{4} & \dfrac{1}{2} \\ \dfrac{2}{3} & -1 \end{bmatrix}$

Solving the equation: $x = A^{-1}B = \begin{bmatrix} -\dfrac{1}{4} & \dfrac{1}{2} \\ \dfrac{2}{3} & -1 \end{bmatrix} \begin{bmatrix} 174 \\ 111 \end{bmatrix} = \begin{bmatrix} 12 \\ 5 \end{bmatrix}$

Adult tickets cost \$12 and child tickets are \$5.

55. Let x represent the calories in a slice of cheese pizza, y represent the calories in a slice of Meaty Delite pizza, and z represent the calories in a slice of Veggie Delite pizza. The system of equations is:

$$2x \quad\;\; + z = 550$$
$$x + y + z = 620$$
$$\quad\; y + 2z = 570$$

First finding the inverse: $A = \begin{bmatrix} 2 & 0 & 1 \\ 1 & 1 & 1 \\ 0 & 1 & 2 \end{bmatrix} \Rightarrow A^{-1} = \begin{bmatrix} \dfrac{1}{3} & \dfrac{1}{3} & -\dfrac{1}{3} \\ -\dfrac{2}{3} & \dfrac{4}{3} & -\dfrac{1}{3} \\ \dfrac{1}{3} & -\dfrac{2}{3} & \dfrac{2}{3} \end{bmatrix}$

Solving the equation: $x = A^{-1}B = \begin{bmatrix} \dfrac{1}{3} & \dfrac{1}{3} & -\dfrac{1}{3} \\ -\dfrac{2}{3} & \dfrac{4}{3} & -\dfrac{1}{3} \\ \dfrac{1}{3} & -\dfrac{2}{3} & \dfrac{2}{3} \end{bmatrix} \begin{bmatrix} 550 \\ 620 \\ 570 \end{bmatrix} = \begin{bmatrix} 200 \\ 270 \\ 150 \end{bmatrix}$

A slice of cheese pizza has 200 calories, a slice of Meaty Delite pizza has 270 calories, and a slice of Veggie Delite pizza has 150 calories.

57. Let x represent the cost per yard for red, y represent the cost per yard for white, and z represent the cost per yard for blue. The system of equations is:

$$\frac{1}{4}x + \frac{5}{12}y + \frac{1}{3}z = 67.50$$
$$\frac{1}{3}x + \frac{1}{3}y + \frac{1}{3}z = 69$$
$$\frac{1}{4}x + \frac{1}{2}y + \frac{1}{4}z = 65.25$$

First finding the inverse: $A = \begin{bmatrix} \dfrac{1}{4} & \dfrac{5}{12} & \dfrac{1}{3} \\ \dfrac{1}{3} & \dfrac{1}{3} & \dfrac{1}{3} \\ \dfrac{1}{4} & \dfrac{1}{2} & \dfrac{1}{4} \end{bmatrix} \Rightarrow A^{-1} = \begin{bmatrix} -12 & 9 & 4 \\ 0 & -3 & 4 \\ 12 & -3 & -8 \end{bmatrix}$

Solving the equation: $x = A^{-1}B = \begin{bmatrix} -12 & 9 & 4 \\ 0 & -3 & 4 \\ 12 & -3 & -8 \end{bmatrix} \begin{bmatrix} 67.5 \\ 69 \\ 65.25 \end{bmatrix} = \begin{bmatrix} 72 \\ 54 \\ 81 \end{bmatrix}$

The red fabric costs $72 per yard, the white fabric costs $54 per yard, and the blue fabric costs $81 per yard.

59. The decoding matrix is the inverse: $\begin{bmatrix} 3 & -7 \\ -2 & 5 \end{bmatrix}$

61. The decoding matrix is the inverse: $\begin{bmatrix} 1.5 & -1.5 & 0.5 & 4.5 \\ 0.5 & -2.5 & 1.5 & 8.5 \\ 0.5 & -0.5 & 0 & 1.5 \\ 0 & 1 & -0.5 & -3 \end{bmatrix}$

63. Using $A = \begin{bmatrix} 1 & -2 & 3 \\ -2 & 3 & -4 \\ 2 & -4 & 5 \end{bmatrix}$, the decoding matrix is $A^{-1} = \begin{bmatrix} -1 & -2 & -1 \\ 2 & -1 & -2 \\ 2 & 0 & -1 \end{bmatrix}$.

Using $B = \begin{bmatrix} 52 \\ -77 \\ 86 \end{bmatrix}$, $C = \begin{bmatrix} -24 \\ 38 \\ -53 \end{bmatrix}$ and $D = \begin{bmatrix} 19 \\ -38 \\ 38 \end{bmatrix}$, apply the decoding matrix:

$X = A^{-1}B = \begin{bmatrix} -1 & -2 & -1 \\ 2 & -1 & -2 \\ 2 & 0 & -1 \end{bmatrix} \begin{bmatrix} 52 \\ -77 \\ 86 \end{bmatrix} = \begin{bmatrix} 16 \\ 9 \\ 18 \end{bmatrix}$ PIR

$Y = A^{-1}C = \begin{bmatrix} -1 & -2 & -1 \\ 2 & -1 & -2 \\ 2 & 0 & -1 \end{bmatrix} \begin{bmatrix} -24 \\ 38 \\ -53 \end{bmatrix} = \begin{bmatrix} 1 \\ 20 \\ 5 \end{bmatrix}$ ATE

$Z = A^{-1}D = \begin{bmatrix} -1 & -2 & -1 \\ 2 & -1 & -2 \\ 2 & 0 & -1 \end{bmatrix} \begin{bmatrix} 19 \\ -38 \\ 38 \end{bmatrix} = \begin{bmatrix} 19 \\ 0 \\ 0 \end{bmatrix}$ S

The decoded message is: PIRATES

65. Using $A = \begin{bmatrix} 1 & -2 & 3 \\ -2 & 3 & -4 \\ 2 & -4 & 5 \end{bmatrix}$, the decoding matrix is $A^{-1} = \begin{bmatrix} -1 & -2 & -1 \\ 2 & -1 & -2 \\ 2 & 0 & -1 \end{bmatrix}$.

Using $B = \begin{bmatrix} 6 \\ -16 \\ 7 \end{bmatrix}$ and $C = \begin{bmatrix} 28 \\ -32 \\ 31 \end{bmatrix}$, apply the decoding matrix:

$X = A^{-1}B = \begin{bmatrix} -1 & -2 & -1 \\ 2 & -1 & -2 \\ 2 & 0 & -1 \end{bmatrix} \begin{bmatrix} 6 \\ -16 \\ 7 \end{bmatrix} = \begin{bmatrix} 19 \\ 14 \\ 5 \end{bmatrix}$ SNE

$Y = A^{-1}C = \begin{bmatrix} -1 & -2 & -1 \\ 2 & -1 & -2 \\ 2 & 0 & -1 \end{bmatrix} \begin{bmatrix} 28 \\ -32 \\ 31 \end{bmatrix} = \begin{bmatrix} 5 \\ 26 \\ 25 \end{bmatrix}$ EZY

The decoded message is: SNEEZY

67. Form the augmented matrix: $\begin{bmatrix} a & a & a & | & 1 & 0 & 0 \\ 0 & 1 & 0 & | & 0 & 1 & 0 \\ 0 & 0 & 1 & | & 0 & 0 & 1 \end{bmatrix}$

Multiply the first row by $\dfrac{1}{a}$: $\begin{bmatrix} 1 & 1 & 1 & | & \dfrac{1}{a} & 0 & 0 \\ 0 & 1 & 0 & | & 0 & 1 & 0 \\ 0 & 0 & 1 & | & 0 & 0 & 1 \end{bmatrix}$

Adding -1 times the second row and -1 times the third row to the first row: $\begin{bmatrix} 1 & 0 & 0 & | & \dfrac{1}{a} & -1 & -1 \\ 0 & 1 & 0 & | & 0 & 1 & 0 \\ 0 & 0 & 1 & | & 0 & 0 & 1 \end{bmatrix}$

The inverse matrix is: $\begin{bmatrix} \dfrac{1}{a} & -1 & -1 \\ 0 & 1 & 0 \\ 0 & 0 & 1 \end{bmatrix}$

For $a = 1$, the inverse matrix is: $\begin{bmatrix} 1 & -1 & -1 \\ 0 & 1 & 0 \\ 0 & 0 & 1 \end{bmatrix}$

69. Finding the power: $A^2 = \begin{bmatrix} 1 & -2 \\ -1 & 3 \end{bmatrix}\begin{bmatrix} 1 & -2 \\ -1 & 3 \end{bmatrix} = \begin{bmatrix} 3 & -8 \\ -4 & 11 \end{bmatrix}$

Form the augmented matrix: $\begin{bmatrix} 1 & -2 & | & 1 & 0 \\ -1 & 3 & | & 0 & 1 \end{bmatrix}$

Adding the first row to the second row: $\begin{bmatrix} 1 & -2 & | & 1 & 0 \\ 0 & 1 & | & 1 & 1 \end{bmatrix}$

Adding 2 times the second row to the first row: $\begin{bmatrix} 1 & 0 & | & 3 & 2 \\ 0 & 1 & | & 1 & 1 \end{bmatrix}$

The inverse is: $A^{-1} = \begin{bmatrix} 3 & 2 \\ 1 & 1 \end{bmatrix}$

Therefore: $\left(A^{-1}\right)^2 = \begin{bmatrix} 3 & 2 \\ 1 & 1 \end{bmatrix}\begin{bmatrix} 3 & 2 \\ 1 & 1 \end{bmatrix} = \begin{bmatrix} 11 & 8 \\ 4 & 3 \end{bmatrix}$

Form the augmented matrix: $\begin{bmatrix} 3 & -8 & | & 1 & 0 \\ -4 & 11 & | & 0 & 1 \end{bmatrix}$

Multiplying the first row by $\dfrac{1}{3}$: $\begin{bmatrix} 1 & -\dfrac{8}{3} & | & \dfrac{1}{3} & 0 \\ -4 & 11 & | & 0 & 1 \end{bmatrix}$

Adding 4 times the first row to the second row: $\begin{bmatrix} 1 & -\dfrac{8}{3} & | & \dfrac{1}{3} & 0 \\ 0 & \dfrac{1}{3} & | & \dfrac{4}{3} & 1 \end{bmatrix}$

Adding 8 times the second row to the first row: $\begin{bmatrix} 1 & 0 & | & 11 & 8 \\ 0 & \frac{1}{3} & | & \frac{4}{3} & 1 \end{bmatrix}$

Multiplying the second row by 3: $\begin{bmatrix} 1 & 0 & | & 11 & 8 \\ 0 & 3 & | & 4 & 3 \end{bmatrix}$

Therefore: $\left(A^2\right)^{-1} = \begin{bmatrix} 11 & 8 \\ 4 & 3 \end{bmatrix}$

This illustrates that $\left(A^2\right)^{-1} = \left(A^{-1}\right)^2$.

71. The results are: $A^{-1} = \begin{bmatrix} -1 & -1 \\ 4 & 5 \end{bmatrix}$, $\left(A^{-1}\right)^3 = \begin{bmatrix} -13 & -17 \\ 68 & 89 \end{bmatrix}$, $A^3 = \begin{bmatrix} -89 & -17 \\ 68 & 13 \end{bmatrix}$, $\left(A^3\right)^{-1} = \begin{bmatrix} -13 & -17 \\ 68 & 89 \end{bmatrix}$

This illustrates that $\left(A^3\right)^{-1} = \left(A^{-1}\right)^3$.

73. Form the augmented matrix: $\begin{bmatrix} 4 & 1 & | & 1 & 0 \\ 3 & 1 & | & 0 & 1 \end{bmatrix}$

Multiplying the first row by $\frac{1}{4}$: $\begin{bmatrix} 1 & \frac{1}{4} & | & \frac{1}{4} & 0 \\ 3 & 1 & | & 0 & 1 \end{bmatrix}$

Adding –3 times the first row to the second row: $\begin{bmatrix} 1 & \frac{1}{4} & | & \frac{1}{4} & 0 \\ 0 & \frac{1}{4} & | & -\frac{3}{4} & 1 \end{bmatrix}$

Adding –1 times the second row to the first row: $\begin{bmatrix} 1 & 0 & | & 1 & -1 \\ 0 & \frac{1}{4} & | & -\frac{3}{4} & 1 \end{bmatrix}$

Multiplying the second row by 4: $\begin{bmatrix} 1 & 0 & | & 1 & -1 \\ 0 & 1 & | & -3 & 4 \end{bmatrix}$

Therefore $A^{-1} = \begin{bmatrix} 1 & -1 \\ -3 & 4 \end{bmatrix}$. Now using the results from the previous exercise:

$$\left(A^2\right)^{-1} = \left(A^{-1}\right)^2 = \begin{bmatrix} 1 & -1 \\ -3 & 4 \end{bmatrix}\begin{bmatrix} 1 & -1 \\ -3 & 4 \end{bmatrix} = \begin{bmatrix} 4 & -5 \\ -15 & 19 \end{bmatrix}$$

$$\left(A^3\right)^{-1} = \left(A^{-1}\right)^3 = \begin{bmatrix} 4 & -5 \\ -15 & 19 \end{bmatrix}\begin{bmatrix} 1 & -1 \\ -3 & 4 \end{bmatrix} = \begin{bmatrix} 19 & -24 \\ -72 & 91 \end{bmatrix}$$

75. a. Finding the product: $AB = \begin{bmatrix} 0 & 1 \\ 1 & 0 \end{bmatrix}\begin{bmatrix} 2 \\ -1 \end{bmatrix} = \begin{bmatrix} -1 \\ 2 \end{bmatrix}$

b. Sketching the graph:

c. Multiply the product by A.

8.6 Determinants and Cramer's Rule

1. Evaluating the determinant: $|A| = \begin{vmatrix} -3 & 1 \\ 2 & 4 \end{vmatrix} = -3(4)-1(2) = -14$

3. Evaluating the determinant: $|A| = \begin{vmatrix} \frac{1}{2} & 3 \\ 2 & -6 \end{vmatrix} = \frac{1}{2}(-6)-(3)(2) = -9$

5. Evaluating the determinant: $|A| = \begin{vmatrix} 4 & 1 \\ -3 & 8 \end{vmatrix} = 4(8)-(-3)(1) = 35$

7. Evaluating the determinant: $|A| = \begin{vmatrix} \frac{1}{3} & -2 \\ 5 & 3 \end{vmatrix} = \frac{1}{3}(3)-(-2)(5) = 11$

9. Finding the minor and cofactor:
$$M_{11} = \begin{vmatrix} 5 & -4 \\ 6 & 5 \end{vmatrix} = 5(5)-(-4)(6) = 49$$
$$C_{11} = (-1)^{1+1} M_{11} = (-1)^2 (49) = 49$$

11. Finding the minor and cofactor:
$$M_{32} = \begin{vmatrix} -3 & 2 \\ 1 & -4 \end{vmatrix} = -3(-4)-2(1) = 10$$
$$C_{32} = (-1)^{3+2} M_{32} = (-1)^5 (10) = -10$$

13. Expand about the first column: $\begin{vmatrix} 0 & 1 & -2 \\ 5 & -2 & 3 \\ 0 & 6 & 5 \end{vmatrix} = (0)C_{11} + (5)C_{21} + (0)C_{31} = (5)(-1)^{2+1}(5-(-12)) = (5)(-1)(17) = -85$

15. Expand about the second row:
$$\begin{vmatrix} -2 & 3 & 5 \\ 6 & -1 & 0 \\ 0 & 1 & -2 \end{vmatrix} = (6)C_{21} + (-1)C_{22} + (0)C_{23}$$
$$= (6)(-1)^{2+1}(-6-5) - (-1)^{2+2}(4-0)$$
$$= (6)(-1)(-11) - (-1)(4)$$
$$= 66 - 4$$
$$= 62$$

17. Expand about the first row: $\begin{vmatrix} 0 & 0 & 0 \\ -7 & 3 & 4 \\ 6 & 3 & 4 \end{vmatrix} = (0)C_{11} + (0)C_{21} + (0)C_{31} = 0$

19. Expand about the first row:
$$\begin{vmatrix} 1 & 1 & 1 \\ 2 & 2 & 2 \\ 3 & 3 & 3 \end{vmatrix} = (1)C_{11} + (1)C_{12} + (1)C_{13} = (-1)^{1+1}(6-6) + (-1)^{1+2}(6-6) + (-1)^{1+3}(6-6) = 0-0+0 = 0$$

21. Expand about the third column:
$$\begin{vmatrix} -2 & 2 & 0 \\ 0 & -1 & 1 \\ -4 & 5 & 2 \end{vmatrix} = (0)C_{13} + (1)C_{23} + (2)C_{33} = (-1)^{2+3}(-10-(-8)) + (2)(-1)^{3+3}(2-0) = (-1)(-2)+2(2) = 6$$

23. Solving the equation:

$$\begin{vmatrix} -1 & x \\ 3 & -4 \end{vmatrix} = -2$$

$$4 - 3x = -2$$
$$-3x = -6$$
$$x = 2$$

25. Expanding about the first column to solve the equation:

$$\begin{vmatrix} -1 & 0 & 2 \\ 0 & 5 & 3 \\ 0 & x & -2 \end{vmatrix} = -2$$

$$(-1)C_{11} = -2$$
$$(-1)(-1)^{1+1}(-10 - 3x) = -2$$
$$10 + 3x = -2$$
$$3x = -12$$
$$x = -4$$

27. Expanding about the second row to solve the equation:

$$\begin{vmatrix} 2 & -3 & 5 \\ x & 0 & -4 \\ 3 & 2 & 1 \end{vmatrix} = 39$$

$$xC_{21} + (-4)C_{23} = 39$$
$$x(-1)^{2+1}(-3 - 10) + (-4)(-1)^{2+3}(4 - (-9)) = 39$$
$$x(-1)(-13) + (-4)(-1)(13) = 39$$
$$13x + 52 = 39$$
$$13x = -13$$
$$x = -1$$

29. Finding the determinants:

$$D = \begin{vmatrix} -3 & -1 \\ 4 & 1 \end{vmatrix} = -3 - (-4) = 1$$

$$D_x = \begin{vmatrix} 5 & -1 \\ 2 & 1 \end{vmatrix} = 5 - (-2) = 7$$

$$D_y = \begin{vmatrix} -3 & 5 \\ 4 & 2 \end{vmatrix} = -6 - 20 = -26$$

Using Cramer's rule: $x = \dfrac{D_x}{D} = \dfrac{7}{1} = 7$, $y = \dfrac{D_y}{D} = \dfrac{-26}{1} = -26$

31. Finding the determinants:

$$D = \begin{vmatrix} 4 & -2 \\ 3 & -1 \end{vmatrix} = -4 - (-6) = 2$$

$$D_x = \begin{vmatrix} 7 & -2 \\ 1 & -1 \end{vmatrix} = -7 - (-2) = -5$$

$$D_y = \begin{vmatrix} 4 & 7 \\ 3 & 1 \end{vmatrix} = 4 - 21 = -17$$

Using Cramer's rule: $x = \dfrac{D_x}{D} = -\dfrac{5}{2}$, $y = \dfrac{D_y}{D} = -\dfrac{17}{2}$

33. Finding the determinants:

$$D = \begin{vmatrix} 1 & -2 \\ -3 & 4 \end{vmatrix} = 4 - 6 = -2$$

$$D_x = \begin{vmatrix} 4 & -2 \\ -8 & 4 \end{vmatrix} = 16 - 16 = 0$$

$$D_y = \begin{vmatrix} 1 & 4 \\ -3 & -8 \end{vmatrix} = -8 - (-12) = 4$$

Using Cramer's rule: $x = \dfrac{D_x}{D} = \dfrac{0}{-2} = 0, \quad y = \dfrac{D_y}{D} = \dfrac{4}{-2} = -2$

35. Finding the determinants:

$$D = \begin{vmatrix} 4 & 1 \\ 5 & 4 \end{vmatrix} = 16 - 5 = 11$$

$$D_x = \begin{vmatrix} -7 & 1 \\ -6 & 4 \end{vmatrix} = -28 - (-6) = -22$$

$$D_y = \begin{vmatrix} 4 & -7 \\ 5 & -6 \end{vmatrix} = -24 - (-35) = 11$$

Using Cramer's rule: $x = \dfrac{D_x}{D} = \dfrac{-22}{11} = -2, \quad y = \dfrac{D_y}{D} = \dfrac{11}{11} = 1$

37. Finding the determinants:

$$D = \begin{vmatrix} 1.4 & 2 \\ 3.5 & 3 \end{vmatrix} = 4.2 - 7 = -2.8$$

$$D_x = \begin{vmatrix} 0 & 2 \\ -9.7 & 3 \end{vmatrix} = 0 - (-19.4) = 19.4$$

$$D_y = \begin{vmatrix} 1.4 & 0 \\ 3.5 & -9.7 \end{vmatrix} = -13.58$$

Using Cramer's rule: $x = \dfrac{D_x}{D} = \dfrac{19.4}{-2.8} \approx -6.9286, \quad y = \dfrac{D_y}{D} = \dfrac{-13.58}{-2.8} = 4.85$

39. Finding the determinants:

$$D = \begin{vmatrix} 1 & 1 & 0 \\ 1 & 0 & -1 \\ 0 & -1 & 1 \end{vmatrix} = C_{11} + C_{12} = (-1)^2(0-1) + (-1)^3(1-0) = -1 - 1 = -2$$

$$D_x = \begin{vmatrix} 1 & 1 & 0 \\ 0 & 0 & -1 \\ 0 & -1 & 1 \end{vmatrix} = C_{11} = (-1)^2(0-1) = -1$$

$$D_y = \begin{vmatrix} 1 & 1 & 0 \\ 1 & 0 & -1 \\ 0 & 0 & 1 \end{vmatrix} = C_{12} = (-1)^3(1-0) = -1$$

$$D_z = \begin{vmatrix} 1 & 1 & 1 \\ 1 & 0 & 0 \\ 0 & -1 & 0 \end{vmatrix} = C_{13} = (-1)^4(-1-0) = -1$$

Using Cramer's rule: $x = \dfrac{D_x}{D} = \dfrac{-1}{-2} = \dfrac{1}{2}, \quad y = \dfrac{D_y}{D} = \dfrac{-1}{-2} = \dfrac{1}{2}, \quad z = \dfrac{D_z}{D} = \dfrac{-1}{-2} = \dfrac{1}{2}$

41. Finding the determinants:

$$D = \begin{vmatrix} 5 & 0 & 3 \\ -2 & 1 & 1 \\ 0 & -3 & 1 \end{vmatrix} = 5C_{11} + 3C_{13} = 5(-1)^2\left(1-(-3)\right) + 3(-1)^4(6-0) = 5(1)(4) + 3(1)(6) = 38$$

$$D_x = \begin{vmatrix} 3 & 0 & 3 \\ -1 & 1 & 1 \\ 7 & -3 & 1 \end{vmatrix} = 3C_{11} + 3C_{13} = 3(-1)^2\left(1-(-3)\right) + 3(-1)^4(3-7) = 3(1)(4) + 3(1)(-4) = 0$$

$$D_y = \begin{vmatrix} 5 & 3 & 3 \\ -2 & -1 & 1 \\ 0 & 7 & 1 \end{vmatrix} = 7C_{32} + C_{33} = 7(-1)^5\left(5-(-6)\right) + (-1)^6\left(-5-(-6)\right) = 7(-1)(11) + (1)(1) = -76$$

$$D_z = \begin{vmatrix} 5 & 0 & 3 \\ -2 & 1 & -1 \\ 0 & -3 & 7 \end{vmatrix} = 5C_{11} + 3C_{13} = 5(-1)^2(7-3) + 3(-1)^4(6-0) = 5(1)(4) + 3(1)(6) = 38$$

Using Cramer's rule: $x = \dfrac{D_x}{D} = \dfrac{0}{38} = 0$, $\quad y = \dfrac{D_y}{D} = \dfrac{-76}{38} = -2$, $\quad z = \dfrac{D_z}{D} = \dfrac{38}{38} = 1$

43. Finding the determinants:

$$D = \begin{vmatrix} 3 & -5 & 1 \\ -3 & 7 & -4 \\ 2 & 0 & 1 \end{vmatrix} = 2C_{31} + C_{33} = 2(-1)^4(20-7) + (-1)^6(21-15) = 2(1)(13) + (1)(6) = 32$$

$$D_x = \begin{vmatrix} -14 & -5 & 1 \\ 9 & 7 & -4 \\ 6 & 0 & 1 \end{vmatrix} = 6C_{31} + C_{33} = 6(-1)^4(20-7) + (-1)^6(-98+45) = 6(1)(13) + (1)(-53) = 25$$

$$D_y = \begin{vmatrix} 3 & -14 & 1 \\ -3 & 9 & -4 \\ 2 & 6 & 1 \end{vmatrix} = 2C_{31} + 6C_{32} + C_{33} = 2(-1)^4(47) + 6(-1)^5(-9) + (-1)^6(-15) = 94 + 54 - 15 = 133$$

$$D_z = \begin{vmatrix} 3 & -5 & -14 \\ -3 & 7 & 9 \\ 2 & 0 & 6 \end{vmatrix} = 2C_{31} + 6C_{33} = 2(-1)^4(-45+98) + 6(-1)^6(21-15) = 2(1)(53) + 6(1)(6) = 142$$

Using Cramer's rule: $x = \dfrac{D_x}{D} = \dfrac{25}{32}$, $\quad y = \dfrac{D_y}{D} = \dfrac{133}{32}$, $\quad z = \dfrac{D_z}{D} = \dfrac{142}{32} = \dfrac{71}{16}$

45. Finding the determinants:

$$D = \begin{vmatrix} 3 & 1 & 1 \\ 2 & 1 & -1 \\ 1 & 3 & -1 \end{vmatrix} = 3C_{11} + C_{12} + C_{13} = 3(1)(-1+3) + (-1)(-2+1) + (1)(6-1) = 3(2) + (-1)(-1) + (5) = 12$$

$$D_x = \begin{vmatrix} 1 & 1 & 1 \\ -\dfrac{3}{2} & 1 & -1 \\ -5 & 3 & -1 \end{vmatrix} = C_{11} + C_{12} + C_{13} = (1)(-1+3) + (-1)\left(\dfrac{3}{2} - 5\right) + (1)\left(-\dfrac{9}{2} + 5\right) = (2) + (-1)\left(-\dfrac{7}{2}\right) + \left(\dfrac{1}{2}\right) = 6$$

$$D_y = \begin{vmatrix} 3 & 1 & 1 \\ 2 & -\dfrac{3}{2} & -1 \\ 1 & -5 & -1 \end{vmatrix} = 3C_{11} + C_{12} + C_{13} = 3\left(\dfrac{3}{2} - 5\right) + (-1)(-1) + 1\left(-10 + \dfrac{3}{2}\right) = 3\left(-\dfrac{7}{2}\right) + 1 + \left(-\dfrac{17}{2}\right) = -18$$

$$D_z = \begin{vmatrix} 3 & 1 & 1 \\ 2 & 1 & -\dfrac{3}{2} \\ 1 & 3 & -5 \end{vmatrix} = 3C_{11} + C_{12} + C_{13} = 3(1)\left(-5 + \dfrac{9}{2}\right) + (-1)\left(-10 + \dfrac{3}{2}\right) + (1)(6-1) = 3\left(-\dfrac{1}{2}\right) + (-1)\left(-\dfrac{17}{2}\right) + 5 = 12$$

Using Cramer's rule: $x = \dfrac{D_x}{D} = \dfrac{6}{12} = \dfrac{1}{2}$, $y = \dfrac{D_y}{D} = \dfrac{-18}{12} = -\dfrac{3}{2}$, $z = \dfrac{D_z}{D} = \dfrac{12}{12} = 1$

47. The entries of the second row are all zeros, so the sum of the products of these entries and their cofactors will be zero.

49. Substituting the values:

$$1 + 2(2) = 5$$
$$4(1) + 2 - 0 = 6$$
$$-2(1) - 4(2) = -10$$

Finding the determinant: $D = \begin{vmatrix} 1 & 2 & 0 \\ 4 & 1 & -1 \\ -2 & -4 & 0 \end{vmatrix} = -1C_{23} = -1(-1)(-4+4) = 0$

Cramer's Rule cannot be used because $D = 0$.

8.7 Partial Fractions

1. The form of the decomposition is: $\dfrac{3}{x^2 - x - 3} = \dfrac{Ax + B}{x^2 - x - 3}$

3. The form of the decomposition is: $\dfrac{4x}{(x+5)^2} = \dfrac{A}{x+5} + \dfrac{B}{(x+5)^2}$

5. The form of the decomposition is: $\dfrac{x+3}{(x^2+2)(2x+1)} = \dfrac{Ax+B}{x^2+2} + \dfrac{C}{2x+1}$

7. The form of the decomposition is: $\dfrac{3x-1}{x^4-16} = \dfrac{3x-1}{(x^2-4)(x^2+4)} = \dfrac{3x-1}{(x-2)(x+2)(x^2+4)} = \dfrac{A}{x-2} + \dfrac{B}{x+2} + \dfrac{Cx+D}{x^2+4}$

9. The form of the decomposition is: $\dfrac{x+6}{3x^3+6x^2+3x} = \dfrac{x+6}{3x(x^2+2x+1)} = \dfrac{x+6}{3x(x+1)^2} = \dfrac{A}{3x} + \dfrac{B}{x+1} + \dfrac{C}{(x+1)^2}$

11. Using $a = 1, b = 0, c = 5$ to find the discriminant: $b^2 - 4ac = (0)^2 - 4(1)(5) = -20 < 0$

So $x^2 + 5$ is irreducible.

13. Using $a = 1, b = 1, c = 1$ to find the discriminant: $b^2 - 4ac = (1)^2 - 4(1)(1) = -3 < 0$

So $x^2 + x + 1$ is irreducible.

15. Using $a = 1, b = 4, c = 4$ to find the discriminant: $b^2 - 4ac = (4)^2 - 4(1)(4) = 0$

So $x^2 + 4x + 4$ is reducible (as a square).

17. The form of the decomposition is: $\dfrac{8}{x^2 - 16} = \dfrac{8}{(x+4)(x-4)} = \dfrac{A}{x+4} + \dfrac{B}{x-4}$

Clearing fractions: $8 = A(x-4) + B(x+4) = Ax - 4A + Bx + 4B = (A+B)x + (-4A+4B)$

This produces the system:
$$A + B = 0$$
$$-4A + 4B = 8$$

Multiplying the first equation by 4:
$$4A + 4B = 0$$
$$-4A + 4B = 8$$

Adding yields:
$$8B = 8$$
$$B = 1$$
$$A = -1$$

Therefore the decomposition is: $\dfrac{8}{x^2 - 16} = \dfrac{-1}{x+4} + \dfrac{1}{x-4}$

19. The form of the decomposition is: $\dfrac{2}{2x^2 - x} = \dfrac{2}{x(2x-1)} = \dfrac{A}{x} + \dfrac{B}{2x-1}$

Clearing fractions: $2 = A(2x-1) + Bx = 2Ax - A + Bx = (2A+B)x - A$

This produces the system:
$$2A + B = 0$$
$$-A = 2$$

Solving the second equation for A:
$$-A = 2$$
$$A = -2$$

Substituting into the first equation:
$$2(-2) + B = 0$$
$$-4 + B = 0$$
$$B = 4$$

Therefore the decomposition is: $\dfrac{2}{2x^2 - x} = \dfrac{-2}{x} + \dfrac{4}{2x-1}$

21. The form of the decomposition is: $\dfrac{x}{x^2 + 5x + 6} = \dfrac{x}{(x+2)(x+3)} = \dfrac{A}{x+2} + \dfrac{B}{x+3}$

Clearing fractions: $x = A(x+3) + B(x+2) = Ax + 3A + Bx + 2B = (A+B)x + (3A+2B)$

This produces the system:
$$A + B = 1$$
$$3A + 2B = 0$$

Multiplying the first equation by –2:
$$-2A - 2B = -2$$
$$3A + 2B = 0$$

Adding yields:
$$A = -2$$
$$-2 + B = 1$$
$$B = 3$$

Therefore the decomposition is: $\dfrac{x}{x^2 + 5x + 6} = \dfrac{-2}{x+2} + \dfrac{3}{x+3}$

23. The form of the decomposition is: $\dfrac{-3x^2 + 2 - 3x}{x^3 - x} = \dfrac{-3x^2 - 3x + 2}{x(x^2 - 1)} = \dfrac{-3x^2 - 3x + 2}{x(x+1)(x-1)} = \dfrac{A}{x} + \dfrac{B}{x+1} + \dfrac{C}{x-1}$

Clearing fractions:
$$-3x^2 - 3x + 2 = A(x+1)(x-1) + Bx(x-1) + Cx(x+1)$$
$$= A(x^2 - 1) + B(x^2 - x) + C(x^2 + x)$$
$$= Ax^2 - A + Bx^2 - Bx + Cx^2 + Cx$$
$$= (A + B + C)x^2 + (-B + C)x - A$$

This produces the system:
$$A + B + C = -3$$
$$-B + C = -3$$
$$-A = 2$$

Solving the third equation for A yields $A = -2$. Substituting into the first equation:
$$-2 + B + C = -3$$
$$-B + C = -3$$

Adding yields:
$$-2 + 2C = -6$$
$$2C = -4$$
$$C = -2$$

Substituting into $-B + C = -3$:
$$-B + (-2) = -3$$
$$-B = -1$$
$$B = 1$$

Therefore the decomposition is: $\dfrac{-3x^2 + 2 - 3x}{x^3 - x} = \dfrac{-2}{x} + \dfrac{1}{x+1} - \dfrac{2}{x-1}$

25. The form of the decomposition is: $\dfrac{-2x + 6}{x^2 - 2x + 1} = \dfrac{-2x + 6}{(x-1)^2} = \dfrac{A}{x-1} + \dfrac{B}{(x-1)^2}$

Clearing fractions: $-2x + 6 = A(x-1) + B = Ax + (-A + B)$

This produces the system:
$$A = -2$$
$$-A + B = 6$$

Substituting into the second equation:
$$2 + B = 6$$
$$B = 4$$

Therefore the decomposition is: $\dfrac{-2x + 6}{x^2 - 2x + 1} = \dfrac{-2}{x-1} + \dfrac{4}{(x-1)^2}$

27. The form of the decomposition is: $\dfrac{-x^2+2x+4}{x^3+2x^2}=\dfrac{-x^2+2x+4}{x^2(x+2)}=\dfrac{A}{x}+\dfrac{B}{x^2}+\dfrac{C}{x+2}$

Clearing fractions:
$$-x^2+2x+4=Ax(x+2)+B(x+2)+Cx^2=Ax^2+2Ax+Bx+2B+Cx^2=(A+C)x^2+(2A+B)x+2B$$

This produces the system:

$A+C=-1$

$2A+B=2$

$2B=4$

Solving the third equation for B yields $B=2$. Substituting into the second equation:

$2A+B=2$

$2A+2=2$

$2A=0$

$A=0$

Substituting into the first equation:

$A+C=-1$

$0+C=-1$

$C=-1$

Therefore the decomposition is: $\dfrac{-x^2+2x+4}{x^3+2x^2}=\dfrac{2}{x^2}-\dfrac{1}{x+2}$

29. The form of the decomposition is: $\dfrac{-2x^2-3x-4}{(x-1)(x+2)^2}=\dfrac{-2x^2-3x-4}{(x-1)(x+2)^2}=\dfrac{A}{x-1}+\dfrac{B}{x+2}+\dfrac{C}{(x+2)^2}$

Clearing fractions:
$$-2x^2-3x-4=A(x+2)^2+B(x-1)(x+2)+C(x-1)$$
$$=A(x^2+4x+4)+B(x^2+x-2)+C(x-1)$$
$$=(A+B)x^2+(4A+B+C)x+(4A-2B-C)$$

This produces the system:

$A+B\quad\;\;=-2$

$4A+B+C=-3$

$4A-2B-C=-4$

Adding -4 times the first equation to the second and third equation yields:

$A+B\quad\;\;=-2$

$-3B+C=5$

$-6B-C=4$

Adding the second equation to the third equation yields:

$A+B\quad\;\;=-2$

$-3B+C=5$

$-9B=9$

Solving the third equation for B yields $B=-1$. Substituting into the first and second equations:

$-3B+C=5$ $\qquad\qquad\qquad\qquad$ $A+B=-2$

$-3(-1)+C=5$ $\qquad\qquad\qquad\quad$ $A-1=-2$

$3+C=5$ $\qquad\qquad\qquad\qquad\quad$ $A=-1$

$C=2$

Therefore the decomposition is: $\dfrac{-2x^2-3x-4}{(x-1)(x+2)^2}=\dfrac{-1}{x-1}-\dfrac{1}{x+2}+\dfrac{2}{(x+2)^2}$

31. The form of the decomposition is: $\dfrac{4x+1}{(x+2)(x^2+3)} = \dfrac{A}{x+2} + \dfrac{Bx+C}{x^2+3}$

Clearing fractions: $4x+1 = A(x^2+3) + (Bx+C)(x+2)$

Substituting $x = -2$:

$$4(-2)+1 = A\big((-2)^2+3\big) + (B(-2)+C)(-2+2)$$
$$-7 = 7A+0$$
$$-1 = A$$

Therefore:

$$4x+1 = -1(x^2+3) + (Bx+C)(x+2) = -x^2-3+Bx^2+2Bx+Cx+2C = (B-1)x^2+(2B+C)x+(2C-3)$$

Equating coefficients:

$$B-1=0 \qquad\qquad\qquad 2B+C = 4$$
$$B=1 \qquad\qquad\qquad 2(1)+C = 4$$
$$\qquad\qquad\qquad C = 2$$

Therefore the decomposition is: $\dfrac{4x+1}{(x+2)(x^2+3)} = \dfrac{-1}{x+2} + \dfrac{x+2}{x^2+3}$

33. The form of the decomposition is: $\dfrac{-3x+3}{(x+2)(x^2+x+1)} = \dfrac{A}{x+2} + \dfrac{Bx+C}{x^2+x+1}$

Clearing fractions: $-3x+3 = A(x^2+x+1) + (Bx+C)(x+2)$

Substituting $x = -2$:

$$-3(-2)+3 = A\big((-2)^2-2+1\big) + (B(-2)+C)(-2+2)$$
$$9 = 3A$$
$$3 = A$$

Therefore:

$$-3x+3 = 3(x^2+x+1) + (Bx+C)(x+2) = 3x^2+3x+3+Bx^2+2Bx+Cx+2C = (B+3)x^2+(2B+C+3)x+(2C+3)$$

Equating coefficients:

$$B+3=0 \qquad\qquad\qquad 2C+3 = 3$$
$$B=-3 \qquad\qquad\qquad 2C = 0$$
$$\qquad\qquad\qquad C = 0$$

Therefore the decomposition is: $\dfrac{-3x+3}{(x+2)(x^2+x+1)} = \dfrac{3}{x+2} - \dfrac{3x}{x^2+x+1}$

35. The form of the decomposition is: $\dfrac{x^2+3}{x^4-1} = \dfrac{x^2+3}{(x^2+1)(x^2-1)} = \dfrac{x^2+3}{(x^2+1)(x+1)(x-1)} = \dfrac{A}{x+1} + \dfrac{B}{x-1} + \dfrac{Cx+D}{x^2+1}$

Clearing fractions: $x^2+3 = A(x-1)(x^2+1) + B(x+1)(x^2+1) + (Cx+D)(x+1)(x-1)$

Substituting $x = 1$: $\qquad\qquad\qquad$ Substituting $x = -1$:

$$1+3 = B(1+1)(1+1) \qquad\qquad 1+3 = A(-1-1)(1+1)$$
$$4 = 4B \qquad\qquad\qquad\qquad 4 = -4A$$
$$B = 1 \qquad\qquad\qquad\qquad\quad A = -1$$

Therefore:

$$x^2+3=-1(x-1)(x^2+1)+1(x+1)(x^2+1)+(Cx+D)(x+1)(x-1)$$

$$=-x^3+x^2-x+1+x^3+x^2+x+1+(Cx+D)(x^2-1)$$

$$=2x^2+2+Cx^3+Dx^2-Cx-D$$

$$=Cx^3+(2+D)x^2-Cx+(2-D)$$

Equating coefficients:

$$2+D=1 \qquad\qquad\qquad\qquad C=0$$
$$D=-1$$

Therefore the decomposition is: $\dfrac{x^2+3}{x^4-1}=\dfrac{-1}{x+1}+\dfrac{1}{x-1}-\dfrac{1}{x^2+1}$

37. The form of the decomposition is: $\dfrac{-x^2-2x-3}{\left(x^2+2\right)^2}=\dfrac{Ax+B}{x^2+2}+\dfrac{Cx+D}{\left(x^2+2\right)^2}$

Clearing fractions:

$$-x^2-2x-3=(Ax+B)(x^2+2)+(Cx+D)=Ax^3+Bx^2+2Ax+2B+Cx+D=Ax^3+Bx^2+(2A+C)x+(2B+D)$$

So $A=0$ and $B=-1$. Substituting to find C and D:

$$2A+C=-2 \qquad\qquad\qquad 2B+D=-3$$
$$2(0)+C=-2 \qquad\qquad\qquad 2(-1)+D=-3$$
$$C=-2 \qquad\qquad\qquad\qquad -2+D=-3$$
$$\qquad\qquad\qquad\qquad\qquad\qquad D=-1$$

Therefore the decomposition is: $\dfrac{-x^2-2x-2}{\left(x^2+2\right)^2}=\dfrac{-1}{x^2+2}-\dfrac{2x+1}{\left(x^2+2\right)^2}$

39. The form of the decomposition is: $\dfrac{x^3-3x^2-x-3}{x^4-1}=\dfrac{x^3-3x^2-x-3}{(x+1)(x-1)(x^2+1)}=\dfrac{A}{x+1}+\dfrac{B}{x-1}+\dfrac{Cx+D}{x^2+1}$

Clearing fractions: $x^3-3x^2-x-3=A(x-1)(x^2+1)+B(x+1)(x^2+1)+(Cx+D)(x+1)(x-1)$

Substituting $x=1$: $\qquad\qquad\qquad\qquad$ Substituting $x=-1$:

$$1-3-1-3=B(1+1)(1+1) \qquad\qquad -1-3+1-3=A(-1-1)(1+1)$$
$$-6=4B \qquad\qquad\qquad\qquad\qquad -6=-4A$$
$$B=-\dfrac{3}{2} \qquad\qquad\qquad\qquad\qquad A=\dfrac{3}{2}$$

Therefore:

$$x^3-3x^2-x-3=\dfrac{3}{2}(x-1)(x^2+1)-\dfrac{3}{2}(x+1)(x^2+1)+(Cx+D)(x+1)(x-1)$$

$$=\dfrac{3}{2}x^3-\dfrac{3}{2}x^2+\dfrac{3}{2}x-\dfrac{3}{2}-\dfrac{3}{2}x^3-\dfrac{3}{2}x^2-\dfrac{3}{2}x-\dfrac{3}{2}+(Cx+D)(x^2-1)$$

$$=-3x^2-3+Cx^3+Dx^2-Cx-D$$

$$=Cx^3+(-3+D)x^2-Cx+(-3-D)$$

Equating coefficients:

$$C=1 \qquad\qquad\qquad\qquad -3+D=-3$$
$$\qquad\qquad\qquad\qquad\qquad D=0$$

Therefore the decomposition is: $\dfrac{x^3-3x^2-x-3}{x^4-1}=\dfrac{3}{2(x+1)}-\dfrac{3}{2(x-1)}+\dfrac{x}{x^2+1}$

41. The form of the decomposition is: $\dfrac{t^2}{t^3+125} = \dfrac{t^2}{(t+5)(t^2-5t+25)} = \dfrac{A}{t+5} + \dfrac{Bt+C}{t^2-5t+25}$

Clearing fractions: $t^2 = A(t^2-5t+25)+(Bt+C)(t+5)$

Substituting $t=-5$:

$$25 = A(25+25+25)$$
$$25 = 75A$$
$$A = \frac{1}{3}$$

Therefore:

$$t^2 = \frac{1}{3}(t^2-5t+25)+(Bt+C)(t+5) = \frac{1}{3}t^2 - \frac{5}{3}t + \frac{25}{3} + Bt^2 + Bt + Ct + 5C = \left(\frac{1}{3}+B\right)t^2 + \left(B+C-\frac{5}{3}\right)t + \left(5C+\frac{25}{3}\right)$$

Equating coefficients:

$\dfrac{1}{3}+B=1 \qquad\qquad\qquad\qquad\qquad 5C+\dfrac{25}{3}=0$

$\qquad B=\dfrac{2}{3} \qquad\qquad\qquad\qquad\qquad\quad 5C=-\dfrac{25}{3}$

$\qquad\qquad\qquad\qquad\qquad\qquad\qquad\qquad\quad C=-\dfrac{5}{3}$

Therefore the decomposition is: $C(t) = \dfrac{t^2}{t^3+125} = \dfrac{1}{3(t+5)} + \dfrac{2t-5}{3(t^2-5t+25)}$

43. The form of the decomposition is: $\dfrac{2}{s(s^2+1)} = \dfrac{A}{s} + \dfrac{Bs+C}{s^2+1}$

Clearing fractions: $2 = A(s^2+1)+(Bs+C)s = As^2 + A + Bs^2 + Cs = (A+B)s^2 + Cs + A$

Equating coefficients yields $A=2, C=0$:

$$A+B=0$$
$$B=-A=-2$$

Therefore the decomposition is: $\dfrac{2}{s(s^2+1)} = \dfrac{2}{s} - \dfrac{2s}{s^2+1}$

45. The quadratic factor is reducible to a product of linear factors: $\dfrac{1}{x(x^2+2x-3)} = \dfrac{1}{x(x+3)(x-1)} = \dfrac{A}{x} + \dfrac{B}{x+3} + \dfrac{C}{x-1}$

47. The form of the decomposition is: $\dfrac{1}{(x-c)^2} = \dfrac{A}{x-c} + \dfrac{B}{(x-c)^2}$

Clearing fractions: $1 = A(x-c)+B = Ax + (-Ac+B)$

Equating coefficients yields $A=0$:

$$-Ac+B=1$$
$$B=1$$

Therefore the decomposition is: $\dfrac{1}{(x-c)^2} = \dfrac{1}{(x-c)^2}$

8.8 Systems of Nonlinear Equations

1. Substituting into the first equation:
$$x^2 + y^2 = 13$$
$$x^2 + (x+1)^2 = 13$$
$$x^2 + x^2 + 2x + 1 = 13$$
$$2x^2 + 2x - 12 = 0$$
$$x^2 + x - 6 = 0$$
$$(x+3)(x-2) = 0$$
$$x = -3, x = 2$$

Substituting into $y = x + 1$:
$$x = -3: \; y = -3 + 1 = -2 \qquad\qquad x = 2: \; y = 2 + 1 = 3$$

The solutions are: $(-3, -2), (2, 3)$

3. Substituting into the first equation:
$$5x^2 + y^2 = 9$$
$$5x^2 + (2x)^2 = 9$$
$$5x^2 + 4x^2 = 9$$
$$9x^2 = 9$$
$$x^2 = 1$$
$$x = \pm 1$$

Substituting into $y = 2x$:
$$x = -1: \; y = 2(-1) = -2 \qquad\qquad x = 1: \; y = 2(1) = 2$$

The solutions are: $(-1, -2), (1, 2)$

5. Substituting into the first equation:
$$2x^2 - y = 1$$
$$2x^2 - (5x + 2) = 1$$
$$2x^2 - 5x - 2 = 1$$
$$2x^2 - 5x - 3 = 0$$
$$(2x + 1)(x - 3) = 0$$
$$x = -\frac{1}{2}, x = 3$$

Substituting into $y = 5x + 2$:
$$x = -\frac{1}{2}: \; y = 5\left(-\frac{1}{2}\right) + 2 = -\frac{1}{2} \qquad\qquad x = 3: \; y = 5(3) + 2 = 17$$

The solutions are: $\left(-\frac{1}{2}, -\frac{1}{2}\right), (3, 17)$

7. Solving the second equation for y:
$$3x + 4y = -2$$
$$4y = -3x - 2$$
$$y = -\frac{3}{4}x - \frac{1}{2}$$

Substituting into the first equation:
$$9x^2 + 4y = 4$$
$$9x^2 + (-3x - 2) = 4$$
$$9x^2 - 3x - 6 = 0$$
$$3x^2 - x - 2 = 0$$
$$(3x + 2)(x - 1) = 0$$
$$x = -\frac{2}{3}, x = 1$$

Substituting into $y = -\frac{3}{4}x - \frac{1}{2}$:

$x = -\frac{2}{3}: \; y = -\frac{3}{4}\left(-\frac{2}{3}\right) - \frac{1}{2} = 0$ $\qquad$ $x = 1: \; y = -\frac{3}{4}(1) - \frac{1}{2} = -\frac{5}{4}$

The solutions are: $\left(-\frac{2}{3}, 0\right), \left(1, -\frac{5}{4}\right)$

9. Solving the second equation for y:
$$x - y = -2$$
$$-y = -x - 2$$
$$y = x + 2$$

Substituting into the first equation:
$$3x^2 - 10y = 5$$
$$3x^2 - 10(x + 2) = 5$$
$$3x^2 - 10x - 25 = 0$$
$$(3x + 5)(x - 5) = 0$$
$$x = -\frac{5}{3}, x = 5$$

Substituting into $y = x + 2$:

$x = -\frac{5}{3}: \; y = -\frac{5}{3} + 2 = \frac{1}{3}$ $\qquad$ $x = 5: \; y = 5 + 2 = 7$

The solutions are: $\left(-\frac{5}{3}, \frac{1}{3}\right), (5, 7)$

11. Solving the second equation for y:
$$-2x + y = 1$$
$$y = 2x + 1$$

Substituting into the first equation:
$$x^2 + 2y = -2$$
$$x^2 + 2(2x + 1) = -2$$
$$x^2 + 4x + 2 = -2$$
$$x^2 + 4x + 4 = 0$$
$$(x + 2)^2 = 0$$
$$x = -2$$

Substituting into $y = 2x + 1$:
$$x = -2: \; y = 2(-2) + 1 = -3$$

The only solution is: $(-2, -3)$

13. Solving the second equation for y:

$$xy = -4$$

$$y = -\frac{4}{x}$$

Substituting into the first equation:

$$x^2 + y^2 = 8$$

$$x^2 + \left(\frac{-4}{x}\right)^2 = 8$$

$$x^2 + \frac{16}{x^2} = 8$$

$$x^4 + 16 = 8x^2$$

$$x^4 - 8x^2 + 16 = 0$$

$$\left(x^2 - 4\right)^2 = 0$$

$$x^2 - 4 = 0$$

$$x = \pm 2$$

Substituting into $y = -\dfrac{4}{x}$:

$$x = -2: \ y = -\frac{4}{-2} = 2 \qquad\qquad x = 2: \ y = -\frac{4}{2} = -2$$

The solutions are: $(-2, 2), (2, -2)$

15. Adding -2 times the first equation to the second equation:

$$-2x^2 - 2y^2 = -18$$

$$2x^2 + \ \ y = 15$$

Adding yields:

$$-2y^2 + y = -3$$

$$2y^2 - y - 3 = 0$$

$$(2y - 3)(y + 1) = 0$$

$$y = \frac{3}{2}, -1$$

Substituting into the second equation:

$$y = \frac{3}{2}: \ 2x^2 + \frac{3}{2} = 15 \qquad\qquad y = -1: \ 2x^2 - 1 = 15$$

$$2x^2 = \frac{27}{2} \qquad\qquad\qquad\qquad\quad 2x^2 = 16$$

$$x^2 = \frac{27}{4} \qquad\qquad\qquad\qquad\qquad x^2 = 8$$

$$x = \pm\frac{3\sqrt{3}}{2} \qquad\qquad\qquad\qquad\quad x = \pm 2\sqrt{2}$$

The solutions are: $\left(\dfrac{3\sqrt{3}}{2}, \dfrac{3}{2}\right), \ \left(-\dfrac{3\sqrt{3}}{2}, \dfrac{3}{2}\right), \ \left(2\sqrt{2}, -1\right), \ \left(-2\sqrt{2}, -1\right)$

17. Adding 2 times the first equation to the second equation:

$$10x^2 - 4y^2 = 20$$
$$3x^2 + 4y^2 = 6$$

Adding yields:

$$13x^2 = 26$$
$$x^2 = 2$$
$$x = \pm\sqrt{2}$$

Substituting into the second equation:

$x = \sqrt{2}: \ 3\left(\sqrt{2}\right)^2 + 4y^2 = 6 \qquad\qquad x = -\sqrt{2}: \ 3\left(-\sqrt{2}\right)^2 + 4y^2 = 6$

$\qquad\qquad 6 + 4y^2 = 6 \qquad\qquad\qquad\qquad\qquad\qquad 6 + 4y^2 = 6$

$\qquad\qquad\qquad 4y^2 = 0 \qquad\qquad\qquad\qquad\qquad\qquad\qquad 4y^2 = 0$

$\qquad\qquad\qquad\quad y = 0 \qquad\qquad\qquad\qquad\qquad\qquad\qquad\quad y = 0$

The solutions are: $\left(\sqrt{2}, 0\right), \left(-\sqrt{2}, 0\right)$

19. Adding –5 times the first equation to the second equation:

$$-5x^2 + 5y^2 - 10y = -5$$
$$5x^2 - 3y^2 \qquad\quad = 17$$

Adding yields:

$$2y^2 - 10y = 12$$
$$2y^2 - 10y - 12 = 0$$
$$y^2 - 5y - 6 = 0$$
$$(y - 6)(y + 1) = 0$$
$$y = 6, -1$$

Substituting into the second equation:

$y = 6: \ 5x^2 - 3(6)^2 = 17 \qquad\qquad\qquad y = -1: \ 5x^2 - 3(-1)^2 = 17$

$\qquad\quad 5x^2 - 108 = 17 \qquad\qquad\qquad\qquad\qquad\quad 5x^2 - 3 = 17$

$\qquad\qquad\quad 5x^2 = 125 \qquad\qquad\qquad\qquad\qquad\qquad\quad 5x^2 = 20$

$\qquad\qquad\quad\ x^2 = 25 \qquad\qquad\qquad\qquad\qquad\qquad\qquad x^2 = 4$

$\qquad\qquad\qquad x = \pm 5 \qquad\qquad\qquad\qquad\qquad\qquad\qquad\ x = \pm 2$

The solutions are: $(-5, 6), (5, 6), (-2, -1), (2, -1)$

21. Adding –1 times the first equation to the second equation:

$$-x^2 - y^2 = -4$$
$$x^2 + 4y^2 = 1$$

Adding yields:

$$3y^2 = -3$$
$$y^2 = -1$$

No real solutions

There is no real solution.

23. Adding 3 times the first equation to –4 times the second equation:

$$6x^2 - 15x - 12y^2 = -12$$
$$-4x^2 \qquad 12y^2 = -16$$

Adding yields:

$$2x^2 - 15x = -28$$
$$2x^2 - 15x + 28 = 0$$
$$(2x - 7)(x - 4) = 0$$
$$x = \frac{7}{2}, 4$$

Substituting into the second equation:

$$x = \frac{7}{2} : \left(\frac{7}{2}\right)^2 - 3y^2 = 4 \qquad\qquad x = 4 : (4)^2 - 3y^2 = 4$$
$$-3y^2 = -\frac{33}{4} \qquad\qquad\qquad\qquad -3y^2 = -12$$
$$y^2 = \frac{11}{4} \qquad\qquad\qquad\qquad\qquad y^2 = 4$$
$$y = \pm\frac{\sqrt{11}}{2} \qquad\qquad\qquad\qquad y = \pm 2$$

The solutions are: $\left(\dfrac{7}{2}, \dfrac{\sqrt{11}}{2}\right), \left(\dfrac{7}{2}, -\dfrac{\sqrt{11}}{2}\right), (4, 2), (4, -2)$

25. Adding –1 times the second equation to the first equation:

$$x^2 + (y - 1)^2 = 9$$
$$-x^2 \qquad - y^2 = -4$$

Adding yields:

$$(y - 1)^2 - y^2 = 5$$
$$y^2 - 2y + 1 - y^2 = 5$$
$$-2y = 4$$
$$y = -2$$

Substituting into the second equation:

$$x^2 + (-2)^2 = 4$$
$$x^2 + 4 = 4$$
$$x^2 = 0$$
$$x = 0$$

The only solution is: $(0, -2)$

27. Adding -1 times the first equation to the second equation:

$$-x^2 + (y-3)^2 = -7$$
$$x^2 \qquad + y^2 = 16$$

Adding yields:

$$(y-3)^2 + y^2 = 9$$
$$y^2 - 6y + 9 + y^2 = 9$$
$$2y^2 - 6y = 0$$
$$2y(y-3) = 0$$
$$y = 0, 3$$

Substituting into the second equation:

$$y = 0: \quad x^2 + (0)^2 = 16 \qquad\qquad y = 3: \quad x^2 + (3)^2 = 16$$
$$x^2 = 16 \qquad\qquad\qquad\qquad x^2 = 7$$
$$x = \pm 4 \qquad\qquad\qquad\qquad x = \pm\sqrt{7}$$

The solutions are: $(4, 0), (-4, 0), (\sqrt{7}, 3), (-\sqrt{7}, 3)$

29. Adding 2 times the first equation to -3 times the second equation:

$$2x^2 + 6xy - 4x = -20$$
$$-6xy - 3x = 42$$

Adding yields:

$$2x^2 - 7x = 22$$
$$2x^2 - 7x - 22 = 0$$
$$(2x - 11)(x + 2) = 0$$
$$x = \frac{11}{2}, -2$$

Substituting into the second equation:

$$x = \frac{11}{2}: \quad 2\left(\frac{11}{2}\right)y + \frac{11}{2} = -14 \qquad\qquad x = -2: \quad 2(-2)y - 2 = -14$$
$$11y + \frac{11}{2} = -14 \qquad\qquad\qquad\qquad -4y = -12$$
$$\qquad\qquad\qquad\qquad\qquad\qquad y = 3$$
$$11y = -\frac{39}{2}$$
$$y = -\frac{39}{22}$$

The solutions are: $\left(\frac{11}{2}, -\frac{39}{22}\right), (-2, 3)$

31. Solving the second equation for x^2: $x^2 = 14 - y^2$

Substituting into the first equation:

$$2^{3(14-y^2)-y^2} = 4$$
$$2^{42-4y^2} = 2^2$$
$$42 - 4y^2 = 2$$
$$-4y^2 = -40$$
$$y^2 = 10$$
$$y = \pm\sqrt{10}$$

Substituting into the second equation:

$y = \sqrt{10}$:

$$x^2 = 14 - \left(\sqrt{10}\right)^2$$
$$x^2 = 4$$
$$x = \pm 2$$

$y = -\sqrt{10}$:

$$x^2 = 14 - \left(-\sqrt{10}\right)^2$$
$$x^2 = 4$$
$$x = \pm 2$$

The solutions are: $\left(2, \sqrt{10}\right), \left(2, -\sqrt{10}\right), \left(-2, \sqrt{10}\right), \left(-2, -\sqrt{10}\right)$

33. Solving the second equation for x : $x = \dfrac{5}{y}$

Substituting into the first equation:

$$\log\left(2y^2\right) + \log\left(x^3\right) = 3$$
$$\log\left(2y^2 x^3\right) = 3$$
$$\log\left(2y^2 x^3\right) = 3$$
$$2y^2 x^3 = 10^3$$
$$2y^2 \left(\frac{5}{y}\right)^3 = 1000$$
$$\frac{250}{y} = 1000$$
$$y = \frac{1}{4}$$
$$x = \frac{5}{y} = \frac{5}{1/4} = 20$$

The only solution is: $\left(20, \dfrac{1}{4}\right)$

35. The point of intersection is $(3, 3)$:

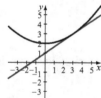

37. The points of intersection are $(3, -1), (7, -5)$:

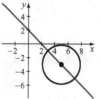

39. The points of intersection are $(1, -3), (5, -3)$:

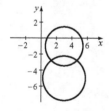

41. The solutions are: $(0.343, -1.646), (-0.834, 0.088)$

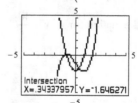

43. The solutions are: $(0.789, 2.378), (-1.686, 0.157)$ **45.** There is no solution.

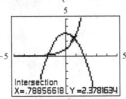

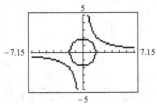

47. The solutions are: $(-1.123, -3.695), (-1.542, 1.895), (1.123, -3.695), (1.542, 1.895)$

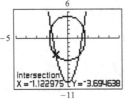

49. Let x represent the length and y represent the width. The system of equations is:

$$2x + 2y = 80$$
$$xy = 336$$

Solving the second equation for y: $y = \dfrac{336}{x}$

Substituting into the first equation:

$$2x + 2\left(\frac{336}{x}\right) = 80$$
$$2x^2 + 672 = 80x$$
$$2x^2 - 80x + 672 = 0$$
$$x^2 - 40x + 336 = 0$$
$$(x - 28)(x - 12) = 0$$
$$x = 28, 12$$

For $x = 28$: $y = \dfrac{336}{28} = 12$ For $x = 12$: $y = \dfrac{336}{12} = 28$

The length is 28 feet and the width is 12 feet.

51. Let x represent the length of one side and y represent the length of the other side. The system of equations is:

$$x^2 + y^2 = 89$$
$$\frac{1}{2}xy = 20$$

Solving the second equation for y: $y = \dfrac{40}{x}$

Substituting into the first equation:

$$x^2 + \left(\frac{40}{x}\right)^2 = 89$$

$$x^2 + \frac{1600}{x^2} = 89$$

$$x^4 + 1600 = 89x^2$$

$$x^4 - 89x^2 + 1600 = 0$$

$$\left(x^2 - 64\right)\left(x^2 - 25\right) = 0$$

$$(x+8)(x-8)(x+5)(x-5) = 0$$

$$x = 5, 8 \quad (x \neq -5, -8)$$

For $x = 8$: $y = \dfrac{40}{8} = 5$ \qquad\qquad For $x = 5$: $y = \dfrac{40}{5} = 8$

The other two sides are 8 inches and 5 inches.

53. The system of equations is:

$$\pi r^2 h = 6.75\pi$$
$$2\pi rh = 9\pi$$
which simplifies to
$$r^2 h = 6.75$$
$$2rh = 9$$

Solving the second equation for h: $h = \dfrac{9}{2r}$

Substituting into the first equation:

$$r^2\left(\frac{9}{2r}\right) = 6.75$$

$$\frac{9r}{2} = 6.75$$

$$r = 1.5$$

$$h = \frac{9}{2r} = \frac{9}{2(1.5)} = 3$$

The radius is 1.5 inches and the height is 3 inches.

55. The system of equations is:

$$\frac{1}{3}\pi r^2 h = 36\pi$$
$$r = \frac{1}{4}h$$
which simplifies to
$$\frac{1}{3}r^2 h = 36$$
$$r = \frac{1}{4}h$$

Substituting into the first equation:

$$\frac{1}{3}r^2 h = 36$$

$$\frac{1}{3}\left(\frac{1}{4}h\right)^2 h = 36$$

$$\frac{1}{48}h^3 = 36$$

$$h^3 = 1728$$

$$h = \sqrt[3]{1728} = 12$$

$$r = \frac{1}{4}(12) = 3$$

The radius is 3 inches and the height is 12 inches.

57. Let x represent one integer and y represent the other integer. The system of equations is:

$$x^2 + y^2 = 85$$

$$x^2 - y^2 = 13$$

Adding the two equations:

$$2x^2 = 98$$

$$x^2 = 49$$

$$x = 7$$

Substituting into the first equation:

$$(7)^2 + y^2 = 85$$

$$49 + y^2 = 85$$

$$y^2 = 36$$

$$y = 6 \qquad (y \neq -6)$$

The integers are 6 and 7.

59. Let w represent the width of the pool and l represent the length of the pool. Then $W = 2w$ is the width of the property, and $L = 2l = 3W$ is the length of the property. The system of equations is:

$$LW = 300$$

$$L = 3W$$

Substituting into the first equation:

$$LW = 300$$

$$(3W)W = 300$$

$$3W^2 = 300$$

$$W^2 = 100$$

$$W = 10$$

$$L = 3W = 3(10) = 30$$

Finding the dimensions of the pool:

$$W = 2w \qquad\qquad\qquad\qquad L = 2l$$

$$w = \frac{W}{2} = \frac{10}{2} = 5 \qquad\qquad l = \frac{L}{2} = \frac{30}{2} = 15$$

The property is 30 feet × 10 feet and the pool is 15 feet × 5 feet.

The area of the pavement is therefore: $A_{paved\ portion} = A_{property} - A_{pool} = (30)(10) - (15)(5) = 300 - 75 = 225 \text{ ft}^2$

61. Substituting into the first equation:

$$y = -x^2 + 2$$

$$x + b = -x^2 + 2$$

$$x^2 + x + (b - 2) = 0$$

Finding the discriminant: $B^2 - 4AC = (1)^2 - 4(1)(b-2) = 1 - 4b + 8 = 9 - 4b$

To have real solutions, the discriminant must be greater than 0:

$$9 - 4b > 0$$

$$-4b > -9$$

$$b < \frac{9}{4}$$

63. Expanding the first equation then substituting the second equation:

$$(x+y)^2 = 36$$
$$x^2 + 2xy + y^2 = 36$$
$$x^2 + 2(18) + y^2 = 36$$
$$x^2 + 36 + y^2 = 36$$
$$x^2 + y^2 = 0$$

The only solution to this is $x = 0$ and $y = 0$, which do not satisfy the second equation. Thus the system has no solution.

65. **a.** If $h = \pm 2r$, the two circles will intersect in only one point.

b. If $0 < h < 2r$ or $-2r < h < 0$, the two circles will intersect in exactly two points.

c. If $h = 0$, the two circles are identical, so they will intersect in infinitely many points.

d. If $h > 2r$ or $h < -2r$, the two circles will not intersect.

Chapter 8 Review Exercises

1. Adding 3 times the first equation to the second equation:

$$-3x - 3y = -21$$
$$3x + 4y = 24$$

Adding yields: $y = 3$
Substituting into the first equation:

$$-x - 3 = -7$$
$$-x = -4$$
$$x = 4$$

The solution is: $x = 4, y = 3$

2. Adding 2 times the first equation to the second equation:

$$-6x + 8y = 18$$
$$6x - 8y = 3$$

Adding yields: $0 = 21$
Since this equation is false, there is no solution.

3. Adding 2 times the first equation to the second equation:

$$2x + 2y = 10$$
$$-2x - 2y = -10$$

Adding yields: $0 = 0$
Solving the first equation for y:

$$x + y = 5$$
$$y = 5 - x$$

The solution is: $y = 5 - x$ (x is any real number)

4. Substituting into the first equation:

$$3x - 6y = 2$$
$$3x - 6(-3) = 2$$
$$3x + 18 = 2$$
$$3x = -16$$
$$x = -\frac{16}{3}$$

The solution is: $x = -\frac{16}{3}, y = -3$

5. Graphing the solution set:

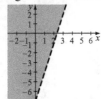

6. Graphing the solution set:

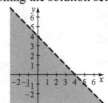

7. Graphing the solution set:

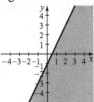

8. Graphing the solution set:

9. Graphing the solution set:

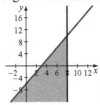

10. Graphing the solution set:

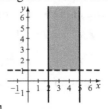

11. Evaluating the function at the corner points:

(x,y)	$P = 5x + 7y$
$(1,10)$	75
$(1,2)$	19
$(7,2)$	49
$(7,10)$	105

The maximum value is $P = 105$ when $x = 7$ and $y = 10$.

12. Evaluating the function at the corner points:

(x,y)	$P = 10x + 20y$
$(1,1)$	30
$(3,3)$	90
$(9,1)$	110

The maximum value is $P = 110$ when $x = 9$ and $y = 1$.

13. Let x represent the number of messages carried on one line, and y represent the number of messages carried on the other line. The system of equations is:

$$x + y = 450$$
$$x = 3.5y$$

Substituting into the first equation:

$$3.5y + y = 450$$
$$4.5y = 450$$
$$y = 100$$
$$x = 3.5(100) = 350$$

One line carries 100 messages and the other line carries 350 messages.

14. Let x represent the gallons used for milk and y represent the gallons used for cheese.
The revenue function is: $R = x + 5y$

The constraints are:
$$x + y \leq 2400$$
$$x \geq 600$$
$$x, y \geq 0$$

Evaluating the function at each of the corner points:

(x, y)	$R = x + 5y$
$(600, 0)$	$600
$(600, 1800)$	$9600
$(2400, 0)$	$2400

The farmer should use 1,800 gallons of milk in the production of cheese in order to maximize the revenue.

15. Adding the first equation to the second equation yields:
$$x - 2y + z = 2$$
$$2y + 4z = -6$$
$$-6y + 2z = 4$$

Adding 3 times the second equation to the third equation yields:
$$x - 2y + z = 2$$
$$2y + 4z = -6$$
$$14z = -14$$

Solving the third equation for z:
$$14z = -14$$
$$z = -1$$

Substituting into the second equation:
$$2y + 4z = -6$$
$$2y - 4 = -6$$
$$2y = -2$$
$$y = -1$$

Substituting into the first equation:
$$x - 2y + z = 2$$
$$x - 2(-1) - 1 = 2$$
$$x + 1 = 2$$
$$x = 1$$

The solution is: $x = 1, y = -1, z = -1$

16. Adding $-\dfrac{3}{2}$ times the first equation to the third equation yields:
$$4x - y \qquad = 2$$
$$y - 2z = 1$$
$$\frac{3}{2}y - z = 0$$

Adding $-\dfrac{3}{2}$ times the second equation to the third equation yields:
$$4x - y \qquad = 2$$
$$y - 2z = 1$$
$$2z = -\frac{3}{2}$$

Solving the third equation for z:
$$2z = -\frac{3}{2}$$
$$z = -\frac{3}{4}$$

Substituting into the second equation:
$$y - 2z = 1$$
$$y - 2\left(-\frac{3}{4}\right) = 1$$
$$y + \frac{3}{2} = 1$$
$$y = -\frac{1}{2}$$

Substituting into the first equation:
$$4x - y = 2$$
$$4x + \frac{1}{2} = 2$$
$$4x = \frac{3}{2}$$
$$x = \frac{3}{8}$$

The solution is: $x = \dfrac{3}{8}, y = -\dfrac{1}{2}, z = -\dfrac{3}{4}$

17. Adding 3 times the first equation to the second equation:
$$x + y + 2z = 4$$
$$5y + 5z = 15$$

Solving the second equation for y:
$$5y + 5z = 15$$
$$5y = 15 - 5z$$
$$y = 3 - z$$

Substituting into the first equation:
$$x + y + 2z = 4$$
$$x + (3 - z) + 2z = 4$$
$$x + 3 + z = 4$$
$$x = 1 - z$$

The solution is: $x = 1 - z, \; y = 3 - z$

18. Adding the first equation to the second equation:
$$2x + y - z = 2$$
$$7x - y = 5$$

Solving the second equation for y:
$$7x - y = 5$$
$$-y = 5 - 7x$$
$$y = 7x - 5$$

Substituting into the first equation:
$$2x + (7x - 5) - z = 2$$
$$9x - 5 - z = 2$$
$$-z = 7 - 9x$$
$$z = 9x - 7$$

The solution is: $y = 7x - 5, \; z = 9x - 7$

19. Let x represent the number of taco calories, y represent the number of tostada calories, and z represent the number of rice calories. The system of equations is:
$$x + y + z = 600$$
$$2x + y = 580$$
$$x + z = 400$$

Adding -2 times the first equation to the second equation, and -1 times the first equation to the third equation:
$$x + y + z = 600$$
$$-y - 2z = -620$$
$$-y = -200$$

Solving the third equation for y:
$$-y = -200$$
$$y = 200$$

Substituting into the second equation:
$$-y - 2z = -620$$
$$-200 - 2z = -620$$
$$-2z = -420$$
$$z = 210$$

Substituting into the first equation:
$$x + y + z = 600$$
$$x + 200 + 210 = 600$$
$$x + 410 = 600$$
$$x = 190$$

The taco contains 190 calories, the tostada contains 200 calories, and the rice contains 210 calories.

20. Writing the augmented matrix: $\begin{bmatrix} 4 & 1 & 1 & | & 0 \\ 0 & -1 & 2 & | & -1 \\ 1 & 0 & 1 & | & 3 \end{bmatrix}$

21. Writing the augmented matrix: $\begin{bmatrix} 1 & 2 & -5 & | & 3 \\ 3 & 0 & 1 & | & -1 \end{bmatrix}$

22. Form the augmented matrix: $\begin{bmatrix} -1 & -1 & | & -10 \\ 3 & 4 & | & 24 \end{bmatrix}$

Adding 3 times the first row to the second row: $\begin{bmatrix} -1 & -1 & | & -10 \\ 0 & 1 & | & -6 \end{bmatrix}$

Substituting $y = -6$ into the first equation:
$$-x - y = -10$$
$$x + y = 16$$
$$x - 6 = 10$$
$$x = 16$$
The solution is: $x = 16, y = -6$

23. Form the augmented matrix: $\begin{bmatrix} 1 & 2 & 1 & | & -3 \\ 3 & 1 & -2 & | & 2 \\ 4 & 3 & -1 & | & 0 \end{bmatrix}$

Adding -3 times the first row to the second row and -4 times the first row to the third row: $\begin{bmatrix} 1 & 2 & 1 & | & -3 \\ 0 & -5 & -5 & | & 11 \\ 0 & -5 & -5 & | & 12 \end{bmatrix}$

Adding -1 times the second row to the third row: $\begin{bmatrix} 1 & 2 & 1 & | & -3 \\ 0 & -5 & -5 & | & 11 \\ 0 & 0 & 0 & | & 1 \end{bmatrix}$

The system is inconsistent. There is no solution.

24. Form the augmented matrix: $\begin{bmatrix} 1 & 1 & -1 & | & 0 \\ 3 & 2 & -1 & | & -1 \\ -2 & 1 & -2 & | & -1 \end{bmatrix}$

Adding -3 times the first row to the second row and 2 times the first row to the third row: $\begin{bmatrix} 1 & 1 & -1 & | & 0 \\ 0 & -1 & 2 & | & -1 \\ 0 & 3 & -4 & | & -1 \end{bmatrix}$

Adding 3 times the second row to the third row: $\begin{bmatrix} 1 & 1 & -1 & | & 0 \\ 0 & -1 & 2 & | & -1 \\ 0 & 0 & 2 & | & -4 \end{bmatrix}$

Solving the third equation for z:
$$2z = -4$$
$$z = -2$$

Substituting into the second equation:
$$-y + 2z = -1$$
$$y - 2z = 1$$
$$y - 2(-2) = 1$$
$$y + 4 = 1$$
$$y = -3$$

Substituting into the first equation:
$$x + y - z = 0$$
$$x - 3 - (-2) = 0$$
$$x - 1 = 0$$
$$x = 1$$

The solution is: $x = 1, y = -3, z = -2$

25. Form the augmented matrix: $\begin{bmatrix} -1 & 4 & 3 & | & 8 \\ 2 & -8 & -4 & | & 3 \end{bmatrix}$

Adding 2 times the first row to the second row: $\begin{bmatrix} -1 & 4 & 3 & | & 8 \\ 0 & 0 & 2 & | & 19 \end{bmatrix}$

Solving the second equation for z:
$$2z = 19$$
$$z = \frac{19}{2}$$

Substituting into the first equation:
$$-x + 4y + 3z = 8$$
$$-x + 4y + 3\left(\frac{19}{2}\right) = 8$$
$$-x + 4y = -\frac{41}{2}$$
$$4y = x - \frac{41}{2}$$
$$y = \frac{1}{4}x - \frac{41}{8}$$

The solution is: $y = -\frac{41}{8} + \frac{1}{4}x, \ z = \frac{19}{2}$

26. The system of equations is: $\begin{cases} x & -2z = 3 \\ y + z = 5 \end{cases}$

This system is consistent. The solution is: $x = 3 + 2z, \ y = 5 - z$

27. The system of equations is: $\begin{cases} x = 7 \\ y = 3 \\ z = 2 \end{cases}$

This system is consistent. The solution is: $x = 7, y = 3, z = 2$

28. Let x represent the number of blazers, y represent the number of trousers, and z represent the number of skirts.
The system of equations is:
$$2.5x + 3y + 3z = 42$$
$$2x + 2y + z = 25$$
$$0.5x + y = 7$$

Form the augmented matrix: $\begin{bmatrix} 2.5 & 3 & 3 & | & 42 \\ 2 & 2 & 1 & | & 25 \\ 0.5 & 1 & 0 & | & 7 \end{bmatrix}$

Multiply the third row by 2 and switch with the first row: $\begin{bmatrix} 1 & 2 & 0 & | & 14 \\ 2 & 2 & 1 & | & 25 \\ 2.5 & 3 & 3 & | & 42 \end{bmatrix}$

Adding -2 times the first row to the second row and -2.5 times the first row to the third row: $\begin{bmatrix} 1 & 2 & 0 & | & 14 \\ 0 & -2 & 1 & | & -3 \\ 0 & -2 & 3 & | & 7 \end{bmatrix}$

Adding -1 times the second row to the third row: $\begin{bmatrix} 1 & 2 & 0 & | & 14 \\ 0 & -2 & 1 & | & -3 \\ 0 & 0 & 2 & | & 10 \end{bmatrix}$

Solving the third equation for z:

$2z = 10$

$z = 5$

Substituting into the second equation:

$-2y + z = -3$

$-2y + 5 = -3$

$-2y = -8$

$y = 4$

Substituting into the first equation:

$x + 2y = 14$

$x + 2(4) = 14$

$x + 8 = 14$

$x = 6$

They can make 6 blazers, 4 pairs of trousers, and 5 skirts.

29. $a_{11} = 0$

30. $a_{22} = -5$

31. The dimension is 3×4.

32. $a_{31} = 5$

33. Performing the operations: $B + C = \begin{bmatrix} -4+3 & 1+5 \\ 2+1 & -3+(-1) \\ 2+2 & -6+(-3) \end{bmatrix} = \begin{bmatrix} -1 & 6 \\ 3 & -4 \\ 4 & -9 \end{bmatrix}$

34. Performing the operations: $C - B = \begin{bmatrix} 3-(-4) & 5-1 \\ 1-2 & -1-(-3) \\ 2-2 & -3-(-6) \end{bmatrix} = \begin{bmatrix} 7 & 4 \\ -1 & 2 \\ 0 & 3 \end{bmatrix}$

35. Performing the operations: $2B + C = \begin{bmatrix} -8 & 2 \\ 4 & -6 \\ 4 & -12 \end{bmatrix} + \begin{bmatrix} 3 & 5 \\ 1 & -1 \\ 2 & -3 \end{bmatrix} = \begin{bmatrix} -5 & 7 \\ 5 & -7 \\ 6 & -15 \end{bmatrix}$

36. Performing the operations: $B - 3C = \begin{bmatrix} -4 & 1 \\ 2 & -3 \\ 2 & -6 \end{bmatrix} - \begin{bmatrix} 9 & 15 \\ 3 & -3 \\ 6 & -9 \end{bmatrix} = \begin{bmatrix} -13 & -14 \\ -1 & 0 \\ -4 & 3 \end{bmatrix}$

37. Performing the operations: $AB = \begin{bmatrix} 4(-4)-1(2)+\frac{1}{2}(2) & 4(1)-1(-3)+\frac{1}{2}(-6) \\ 0(-4)+3(2)-1(2) & 0(1)+3(-3)-1(-6) \end{bmatrix} = \begin{bmatrix} -17 & 4 \\ 4 & -3 \end{bmatrix}$

38. Performing the operations: $AC = \begin{bmatrix} 4(3)-1(1)+\frac{1}{2}(2) & 4(5)-1(-1)+\frac{1}{2}(-3) \\ 0(3)+3(1)-1(2) & 0(5)+3(-1)-1(-3) \end{bmatrix} = \begin{bmatrix} 12 & \frac{39}{2} \\ 1 & 0 \end{bmatrix}$

39. Form the augmented matrix: $\begin{bmatrix} 4 & 5 & | & 1 & 0 \\ 1 & 1 & | & 0 & 1 \end{bmatrix}$

Switching the first and second rows: $\begin{bmatrix} 1 & 1 & | & 0 & 1 \\ 4 & 5 & | & 1 & 0 \end{bmatrix}$

Adding -4 times the first row to the second row: $\begin{bmatrix} 1 & 1 & | & 0 & 1 \\ 0 & 1 & | & 1 & -4 \end{bmatrix}$

Adding -1 times the second row to the first row: $\begin{bmatrix} 1 & 0 & | & -1 & 5 \\ 0 & 1 & | & 1 & -4 \end{bmatrix}$

The inverse matrix is: $\begin{bmatrix} -1 & 5 \\ 1 & -4 \end{bmatrix}$

40. Form the augmented matrix: $\begin{bmatrix} 5 & 3 & | & 1 & 0 \\ 3 & 2 & | & 0 & 1 \end{bmatrix}$

Multiplying the first row by $\dfrac{1}{5}$: $\begin{bmatrix} 1 & \dfrac{3}{5} & | & \dfrac{1}{5} & 0 \\ 3 & 2 & | & 0 & 1 \end{bmatrix}$

Adding -3 times the first row to the second row: $\begin{bmatrix} 1 & \dfrac{3}{5} & | & \dfrac{1}{5} & 0 \\ 0 & \dfrac{1}{5} & | & -\dfrac{3}{5} & 1 \end{bmatrix}$

Multiplying the second row by 5: $\begin{bmatrix} 1 & \dfrac{3}{5} & | & \dfrac{1}{5} & 0 \\ 0 & 1 & | & -3 & 5 \end{bmatrix}$

Adding $-\dfrac{3}{5}$ times the second row to the first row: $\begin{bmatrix} 1 & 0 & | & 2 & -3 \\ 0 & 1 & | & -3 & 5 \end{bmatrix}$

The inverse matrix is: $\begin{bmatrix} 2 & -3 \\ -3 & 5 \end{bmatrix}$

41. Form the augmented matrix: $\begin{bmatrix} -4 & 1 & | & 1 & 0 \\ -3 & 1 & | & 0 & 1 \end{bmatrix}$

Multiplying the first row by $-\dfrac{1}{4}$: $\begin{bmatrix} 1 & -\dfrac{1}{4} & | & -\dfrac{1}{4} & 0 \\ -3 & 2 & | & 0 & 1 \end{bmatrix}$

Adding 3 times the first row to the second row: $\begin{bmatrix} 1 & -\dfrac{1}{4} & | & -\dfrac{1}{4} & 0 \\ 0 & \dfrac{1}{4} & | & -\dfrac{3}{4} & 1 \end{bmatrix}$

Adding the second row to the first row: $\begin{bmatrix} 1 & 0 & | & -1 & 1 \\ 0 & \dfrac{1}{4} & | & -\dfrac{3}{4} & 1 \end{bmatrix}$

Multiplying the second row by 4: $\begin{bmatrix} 1 & 0 & | & -1 & 1 \\ 0 & 1 & | & -3 & 4 \end{bmatrix}$

The inverse matrix is: $\begin{bmatrix} -1 & 1 \\ -3 & 4 \end{bmatrix}$

42. Form the augmented matrix: $\begin{bmatrix} 4 & 3 & | & 1 & 0 \\ 5 & 4 & | & 0 & 1 \end{bmatrix}$

Multiplying the first row by $\dfrac{1}{4}$: $\begin{bmatrix} 1 & \frac{3}{4} & | & \frac{1}{4} & 0 \\ 5 & 4 & | & 0 & 1 \end{bmatrix}$

Adding –5 times the first row to the second row: $\begin{bmatrix} 1 & \frac{3}{4} & | & \frac{1}{4} & 0 \\ 0 & \frac{1}{4} & | & -\frac{5}{4} & 1 \end{bmatrix}$

Adding –3 times the second row to the first row: $\begin{bmatrix} 1 & 0 & | & 4 & -3 \\ 0 & \frac{1}{4} & | & -\frac{5}{4} & 1 \end{bmatrix}$

Multiplying the second row by 4: $\begin{bmatrix} 1 & 0 & | & 4 & -3 \\ 0 & 1 & | & -5 & 4 \end{bmatrix}$

The inverse matrix is: $\begin{bmatrix} 4 & -3 \\ -5 & 4 \end{bmatrix}$

43. Form the augmented matrix: $\begin{bmatrix} 1 & -1 & 0 & | & 1 & 0 & 0 \\ -2 & 0 & 1 & | & 0 & 1 & 0 \\ -2 & 5 & -1 & | & 0 & 0 & 1 \end{bmatrix}$

Adding 2 times the first row to the second row and third row: $\begin{bmatrix} 1 & -1 & 0 & | & 1 & 0 & 0 \\ 0 & -2 & 1 & | & 2 & 1 & 0 \\ 0 & 3 & -1 & | & 2 & 0 & 1 \end{bmatrix}$

Multiplying the second row by $-\dfrac{1}{2}$: $\begin{bmatrix} 1 & -1 & 0 & | & 1 & 0 & 0 \\ 0 & 1 & -\frac{1}{2} & | & -1 & -\frac{1}{2} & 0 \\ 0 & 3 & -1 & | & 2 & 0 & 1 \end{bmatrix}$

Adding the second row to the first row and –3 times the second row to the third row: $\begin{bmatrix} 1 & 0 & -\frac{1}{2} & | & 0 & -\frac{1}{2} & 0 \\ 0 & 1 & -\frac{1}{2} & | & -1 & -\frac{1}{2} & 0 \\ 0 & 0 & \frac{1}{2} & | & 5 & \frac{3}{2} & 1 \end{bmatrix}$

Adding the third row to the first row and the second row: $\begin{bmatrix} 1 & 0 & 0 & | & 5 & 1 & 1 \\ 0 & 1 & 0 & | & 4 & 1 & 1 \\ 0 & 0 & \frac{1}{2} & | & 5 & \frac{3}{2} & 1 \end{bmatrix}$

Multiplying the third row by 2: $\begin{bmatrix} 1 & 0 & 0 & | & 5 & 1 & 1 \\ 0 & 1 & 0 & | & 4 & 1 & 1 \\ 0 & 0 & 1 & | & 10 & 3 & 2 \end{bmatrix}$

The inverse matrix is: $\begin{bmatrix} 5 & 1 & 1 \\ 4 & 1 & 1 \\ 10 & 3 & 2 \end{bmatrix}$

44. Form the augmented matrix: $\begin{bmatrix} 4 & -2 & 1 & | & 1 & 0 & 0 \\ -2 & 1 & 2 & | & 0 & 1 & 0 \\ 1 & 2 & 4 & | & 0 & 0 & 1 \end{bmatrix}$

Switching the first and third rows: $\begin{bmatrix} 1 & 2 & 4 & | & 0 & 0 & 1 \\ -2 & 1 & 2 & | & 0 & 1 & 0 \\ 4 & -2 & 1 & | & 1 & 0 & 0 \end{bmatrix}$

Adding 2 times the first row to the second row and –4 times the first row to the third row:

$\begin{bmatrix} 1 & 2 & 4 & | & 0 & 0 & 1 \\ 0 & 5 & 10 & | & 0 & 1 & 2 \\ 0 & -10 & -15 & | & 1 & 0 & -4 \end{bmatrix}$

Multiplying the second row by $\dfrac{1}{5}$: $\begin{bmatrix} 1 & 2 & 4 & | & 0 & 0 & 1 \\ 0 & 1 & 2 & | & 0 & \dfrac{1}{5} & \dfrac{2}{5} \\ 0 & -10 & -15 & | & 1 & 0 & -4 \end{bmatrix}$

Adding –2 times the second row to the first row and 10 times the second row to the third row:

$\begin{bmatrix} 1 & 0 & 0 & | & 0 & -\dfrac{2}{5} & \dfrac{1}{5} \\ 0 & 1 & 2 & | & 0 & \dfrac{1}{5} & \dfrac{2}{5} \\ 0 & 0 & 5 & | & 1 & 2 & 0 \end{bmatrix}$

Multiplying the third row by $\dfrac{1}{5}$: $\begin{bmatrix} 1 & 0 & 0 & | & 0 & -\dfrac{2}{5} & \dfrac{1}{5} \\ 0 & 1 & 2 & | & 0 & \dfrac{1}{5} & \dfrac{2}{5} \\ 0 & 0 & 1 & | & \dfrac{1}{5} & \dfrac{2}{5} & 0 \end{bmatrix}$

Adding –2 times the third row to the second row: $\begin{bmatrix} 1 & 0 & 0 & | & 0 & -\dfrac{2}{5} & \dfrac{1}{5} \\ 0 & 1 & 0 & | & -\dfrac{2}{5} & -\dfrac{3}{5} & \dfrac{2}{5} \\ 0 & 0 & 1 & | & \dfrac{1}{5} & \dfrac{2}{5} & 0 \end{bmatrix}$

The inverse matrix is: $\begin{bmatrix} 0 & -\dfrac{2}{5} & \dfrac{1}{5} \\ -\dfrac{2}{5} & -\dfrac{3}{5} & \dfrac{2}{5} \\ \dfrac{1}{5} & \dfrac{2}{5} & 0 \end{bmatrix}$

45. First finding the inverse: $A = \begin{bmatrix} 1 & 2 \\ -1 & -1 \end{bmatrix} \Rightarrow A^{-1} = \begin{bmatrix} -1 & -2 \\ 1 & 1 \end{bmatrix}$

Solving the equation: $X = A^{-1}B \Rightarrow \begin{bmatrix} x \\ y \end{bmatrix} = \begin{bmatrix} -1 & -2 \\ 1 & 1 \end{bmatrix}\begin{bmatrix} -4 \\ 5 \end{bmatrix} = \begin{bmatrix} -6 \\ 1 \end{bmatrix}$

The solution is: $x = -6, y = 1$

46. First finding the inverse: $A = \begin{bmatrix} 1 & -3 & 2 \\ 0 & 1 & 1 \\ 2 & -6 & 3 \end{bmatrix} \Rightarrow A^{-1} = \begin{bmatrix} -9 & 3 & 5 \\ -2 & 1 & 1 \\ 2 & 0 & -1 \end{bmatrix}$

Solving the equation: $X = A^{-1}B \Rightarrow \begin{bmatrix} x \\ y \\ z \end{bmatrix} = \begin{bmatrix} -9 & 3 & 5 \\ -2 & 1 & 1 \\ 2 & 0 & -1 \end{bmatrix}\begin{bmatrix} -1 \\ 4 \\ 3 \end{bmatrix} = \begin{bmatrix} 36 \\ 9 \\ -5 \end{bmatrix}$

The solution is: $x = 36, y = 9, z = -5$

47. Finding the determinant: $|A| = \begin{vmatrix} 4 & 2 \\ -3 & 1 \end{vmatrix} = 4(1) - 2(-3) = 10$

48. Finding the determinant: $|A| = \begin{vmatrix} -2 & -3 \\ 1 & 5 \end{vmatrix} = -2(5) - 1(-3) = -7$

49. Expand about the third column:

$$|A| = \begin{vmatrix} -7 & 5 & 0 \\ 0 & 3 & 0 \\ -3 & -2 & 2 \end{vmatrix} = 0C_{13} + 0C_{23} + 2C_{33} = (2)(-1)^{3+3}(-7(3) - 5(0)) = (2)(-1)^6(-21) = -42$$

50. Expand about the third row:

$$|A| = \begin{vmatrix} -2 & 3 & 5 \\ 6 & -1 & 0 \\ 0 & 1 & -2 \end{vmatrix} = 0C_{31} + 1C_{32} - 2C_{33} = (-1)^5(-2(0) - 5(6)) - 2(-1)^6(-2(-1) - 3(6)) = 30 + 32 = 62$$

51. Finding the determinants:

$$D = \begin{vmatrix} -1 & -1 \\ 2 & 1 \end{vmatrix} = -1 - (-2) = 1$$

$$D_x = \begin{vmatrix} -2 & -1 \\ 0 & 1 \end{vmatrix} = -2 - 0 = -2$$

$$D_y = \begin{vmatrix} -1 & -2 \\ 2 & 0 \end{vmatrix} = 0 - (-4) = 4$$

Using Cramer's rule: $x = \dfrac{D_x}{D} = \dfrac{-2}{1} = -2, \quad y = \dfrac{D_y}{D} = \dfrac{4}{1} = 4$

52. Finding the determinants:

$$D = \begin{vmatrix} -3 & 2 \\ -2 & -1 \end{vmatrix} = 3 - (-4) = 7$$

$$D_x = \begin{vmatrix} 1 & 2 \\ 2 & -1 \end{vmatrix} = -1 - 4 = -5$$

$$D_y = \begin{vmatrix} -3 & 1 \\ -2 & 2 \end{vmatrix} = -6 - (-2) = -4$$

Using Cramer's rule: $x = \dfrac{D_x}{D} = \dfrac{-5}{7} = -\dfrac{5}{7}, \quad y = \dfrac{D_y}{D} = \dfrac{-4}{7} = -\dfrac{4}{7}$

53. Finding the determinants:

$$D = \begin{vmatrix} -2 & 1 & 1 \\ 0 & 1 & 1 \\ 0 & -3 & 1 \end{vmatrix} = -2C_{11} = -2(-1)^2(1+3) = -8$$

$$D_x = \begin{vmatrix} 0 & 1 & 1 \\ 4 & 1 & 1 \\ 1 & -3 & 1 \end{vmatrix} = C_{12} + C_{13} = (-1)^3(4-1) + (-1)^4(-12-1) = (-1)(3) + (1)(-13) = -16$$

$$D_y = \begin{vmatrix} -2 & 0 & 1 \\ 0 & 4 & 1 \\ 0 & 1 & 1 \end{vmatrix} = -2C_{11} = -2(-1)^2(4-1) = -2(1)(3) = -6$$

$$D_z = \begin{vmatrix} -2 & 1 & 0 \\ 0 & 1 & 4 \\ 0 & -3 & 1 \end{vmatrix} = -2C_{11} = -2(-1)^2(1-(-12)) = -2(1)(13) = -26$$

Using Cramer's rule: $x = \dfrac{D_x}{D} = \dfrac{-16}{-8} = 2$, $y = \dfrac{D_y}{D} = \dfrac{-6}{-8} = \dfrac{3}{4}$, $z = \dfrac{D_z}{D} = \dfrac{-26}{-8} = \dfrac{13}{4}$

54. Finding the determinants:

$$D = \begin{vmatrix} 1 & 3 & -1 \\ 1 & 0 & -1 \\ 1 & -1 & 0 \end{vmatrix} = C_{21} - C_{23} = (-1)^3(0-1) - (-1)^5(-1-3) = (-1)(-1) - (-1)(-4) = -3$$

$$D_x = \begin{vmatrix} 3 & 3 & -1 \\ 0 & 0 & -1 \\ 2 & -1 & 0 \end{vmatrix} = -C_{23} = -(-1)^5(-3-6) = -9$$

$$D_y = \begin{vmatrix} 1 & 3 & -1 \\ 1 & 0 & -1 \\ 1 & 2 & 0 \end{vmatrix} = C_{21} - C_{23} = (-1)^3(0+2) - (-1)^5(2-3) = (-1)(2) - (-1)(-1) = -3$$

$$D_z = \begin{vmatrix} 1 & 3 & 3 \\ 1 & 0 & 0 \\ 1 & -1 & 2 \end{vmatrix} = C_{21} = (-1)^3(6+3) = (-1)(9) = -9$$

Using Cramer's rule: $x = \dfrac{D_x}{D} = \dfrac{-9}{-3} = 3$, $y = \dfrac{D_y}{D} = \dfrac{-3}{-3} = 1$, $z = \dfrac{D_z}{D} = \dfrac{-9}{-3} = 3$

55. The form of the decomposition is: $\dfrac{-3x+8}{x^2+5x+6} = \dfrac{-3x+8}{(x+3)(x+2)} = \dfrac{A}{x+3} + \dfrac{B}{x+2}$

Clearing fractions: $-3x+8 = A(x+2) + B(x+3) = Ax + 2A + Bx + 3B = (A+B)x + (2A+3B)$

Equating coefficients:

$$A + B = -3$$

$$2A + 3B = 8$$

Adding −2 times the first equation to the second equation:

$$-2A - 2B = 6$$

$$2A + 3B = 8$$

Adding yields $B = 14$. Substituting into the first equation:

$$A + B = -3$$

$$A + 14 = -3$$

$$A = -17$$

Therefore the decomposition is: $\dfrac{-3x+8}{x^2+5x+6} = \dfrac{-17}{x+3} + \dfrac{14}{x+2}$

56. The form of the decomposition is: $\dfrac{-2x^2-x+1}{x^3-x^2}=\dfrac{-2x^2-x+1}{x^2(x-1)}=\dfrac{A}{x}+\dfrac{B}{x^2}+\dfrac{C}{x-1}$

Clearing fractions: $-2x^2-x+1=Ax(x-1)+B(x-1)+Cx^2$

Substituting $x=0$:

$\qquad 1=B(0-1)$

$\qquad 1=-B$

$\qquad B=-1$

Substituting $x=1$:

$\qquad -2-1+1=C(1)^2$

$\qquad -2=C$

Therefore:

$\qquad -2x^2-x+1=Ax(x-1)-(x-1)-2x^2=Ax^2-Ax-x+1-2x^2=(A-2)x^2+(-A-1)x+1$

Equating coefficients:

$\qquad A-2=-2$

$\qquad A=0$

Therefore the decomposition is: $\dfrac{-2x^2-x+1}{x^3-x^2}=\dfrac{-1}{x^2}-\dfrac{2}{x-1}$

57. The form of the decomposition is: $\dfrac{9}{(x+2)(x^2+5)}=\dfrac{A}{x+2}+\dfrac{Bx+C}{x^2+5}$

Clearing fractions: $9=A(x^2+5)+(Bx+C)(x+2)$

Substituting $x=-2$:

$\qquad 9=A(4+5)$

$\qquad 9=9A$

$\qquad A=1$

Therefore:

$\qquad 9=(x^2+5)+(Bx+C)(x+2)=x^2+5+Bx^2+2Bx+Cx+2C=(1+B)x^2+(2B+C)x+(5+2C)$

Equating coefficients:

$\qquad 1+B=0 \qquad\qquad\qquad\qquad\qquad 2B+C=0$

$\qquad\quad B=-1 \qquad\qquad\qquad\qquad\qquad -2+C=0$

$\qquad\qquad\qquad\qquad\qquad\qquad\qquad\qquad\quad C=2$

Therefore the decomposition is: $\dfrac{9}{(x+2)(x^2+5)}=\dfrac{1}{x+2}+\dfrac{-x+2}{x^2+5}=\dfrac{1}{x+2}-\dfrac{x-2}{x^2+5}$

58. The form of the decomposition is: $\dfrac{-x^3-x+x^2+2}{x^4+4x^2+4}=\dfrac{-x^3-x+x^2+2}{(x^2+2)^2}=\dfrac{Ax+B}{x^2+2}+\dfrac{Cx+D}{(x^2+2)^2}$

Clearing fractions:

$\qquad -x^3+x^2-x+2=(Ax+B)(x^2+2)+(Cx+D)=Ax^3+Bx^2+2Ax+2B+Cx+D=Ax^3+Bx^2+(2A+C)x+(2B+D)$

Equating coefficients results in $A=-1$ and $B=1$. Substituting:

$\qquad 2A+C=-1 \qquad\qquad\qquad\qquad\qquad 2B+D=2$

$\qquad -2+C=-1 \qquad\qquad\qquad\qquad\qquad 2+D=2$

$\qquad\qquad\ \ C=1 \qquad\qquad\qquad\qquad\qquad\qquad D=0$

Therefore the decomposition is: $\dfrac{-x^3-x+x^2+2}{x^4+4x^2+4}=\dfrac{-x+1}{x^2+2}+\dfrac{x}{(x^2+2)^2}$

59. Substituting into the first equation:

$$x^2 + y^2 = 9$$
$$x^2 + (x+1)^2 = 9$$
$$x^2 + x^2 + 2x + 1 = 9$$
$$2x^2 + 2x - 8 = 0$$
$$x^2 + x - 4 = 0$$

$$x = \frac{-1 \pm \sqrt{(1)^2 - 4(1)(-4)}}{2(1)} = \frac{-1 \pm \sqrt{17}}{2} \approx 1.56, -2.56$$

Substituting into the second equation:

$x \approx 1.56$: $y \approx 1.56 + 1 = 2.56$

$x \approx -2.56$: $y \approx -2.56 + 1 = -1.56$

The solutions are: $(1.56, 2.56), (-2.56, -1.56)$

60. Adding -2 times the first equation to the second equation:

$$-2x^2 + 4y^2 = -8$$
$$2x^2 + 5y^2 = 12$$

Adding yields:

$$9y^2 = 4$$
$$y^2 = \frac{4}{9}$$
$$y = \pm\frac{2}{3}$$

Substituting into the first equation:

$y = \frac{2}{3}$: $x^2 - 2\left(\frac{2}{3}\right)^2 = 4$

$$x^2 - \frac{8}{9} = 4$$
$$x^2 = \frac{44}{9}$$
$$x = \pm\sqrt{\frac{44}{9}} = \pm\frac{2\sqrt{11}}{3}$$

$y = -\frac{2}{3}$: $x^2 - 2\left(-\frac{2}{3}\right)^2 = 4$

$$x^2 - \frac{8}{9} = 4$$
$$x^2 = \frac{44}{9}$$
$$x = \pm\sqrt{\frac{44}{9}} = \pm\frac{2\sqrt{11}}{3}$$

The solutions are: $\left(\frac{2\sqrt{11}}{3}, \frac{2}{3}\right), \left(-\frac{2\sqrt{11}}{3}, \frac{2}{3}\right), \left(\frac{2\sqrt{11}}{3}, -\frac{2}{3}\right), \left(-\frac{2\sqrt{11}}{3}, -\frac{2}{3}\right)$

61. Multiplying out terms in each equation results in the system:

$$x^2 + 6x + 9 + y^2 - 8y + 16 = 25$$
$$x^2 - 8x \quad + y^2 + 6y + 9 = 9$$

The system simplifies to:

$$x^2 + 6x + y^2 - 8y = 0$$
$$x^2 - 8x + y^2 + 6y = 0$$

Adding -1 times the second equation to the first equation:

$$x^2 + 6x + y^2 - 8y = 0$$
$$-x^2 + 8x - y^2 - 6y = 0$$

Adding yields:
$$14x - 14y = 0$$
$$14x = 14y$$
$$x = y$$
Substituting into the second equation:
$$x^2 - 8x + y^2 + 6y = 0$$
$$x^2 - 8x + x^2 + 6x = 0$$
$$2x^2 - 2x = 0$$
$$2x(x - 1) = 0$$
$$x = 0, 1$$
$$y = 0, 1$$
The solutions are: $(0,0), (1,1)$

62. Multiplying out terms in the first equation results in the system:
$$x^2 - 2x + 1 + y^2 + 2y + 1 = 0$$
$$x^2 \qquad + y^2 + 2y \quad = 0$$
The system simplifies to:
$$x^2 - 2x + y^2 + 2y = -2$$
$$x^2 \qquad + y^2 + 2y = 0$$
Adding -1 times the second equation to the first equation:
$$x^2 - 2x + y^2 + 2y = -2$$
$$-x^2 \qquad - y^2 - 2y = 0$$
Adding yields:
$$-2x = -2$$
$$x = 1$$
Substituting into the second equation:
$$x^2 + y^2 + 2y = 0$$
$$(1)^2 + y^2 + 2y = 0$$
$$y^2 + 2y + 1 = 0$$
$$(y + 1)^2 = 0$$
$$y = -1$$
The only solution is: $(1, -1)$

63. Let x represent the length of a side of the smaller square, and y represent the length of a side of the larger square. The system of equations is:

$$x^2 + y^2 = 549$$
$$y = x + 3$$

Substituting into the first equation:

$$x^2 + y^2 = 549$$
$$x^2 + (x+3)^2 = 549$$
$$x^2 + x^2 + 6x + 9 = 549$$
$$2x^2 + 6x - 540 = 0$$
$$x^2 + 3x - 270 = 0$$
$$(x+18)(x-15) = 0$$
$$x = 15 \quad (x \neq -18)$$

Substituting into the second equation: $y = x + 3 = 15 + 3 = 18$

The length of the small square is 15 inches and the length of the large square is 18 inches.

Chapter 8 Test

1. Adding 2 times the second equation to the first equation results in the system:

$$x + 2y = 4$$
$$8x - 2y = -22$$

Adding yields: Substituting into the first equation:
$$9x = -18 \qquad\qquad\qquad -2 + 2y = 4$$
$$x = -2 \qquad\qquad\qquad\qquad 2y = 6$$
$$\qquad\qquad\qquad\qquad\qquad y = 3$$

The solution is: $x = -2, y = 3$

2. Adding 5 times the first equation to 2 times the second equation results in the system:

$$-10x + 15y = -40$$
$$10x - 4y = 18$$

Adding yields: Substituting into the second equation:
$$11y = -22 \qquad\qquad\qquad 5x - 2y = 9$$
$$y = -2 \qquad\qquad\qquad 5x - 2(-2) = 9$$
$$\qquad\qquad\qquad\qquad\qquad 5x + 4 = 9$$
$$\qquad\qquad\qquad\qquad\qquad 5x = 5$$
$$\qquad\qquad\qquad\qquad\qquad x = 1$$

The solution is: $x = 1, y = -2$

3. Sketching the graph:

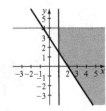

4. Evaluating the function at the corner points:

(x,y)	$P = 15x + 10y$
$(0,0)$	0
$(0.5,1)$	17.5
$(3.5,1)$	62.5
$(4,0)$	60

The maximum value is $P = 62.5$ when $x = 3.5$ and $y = 1$.

5. Reversing the first and third equations results in the system:
$$\begin{aligned} x + 2y \quad &= -5 \\ -3x \quad + z &= 11 \\ 2x - y + z &= -3 \end{aligned}$$

Adding 3 times the first equation to the second equation and -2 times the first equation to the third equation:
$$\begin{aligned} x + 2y \quad &= -5 \\ 6y + z &= -4 \\ -5y + z &= 7 \end{aligned}$$

Adding -1 times the second equation to the third equation:
$$\begin{aligned} x + 2y \quad &= -5 \\ 6y + z &= -4 \\ -11y \quad &= 11 \end{aligned}$$

Solving the third equation for y:
$$\begin{aligned} -11y &= 11 \\ y &= -1 \end{aligned}$$

Substituting into the second equation:
$$\begin{aligned} 6y + z &= -4 \\ 6(-1) + z &= -4 \\ -6 + z &= -4 \\ z &= 2 \end{aligned}$$

Substituting into the first equation:
$$\begin{aligned} x + 2y &= -5 \\ x + 2(-1) &= -5 \\ x - 2 &= -5 \\ x &= -3 \end{aligned}$$

The solution is: $x = -3, y = -1, z = 2$

6. Adding 2 times the first equation to the second equation:
$$\begin{aligned} -x + 2y - z &= 0 \\ 3y - 2z &= 2 \end{aligned}$$

Solving the second equation for y:
$$\begin{aligned} 3y - 2z &= 2 \\ 3y &= 2 + 2z \\ y &= \frac{2}{3} + \frac{2}{3}z \end{aligned}$$

Substituting into the first equation:
$$\begin{aligned} -x + 2y - z &= 0 \\ -x + 2\left(\frac{2}{3} + \frac{2}{3}z\right) - z &= 0 \\ -x + \frac{4}{3} + \frac{4}{3}z - z &= 0 \\ -x + \frac{4}{3} + \frac{1}{3}z &= 0 \\ -x &= -\frac{4}{3} - \frac{1}{3}z \\ x &= \frac{4}{3} + \frac{1}{3}z \end{aligned}$$

The solution is: $x = \frac{4}{3} + \frac{1}{3}z, y = \frac{2}{3} + \frac{2}{3}z$

7. Performing the operations: $B - 2C = \begin{bmatrix} -3 & 4 \\ -1 & 2 \\ 7 & -3 \end{bmatrix} - \begin{bmatrix} 16 & 6 \\ -12 & 10 \\ 10 & -4 \end{bmatrix} = \begin{bmatrix} -19 & -2 \\ 11 & -8 \\ -3 & 1 \end{bmatrix}$

8. Performing the operations: $CA = \begin{bmatrix} 8 & 3 \\ -6 & 5 \\ 5 & -2 \end{bmatrix} \begin{bmatrix} 5 & 0 & 3 \\ 2 & -4 & 3 \end{bmatrix} = \begin{bmatrix} 46 & -12 & 33 \\ -22 & -20 & -3 \\ 21 & 8 & 9 \end{bmatrix}$

9. Form the augmented matrix: $\left[\begin{array}{cc|cc} 3 & 5 & 1 & 0 \\ 1 & 2 & 0 & 1 \end{array} \right]$

Reversing the first and second rows: $\left[\begin{array}{cc|cc} 1 & 2 & 0 & 1 \\ 3 & 5 & 1 & 0 \end{array} \right]$

Adding -3 times the first row to the second row: $\left[\begin{array}{cc|cc} 1 & 2 & 0 & 1 \\ 0 & -1 & 1 & -3 \end{array} \right]$

Adding 2 times the second row to the first row: $\left[\begin{array}{cc|cc} 1 & 0 & 2 & -5 \\ 0 & -1 & 1 & -3 \end{array} \right]$

Multiplying the second row by -1: $\left[\begin{array}{cc|cc} 1 & 0 & 2 & -5 \\ 0 & 1 & -1 & 3 \end{array} \right]$

The inverse matrix is: $\begin{bmatrix} 2 & -5 \\ -1 & 3 \end{bmatrix}$

10. Form the augmented matrix: $\left[\begin{array}{ccc|ccc} 1 & 4 & 2 & 1 & 0 & 0 \\ -2 & 1 & 0 & 0 & 1 & 0 \\ 0 & 2 & 1 & 0 & 0 & 1 \end{array} \right]$

Adding 2 times the first row to the second row: $\left[\begin{array}{ccc|ccc} 1 & 4 & 2 & 1 & 0 & 0 \\ 0 & 9 & 4 & 2 & 1 & 0 \\ 0 & 2 & 1 & 0 & 0 & 1 \end{array} \right]$

Multiplying the third row by $\dfrac{1}{2}$ and switching with the second row: $\left[\begin{array}{ccc|ccc} 1 & 4 & 2 & 1 & 0 & 0 \\ 0 & 1 & \frac{1}{2} & 0 & 0 & \frac{1}{2} \\ 0 & 9 & 4 & 2 & 1 & 0 \end{array} \right]$

Adding -4 times the second row to the first row and -9 times the second row to the third row:
$\left[\begin{array}{ccc|ccc} 1 & 0 & 0 & 1 & 0 & -2 \\ 0 & 1 & \frac{1}{2} & 0 & 0 & \frac{1}{2} \\ 0 & 0 & -\frac{1}{2} & 2 & 1 & -\frac{9}{2} \end{array} \right]$

Adding the third row to the second row: $\left[\begin{array}{ccc|ccc} 1 & 0 & 0 & 1 & 0 & -2 \\ 0 & 1 & 0 & 2 & 1 & -4 \\ 0 & 0 & -\frac{1}{2} & 2 & 1 & -\frac{9}{2} \end{array} \right]$

Multiplying the third row by –2: $\begin{bmatrix} 1 & 0 & 0 & | & 1 & 0 & -2 \\ 0 & 1 & 0 & | & 2 & 1 & -4 \\ 0 & 0 & 1 & | & -4 & -2 & 9 \end{bmatrix}$

The inverse matrix is: $\begin{bmatrix} 1 & 0 & -2 \\ 2 & 1 & -4 \\ -4 & -2 & 9 \end{bmatrix}$

11. First finding the inverse: $A = \begin{bmatrix} 1 & 3 & -1 \\ 1 & 4 & 1 \\ 2 & 6 & -1 \end{bmatrix} \Rightarrow A^{-1} = \begin{bmatrix} -10 & -3 & 7 \\ 3 & 1 & -2 \\ -2 & 0 & 1 \end{bmatrix}$

Solving the equation: $X = A^{-1}B \Rightarrow \begin{bmatrix} x \\ y \\ z \end{bmatrix} = \begin{bmatrix} -10 & -3 & 7 \\ 3 & 1 & -2 \\ -2 & 0 & 1 \end{bmatrix} \begin{bmatrix} 0 \\ -2 \\ 1 \end{bmatrix} = \begin{bmatrix} 13 \\ -4 \\ 1 \end{bmatrix}$

The solution is: $x = 13, y = -4, z = 1$

12. Expand about the third column:

$|A| = \begin{vmatrix} 2 & -3 & 1 \\ 0 & 5 & 2 \\ -4 & 2 & 0 \end{vmatrix} = C_{13} + 2C_{23} + 0C_{33} = (-1)^{1+3}(0-(-20)) + 2(-1)^{2+3}(4-12) = (1)(20) + 2(-1)(-8) = 36$

13. Finding the determinants:

$D = \begin{vmatrix} 1 & 3 \\ 1 & 1 \end{vmatrix} = 1 - 3 = -2$

$D_x = \begin{vmatrix} 6 & 3 \\ 2 & 1 \end{vmatrix} = 6 - 6 = 0$

$D_y = \begin{vmatrix} 1 & 6 \\ 1 & 2 \end{vmatrix} = 2 - 6 = -4$

Using Cramer's rule: $x = \dfrac{D_x}{D} = \dfrac{0}{-2} = 0, \quad y = \dfrac{D_y}{D} = \dfrac{-4}{-2} = 2$

14. Finding the determinants:

$D = \begin{vmatrix} 1 & -2 & -1 \\ -1 & -1 & 0 \\ 1 & 0 & 1 \end{vmatrix} = C_{31} + C_{33} = (-1)^4(0-1) + (-1)^6(-1-2) = -1 - 3 = -4$

$D_x = \begin{vmatrix} 0 & -2 & -1 \\ 3 & -1 & 0 \\ -1 & 0 & 1 \end{vmatrix} = -C_{31} + C_{33} = -(-1)^4(0-1) + (-1)^6(0+6) = 1 + 6 = 7$

$D_y = \begin{vmatrix} 1 & 0 & -1 \\ -1 & 3 & 0 \\ 1 & -1 & 1 \end{vmatrix} = C_{11} - C_{13} = (-1)^2(3-0) - (-1)^4(1-3) = 3 + 2 = 5$

$D_z = \begin{vmatrix} 1 & -2 & 0 \\ -1 & -1 & 3 \\ 1 & 0 & -1 \end{vmatrix} = C_{31} - C_{33} = (-1)^4(-6-0) - (-1)^6(-1-2) = -6 + 3 = -3$

Using Cramer's rule: $x = \dfrac{D_x}{D} = \dfrac{7}{-4} = -\dfrac{7}{4}, \quad y = \dfrac{D_y}{D} = \dfrac{5}{-4} = -\dfrac{5}{4}, \quad z = \dfrac{D_z}{D} = \dfrac{-3}{-4} = \dfrac{3}{4}$

15. The form of the decomposition is: $\dfrac{-x^2+2x+2}{x^3+2x^2+x} = \dfrac{-x^2+2x+2}{x(x^2+2x+1)} = \dfrac{-x^2+2x+2}{x(x+1)^2} = \dfrac{A}{x} + \dfrac{B}{x+1} + \dfrac{C}{(x+1)^2}$

Clearing fractions: $-x^2+2x+2 = A(x+1)^2 + Bx(x+1) + Cx$

Substituting $x=-1$:

$$-1-2+2 = C(-1)$$
$$-1 = -C$$
$$C = 1$$

Therefore:

$$-x^2+2x+2 = A(x+1)^2 + Bx(x+1) + x = Ax^2+2Ax+A+Bx^2+Bx+x = (A+B)x^2 + (2A+B+1)x + A$$

Equating coefficients:

$A = 2$

$A+B = -1$
$2+B = -1$
$B = -3$

Therefore the decomposition is: $\dfrac{-x^2+2x+2}{x^3+2x^2+x} = \dfrac{2}{x} - \dfrac{3}{x+1} + \dfrac{1}{(x+1)^2}$

16. The form of the decomposition is: $\dfrac{5x^2-7x+6}{(x^2+1)(x-3)} = \dfrac{A}{x-3} + \dfrac{Bx+C}{x^2+1}$

Clearing fractions: $5x^2-7x+6 = A(x^2+1) + (Bx+C)(x-3)$

Substituting $x=3$:

$$5(9) - 7(3) + 6 = A(9+1)$$
$$30 = 10A$$
$$A = 3$$

Therefore:

$$5x^2-7x+6 = 3(x^2+1) + (Bx+C)(x-3) = 3x^2+3+Bx^2-3Bx+Cx-3C = (B+3)x^2 + (-3B+C)x + (-3C+3)$$

Equating coefficients:

$3+B = 5$
$B = 2$

$-3C+3 = 6$
$-3C = 3$
$C = -1$

Therefore the decomposition is: $\dfrac{5x^2-7x+6}{(x^2+1)(x-3)} = \dfrac{3}{x-3} + \dfrac{2x-1}{x^2+1}$

17. Solving the second equation for y: $y = 3x$

Substituting into the first equation:

$$x^2+y^2 = 4$$
$$x^2+(3x)^2 = 4$$
$$x^2+9x^2 = 4$$
$$10x^2 = 4$$
$$x^2 = \frac{2}{5}$$
$$x = \pm\frac{\sqrt{2}}{\sqrt{5}} = \pm\frac{\sqrt{10}}{5}$$

Finding the y-values:

$$x = \frac{\sqrt{10}}{5} : \quad y = 3\left(\frac{\sqrt{10}}{5}\right) = \frac{3\sqrt{10}}{5}$$

$$x = -\frac{\sqrt{10}}{5} : \quad y = 3\left(-\frac{\sqrt{10}}{5}\right) = -\frac{3\sqrt{10}}{5}$$

The solutions are: $\left(\frac{\sqrt{10}}{5}, \frac{3\sqrt{10}}{5}\right), \left(-\frac{\sqrt{10}}{5}, -\frac{3\sqrt{10}}{5}\right)$

18. Multiplying out terms in the first equation results in the system:

$$x^2 + 2x + 1 + y^2 - 2y + 1 = 9$$
$$x^2 + 2x \quad + y^2 \qquad = 9$$

The system simplifies to:

$$x^2 + 2x + y^2 - 2y = 7$$
$$x^2 + 2x + y^2 \qquad = 9$$

Adding -1 times the second equation to the first equation:

$$x^2 + 2x + y^2 - 2y = 7$$
$$-x^2 - 2x - y^2 \qquad = -9$$

Adding yields:

$$-2y = -2$$
$$y = 1$$

Substituting into the second equation:

$$x^2 + 2x + (1)^2 = 9$$
$$x^2 + 2x - 8 = 0$$
$$(x+4)(x-2) = 0$$
$$x = -4, 2$$

The solutions are: $(-4,1), (2,1)$

19. Let x represent the number of CX100 laptops and y represent the number of FX100 laptops produced.
The profit function is: $P = 150x + 100y$

The constraints are:

$$x + 2y \le 800$$
$$y \ge 100$$
$$x, y \ge 0$$

Evaluating the profit at the corner points:

(x,y)	$P = 150x + 100y$
$(0,100)$	$10,000
$(0,400)$	$40,000
$(600,100)$	$100,000

They should produce 600 CX100 models and 100 FX100 models to realize a maximum profit of $100,000.

20. Let x represent the number of first-class tickets, y represent the number of business class tickets, and z represent the number of coach tickets. The system of equations is:

$$x + y + z = 10$$
$$2500x + 1500y + 300z = 14{,}200$$
$$z = 2y$$

Form the augmented matrix: $\begin{bmatrix} 1 & 1 & 1 & | & 10 \\ 2500 & 1500 & 300 & | & 14200 \\ 0 & -2 & 1 & | & 0 \end{bmatrix}$

Dividing the second row by 100: $\begin{bmatrix} 1 & 1 & 1 & | & 10 \\ 25 & 15 & 3 & | & 142 \\ 0 & -2 & 1 & | & 0 \end{bmatrix}$

Adding –25 times the first row to the second row: $\begin{bmatrix} 1 & 1 & 1 & | & 10 \\ 0 & -10 & -22 & | & -108 \\ 0 & -2 & 1 & | & 0 \end{bmatrix}$

Adding –5 times the third row to the second row: $\begin{bmatrix} 1 & 1 & 1 & | & 10 \\ 0 & 0 & -27 & | & -108 \\ 0 & -2 & 1 & | & 0 \end{bmatrix}$

Switching the second the third rows: $\begin{bmatrix} 1 & 1 & 1 & | & 10 \\ 0 & -2 & 1 & | & 0 \\ 0 & 0 & -27 & | & -108 \end{bmatrix}$

Dividing the third row by –27: $\begin{bmatrix} 1 & 1 & 1 & | & 10 \\ 0 & -2 & 1 & | & 0 \\ 0 & 0 & 1 & | & 4 \end{bmatrix}$

Adding –1 times the third row to the first and second rows: $\begin{bmatrix} 1 & 1 & 0 & | & 6 \\ 0 & -2 & 0 & | & -4 \\ 0 & 0 & 1 & | & 4 \end{bmatrix}$

Dividing the second row by –2: $\begin{bmatrix} 1 & 1 & 0 & | & 6 \\ 0 & 1 & 0 & | & 2 \\ 0 & 0 & 1 & | & 4 \end{bmatrix}$

Adding –1 times the second row to the first row: $\begin{bmatrix} 1 & 0 & 0 & | & 4 \\ 0 & 1 & 0 & | & 2 \\ 0 & 0 & 1 & | & 4 \end{bmatrix}$

There were 4 first-class, 2 business class, and 4 coach tickets purchased.

21. The minutes matrix is: $\begin{bmatrix} 200 & 400 \\ 300 & 200 \\ 150 & 300 \end{bmatrix}$

The cost matrix is: $\begin{bmatrix} 0.10 \\ 0.05 \end{bmatrix}$

Finding the product: $\begin{bmatrix} 200 & 400 \\ 300 & 200 \\ 150 & 300 \end{bmatrix} \begin{bmatrix} 0.10 \\ 0.05 \end{bmatrix} = \begin{bmatrix} \$40 \\ \$40 \\ \$30 \end{bmatrix}$

The costs are $40 for customer 1, $40 for customer 2, and $30 for customer 3.

Chapter 9
Conic Sections

9.1 The Parabola

1. This statement is true.

3. Using the distance formula: $d = \sqrt{(2-(-8))^2 + (6-6)^2} = \sqrt{10^2 + 0^2} = 10$

5. The function is $f(x) = (x-1)^2$.

7. This statement is true.

9. Completing the square: $x^2 + 6x + \left(\frac{1}{2}(6)\right)^2 = x^2 + 6x + (3)^2 = x^2 + 6x + 9$

11. This graph is c.

13. This graph is b.

15. Finding p:
$$4p = 12$$
$$p = 3$$

The vertex is $(0,0)$, the focus is $(3,0)$, and the directrix is $x = -3$. Sketching the graph:

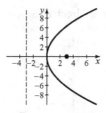

17. Finding p:
$$4p = 8$$
$$p = 2$$

The vertex is $(0,0)$, the focus is $(2,0)$, and the directrix is $x = -2$. Sketching the graph:

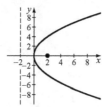

19. Changing the form of the equation:
$$y = -\frac{1}{4}x^2$$
$$4y = -x^2$$
$$x^2 = -4y$$
Finding p:
$$4p = -4$$
$$p = -1$$
The vertex is $(0,0)$, the focus is $(0,-1)$, and the directrix is $y = 1$. Sketching the graph:

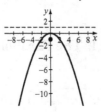

21. Changing the form of the equation:
$$8x = 3y^2$$
$$y^2 = \frac{8}{3}x$$
Finding p:
$$4p = \frac{8}{3}$$
$$p = \frac{2}{3}$$
The vertex is $(0,0)$, the focus is $\left(\frac{2}{3},0\right)$, and the directrix is $x = -\frac{2}{3}$. Sketching the graph:

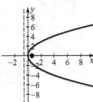

23. Changing the form of the equation:
$$5y^2 = 4x$$
$$y^2 = \frac{4}{5}x$$
Finding p:
$$4p = \frac{4}{5}$$
$$p = \frac{1}{5}$$

The vertex is $(0,0)$, the focus is $\left(\dfrac{1}{5},0\right)$, and the directrix is $x=-\dfrac{1}{5}$. Sketching the graph:

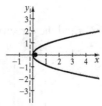

25. Finding p:
$$4p=-12$$
$$p=-3$$

The vertex is $(2,0)$, the focus is $(2-3,0)=(-1,0)$, and the directrix is $x=2+3=5$. Sketching the graph:

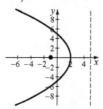

27. Finding p:
$$4p=-4$$
$$p=-1$$

The vertex is $(5,-1)$, the focus is $(5,-1-1)=(5,-2)$, and the directrix is $y=-1+1=0$. Sketching the graph:

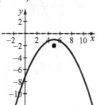

29. Finding p:
$$4p=-1$$
$$p=-\dfrac{1}{4}$$

The vertex is $(1,4)$, the focus is $\left(1-\dfrac{1}{4},4\right)=\left(\dfrac{3}{4},4\right)$, and the directrix is $x=1+\dfrac{1}{4}=\dfrac{5}{4}$. Sketching the graph:

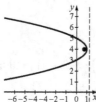

31. First complete the square:
$$y^2-4y+4x=0$$
$$y^2-4y=-4x$$
$$y^2-4y+4=-4x+4$$
$$(y-2)^2=-4(x-1)$$

Finding p:
$$4p = -4$$
$$p = -1$$

The vertex is $(1,2)$, the focus is $(1-1,2) = (0,2)$, and the directrix is $x = 1+1 = 2$. Sketching the graph:

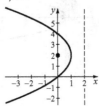

33.   First complete the square:
$$x^2 - 2x = -y$$
$$x^2 - 2x + 1 = -y + 1$$
$$(x-1)^2 = -(y-1)$$

Finding p:
$$4p = -1$$
$$p = -\frac{1}{4}$$

The vertex is $(1,1)$, the focus is $\left(1, 1 - \frac{1}{4}\right) = \left(1, \frac{3}{4}\right)$, and the directrix is $y = 1 + \frac{1}{4} = \frac{5}{4}$. Sketching the graph:

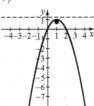

35.   First complete the square:
$$x^2 + 6x + 4y + 25 = 0$$
$$x^2 + 6x = -4y - 25$$
$$x^2 + 6x + 9 = -4y - 25 + 9$$
$$(x+3)^2 = -4y - 16$$
$$(x+3)^2 = -4(y+4)$$

Finding p:
$$4p = -4$$
$$p = -1$$

The vertex is $(-3,-4)$, the focus is $(-3, -4-1) = (-3,-5)$, and the directrix is $y = -4+1 = -3$. Sketching the graph:

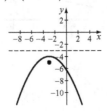

37. First complete the square:
$$x^2 - 5y + 1 = 8x$$
$$x^2 - 8x = 5y - 1$$
$$x^2 - 8x + 16 = 5y - 1 + 16$$
$$(x-4)^2 = 5y + 15$$
$$(x-4)^2 = 5(x+3)$$

Finding p:
$$4p = 5$$
$$p = \frac{5}{4}$$

The vertex is $(4,-3)$, the focus is $\left(4, -3+\frac{5}{4}\right) = \left(4, -\frac{7}{4}\right)$, and the directrix is $y = -3 - \frac{5}{4} = -\frac{17}{4}$. Sketching the graph:

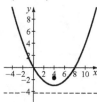

39. The directrix is $x = -1$, so the focus is $(1,0)$ and $p = 1$. The equation is: $y^2 = 4(1)x = 4x$

41. The directrix is $y = -3$, so the focus is $(0,3)$ and $p = 3$. The equation is: $x^2 = 4(3)y = 12y$

43. The focus is $(0,2)$, so $p = 2$ and the parabola opens up. The equation is: $x^2 = 4(2)y = 8y$

45. The focus is $(-2,0)$, so $p = -2$ and the parabola opens to the left. The equation is: $y^2 = 4(-2)x = -8x$

47. The vertex is $(0,0)$ and the parabola is opening up. Since $p = 4$, the equation is: $x^2 = 4(4)y = 16y$

49. The vertex is $(0,0)$ and the parabola is opening to the left. Since $p = -5$, the equation is: $y^2 = 4(-5)x = -20x$

51. The vertex is $(-2,1)$ and the directrix is $y = -2$, so the parabola is opening up. Since $p = 3$, the equation is:
$$(x+2)^2 = 4(3)(y-1)$$
$$(x+2)^2 = 12(y-1)$$

53. The vertex is $(0,0)$ and the focus is $(0,4)$, so the parabola is opening upward. Since $p = 4$, the equation is:
$$x^2 = 4(4)y$$
$$x^2 = 16y$$

55. The vertex is $(0,0)$ and the axis is horizontal, so the form of the equation is $y^2 = 4px$. Substituting the point $(1,3)$:
$$(3)^2 = 4p(1)$$
$$9 = 4p$$
$$p = \frac{9}{4}$$

The equation is:
$$y^2 = 4\left(\frac{9}{4}\right)x$$
$$y^2 = 9x$$

57. The vertex is $(4,3)$ and the axis is vertical, so the form of the equation is $(x-4)^2 = 4p(y-3)$.

Substituting the point $(5,2)$:

$$(5-4)^2 = 4p(2-3)$$
$$1 = -4p$$
$$p = -\frac{1}{4}$$

The equation is:

$$(x-4)^2 = 4\left(-\frac{1}{4}\right)(y-3)$$
$$(x-4)^2 = -(y-3)$$

59. The vertex is $(4,1)$ and the parabola opens upward, so the form of the equation is $(x-4)^2 = 4p(y-1)$.

Substituting the point $(8,3)$:

$$(8-4)^2 = 4p(3-1)$$
$$16 = 8p$$
$$p = 2$$

The equation is:

$$(x-4)^2 = 4(2)(y-1)$$
$$(x-4)^2 = 8(y-1)$$

61. The vertex is $(5,3)$ and the parabola opens downward, so the form of the equation is $(x-5)^2 = 4p(y-3)$.

Substituting the point $(2,0)$:

$$(2-5)^2 = 4p(0-3)$$
$$9 = -12p$$
$$p = -\frac{3}{4}$$

The equation is:

$$(x-5)^2 = 4\left(-\frac{3}{4}\right)(y-3)$$
$$(x-5)^2 = -3(y-3)$$

63. Positioning the satellite so that its vertex is at the origin and opens up, its equation is $x^2 = 4py$.

The cross-section ends at the point $(18,16)$, so:

$$(18)^2 = 4(16)y$$
$$324 = 64p$$
$$p = 5.0625$$

The receptor must be located 5.0625 inches from the vertex.

65. a. Using $(0,144)$ as the vertex, the form of the equation is $x^2 = 4p(y-144)$. Substituting the point $(48,0)$:

$$(48)^2 = 4p(0-144)$$
$$2304 = -576p$$
$$p = -4$$

The equation of the parabola is: $x^2 = 4(-4)(y-144) = -16(y-144)$

At a point 32 inches from the ends, $x = 48 - 32 = 16$. Substituting to find y:

$$(16)^2 = -16(y - 144)$$
$$256 = -16y + 2304$$
$$-2048 = -16y$$
$$128 = y$$

The parabola is 128 inches high at a point 32 inches from the ends.

b. At a point 63 inches high, $y = 63$. Substituting to find x:

$$x^2 = -16(63 - 144)$$
$$x^2 = 1296$$
$$x = 36$$

The locations are $48 - 36 = 12$ inches from the ends of the base.

67. Set the vertex at the point $(0,5)$ and the x-intercept is at $(30,0)$. Therefore:

$$x^2 = 4p(y - 5)$$
$$(30)^2 = 4p(0 - 5)$$
$$900 = -20p$$
$$p = -45$$

So the equation of the parabola is:

$$x^2 = 4(-45)(y - 5)$$
$$x^2 = -180(y - 5)$$

At a point 12 feet from the end, $x = 30 - 12 = 18$. Substituting to find y:

$$(18)^2 = -180(y - 5)$$
$$324 = -180y + 900$$
$$-576 = -180y$$
$$y = 3.2$$

The point is 3.2 feet above the base.

69. Since $(4, -7)$ is a point on the parabola, its distance from the focus is the same as its distance from the directrix. Since the point is 5 units from the directrix, it is 5 units from the focus.

71. The focus is $(-2,1)$ and the axis is horizontal, so its equation is $y = 1$. The distance from the point $(0,5)$ to this axis is 4 units.

73. The form of the parabola is $y = ax^2 + bx + c$. Substituting the given points:

$$4 = a(-7)^2 + b(-7) + c$$
$$5 = a(-5)^2 + b(-5) + c$$
$$29 = a(3)^2 + b(3) + c$$

This results in the system of equations:

$$49a - 7b + c = 4$$
$$25a - 5b + c = 5$$
$$9a + 3b + c = 29$$

Using $A = \begin{bmatrix} 49 & -7 & 1 \\ 25 & -5 & 1 \\ 9 & 3 & 1 \end{bmatrix}$, the inverse is given by: $A^{-1} = \begin{bmatrix} \dfrac{1}{80} & -\dfrac{1}{16} & \dfrac{1}{20} \\[6pt] \dfrac{3}{20} & -\dfrac{1}{4} & \dfrac{1}{10} \\[6pt] \dfrac{7}{16} & \dfrac{21}{16} & -\dfrac{3}{4} \end{bmatrix}$

Therefore: $X = A^{-1}B = \begin{bmatrix} \dfrac{1}{80} & -\dfrac{1}{16} & \dfrac{1}{20} \\[6pt] \dfrac{3}{20} & -\dfrac{1}{4} & \dfrac{1}{10} \\[6pt] \dfrac{7}{16} & \dfrac{21}{16} & -\dfrac{3}{4} \end{bmatrix} \begin{bmatrix} 4 \\ 5 \\ 29 \end{bmatrix} = \begin{bmatrix} \dfrac{1}{4} \\[6pt] \dfrac{7}{2} \\[6pt] \dfrac{65}{4} \end{bmatrix}$

The equation (in standard form) is given by:

$$y = \frac{1}{4}x^2 + \frac{7}{2}x + \frac{65}{4}$$
$$4y = x^2 + 14x + 65$$
$$x^2 + 14x = 4y - 65$$
$$x^2 + 14x + 49 = 4y - 16$$
$$(x+7)^2 = 4(y-4)$$

75. The axis of symmetry is $y = 1$. Since $(4, -6)$ is 7 units below the axis so its mirror image will be 7 units above the axis, or 14 units above the point $(4, -6 + 14) = (4, 8)$.

9.2 The Ellipse

1. This statement is true.

3. Using the distance formula: $d = \sqrt{(3-1)^2 + (4-(-2))^2} = \sqrt{2^2 + 6^2} = \sqrt{40} = 2\sqrt{10}$

5. The number is: $\left[\dfrac{1}{2}(-12)\right]^2 = (-6)^2 = 36$

7. The corresponding graph is c.

9. The corresponding graph is d.

11. Using $a = 5$ and $b = 4$, find c: $c = \sqrt{a^2 - b^2} = \sqrt{5^2 - 4^2} = \sqrt{9} = 3$

The center is $(0,0)$, the vertices are $(-5,0)$ and $(5,0)$, and the foci are $(-3,0)$ and $(3,0)$. Sketching the graph:

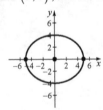

13. Using $a = 5$ and $b = 4$, find c: $c = \sqrt{a^2 - b^2} = \sqrt{5^2 - 4^2} = \sqrt{9} = 3$

The center is $(0,0)$, the vertices are $(0,-5)$ and $(0,5)$, and the foci are $(0,-3)$ and $(0,3)$. Sketching the graph:

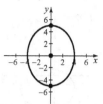

15. Using $a = 3$ and $b = 2$, find c: $c = \sqrt{a^2 - b^2} = \sqrt{3^2 - 2^2} = \sqrt{5}$

The center is $(0,0)$, the vertices are $(-3,0)$ and $(3,0)$, and the foci are $\left(-\sqrt{5},0\right)$ and $\left(\sqrt{5},0\right)$. Sketching the graph:

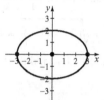

17. Using $a = \dfrac{3}{2}$ and $b = \dfrac{4}{3}$, find c: $c = \sqrt{a^2 - b^2} = \sqrt{\left(\dfrac{3}{2}\right)^2 - \left(\dfrac{4}{3}\right)^2} = \sqrt{\dfrac{17}{36}} = \dfrac{\sqrt{17}}{6}$

The center is $(0,0)$, the vertices are $\left(-\dfrac{3}{2},0\right)$ and $\left(\dfrac{3}{2},0\right)$, and the foci are $\left(-\dfrac{\sqrt{17}}{6},0\right)$ and $\left(\dfrac{\sqrt{17}}{6},0\right)$.

Sketching the graph:

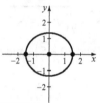

19. Using $a = 4$ and $b = 3$, find c: $c = \sqrt{a^2 - b^2} = \sqrt{4^2 - 3^2} = \sqrt{7}$

The center is $(-3,-1)$, the vertices are $(-3,-1-4) = (-3,-5)$ and $(-3,-1+4) = (-3,3)$, and the foci are $\left(-3,-1-\sqrt{7}\right)$ and $\left(-3,-1+\sqrt{7}\right)$. Sketching the graph:

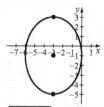

21. Using $a = 10$ and $b = 6$, find c: $c = \sqrt{a^2 - b^2} = \sqrt{10^2 - 6^2} = \sqrt{64} = 8$

The center is $(1,-1)$, the vertices are $(1-10,-1) = (-9,-1)$ and $(1+10,-1) = (11,-1)$, and the foci are $(1-8,-1) = (-7,-1)$ and $(1+8,-1) = (9,-1)$. Sketching the graph:

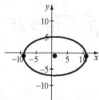

23. Using $a = 4$ and $b = 3$, find c: $c = \sqrt{a^2 - b^2} = \sqrt{4^2 - 3^2} = \sqrt{7}$

The center is $(1, -2)$, the vertices are $(1 - 4, -2) = (-3, -2)$ and $(1 + 4, -2) = (5, -2)$, and the foci are $(1 - \sqrt{7}, -2)$ and $(1 + \sqrt{7}, -2)$. Sketching the graph:

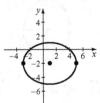

25. First divide by 12 to write the equation in standard form: $\dfrac{x^2}{4} + \dfrac{y^2}{3} = 1$

Using $a = 2$ and $b = \sqrt{3}$, find c: $c = \sqrt{a^2 - b^2} = \sqrt{(2)^2 - (\sqrt{3})^2} = \sqrt{1} = 1$

The center is $(0, 0)$, the vertices are $(-2, 0)$ and $(2, 0)$, and the foci are $(-1, 0)$ and $(1, 0)$. Sketching the graph:

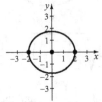

27. First divide by 10 to write the equation in standard form: $\dfrac{x^2}{2} + \dfrac{y^2}{5} = 1$

Using $a = \sqrt{5}$ and $b = \sqrt{2}$, find c: $c = \sqrt{a^2 - b^2} = \sqrt{(\sqrt{5})^2 - (\sqrt{2})^2} = \sqrt{3}$

The center is $(0, 0)$, the vertices are $(0, -\sqrt{5})$ and $(0, \sqrt{5})$, and the foci are $(0, -\sqrt{3})$ and $(0, \sqrt{3})$.
Sketching the graph:

29. Completing the square:
$$4x^2 + y^2 - 24x - 8y + 48 = 0$$
$$4x^2 - 24x + y^2 - 8y + 48 = 0$$
$$4(x^2 - 6x) + (y^2 - 8y) = -48$$
$$4(x^2 - 6x + 9) + (y^2 - 8y + 16) = -48 + 36 + 16$$
$$4(x - 3)^2 + (y - 4)^2 = 4$$
$$\frac{(x - 3)^2}{1} + \frac{(y - 4)^2}{4} = 1$$

Using $a = 2$ and $b = 1$, find c: $c = \sqrt{a^2 - b^2} = \sqrt{(2)^2 - (1)^2} = \sqrt{3}$

The center is $(3,4)$, the vertices are $(3,4-2)=(3,2)$ and $(3,4+2)=(3,6)$, and the foci are $\left(3,4-\sqrt{3}\right)$ and $\left(3,4+\sqrt{3}\right)$. Sketching the graph:

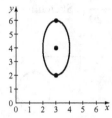

31. Completing the square:
$$5x^2+9y^2-20x+54y+56=0$$
$$5x^2-20x+9y^2+54y+56=0$$
$$5\left(x^2-4x\right)+9\left(y^2+6y\right)=-56$$
$$5\left(x^2-4x+4\right)+9\left(y^2+6y+9\right)=-56+20+81$$
$$5(x-2)^2+9(y+3)^2=45$$
$$\frac{(x-2)^2}{9}+\frac{(y+3)^2}{5}=1$$

Using $a=3$ and $b=\sqrt{5}$, find c: $c=\sqrt{a^2-b^2}=\sqrt{(3)^2-\left(\sqrt{5}\right)^2}=\sqrt{4}=2$

The center is $(2,-3)$, the vertices are $(2-3,-3)=(-1,-3)$ and $(2+3,-3)=(5,-3)$, and the foci are $(2-2,-3)=(0,-3)$ and $(2+2,-3)=(4,-3)$. Sketching the graph:

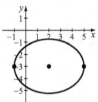

33. Completing the square:
$$25x^2+16y^2-200x+96y+495=0$$
$$25x^2-200x+16y^2+96y=-495$$
$$25\left(x^2-8x\right)+16\left(y^2+6x\right)=-495$$
$$25\left(x^2-8x+16\right)+16\left(y^2+6x+9\right)=-495+400+144$$
$$25(x-4)^2+16(y+3)^2=49$$
$$\frac{(x-4)^2}{\frac{49}{25}}+\frac{(y+3)^2}{\frac{49}{16}}=1$$

Using $a=\frac{7}{4}$ and $b=\frac{7}{5}$, find c: $c=\sqrt{a^2-b^2}=\sqrt{\left(\frac{7}{4}\right)^2-\left(\frac{7}{5}\right)^2}=\sqrt{\frac{441}{400}}=\frac{21}{20}$

The center is $(4,-3)$, the vertices are $\left(4,-3-\frac{7}{4}\right)=\left(4,-\frac{19}{4}\right)$ and $\left(4,-3+\frac{7}{4}\right)=\left(4,-\frac{5}{4}\right)$, and the foci are $\left(4,-3-\frac{21}{20}\right)=\left(4,-\frac{81}{20}\right)$ and $\left(4,-3+\frac{21}{20}\right)=\left(4,-\frac{39}{20}\right)$. Sketching the graph:

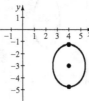

35. Solving the equation for y:

$$3x^2 + 7y^2 = 20$$
$$7y^2 = 20 - 3x^2$$
$$y^2 = \frac{20 - 3x^2}{7}$$
$$y = \pm\sqrt{\frac{20 - 3x^2}{7}}$$

Graphing the equation:

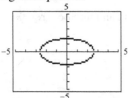

37. Solving the equation for y:

$$\frac{x^2}{6} + \frac{y^2}{11} = 1$$
$$11x^2 + 6y^2 = 66$$
$$6y^2 = 66 - 11x^2$$
$$y^2 = 11 - \frac{11x^2}{6}$$
$$y = \pm\sqrt{11 - \frac{11x^2}{6}}$$

Graphing the equation:

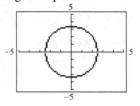

39. Solving the equation for y:

$$\frac{(x-1)^2}{5} + \frac{(y+3)^2}{6} = 1$$
$$\frac{(y+3)^2}{6} = 1 - \frac{(x-1)^2}{5}$$
$$(y+3)^2 = 6 - \frac{6(x-1)^2}{5}$$
$$y+3 = \pm\sqrt{6 - \frac{6(x-1)^2}{5}}$$
$$y = -3 \pm\sqrt{6 - \frac{6(x-1)^2}{5}}$$

Graphing the equation:

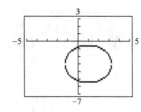

41. Since the vertex is to the right of the focus, the ellipse has a horizontal major axis: $\dfrac{x^2}{a^2}+\dfrac{y^2}{b^2}=1$.

Vertex: $(6,0)=(a,k) \Rightarrow a=6 \Rightarrow a^2=36$

Foci: $(3,0)=(c,k) \Rightarrow c=3 \Rightarrow c^2=9$

Finding b: $c^2=a^2-b^2 \Rightarrow b^2=a^2-c^2=36-9=27$

The equation is: $\dfrac{x^2}{36}+\dfrac{y^2}{27}=1$

43. The y-coordinate of the focus is 0, so they lie on the x-axis; hence the major axis is horizontal: $\dfrac{x^2}{a^2}+\dfrac{y^2}{b^2}=1$.

Finding b: $2b=2\sqrt{39} \Rightarrow b=\sqrt{39} \Rightarrow b^2=39$

Foci: $(5,0)=(c,k) \Rightarrow c=5 \Rightarrow c^2=25$

Finding a: $c^2=a^2-b^2 \Rightarrow a^2=c^2+b^2=25+39=64$

The equation is: $\dfrac{x^2}{64}+\dfrac{y^2}{39}=1$

45. The major axis is vertical: $\dfrac{x^2}{b^2}+\dfrac{y^2}{a^2}=1$

Finding b: $2b=7 \Rightarrow b=\dfrac{7}{2} \Rightarrow b^2=\dfrac{49}{4}$

Finding a: $2a=9 \Rightarrow a=\dfrac{9}{2} \Rightarrow a^2=\dfrac{81}{4}$

The equation is: $\dfrac{x^2}{\frac{49}{4}}+\dfrac{y^2}{\frac{81}{4}}=1 \Rightarrow \dfrac{4x^2}{49}+\dfrac{4y^2}{81}=1$

47. Endpoint of minor axis on the x-axis $\Rightarrow$ major axis is vertical: $\dfrac{x^2}{b^2}+\dfrac{y^2}{a^2}=1$

Endpoint of minor axis $(2,0) \Rightarrow b=2 \Rightarrow b^2=4$

Finding a: $2a=18 \Rightarrow a=9 \Rightarrow a^2=81$

The equation is: $\dfrac{x^2}{4}+\dfrac{y^2}{81}=1$

49. The y-coordinate of the vertex and focus is 4, so the major axis coincides with the horizontal line $y=4$ and

is therefore horizontal: $\dfrac{(x-h)^2}{a^2}+\dfrac{(y-k)^2}{b^2}=1$

The center is $(-2,4) \Rightarrow h=-2, k=4$

Vertex: $(-6,4)$ is 4 units left of center $\Rightarrow a=4; a^2=16$

Focus: $(1,4)$ is 3 units right of center $\Rightarrow c=3; c^2=9$

Finding b: $c^2=a^2-b^2 \Rightarrow b^2=a^2-c^2=16-9=7$

The equation is: $\dfrac{(x+2)^2}{16}+\dfrac{(y-4)^2}{7}=1$

51. The *x*-coordinate of each vertex and focus is –3, so they lie on the vertical line $x = -3$; hence the major axis is vertical:

$$\frac{(x-h)^2}{b^2} + \frac{(y-k)^2}{a^2} = 1$$

Center = midpoint of foci: $\left(\frac{-3+(-3)}{2}, \frac{4+(-2)}{2}\right) = (-3, 1)$

The distance from center to vertex: $a = \sqrt{(-3-(-3))^2 + (4-1)^2} = 4$ and $a^2 = 9$

The distance from center to foci: $c = \sqrt{(-3-(-3))^2 + (3-1)^2} = 2$ and $c^2 = 4$

Finding *b*: $c^2 = a^2 - b^2 \Rightarrow b^2 = a^2 - c^2 = 9 - 4 = 5$

The equation is: $\dfrac{(x+3)^2}{5} + \dfrac{(y-1)^2}{9} = 1$

53. The *x*-coordinate of each vertex and focus is 4, so they line on the vertical line $x = 4$; hence the major axis is vertical:

$$\frac{(x-h)^2}{b^2} + \frac{(y-k)^2}{a^2} = 1$$

Center = midpoint of foci: $\left(\frac{4+4}{2}, \frac{1+(-3)}{2}\right) = (4, -1)$

Major axis length 8: $2a = 8 \Rightarrow a = 4;\ a^2 = 16$

The distance from center to foci: $c = \sqrt{(4-4)^2 + (-1-1)^2} = 2;\ c^2 = 4$

Finding *b*: $c^2 = a^2 - b^2 \Rightarrow b^2 = a^2 - c^2 = 16 - 4 = 12$

The equation is: $\dfrac{(x-4)^2}{12} + \dfrac{(y+1)^2}{16} = 1$

55. Endpoint of minor axis is above the center so the major axis has to be horizontal: $\dfrac{(x-h)^2}{a^2} + \dfrac{(y-k)^2}{b^2} = 1$

Center: $(7, -8) \Rightarrow h = 7, k = -8$

Endpoint of minor axis $(7, -4)$: $b = \sqrt{(7-7)^2 + (-8-(-4))^2} = 4;\ b^2 = 16$

Major axis length 12: $2a = 12 \Rightarrow a = 6;\ a^2 = 36$

The equation is: $\dfrac{(x-7)^2}{36} + \dfrac{(y+8)^2}{16} = 1$

57. Major axis length 9: $2a = 9 \Rightarrow a = \dfrac{9}{2};\ a^2 = \dfrac{81}{4}$

Minor axis length 5: $2b = 5 \Rightarrow b = \dfrac{5}{2};\ b^2 = \dfrac{25}{4}$

The two equations are: $\dfrac{x^2}{\frac{81}{4}} + \dfrac{y^2}{\frac{25}{4}} = 1 \Rightarrow \dfrac{4x^2}{81} + \dfrac{4y^2}{25} = 1;\ \dfrac{x^2}{\frac{25}{4}} + \dfrac{y^2}{\frac{81}{4}} = 1 \Rightarrow \dfrac{4x^2}{25} + \dfrac{4y^2}{81} = 1$

59. Major axis length 12: $2a = 12$; $a = 6$; $a^2 = 36$

Minor axis length 8: $2b = 8$; $b = 4$; $b^2 = 16$

Going 4 units left from the minor axis endpoint gives a center of $(5-4,0) = (1,0)$ and a vertical major axis.

Equation: $\dfrac{(x-1)^2}{16} + \dfrac{y^2}{36} = 1$

Going 4 units right of the minor axis endpoint gives a center of $(5+4,0) = (9,0)$ and a vertical major axis.

Equation: $\dfrac{(x-9)^2}{16} + \dfrac{y^2}{36} = 1$

61. Using $a = 6$ and $b = 2.5$, finding c: $c = \sqrt{a^2 - b^2} = \sqrt{(6)^2 - (2.5)^2} = \sqrt{29.75}$

The coordinates of the foci are $\left(-\sqrt{29.75}, 0\right)$ and $\left(\sqrt{29.75}, 0\right)$.

63. Using the major axis length of 477,736:

$2a = 477,736$

$a = 238,868$

Using the minor axis length of 477,078:

$2b = 477,078$

$b = 238,539$

Finding c: $c = \sqrt{a^2 - b^2} = \sqrt{(238,868)^2 - (238,539)^2} = \sqrt{157,066,903} \approx 12,532.6$

Assuming the center of the moon's orbit is the origin, the endpoints of the orbits major axis are:

$(12,532.6, 0), (-12,532.6, 0)$

The shortest distance is therefore: $a - c = 238,868 - 12,532.6 \approx 226,335$ miles

The longest distance is therefore: $a + c = 238,868 + 12,532.6 \approx 251,401$ miles

65. Since the foci are 20 feet apart:

$2c = 20$

$c = 10$

Since the shorter dimension is 12 feet:

$2b = 12$

$b = 6$

Finding a: $a = \sqrt{c^2 + b^2} = \sqrt{(10)^2 - (6)^2} = \sqrt{136} = 2\sqrt{34}$

The greatest distance is therefore: $2 \cdot 2\sqrt{34} = 4\sqrt{34}$ feet

67. Assume the center of the hole is at the origin.

Foci 12 feet apart $\Rightarrow c = 6$; foci located at $(-6,0), (6,0)$

Minor axis 8 feet long $\Rightarrow b = 4$; one endpoint of minor axis at $(0,4)$

Finding the distance from a focus to the endpoint of the diameter:

$d = \sqrt{(-6-0)^2 + (0-4)^2} + \sqrt{(6-0)^2 + (0-4)^2} = \sqrt{36+16} + \sqrt{36+16} = 2\sqrt{52} = 2 \cdot 2\sqrt{13} = 4\sqrt{13}$ feet

69. The distance from the center of one endpoint of the major axis is:

$a^2 = 16$

$a = 4$

The distance from the center of one endpoint of the minor axis is:

$b^2 = 9$

$b = 3$

Therefore the required distance is: $D = \sqrt{4^2 + 3^2} = \sqrt{25} = 5$

71. Let (x,y) be an arbitrary point. Using the distance formula:

$$\sqrt{(x+3)^2 + y^2} + \sqrt{(x-3)^2 + y^2} = 8$$

$$\sqrt{(x+3)^2 + y^2} = 8 - \sqrt{(x-3)^2 + y^2}$$

$$(x+3)^2 + y^2 = 64 - 16\sqrt{(x-3)^2 + y^2} + (x-3)^2 + y^2$$

$$x^2 + 6x + 9 = 64 - 16\sqrt{(x-3)^2 + y^2} + x^2 - 6x + 9$$

$$12x - 64 = -16\sqrt{(x-3)^2 + y^2}$$

$$3x - 16 = -4\sqrt{(x-3)^2 + y^2}$$

$$9x^2 - 96x + 256 = 16\left(x^2 - 6x + 9 + y^2\right)$$

$$7x^2 + 16y^2 = 112$$

$$\frac{x^2}{16} + \frac{y^2}{7} = 1$$

73. Given $a = b$, then:

$$\frac{x^2}{a^2} + \frac{y^2}{a^2} = 1$$

$$x^2 + y^2 = a^2$$

$$y^2 = a^2 - x^2$$

$$y = \pm\sqrt{a^2 - x^2}$$

The curve is a circle.

9.3 The Hyperbola

1. Using the distance formula: $d = \sqrt{(c-w)^2 + (d-v)^2}$

3. Using the distance formula: $d = \sqrt{(-3-0)^2 + (5-5)^2} = \sqrt{9} = 3$

5. Completing the square: $x^2 + 22x + \left[\frac{1}{2}(22)\right]^2 = x^2 + 22x + (11)^2 = x^2 + 22x + 121$

7. The correct graph is d.

9. The correct graph is c.

11. The transverse axis is horizontal with $a = 4$ and $b = 3$. Finding c: $c = \sqrt{a^2 + b^2} = \sqrt{16+9} = \sqrt{25} = 5$

The center is $(0,0)$, the vertices are $(-4,0)$ and $(4,0)$, the foci are $(-5,0)$ and $(5,0)$, and the asymptotes

are $y = -\frac{3}{4}x$, $y = \frac{3}{4}x$. Sketching the graph:

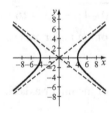

13. The transverse axis is vertical with $a = 3$ and $b = 4$. Finding c: $c = \sqrt{a^2 + b^2} = \sqrt{9 + 16} = \sqrt{25} = 5$

The center is $(0,0)$, the vertices are $(0,-3)$ and $(0,3)$, the foci are $(0,-5)$ and $(0,5)$, and the asymptotes

are $y = -\dfrac{3}{4}x$, $y = \dfrac{3}{4}x$. Sketching the graph:

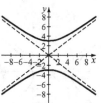

15. The transverse axis is vertical with $a = 8$ and $b = 6$. Finding c: $c = \sqrt{a^2 + b^2} = \sqrt{64 + 36} = \sqrt{100} = 10$

The center is $(0,0)$, the vertices are $(0,-8)$ and $(0,8)$, the foci are $(0,-10)$ and $(0,10)$, and the asymptotes

are $y = -\dfrac{8}{6}x = -\dfrac{4}{3}x$, $y = \dfrac{8}{6}x = \dfrac{4}{3}x$. Sketching the graph:

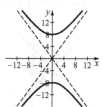

17. First write the equation as: $\dfrac{x^2}{9} - \dfrac{y^2}{9} = 1$

The transverse axis is horizontal with $a = 3$ and $b = 3$. Finding c: $c = \sqrt{a^2 + b^2} = \sqrt{9 + 9} = \sqrt{18} = 3\sqrt{2}$

The center is $(0,0)$, the vertices are $(-3,0)$ and $(3,0)$, the foci are $\left(-3\sqrt{2},0\right)$ and $\left(3\sqrt{2},0\right)$, and the asymptotes

are $y = -\dfrac{9}{9}x = -x$, $y = \dfrac{9}{9}x = x$. Sketching the graph:

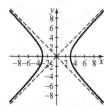

19. The transverse axis is horizontal with $a = 4$ and $b = 3$. Finding c: $c = \sqrt{a^2 + b^2} = \sqrt{16 + 9} = \sqrt{25} = 5$

The center is $(-3,-1)$, the vertices are $(-3-4,-1) = (-7,-1)$ and $(-3+4,-1) = (1,-1)$, the foci are

$(-3-5,-1) = (-8,-1)$ and $(-3+5,-1) = (2,-1)$, and the asymptotes are

$y = -\dfrac{3}{4}(x+3) - 1 = -\dfrac{3}{4}x - \dfrac{13}{4}$, $y = \dfrac{3}{4}(x+3) - 1 = \dfrac{3}{4}x + \dfrac{5}{4}$. Sketching the graph:

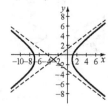

21. The transverse axis is horizontal with $a = 5$ and $b = 4$. Finding c: $c = \sqrt{a^2 + b^2} = \sqrt{25 + 16} = \sqrt{41}$

The center is $(-5, -1)$, the vertices are $(-5 - 5, -1) = (-10, -1)$ and $(-5 + 5, -1) = (0, -1)$, the foci are

$\left(-5 - \sqrt{41}, -1\right)$ and $\left(-5 + \sqrt{41}, -1\right)$, and the asymptotes are $y = -\dfrac{4}{5}(x + 5) - 1 = -\dfrac{4}{5}x - 5$, $y = \dfrac{4}{5}(x + 5) - 1 = \dfrac{4}{5}x + 3$.

Sketching the graph:

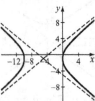

23. The transverse axis is vertical with $a = 1$ and $b = 1$. Finding c: $c = \sqrt{a^2 + b^2} = \sqrt{1 + 1} = \sqrt{2}$

The center is $(-4, 0)$, the vertices are $(-4, 0 - 1) = (-4, -1)$ and $(-4, 0 + 1) = (-4, 1)$, the foci are

$\left(-4, -\sqrt{2}\right)$ and $\left(-4, \sqrt{2}\right)$, and the asymptotes are $y = -(x + 4) = -x - 4$, $y = x + 4$. Sketching the graph:

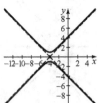

25. The transverse axis is vertical with $a = 3$ and $b = 5$. Finding c: $c = \sqrt{a^2 + b^2} = \sqrt{9 + 25} = \sqrt{34}$

The center is $(-1, 3)$, the vertices are $(-1, 3 - 3) = (-1, 0)$ and $(-1, 3 + 3) = (-1, 6)$, the foci are

$\left(-1, 3 - \sqrt{34}\right)$ and $\left(-1, 3 + \sqrt{34}\right)$, and the asymptotes are $y = -\dfrac{3}{5}(x + 1) + 3 = -\dfrac{3}{5}x + \dfrac{12}{5}$, $y = \dfrac{3}{5}(x + 1) + 3 = \dfrac{3}{5}x + \dfrac{18}{5}$.

Sketching the graph:

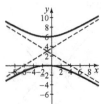

27. The transverse axis is horizontal with $a = 12$ and $b = 5$. Finding c: $c = \sqrt{a^2 + b^2} = \sqrt{144 + 25} = \sqrt{169} = 13$

The center is $(-2, 3)$, the vertices are $(-2 - 12, 3) = (-14, 3)$ and $(-2 + 12, 3) = (10, 3)$, the foci are

$(-2 - 13, 3) = (-15, 3)$ and $(-2 + 13, 3) = (11, 3)$, and the asymptotes are

$y = -\dfrac{5}{12}(x + 2) + 3 = -\dfrac{5}{12}x + \dfrac{13}{6}$, $y = \dfrac{5}{12}(x + 2) + 3 = \dfrac{5}{12}x + \dfrac{23}{6}$. Sketching the graph:

29. Converting the equation to standard form:

$$36x^2 - 16y^2 = 225$$

$$\frac{36x^2}{225} - \frac{16y^2}{225} = 1$$

$$\frac{x^2}{\frac{25}{4}} - \frac{y^2}{\frac{225}{16}} = 1$$

The transverse axis is horizontal with $a = \frac{5}{2}$ and $b = \frac{15}{4}$. Finding c: $c = \sqrt{a^2 + b^2} = \sqrt{\frac{25}{4} + \frac{225}{16}} = \sqrt{\frac{325}{16}} = \frac{5\sqrt{13}}{4}$

The center is $(0,0)$, the vertices are $\left(0 - \frac{5}{2}, 0\right) = \left(-\frac{5}{2}, 0\right)$ and $\left(0 + \frac{5}{2}, 0\right) = \left(\frac{5}{2}, 0\right)$, the foci are

$\left(0 - \frac{5\sqrt{13}}{4}, 0\right) = \left(-\frac{5\sqrt{13}}{4}, 0\right)$ and $\left(0 + \frac{5\sqrt{13}}{4}, 0\right) = \left(\frac{5\sqrt{13}}{4}, 0\right)$, and the asymptotes are

$y = -\frac{15/4}{5/2}x = -\frac{3}{2}x$, $y = \frac{15/4}{5/2}x = \frac{3}{2}x$. Sketching the graph:

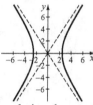

31. Converting the equation to standard form by completing the square:

$$9x^2 + 54x - y^2 = 0$$

$$9\left(x^2 + 6x\right) - y^2 = 0$$

$$9\left(x^2 + 6x + 9\right) - y^2 = 81$$

$$9(x + 3)^2 - y^2 = 81$$

$$\frac{(x + 3)^2}{9} - \frac{y^2}{81} = 1$$

The transverse axis is horizontal with $a = 3$ and $b = 9$. Finding c: $c = \sqrt{a^2 + b^2} = \sqrt{9 + 81} = \sqrt{90} = 3\sqrt{10}$

The center is $(-3, 0)$, the vertices are $(-3 - 3, 0) = (-6, 0)$ and $(-3 + 3, 0) = (0, 0)$, the foci are

$\left(-3 - 3\sqrt{10}, 0\right)$ and $\left(-3 + 3\sqrt{10}, 0\right)$, and the asymptotes are $y = -\frac{9}{3}(x + 3) = -3x - 9$, $y = \frac{9}{3}(x + 3) = 3x + 9$.

Sketching the graph:

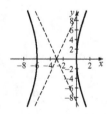

33. Converting the equation to standard form by completing the square:
$$8x^2 - 32x - y^2 - 6y = 41$$
$$8(x^2 - 4x) - (y^2 + 6y) = 41$$
$$8(x^2 - 4x + 4) - (y^2 + 6y + 9) = 41 + 32 - 9$$
$$8(x - 2)^2 - (y + 3)^2 = 64$$
$$\frac{(x - 2)^2}{8} - \frac{(y + 3)^2}{64} = 1$$

The transverse axis is horizontal with $a = 2\sqrt{2}$ and $b = 8$. Finding c: $c = \sqrt{a^2 + b^2} = \sqrt{8 + 64} = \sqrt{72} = 6\sqrt{2}$

The center is $(2, -3)$, the vertices are $(2 - 2\sqrt{2}, -3)$ and $(2 + 2\sqrt{2}, -3)$, the foci are

$(2 - 6\sqrt{2}, -3)$ and $(2 + 6\sqrt{2}, -3)$, and the asymptotes are:

$$y = -\frac{8}{2\sqrt{2}}(x - 2) - 3 = -2\sqrt{2}(x - 2) - 3 = -2\sqrt{2}x + 4\sqrt{2} - 3$$

$$y = \frac{8}{2\sqrt{2}}(x - 2) - 3 = 2\sqrt{2}(x - 2) - 3 = 2\sqrt{2}x - 4\sqrt{2} - 3$$

Sketching the graph:

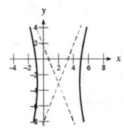

35. Vertices and foci on the x-axis $\Rightarrow$ horizontal transverse axis: $\dfrac{(x - h)^2}{a^2} - \dfrac{(y - k)^2}{b^2} = 1$

Center = midpoint of vertices: $(0, 0)$

Vertex $(3, 0) \Rightarrow a = 3;\ a^2 = 9$

Foci $(4, 0) \Rightarrow c = 4;\ c^2 = 16$

Finding b: $c^2 = a^2 + b^2 \Rightarrow b^2 = c^2 - a^2 = 16 - 9 = 7$

The equation is: $\dfrac{x^2}{9} - \dfrac{y^2}{7} = 1$

37. Vertices and foci on the x-axis $\Rightarrow$ horizontal transverse axis: $\dfrac{(x - h)^2}{a^2} - \dfrac{(y - k)^2}{b^2} = 1$

Center = midpoint of foci: $(0, 0)$

Foci $(4, 0) \Rightarrow c = 4;\ c^2 = 16$

Asymptote: $y = \pm 2x = \pm \dfrac{b}{a}x \Rightarrow \dfrac{b}{a} = 2 \Rightarrow b = 2a$

Finding a: $c^2 = a^2 + b^2 \Rightarrow 16 = a^2 + (2a)^2 = 5a^2 \Rightarrow a^2 = \dfrac{16}{5}$

Finding b: $b^2 = 4a^2 = 4\left(\dfrac{16}{5}\right) = \dfrac{64}{5}$

The equation is: $\dfrac{x^2}{\frac{16}{5}} - \dfrac{y^2}{\frac{64}{5}} = 1 \Rightarrow \dfrac{5x^2}{16} - \dfrac{5y^2}{64} = 1$

39. Foci on the x-axis $\Rightarrow$ horizontal transverse axis: $\dfrac{(x-h)^2}{a^2} - \dfrac{(y-k)^2}{b^2} = 1$

Center = midpoint of foci: $(0,0)$

Foci $(2,0) \Rightarrow c = 2;\ c^2 = 4$

Distance from $(2,3)$ to $(2,0)$: $d_1 = \sqrt{(2-2)^2 + (3-0)^2} = 3$

Distance from $(2,3)$ to $(-2,0)$: $d_2 = \sqrt{(2-(-2))^2 + (3-0)^2} = \sqrt{16+9} = 5$

Finding a: $|d_2 - d_1| = 2a \Rightarrow |5-3| = 2a \Rightarrow 2 = 2a \Rightarrow a = 1;\ a^2 = 1$

Finding b: $c^2 = a^2 + b^2 \Rightarrow 4 = 1 + b^2 \Rightarrow b^2 = 3$

The equation is: $\dfrac{x^2}{1} - \dfrac{y^2}{3} = 1$

41. Vertices on the x-axis $\Rightarrow$ horizontal transverse axis: $\dfrac{(x-h)^2}{a^2} - \dfrac{(y-k)^2}{b^2} = 1$

Center = midpoint of vertices: $(0,0)$

Vertex $(4,0) \Rightarrow a = 4;\ a^2 = 16$

Passes through $(8,2)$: $\dfrac{8^2}{16} - \dfrac{2^2}{b^2} = 1$

$$4 - \dfrac{4}{b^2} = 1$$

$$-\dfrac{4}{b^2} = -3 \Rightarrow b^2 = \dfrac{4}{3}$$

The equation is: $\dfrac{x^2}{16} - \dfrac{y^2}{\frac{4}{3}} = 1 \Rightarrow \dfrac{x^2}{16} - \dfrac{3y^2}{4} = 1$

43. The foci are located on the line $x = -3$ so the transverse axis is vertical: $\dfrac{(y-k)^2}{a^2} - \dfrac{(x-h)^2}{b^2} = 1$

Center = midpoint of foci: $\left(\dfrac{-3+(-3)}{2}, \dfrac{-6+(-2)}{2}\right) = (-3,-4)$

Distance from $(-3,-6)$ to $(-3,-4)$: $c = -4 - (-6) = 2$

Slope of asymptote = 1: $\dfrac{a}{b} = 1 \Rightarrow a = b$

Finding a: $c^2 = a^2 + b^2 \Rightarrow 4 = 2a^2 \Rightarrow a^2 = b^2 = 2$

The equation is: $\dfrac{(y+4)^2}{2} - \dfrac{(x+3)^2}{2} = 1$

45. The vertices are located on the line $y = -2$ so the transverse axis is horizontal: $\dfrac{(x-h)^2}{a^2} - \dfrac{(y-k)^2}{b^2} = 1$

Center = midpoint of vertices: $\left(\dfrac{5+1}{2}, \dfrac{-2+(-2)}{2}\right) = (3, -2)$

Distance from $(5, -2)$ to $(3, -2)$: $a = 5 - 3 = 2$

Slope of asymptote = $\dfrac{\sqrt{5}}{2}$: $\dfrac{b}{a} = \dfrac{5}{2} \Rightarrow b = \dfrac{5}{2}a = \dfrac{5}{2}(2) = 5$

The equation is: $\dfrac{(x-3)^2}{4} - \dfrac{(y+2)^2}{25} = 1$

47. The center and focus are located on the line $y = -4$ so the transverse axis is horizontal: $\dfrac{(x-h)^2}{a^2} - \dfrac{(y-k)^2}{b^2} = 1$

Center: $(1, -4)$

Transverse axis length 10: $2a = 10 \Rightarrow a = 5$

Distance from focus to center: $c = 9 - 1 = 8$

Finding b: $c^2 = a^2 + b^2 \Rightarrow 64 = 25 + b^2 \Rightarrow b^2 = 39$

The equation is: $\dfrac{(x-1)^2}{25} - \dfrac{(y+4)^2}{39} = 1$

49. Solving the equation for y:

$$x^2 - 5y^2 = 10$$

$$-5y^2 = 10 - x^2$$

$$y^2 = \dfrac{x^2}{5} - 2$$

$$y = \pm\sqrt{\dfrac{x^2}{5} - 2}$$

Graphing the equation:

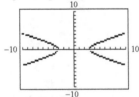

51. Solving the equation for y:

$$\dfrac{x^2}{5} - \dfrac{y^2}{7} = 1$$

$$-\dfrac{y^2}{7} = 1 - \dfrac{x^2}{5}$$

$$y^2 = \dfrac{7x^2}{5} - 7$$

$$y = \pm\sqrt{\dfrac{7x^2}{5} - 7}$$

Graphing the equation:

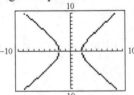

53. Solving the equation for y:

$$\dfrac{(x+1)^2}{15} - \dfrac{(y-3)^2}{3} = 1$$

$$\dfrac{(y-3)^2}{3} = 1 - \dfrac{(x+1)^2}{15}$$

$$(y-3)^2 = 3 - \dfrac{(x+1)^2}{5}$$

$$y - 3 = \pm\sqrt{3 - \dfrac{(x+1)^2}{5}}$$

$$y = 3 \pm \sqrt{3 - \dfrac{(x+1)^2}{5}}$$

Graphing the equation:

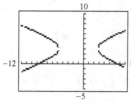

55. Transverse axis length 12: $2a = 12 \Rightarrow a = 6$; $a^2 = 36$

Slope of asymptote = 4: $\dfrac{b}{a} = 4 \Rightarrow b = 4a = 24$; $b^2 = 576$ or $\dfrac{a}{b} = 4 \Rightarrow a = 4b = 6 \Rightarrow b = \dfrac{3}{2}$; $b^2 = \dfrac{9}{4}$

The equations are: $\dfrac{x^2}{36} - \dfrac{y^2}{576} = 1$; $\dfrac{y^2}{36} - \dfrac{4x^2}{9} = 1$

57. Transverse axis length 6: $2a = 6 \Rightarrow a = 3$; $a^2 = 9$

Transverse axis vertical: $\dfrac{(y-k)^2}{a^2} - \dfrac{(x-h)^2}{b^2} = 1$

Distance from focus to nearest vertex = 4: $c - a = 4 \Rightarrow c = 4 + a = 7$; $c^2 = 49$

Finding b: $c^2 = a^2 + b^2 \Rightarrow 49 = 9 + b^2 \Rightarrow b^2 = 40$

Vertex $(h, k \pm a) = (-1, 1) \Rightarrow h = -1$ and $k \pm a = 1 \Rightarrow k = 1 \pm a = 1 \pm 3 = 4$ or -2

Center: $(-1, -2)$ or $(-1, 4)$

The equations are: $\dfrac{(y+2)^2}{9} - \dfrac{(x+1)^2}{40} = 1$; $\dfrac{(y-4)^2}{9} - \dfrac{(x+1)^2}{40} = 1$

59. Length of transverse axis = 4: $2a = 4 \Rightarrow a = 2$; $a^2 = 4$

Horizontal transverse axis and slope of asymptote = 1: $\dfrac{a}{b} = 1 \Rightarrow a = b = 2 \Rightarrow b^2 = 4$

The equation is: $\dfrac{x^2}{4} - \dfrac{y^2}{4} = 1 \Rightarrow x^2 - y^2 = 4$

Base 2 inches below the transverse axis $\Rightarrow y = -2$: $x^2 - (-2)^2 = 4 \Rightarrow x^2 = 8 \Rightarrow x = \pm 2\sqrt{2}$

The width is: $2(2\sqrt{2}) = 4\sqrt{2}$ inches

61. Using $c = 13$ million and $a = 5$ million, we can find b:

$c^2 = a^2 + b^2$

$b^2 = 169 - 25 = 144$ million^2

The equation is: $\dfrac{x^2}{25,000,000,000,000} - \dfrac{y^2}{144,000,000,000,000} = 1$

63. Solving the inequality:

$\dfrac{16x^2 - 144}{9} \geq 0$

$16x^2 - 144 \geq 0$

$16(x^2 - 9) \geq 0$

$16(x+3)(x-3) \geq 0$

This inequality is true on the domain $(-\infty, -3] \cup [3, \infty)$.

65. Let l represent the length of the diagonal. Therefore:

$l^2 = (2a)^2 + (2b)^2 = 4a^2 + 4b^2 = 4(a^2 + b^2) = 4c^2$

$l = \sqrt{4c^2} = 2c$

67. Solving for a: $6 = 2a \Rightarrow a = 3$; $a^2 = 9$

Distance between given points: $2c = 2 - (-8) = 10 \Rightarrow c = 5$

Finding b: $c^2 = a^2 + b^2 \Rightarrow 25 = 9 + b^2 \Rightarrow b^2 = 16$

Midpoint of the two points (foci) is the center: $(3, -3)$

Foci on vertical line $x = 3 \Rightarrow$ horizontal transverse axis

The equation is: $\dfrac{(y+3)^2}{9} - \dfrac{(x-3)^2}{16} = 1$

69. $xy = 10 > 0 \Rightarrow x, y$ have the same sign, which occurs in quadrants I and III, so the hyperbola lies in these quadrants. $xy = -10 < 0 \Rightarrow x, y$ have different signs, which occur in quadrants II and IV, so this hyperbola lies in these quadrants.

9.4 Rotation of Axes; General Form of Conic Sections

1. Converting the coordinates:
$$x = u\cos\theta - v\sin\theta = 1\cos\frac{\pi}{4} - 0\sin\frac{\pi}{4} = \frac{\sqrt{2}}{2}$$
$$y = u\sin\theta + v\cos\theta = 1\sin\frac{\pi}{4} + 0\cos\frac{\pi}{4} = \frac{\sqrt{2}}{2}$$

The rotated point is: $\left(\dfrac{\sqrt{2}}{2}, \dfrac{\sqrt{2}}{2} \right)$

3. Converting the coordinates:
$$x = u\cos\theta - v\sin\theta = 1\cos\frac{\pi}{3} - 2\sin\frac{\pi}{3} = \frac{1}{2} - \frac{2\sqrt{3}}{2}$$
$$y = u\sin\theta + v\cos\theta = 1\sin\frac{\pi}{3} + 2\cos\frac{\pi}{3} = \frac{\sqrt{3}}{2} + 1$$

The rotated point is: $\left(\dfrac{1 - 2\sqrt{3}}{2}, \dfrac{\sqrt{3} + 2}{2} \right)$

5. Converting the coordinates:
$$x = u\cos\theta - v\sin\theta = -2\cos\frac{\pi}{6} - 4\sin\frac{\pi}{6} = -2\left(\frac{\sqrt{3}}{2}\right) - 4\left(\frac{1}{2}\right) = -\sqrt{3} - 2$$
$$y = u\sin\theta + v\cos\theta = -2\sin\frac{\pi}{6} + 4\cos\frac{\pi}{6} = -2\left(\frac{1}{2}\right) + 4\left(\frac{\sqrt{3}}{2}\right) = -1 + 2\sqrt{3}$$

The rotated point is: $\left(-\sqrt{3} - 2, -1 + 2\sqrt{3} \right)$

7. Converting the coordinates:
$$x = u\cos\theta - v\sin\theta = -1\cos\frac{\pi}{4} - (-1)\sin\frac{\pi}{4} = -\frac{\sqrt{2}}{2} + \frac{\sqrt{2}}{2} = 0$$
$$y = u\sin\theta + v\cos\theta = -1\sin\frac{\pi}{4} + (-1)\cos\frac{\pi}{4} = -\frac{\sqrt{2}}{2} - \frac{\sqrt{2}}{2} = -\sqrt{2}$$

The rotated point is: $\left(0, -\sqrt{2} \right)$

9. Let $A = 3, B = 0, C = 0$: $B^2 - 4AC = 0^2 - 4(3)(0) = 0$

The conic is a parabola.

11. Let $A = 1, B = 0, C = 1$: $B^2 - 4AC = 0^2 - 4(1)(1) = -4 < 0$

The conic is an ellipse.

13. Let $A = 2, B = 2, C = -1$: $B^2 - 4AC = 2^2 - 4(2)(-1) = 12 > 0$

The conic is a hyperbola.

15. Let $A = 1, B = -2, C = 1$: $B^2 - 4AC = (-2)^2 - 4(1)(1) = 0$

The conic is a parabola.

17. $v^2 = 16u$ is a parabola with vertex at the origin. The vertex is: $(0, 0)$

19. $\dfrac{u^2}{1} + \dfrac{v^2}{4} = 1$ is an ellipse centered at the origin with major axis on the v-axis of length $2a = 2(2) = 4$.

The vertices are: $(0, -2), (0, 2)$

21. $\dfrac{u^2}{9} - \dfrac{v^2}{4} = 1$ is a hyperbola centered at the origin with transverse axis on the u-axis of length $2a = 2(3) = 6$.

The vertices are: $(-3, 0), (3, 0)$

23. $u^2 - 9v^2 = 36 \implies \dfrac{u^2}{36} - \dfrac{v^2}{9} = 1$

This is a hyperbola centered at the origin with transverse axis on the u-axis of length $2a = 2(6) = 12$.

The vertices are: $(-6, 0), (6, 0)$

25. **a.** Let $A = 0, B = 1, C = 0$: $B^2 - 4AC = 1^2 - 4(0)(0) = 1 > 0$

The conic is a hyperbola.

b. Finding the angle of rotation: $\cot 2\theta = \dfrac{A - C}{B} = 0 \implies 2\theta = \dfrac{\pi}{2} \implies \theta = \dfrac{\pi}{4}$

Finding the coordinate conversions:

$$x = u\cos\frac{\pi}{4} - v\sin\frac{\pi}{4} = \frac{\sqrt{2}}{2}u - \frac{\sqrt{2}}{2}v = \frac{\sqrt{2}}{2}(u - v)$$

$$y = u\sin\frac{\pi}{4} + v\cos\frac{\pi}{4} = \frac{\sqrt{2}}{2}u + \frac{\sqrt{2}}{2}v = \frac{\sqrt{2}}{2}(u + v)$$

Converting the equation:

$$xy = 4$$

$$\left[\frac{\sqrt{2}}{2}(u - v)\right]\left[\frac{\sqrt{2}}{2}(u + v)\right] = 4$$

$$\frac{1}{2}(u^2 - v^2) = 4$$

$$\frac{1}{2}u^2 - \frac{1}{2}v^2 = 4$$

$$\frac{u^2}{8} - \frac{v^2}{8} = 1$$

c. Finding a: $a^2 = 8 \Rightarrow a = 2\sqrt{2}$

The vertices are: $(u,v) = \left(-2\sqrt{2}, 0\right), \left(2\sqrt{2}, 0\right)$

Sketching the graph:

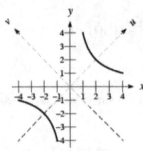

27. a. Let $A = 3, B = 10, C = 3$: $B^2 - 4AC = 10^2 - 4(3)(3) = 64 > 0$

The conic is a hyperbola.

b. Finding the angle of rotation: $\cot 2\theta = \dfrac{A-C}{B} = \dfrac{0}{10} = 0 \Rightarrow 2\theta = \dfrac{\pi}{2} \Rightarrow \theta = \dfrac{\pi}{4}$

Finding the coordinate conversions:

$$x = u\cos\frac{\pi}{4} - v\sin\frac{\pi}{4} = \frac{\sqrt{2}}{2}u - \frac{\sqrt{2}}{2}v = \frac{\sqrt{2}}{2}(u-v)$$

$$y = u\sin\frac{\pi}{4} + v\cos\frac{\pi}{4} = \frac{\sqrt{2}}{2}u + \frac{\sqrt{2}}{2}v = \frac{\sqrt{2}}{2}(u+v)$$

Simplifying parts of the equation:

$$3x^2 = 3\left[\frac{\sqrt{2}}{2}(u-v)\right]^2 = \frac{3}{2}\left(u^2 - 2uv + v^2\right) = \frac{3}{2}u^2 - 3uv + \frac{3}{2}v^2$$

$$10xy = 10\left[\frac{\sqrt{2}}{2}(u-v)\right]\left[\frac{\sqrt{2}}{2}(u+v)\right] = 5\left(u^2 - v^2\right) = 5u^2 - 5v^2$$

$$3y^2 = 3\left[\frac{\sqrt{2}}{2}(u+v)\right]^2 = \frac{3}{2}\left(u^2 + 2uv + v^2\right) = \frac{3}{2}u^2 + 3uv + \frac{3}{2}v^2$$

Converting the equation:

$$3x^2 + 10xy + 3y^2 - 8 = 0$$

$$\frac{3}{2}u^2 - 3uv + \frac{3}{2}v^2 + 5u^2 - 5v^2 + \frac{3}{2}u^2 + 3uv + \frac{3}{2}v^2 - 8 = 0$$

$$3u^2 + 5u^2 - 5v^2 + 3v^2 - 8 = 0$$

$$8u^2 - 2v^2 = 8$$

$$\frac{u^2}{1} - \frac{v^2}{4} = 1$$

c. Finding a: $a^2 = 1 \Rightarrow a = 1$

The vertices are: $(u,v) = (-1,0), (1,0)$

Sketching the graph:

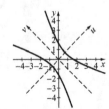

29. **a.** Let $A = 5, B = -8, C = 5$: $B^2 - 4AC = (-8)^2 - 4(5)(5) = -36 < 0$

The conic is an ellipse.

b. Finding the angle of rotation: $\cot 2\theta = \dfrac{A-C}{B} = \dfrac{0}{-8} = 0 \Rightarrow 2\theta = \dfrac{\pi}{2} \Rightarrow \theta = \dfrac{\pi}{4}$

Finding the coordinate conversions:

$$x = u\cos\frac{\pi}{4} - v\sin\frac{\pi}{4} = \frac{\sqrt{2}}{2}u - \frac{\sqrt{2}}{2}v = \frac{\sqrt{2}}{2}(u-v)$$

$$y = u\sin\frac{\pi}{4} + v\cos\frac{\pi}{4} = \frac{\sqrt{2}}{2}u + \frac{\sqrt{2}}{2}v = \frac{\sqrt{2}}{2}(u+v)$$

Simplifying parts of the equation:

$$5x^2 = 5\left[\frac{\sqrt{2}}{2}(u-v)\right]^2 = \frac{5}{2}(u^2 - 2uv + v^2) = \frac{5}{2}u^2 - 5uv + \frac{5}{2}v^2$$

$$-8xy = -8\left[\frac{\sqrt{2}}{2}(u-v)\right]\left[\frac{\sqrt{2}}{2}(u+v)\right] = -4(u^2 - v^2) = -4u^2 + 4v^2$$

$$5y^2 = 5\left[\frac{\sqrt{2}}{2}(u+v)\right]^2 = \frac{5}{2}(u^2 + 2uv + v^2) = \frac{5}{2}u^2 + 5uv + \frac{5}{2}v^2$$

Converting the equation:

$$5x^2 - 8xy + 5y^2 - 9 = 0$$

$$\frac{5}{2}u^2 - 5uv + \frac{5}{2}v^2 - 4u^2 + 4v^2 + \frac{5}{2}u^2 + 5uv + \frac{5}{2}v^2 - 9 = 0$$

$$5u^2 - 4u^2 + 4v^2 + 5v^2 - 9 = 0$$

$$u^2 + 9v^2 = 9$$

$$\frac{u^2}{9} + \frac{v^2}{1} = 1$$

c. Finding a: $a^2 = 9 \Rightarrow a = 3$

The vertices are: $(u, v) = (-3, 0), (3, 0)$

Sketching the graph:

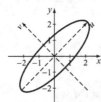

31. **a.** Let $A = 1, B = -10\sqrt{3}, C = 11$: $B^2 - 4AC = (-10\sqrt{3})^2 - 4(1)(11) = 256 > 0$

The conic is a hyperbola.

b. Finding the angle of rotation: $\cot 2\theta = \dfrac{A-C}{B} = \dfrac{1-11}{-10\sqrt{3}} = \dfrac{1}{\sqrt{3}} \Rightarrow 2\theta = \dfrac{\pi}{3} \Rightarrow \theta = \dfrac{\pi}{6}$

Finding the coordinate conversions:

$$x = u\cos\frac{\pi}{6} - v\sin\frac{\pi}{6} = \frac{\sqrt{3}}{2}u - \frac{1}{2}v = \frac{1}{2}(\sqrt{3}u - v)$$

$$y = u\sin\frac{\pi}{6} + v\cos\frac{\pi}{6} = \frac{1}{2}u + \frac{\sqrt{3}}{2}v = \frac{1}{2}(u + \sqrt{3}v)$$

Simplifying parts of the equation:

$$x^2 = \left[\frac{1}{2}\left(\sqrt{3}u - v\right)\right]^2 = \frac{1}{4}\left(3u^2 - 2\sqrt{3}uv + v^2\right) = \frac{3}{4}u^2 - \frac{\sqrt{3}}{2}uv + \frac{1}{4}v^2$$

$$-10\sqrt{3}xy = -10\sqrt{3}\left[\frac{1}{2}\left(\sqrt{3}u - v\right)\right]\left[\frac{1}{2}\left(u + \sqrt{3}v\right)\right] = -10\sqrt{3} \cdot \frac{1}{4}\left(\sqrt{3}u^2 + 3uv - uv - \sqrt{3}v^2\right) = -\frac{15}{2}u^2 - 5\sqrt{3}uv + \frac{15}{2}v^2$$

$$11y^2 = 11\left[\frac{1}{2}\left(u + \sqrt{3}v\right)\right]^2 = 11 \cdot \frac{1}{4}\left(u^2 + 2\sqrt{3}uv + 3v^2\right) = \frac{11}{4}u^2 + \frac{11\sqrt{3}}{2}uv + \frac{33}{4}v^2$$

Converting the equation:

$$x^2 - 10\sqrt{3}xy + 11y^2 - 16 = 0$$

$$\frac{3}{4}u^2 - \frac{\sqrt{3}}{2}uv + \frac{1}{4}v^2 - \frac{15}{2}u^2 - 5\sqrt{3}uv + \frac{15}{2}v^2 + \frac{11}{4}u^2 + \frac{11\sqrt{3}}{2}uv + \frac{33}{4}v^2 - 16 = 0$$

$$\frac{7}{2}u^2 - \frac{15}{2}u^2 + \frac{17}{2}v^2 + \frac{15}{2}v^2 - 16 = 0$$

$$-4u^2 + 16v^2 = 16$$

$$\frac{v^2}{1} - \frac{u^2}{4} = 1$$

c. Finding a: $a^2 = 1 \Rightarrow a = 1$

The vertices are: $(u, v) = (0, -1), (0, 1)$

Sketching the graph:

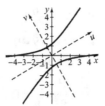

33. a. Let $A = 1$, $B = -2\sqrt{3}$, $C = 3$: $B^2 - 4AC = \left(-2\sqrt{3}\right)^2 - 4(1)(3) = 0$

The conic is a parabola.

b. Finding the angle of rotation: $\cot 2\theta = \dfrac{A - C}{B} = \dfrac{1 - 3}{-2\sqrt{3}} = \dfrac{1}{\sqrt{3}} \Rightarrow 2\theta = \dfrac{\pi}{3}; \theta = \dfrac{\pi}{6}$

Finding the coordinate conversions:

$$x = u\cos\frac{\pi}{6} - v\sin\frac{\pi}{6} = \frac{\sqrt{3}}{2}u - \frac{1}{2}v = \frac{1}{2}\left(\sqrt{3}u - v\right)$$

$$y = u\sin\frac{\pi}{6} + v\cos\frac{\pi}{6} = \frac{1}{2}u + \frac{\sqrt{3}}{2}v = \frac{1}{2}\left(u + \sqrt{3}v\right)$$

Simplifying parts of the equation:

$$x^2 = \left[\frac{1}{2}\left(\sqrt{3}u - v\right)\right]^2 = \frac{1}{4}\left(3u^2 - 2\sqrt{3}uv + v^2\right) = \frac{3}{4}u^2 - \frac{\sqrt{3}}{2}uv + \frac{1}{4}v^2$$

$$-2\sqrt{3}xy = -2\sqrt{3}\left[\frac{1}{2}\left(\sqrt{3}u - v\right)\right]\left[\frac{1}{2}\left(u + \sqrt{3}v\right)\right] = -2\sqrt{3}\cdot\frac{1}{4}\left(\sqrt{3}u^2 + 2uv - \sqrt{3}v^2\right) = -\frac{3}{2}u^2 - \sqrt{3}uv + \frac{3}{2}v^2$$

$$3y^2 = 3\left[\frac{1}{2}\left(u + \sqrt{3}v\right)\right]^2 = 3\cdot\frac{1}{4}\left(u^2 + 2\sqrt{3}uv + 3v^2\right) = \frac{3}{4}u^2 + \frac{3\sqrt{3}}{2}uv + \frac{9}{4}v^2$$

$$\frac{\sqrt{3}}{2}x = \frac{\sqrt{3}}{2}\left[\frac{1}{2}\left(\sqrt{3}u - v\right)\right] = \frac{3}{4}u - \frac{\sqrt{3}}{4}v$$

$$\frac{1}{2}y = \frac{1}{2}\left[\frac{1}{2}\left(u + \sqrt{3}v\right)\right] = \frac{1}{4}u + \frac{\sqrt{3}}{4}v$$

Converting the equation:

$$x^2 - 2\sqrt{3}xy + 3y^2 + \frac{\sqrt{3}}{2}x + \frac{1}{2}y = 0$$

$$\frac{3}{4}u^2 - \frac{\sqrt{3}}{2}uv + \frac{1}{4}v^2 - \frac{3}{2}u^2 - \sqrt{3}uv + \frac{3}{2}v^2 + \frac{3}{4}u^2 + \frac{3\sqrt{3}}{2}uv + \frac{9}{4}v^2 + \frac{3}{4}u - \frac{\sqrt{3}}{4}v + \frac{1}{4}u + \frac{\sqrt{3}}{4}v = 0$$

$$4v^2 + u = 0$$

$$v^2 = -\frac{1}{4}u$$

c. The vertex is: $(u, v) = (0, 0)$

Sketching the graph:

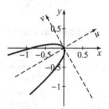

35. Starting with Equations (1) of the change-of-coordinates formula:

$$x = u\cos\theta - v\sin\theta$$

$$y = u\sin\theta + v\cos\theta$$

Multiplying the first equation by $-\sin\theta$ and the second equation by $\cos\theta$:

$$(-\sin\theta)x = (u\cos\theta - v\sin\theta)(-\sin\theta)$$

$$\underline{(\cos\theta)y = (u\sin\theta + v\cos\theta)(\cos\theta)}$$

$$-x\sin\theta + y\cos\theta = v\left(\sin^2\theta + \cos^2\theta\right)$$

$$v = -x\sin\theta + y\cos\theta$$

Multiplying the first equation by $\cos\theta$ and the second equation by $\sin\theta$:

$$(\cos\theta)x = (u\cos\theta - v\sin\theta)(\cos\theta)$$

$$\underline{(\sin\theta)y = (u\sin\theta + v\cos\theta)(\sin\theta)}$$

$$x\cos\theta + y\sin\theta = u\left(\cos^2\theta + \sin^2\theta\right)$$

$$u = x\cos\theta + y\sin\theta$$

This proves Equations (2).

37. Using $A = 1$ and $B = 1$: $B^2 - 4AC = 1 - 4C$

For a parabola, we have:

$$1 - 4C = 0$$

$$4C = 1$$

$$C = \frac{1}{4}$$

9.5 Polar Equations of Conic Sections

1. This statement is true.

3. The graph of $r = 5$ is a circle.

5. Since $e = 6$, this is the equation of a hyperbola.

7. Since $e = 1$, this is the equation of a parabola.

9. Since $e = 1$, this is the equation of a parabola.

11. Since $e = 0.6$, this is the equation of an ellipse.

13. Given: $r = \dfrac{1}{1 - \sin\theta} \Rightarrow e = 1$; parabola opening upward

Because the vertex lies on the ray $\theta = \dfrac{3\pi}{2}$, we have $r = \dfrac{1}{1 - \sin\dfrac{3\pi}{2}} = \dfrac{1}{2} \Rightarrow$ vertex $= \left(\dfrac{1}{2}, \dfrac{3\pi}{2}\right)$.

Two other points: $(1, 0), (1, \pi)$. Sketching the graph:

15. Given: $r = \dfrac{4}{1 + 2\cos\theta} \Rightarrow e = 2$; hyperbola with horizontal transverse axis

$\theta = 0$ gives $r = \dfrac{4}{1 + 2\cos 0} = \dfrac{4}{3}$ and $\theta = \pi$ gives $r = \dfrac{4}{1 + 2\cos\pi} = -4$.

Vertices: $\left(\dfrac{4}{3}, 0\right), (-4, \pi)$. Other points: $\left(4, \dfrac{\pi}{2}\right), \left(4, \dfrac{3\pi}{2}\right), \left(2, \dfrac{\pi}{3}\right), \left(2, \dfrac{5\pi}{3}\right)$. Sketching the graph:

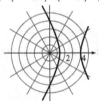

17. Given: $r = \dfrac{1}{1 - 0.5\cos\theta} \Rightarrow e = 0.5$; ellipse

$\theta = 0$ gives $r = \dfrac{1}{1 - 0.5\cos 0} = 2$ and $\theta = \pi$ gives $r = \dfrac{1}{1 - 0.5\cos\pi} = \dfrac{2}{3}$.

Vertices: $(2, 0), \left(\dfrac{2}{3}, \pi\right)$. Other points: $\left(1, \dfrac{\pi}{2}\right), \left(1, \dfrac{3\pi}{2}\right), \left(\dfrac{4}{3}, \dfrac{\pi}{3}\right), \left(\dfrac{4}{5}, \dfrac{2\pi}{3}\right)$. Sketching the graph:

19. Given: $r = \dfrac{6}{6+3\sin\theta} \Rightarrow e = \dfrac{1}{2}$; ellipse

$\theta = \dfrac{\pi}{2}$ gives $r = \dfrac{6}{6+3\sin\dfrac{\pi}{2}} = \dfrac{2}{3}$ and $\theta = \dfrac{3\pi}{2}$ gives $r = \dfrac{6}{6+3\sin\dfrac{3\pi}{2}} = 2$.

Vertices: $\left(\dfrac{2}{3}, \dfrac{\pi}{2}\right), \left(2, \dfrac{3\pi}{2}\right)$. Other points: $(1,0), (1,\pi), \left(\dfrac{4}{5}, \dfrac{\pi}{6}\right), \left(\dfrac{4}{4}, \dfrac{5\pi}{6}\right), \left(\dfrac{4}{3}, \dfrac{7\pi}{6}\right), \left(\dfrac{4}{3}, \dfrac{11\pi}{6}\right)$. Sketching the graph:

21. Given: $r = \dfrac{18}{6+12\cos\theta} \Rightarrow e = 2$; hyperbola with vertical transverse axis

$\theta = 0$ gives $r = \dfrac{18}{6+12\cos 0} = 1$ and $\theta = \pi$ gives $r = \dfrac{18}{6+12\cos\pi} = -3$.

Vertices: $(1,0), (-3,\pi)$. Other points: $\left(3, \dfrac{\pi}{2}\right), \left(3, \dfrac{3\pi}{2}\right), \left(\dfrac{3}{2}, \dfrac{\pi}{3}\right), \left(\dfrac{3}{2}, \dfrac{5\pi}{3}\right)$. Sketching the graph:

23. Given: $r = \dfrac{6}{6-8\sin\theta} \Rightarrow e = \dfrac{4}{3}$; hyperbola with horizontal transverse axis

$\theta = \dfrac{\pi}{2}$ gives $r = \dfrac{6}{6-8\sin\dfrac{\pi}{2}} = -3$ and $\theta = \dfrac{3\pi}{2}$ gives $r = \dfrac{6}{6-8\sin\dfrac{\pi}{2}} = \dfrac{3}{7}$.

Vertices: $\left(-3, \dfrac{\pi}{2}\right), \left(\dfrac{3}{7}, \dfrac{3\pi}{2}\right)$. Other points: $(1,0), \left(3, \dfrac{\pi}{6}\right), \left(3, \dfrac{5\pi}{6}\right), (1,\pi)$. Sketching the graph:

25. Given: $r = \dfrac{4}{3-3\cos\theta} \Rightarrow e = 1$; parabola opening to the right

Because the vertex lies on the ray $\theta = \pi$, we have $r = \dfrac{4}{3-3\cos\pi} = \dfrac{2}{3} \Rightarrow$ vertex $= \left(\dfrac{2}{3}, \pi\right)$.

Other points: $\left(\dfrac{8}{3}, \dfrac{\pi}{3}\right), \left(\dfrac{4}{3}, \dfrac{\pi}{2}\right), \left(\dfrac{8}{9}, \dfrac{2\pi}{3}\right), \left(\dfrac{4}{3}, \dfrac{3\pi}{2}\right)$. Sketching the graph:

27. Transforming the equation: $r = \dfrac{1}{1-\sin\left(\theta-\dfrac{\pi}{2}\right)} = \dfrac{1}{1-\sin\left[-\left(\dfrac{\pi}{2}-\theta\right)\right]} = \dfrac{1}{1+\sin\left(\dfrac{\pi}{2}-\theta\right)} = \dfrac{1}{1+\cos\theta}$

This is a parabola.

29. Transforming the equation: $r = \dfrac{1}{3+\sin(\theta+\pi)} = \dfrac{1}{3+(\sin\theta\cos\pi+\cos\theta\sin\pi)} = \dfrac{1}{3-\sin\theta} = \dfrac{\dfrac{1}{3}}{1-\dfrac{1}{3}\sin\theta}$

This is an ellipse.

31. Transforming the equation: $r = \dfrac{4}{1+4\cos(\theta+\pi)} = \dfrac{4}{1+4(\cos\theta\cos\pi-\sin\theta\sin\pi)} = \dfrac{4}{1-4\cos\theta}$

This is a hyperbola.

33. Sketching the graph of $r = \dfrac{\sqrt{2}}{1+\sin\theta}$:

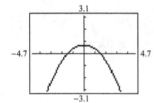

35. Sketching the graph of $r = \dfrac{5}{1-3\cos\left(\theta+\dfrac{\pi}{6}\right)}$:

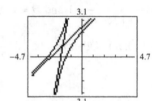

Note that the graph is a rotation.

37. A parabola $\Rightarrow e = 1$, and vertex $(1,\pi)$ and focus at the pole indicates a parabola that opens to the right:

$$r = \dfrac{ed}{1-e\cos\theta} = \dfrac{d}{1-\cos\theta}$$

Using $(1,\pi)$ we get: $1 = \dfrac{d}{1-\cos\pi} = \dfrac{d}{2} \Rightarrow d = 2$

Therefore the equation is $r = \dfrac{2}{1-\cos\theta}$.

39. Directrix $y = -3 \Rightarrow d = 3$ (assuming the focus is at the pole). Also, a horizontal directrix $\Rightarrow$ the vertices are at

$\theta = \dfrac{\pi}{2}$ and $\theta = \dfrac{3\pi}{2}$. Thus: $r = \dfrac{ed}{1-e\sin\theta} = \dfrac{\dfrac{3}{10}(3)}{1-\dfrac{3}{10}\sin\theta} = \dfrac{9}{10-3\sin\theta}$

9.6 Parametric Equations

1. Completing the table:

t	0	1	2	3
$x = t$	0	1	2	3
$y = t-2$	−2	−1	0	1

Sketching the graph:

3. Completing the table:

t	−1	0	1	2
$x = -t$	1	0	−1	−2
$y = 2t + 3$	1	3	5	7

Sketching the graph:

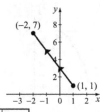

5. Completing the table:

t	−1	0	1	2
$x = -t$	1	0	−1	−2
$y = t^2 + 1$	2	1	2	5

Sketching the graph:

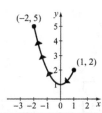

7. Completing the table:

t	−3	−2	−1	0	1	2	3
$x = t + 1$	−2	−1	0	1	2	3	4
$y = -2t^2 - 1$	−19	−9	−3	−1	−3	−9	−19

Sketching the graph:

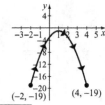

9. Completing the table:

t	−2	−1	0	1	2
$x = t^2$	4	1	0	1	4
$y = t$	−2	−1	0	1	2

Sketching the graph:

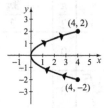

11. Solving for t:

$$x = t - 2$$
$$t = x + 2$$

Substituting:

$$y = -t^2$$
$$y = -(x+2)^2, \ -5 \le x \le 0$$

Completing the table:

t	-3	-2	-1	0	1	2
$x = t - 2$	-5	-4	-3	-2	-1	0
$y = -t^2$	-9	-4	-1	0	-1	-4

Sketching the graph:

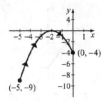

13. Solving for t:

$$x = e^{-t} = \frac{1}{e^t}$$

$$e^t = \frac{1}{x}$$

Substituting:

$$y = e^t$$

$$y = \frac{1}{x}, \, 0 < x \le 1$$

Completing the table:

t	0	1	2	3
$x = e^{-t}$	1	e^{-1}	e^{-2}	e^{-3}
$y = e^t$	1	e	e^2	e^3

Sketching the graph:

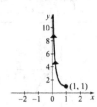

15. Substituting:

$$x^2 + y^2 = (3\cos t)^2 + (3\sin t)^2$$
$$x^2 + y^2 = 9\cos^2 t + 9\sin^2 t$$
$$x^2 + y^2 = 9(\cos^2 t + \sin^2 t)$$
$$x^2 + y^2 = 9, \, -3 \le x \le 3$$

Completing the table:

t	0	$\frac{\pi}{6}$	$\frac{\pi}{3}$	$\frac{\pi}{2}$	π	$\frac{3\pi}{2}$	2π
$x = 3\cos t$	3	$\frac{3\sqrt{3}}{2}$	$\frac{3}{2}$	0	-3	0	3
$y = 3\sin t$	0	$\frac{3}{2}$	$\frac{3\sqrt{3}}{2}$	3	0	-3	0

Sketching the graph:

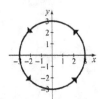

17. Solving for $\cos t$ and $\sin t$:

$$x = 3\cos t \;\Rightarrow\; \frac{x}{3} = \cos t$$

$$y = 4\sin t \;\Rightarrow\; \frac{y}{4} = \sin t$$

Substituting:

$$\left(\frac{x}{3}\right)^2 + \left(\frac{y}{4}\right)^2 = \cos^2 t + \sin^2 t$$

$$\frac{x^2}{9} + \frac{y^2}{16} = 1, \; -3 \le x \le 3$$

Completing the table:

t	0	$\dfrac{\pi}{6}$	$\dfrac{\pi}{3}$	$\dfrac{\pi}{2}$	π	$\dfrac{3\pi}{2}$	2π
$x = 3\cos t$	3	$\dfrac{3\sqrt{3}}{2}$	$\dfrac{3}{2}$	0	-3	0	3
$y = 4\sin t$	0	2	$2\sqrt{3}$	4	0	-4	0

Sketching the graph:

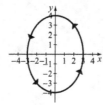

19. Substituting: $y = \sec t = \dfrac{1}{\cos t} \;\Rightarrow\; y = \dfrac{1}{x}, \; 0 < x \le 1$

Completing the table:

t	0	$\dfrac{\pi}{6}$	$\dfrac{\pi}{4}$	$\dfrac{\pi}{3}$	$\dfrac{\pi}{2}$
$x = \cos t$	1	$\dfrac{\sqrt{3}}{2}$	$\dfrac{\sqrt{2}}{2}$	$\dfrac{1}{2}$	0
$y = \sec t$	1	$\dfrac{2}{\sqrt{3}}$	$\sqrt{2}$	2	undefined

Sketching the graph:

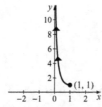

21. It is the same graph for both intervals. The point moves from $(1,1)$ to $(-1,1)$ and back again:

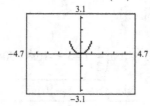

23. No, y will never be negative. Note that $-1 \le \cos t \le 1, 0 \le y \le 4$:

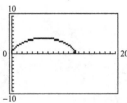

25. The common rectangular equation is: $y = x$

    a. Restrictions: $0 \le x \le 2, 0 \le y \le 2$ **b.** Restrictions: $0 \le x \le 4, 0 \le y \le 4$

27. The common rectangular equation is: $y = x + 1$

    a. Restrictions: $-1 \le x \le 2, 0 \le y \le 3$ **b.** Restrictions: $0 \le x \le 4, 1 \le y \le 5$

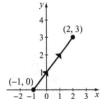   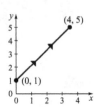

29.   **a.** Finding the parametric equations:

$$x = v_0 (\cos \theta) t = 120 (\cos 30°) t = 120 \left(\frac{\sqrt{3}}{2} \right) t = \left(60\sqrt{3} \right) t$$

$$y = -16t^2 + v_0 (\sin \theta) t + h = -16t^2 + 120 (\sin 30°) t + 0 = -16t^2 + 120 \left(\frac{1}{2} \right) t = -16t^2 + 60t$$

    b. Using the vertex formula: $t = \dfrac{-b}{2a} = \dfrac{-60}{2(-16)} \approx 1.875$ seconds

    The maximum height is: $y = -16(1.875)^2 + 60(1.875) \approx 56.25$ feet

    c. Finding when the ball hits the ground:

$$-16t^2 + 60t = 0$$
$$-4t(4t - 15) = 0$$
$$t = \frac{15}{4} = 3.75$$

    The horizontal distance traveled is: $x(3.75) = 60\sqrt{3}(3.75) \approx 390$ feet

31. Finding the parametric equations:

$$x = 100 (\cos 60°) t = 100 \left(\frac{\sqrt{3}}{2} \right) t = \left(50\sqrt{3} \right) t$$

$$y = -16t^2 + 100 (\sin 60°) t + 3 = -16t^2 + 100 \left(\frac{1}{2} \right) t + 3 = -16t^2 + 50t + 3$$

Finding when the ball hits the ground: $t = \dfrac{-50 \pm \sqrt{50^2 - 4(-16)(3)}}{2(-16)} = \dfrac{-50 - \sqrt{2692}}{-32} \approx 3.18$ seconds

The horizontal distance traveled is: $x(3.18) = 50\sqrt{3}(3.18) \approx 275$ feet

33. Substituting into the equation of the circle:
$$\left(a\cos bt\right)^2 + \left(a\sin bt\right)^2 = 100$$
$$a^2\cos^2 bt + a^2\sin^2 bt = 100$$
$$a^2\left(\cos^2 bt + \sin^2 bt\right) = 100$$
$$a^2 = 100$$
$$a = 10$$

Converting from radians to seconds:
$$1 \text{ rev} = 15 \text{ sec}$$
$$2\pi \text{ rad} = 15 \text{ sec}$$
$$\frac{2\pi}{15} \text{ rad} = 1 \text{ sec}$$

The parametric equations are: $x = 10\cos\left(\frac{2\pi}{15}t\right), y = 10\sin\left(\frac{2\pi}{15}t\right), 0 \le t \le 15$

35. Solving the equation:
$$x = v_0\left(\cos\theta\right)t$$
$$350 = v_0\left(\cos 30°\right)\cdot 4$$
$$v_0 = \frac{350}{4\cos 30°} \approx 101 \text{ ft/sec}$$

37. Sketching the motion:

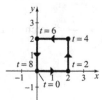

39. No. There is no value of t for which $x(t) = y(t) = 0$:

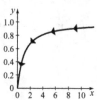

41. Despite the two having the common rectangular equation $y = x + 1$, the restrictions on x and y are different. For part (a), $0 \le x \le 1, 1 \le y \le 2$; for part (b), $-1 \le x \le 0, 0 \le y \le 1$.

Chapter 9 Review Exercises

1. Finding p:
$$4p = 12$$
$$p = 3$$

The vertex is $(0,0)$, the focus is $(0,3)$, and the directrix is $y = -3$. Sketching the graph:

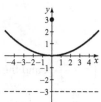

2. Finding p:
$$4p = 1$$
$$p = \frac{1}{4}$$

The vertex is $(7,1)$, the focus is $\left(7, 1+\dfrac{1}{4}\right) = \left(7, \dfrac{5}{4}\right)$, and the directrix is $y = 1 - \dfrac{1}{4} = \dfrac{3}{4}$. Sketching the graph:

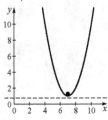

3. Finding p:
$$4p = 4$$
$$p = 1$$

The vertex is $(0,0)$, the focus is $(1,0)$, and the directrix is $x = -1$. Sketching the graph:

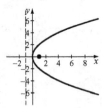

4. Finding p:
$$4p = -1$$
$$p = -\dfrac{1}{4}$$

The vertex is $(-2,4)$, the focus is $\left(-2 - \dfrac{1}{4}, 4\right) = \left(-\dfrac{9}{4}, 4\right)$, and the directrix is $x = -2 + \dfrac{1}{4} = -\dfrac{7}{4}$. Sketching the graph:

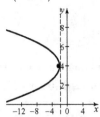

5. First complete the square:
$$x^2 - 6x = y$$
$$x^2 - 6x + 9 = y + 9$$
$$(x-3)^2 = y + 9$$

Finding p:
$$4p = 1$$
$$p = \dfrac{1}{4}$$

The vertex is $(3,-9)$, the focus is $\left(3, -9 + \dfrac{1}{4}\right) = \left(3, -\dfrac{35}{4}\right)$, and the directrix is $y = -9 - \dfrac{1}{4} = -\dfrac{37}{4}$. Sketching the graph:

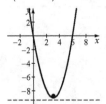

6. First complete the square:
$$x^2 + 2x + 3y = 5$$
$$\left(x^2 + 2x + 1\right) = 5 - 3y + 1$$
$$(x+1)^2 = -3y + 6$$
$$(x+1)^2 = -3(y-2)$$

Finding p:
$$4p = -3$$
$$p = -\frac{3}{4}$$

The vertex is $(-1,2)$, the focus is $\left(-1, 2 - \frac{3}{4}\right) = \left(-1, \frac{5}{4}\right)$, and the directrix is $y = 2 + \frac{3}{4} = \frac{11}{4}$. Sketching the graph:

7. First complete the square:
$$y^2 + 10y + 5x = 0$$
$$y^2 + 10y = -5x$$
$$\left(y^2 + 10y + 25\right) = -5x + 25$$
$$(y+5)^2 = -5(x-5)$$

Finding p:
$$4p = -5$$
$$p = -\frac{5}{4}$$

The vertex is $(5,-5)$, the focus is $\left(5 - \frac{5}{4}, -5\right) = \left(\frac{15}{4}, -5\right)$, and the directrix is $x = 5 + \frac{5}{4} = \frac{25}{4}$. Sketching the graph:

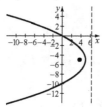

8. First complete the square:
$$y^2 - 8y + 4 = 4x$$
$$y^2 - 8y = 4x - 4$$
$$y^2 - 8y + 16 = 4x - 4 + 16$$
$$(y-4)^2 = 4x + 12$$
$$(y-4)^2 = 4(x+3)$$

Finding p:
$$4p = 4$$
$$p = 1$$

The vertex is $(-3,4)$, the focus is $(-3+1,4)=(-2,4)$, and the directrix is $x=-3-1=-4$. Sketching the graph:

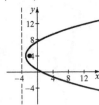

9.   Converting the equation to standard form:

$$7y^2 = x$$

$$y^2 = \frac{1}{7}x$$

Finding p:

$$4p = \frac{1}{7}$$

$$p = \frac{1}{28}$$

The vertex is $(0,0)$, the focus is $\left(\frac{1}{28},0\right)$, and the directrix is $x = -\frac{1}{28}$. Sketching the graph:

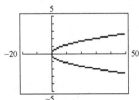

10.   First complete the square:

$$x^2 + 3x - y = 0$$

$$x^2 + 3x = y$$

$$x^2 + 3x + \frac{9}{4} = y + \frac{9}{4}$$

$$\left(x+\frac{3}{2}\right)^2 = y + \frac{9}{4}$$

Finding p:

$$4p = 1$$

$$p = \frac{1}{4}$$

The vertex is $\left(-\frac{3}{2},-\frac{9}{4}\right)$, the focus is $\left(-\frac{3}{2},-\frac{9}{4}+\frac{1}{4}\right)=\left(-\frac{3}{2},-2\right)$, and the directrix is $y = -\frac{9}{4}-\frac{1}{4}=-\frac{5}{2}$.

Sketching the graph:

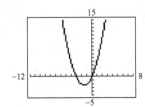

11. Vertical axis and vertex $(0,0)$: $x^2 = 4py$

Substituting the point $(-2, -6)$:

$$4 = 4p(-6)$$
$$4 = -24p$$
$$4p = -\frac{2}{3}$$

The equation is $x^2 = -\frac{2}{3}y$. Sketching the graph:

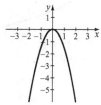

12. Horizontal directrix $\Rightarrow$ a vertical axis through the focus $(0,2)$ of $x = 0$ and equation $(x-h)^2 = 4p(y-k)$

Point of intersection of axis and directrix: $(0, -2)$

The vertex is the midpoint of segment joining this point and the focus: $\left(0, \dfrac{-2+2}{2}\right) = (0,0)$

Position of focus relative to vertex $\Rightarrow p = 2$; $4p = 8$

The equation is $x^2 = 8y$. Sketching the graph:

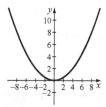

13. Horizontal directrix $\Rightarrow$ a vertical axis through the focus $(0, -5)$ of $x = 0$ and equation $(x-h)^2 = 4p(y-k)$

Point of intersection of axis and directrix: $(0, 5)$

The vertex is the midpoint of segment joining this point and the focus: $\left(0, \dfrac{-5+5}{2}\right) = (0,0)$

Position of focus relative to vertex $\Rightarrow p = -5$; $4p = -20$

The equation is $x^2 = -20y$. Sketching the graph:

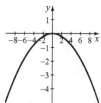

14. Substituting $(1,6)$ into $y^2 = 4px$:

$$36 = 4p(1)$$
$$4p = 36$$

The equation is $y^2 = 36x$. Sketching the graph:

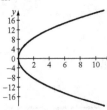

15. Vertex $(2,0)$ and vertical directrix $\Rightarrow y^2 = 4p(x-2)$

Directrix 4 units left of vertex so focus is 4 units right:

$$p = 4$$
$$4p = 16$$

The equation is $y^2 = 16(x-2)$. Sketching the graph:

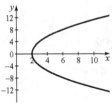

16. Vertex $(1,-4)$ and vertical directrix $\Rightarrow (y+4)^2 = 4p(x-1)$

Directrix 5 units right of vertex so focus is 5 units left:

$$p = -5$$
$$4p = -20$$

The equation is $(y+4)^2 = -20(x-1)$. Sketching the graph:

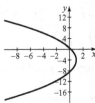

17. Having the axis of symmetry coincide with the y-axis, the vertex is $(0,6)$ and the parabola opens down so the equation has the form $x^2 = 4p(y-6)$.

The x-intercepts are $(\pm 5, 0)$. Using $(5,0)$ we get:

$$5^2 = 4p(0-6)$$
$$25 = -24p$$
$$4p = -\frac{25}{6}$$

Hence the equation is $x^2 = -\dfrac{25}{6}(y-6)$. Substituting $y = 4$:

$$x^2 = -\frac{25}{6}(4-6) = \frac{25}{3}$$

$$x = \frac{5}{\sqrt{3}} = \frac{5\sqrt{3}}{3}$$

They are $\dfrac{5\sqrt{3}}{3}$ feet from the center.

18. Substituting $x = 3$: $y = -64(3)^2 = -576$

The cliff is 576 feet high.

19. Using $a = 2$ and $b = 1$, find c: $c = \sqrt{a^2 - b^2} = \sqrt{2^2 - 1^2} = \sqrt{3}$

The center is $(0,0)$, the vertices are $(-2,0)$ and $(2,0)$, and the foci are $\left(-\sqrt{3},0\right)$ and $\left(\sqrt{3},0\right)$. Sketching the graph:

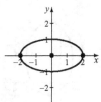

20. Using $a = 8$ and $b = 5$, find c: $c = \sqrt{a^2 - b^2} = \sqrt{8^2 - 5^2} = \sqrt{39}$

The center is $(1,0)$, the vertices are $(1-8,0) = (-7,0)$ and $(1+8,0) = (9,0)$, and the foci are $\left(1-\sqrt{39},0\right)$ and $\left(1+\sqrt{39},0\right)$. Sketching the graph:

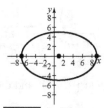

21. Using $a = 5$ and $b = 4$, find c: $c = \sqrt{a^2 - b^2} = \sqrt{5^2 - 4^2} = \sqrt{9} = 3$

The center is $(-2,1)$, the vertices are $(-2-5,1) = (-7,1)$ and $(-2+5,1) = (3,1)$, and the foci are $(-2-3,1) = (-5,1)$ and $(-2+3,1) = (1,1)$. Sketching the graph:

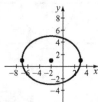

22. Using $a = 3$ and $b = 2$, find c: $c = \sqrt{a^2 - b^2} = \sqrt{3^2 - 2^2} = \sqrt{5}$

The center is $(0,0)$, the vertices are $(0,-3)$ and $(0,3)$, and the foci are $\left(0,-\sqrt{5}\right)$ and $\left(0,\sqrt{5}\right)$. Sketching the graph:

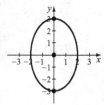

23. Using $a = 4$ and $b = 3$, find c: $c = \sqrt{a^2 - b^2} = \sqrt{4^2 - 3^2} = \sqrt{7}$

The center is $(-2, 0)$, the vertices are $(-2, 0-4) = (-2, -4)$ and $(-2, 0+4) = (-2, 4)$, and the foci are

$\left(-2, -\sqrt{7}\right)$ and $\left(-2, \sqrt{7}\right)$. Sketching the graph:

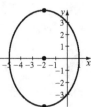

24. Using $a = 3$ and $b = 2$, find c: $c = \sqrt{a^2 - b^2} = \sqrt{3^2 - 2^2} = \sqrt{5}$

The center is $(1, 2)$, the vertices are $(1, 2-3) = (1, -1)$ and $(1, 2+3) = (1, 5)$, and the foci are $\left(1, 2-\sqrt{5}\right)$ and $\left(1, 2+\sqrt{5}\right)$.
Sketching the graph:

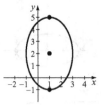

25. Converting the equation to standard form:

$$3x^2 + y^2 = 7$$

$$\frac{x^2}{\frac{7}{3}} + \frac{y^2}{7} = 1$$

Using $a = \sqrt{7}$ and $b = \sqrt{\frac{7}{3}} = \frac{\sqrt{21}}{3}$, find c: $c = \sqrt{a^2 - b^2} = \sqrt{7 - \frac{7}{3}} = \sqrt{\frac{14}{3}} = \frac{\sqrt{42}}{3}$

The center is $(0, 0)$, the vertices are $\left(0, -\sqrt{7}\right)$ and $\left(0, \sqrt{7}\right)$, and the foci are $\left(0, -\frac{\sqrt{42}}{3}\right)$ and $\left(0, \frac{\sqrt{42}}{3}\right)$.

Sketching the graph:

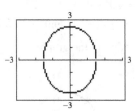

26. Converting the equation to standard form:

$$2x^2 + 3y^2 = 10$$

$$\frac{x^2}{5} + \frac{y^2}{\frac{10}{3}} = 1$$

Using $a = \sqrt{5}$ and $b = \sqrt{\frac{10}{3}} = \frac{\sqrt{30}}{3}$, find c: $c = \sqrt{a^2 - b^2} = \sqrt{5 - \frac{10}{3}} = \sqrt{\frac{5}{3}} = \frac{\sqrt{15}}{3}$

The center is $(0, 0)$, the vertices are $\left(-\sqrt{5}, 0\right)$ and $\left(\sqrt{5}, 0\right)$, and the foci are $\left(-\frac{\sqrt{15}}{3}, 0\right)$ and $\left(\frac{\sqrt{15}}{3}, 0\right)$.

Sketching the graph:

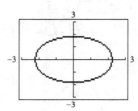

27.   First complete the square:

$$x^2 - 4x + 6y^2 - 20 = 0$$

$$\left(x^2 - 4x + 4\right) + 6y^2 = 20 + 4$$

$$\left(x - 2\right)^2 + 6y^2 = 24$$

$$\frac{\left(x - 2\right)^2}{24} + \frac{y^2}{4} = 1$$

Using $a = \sqrt{24} = 2\sqrt{6}$ and $b = 2$, find c: $c = \sqrt{a^2 - b^2} = \sqrt{24 - 4} = \sqrt{20} = 2\sqrt{5}$

The center is $(2,0)$, the vertices are $\left(2 - 2\sqrt{6}, 0\right)$ and $\left(2 + 2\sqrt{6}, 0\right)$, and the foci are $\left(2 - 2\sqrt{5}, 0\right)$ and $\left(2 + 2\sqrt{5}, 0\right)$.

Sketching the graph:

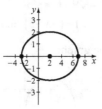

28.   First complete the square:

$$4y^2 - 32y + 3x^2 + 12x + 40 = 0$$

$$4\left(y^2 - 8y + 16\right) + 3\left(x^2 + 4x + 4\right) = -40 + 64 + 12$$

$$4\left(y - 4\right)^2 + 3\left(x + 2\right)^2 = 36$$

$$\frac{\left(y - 4\right)^2}{9} + \frac{\left(x + 2\right)^2}{12} = 1$$

Using $a = \sqrt{12} = 2\sqrt{3}$ and $b = 3$, find c: $c = \sqrt{a^2 - b^2} = \sqrt{12 - 9} = \sqrt{3}$

The center is $(-2,4)$, the vertices are $\left(-2 - 2\sqrt{3}, 4\right)$ and $\left(-2 + 2\sqrt{3}, 4\right)$, and the foci are $\left(-2 - \sqrt{3}, 4\right)$ and $\left(-2 + \sqrt{3}, 4\right)$.

Sketching the graph:

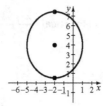

29.   First complete the square:

$$4y^2 - 24y + 7x^2 + 42x + 71 = 0$$

$$4\left(y^2 - 6y + 9\right) + 7\left(x^2 + 6x + 9\right) = -71 + 36 + 63$$

$$4\left(y - 3\right)^2 + 7\left(x + 3\right)^2 = 28$$

$$\frac{\left(y - 3\right)^2}{7} + \frac{\left(x + 3\right)^2}{4} = 1$$

Using $a = \sqrt{7}$ and $b = 2$, find c: $c = \sqrt{a^2 - b^2} = \sqrt{7-4} = \sqrt{3}$

The center is $(-3,3)$, the vertices are $\left(-3, 3-\sqrt{7}\right)$ and $\left(-3, 3+\sqrt{7}\right)$, and the foci are $\left(-3, 3-\sqrt{3}\right)$ and $\left(-3, 3+\sqrt{3}\right)$.

Sketching the graph:

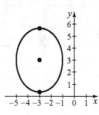

30. First complete the square:
$$3x^2 + 18x + 2y^2 + 8y + 17 = 0$$
$$3\left(x^2 + 6x + 9\right) + 2\left(y^2 + 4y + 4\right) = -17 + 27 + 8$$
$$3(x+3)^2 + 2(y+2)^2 = 18$$
$$\frac{(x+3)^2}{6} + \frac{(y+2)^2}{9} = 1$$

Using $a = 3$ and $b = \sqrt{6}$, find c: $c = \sqrt{a^2 - b^2} = \sqrt{9-6} = \sqrt{3}$

The center is $(-3,-2)$, the vertices are $(-3,-2-3) = (-3,-5)$ and $(-3,-2+3) = (-3,1)$, and the foci are

$\left(-3, -2-\sqrt{3}\right)$ and $\left(-3, -2+\sqrt{3}\right)$. Sketching the graph:

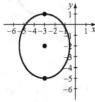

31. The vertex and focus is on the line $x = 0$ so the major axis is vertical: $\dfrac{x^2}{b^2} + \dfrac{y^2}{a^2} = 1$

Vertex $(0,5) \Rightarrow a = 5$; Focus $(0,3) \Rightarrow c = 3$

Finding b: $c^2 = a^2 - b^2 \Rightarrow b^2 = a^2 - c^2 = 25 - 9 = 16$

The equation is: $\dfrac{x^2}{16} + \dfrac{y^2}{25} = 1$

32. Major axis length 8: $2a = 8 \Rightarrow a = 4$

The foci are on the line $x = 0$ so the major axis is vertical: $\dfrac{x^2}{b^2} + \dfrac{y^2}{a^2} = 1$

Focus $(0,2) \Rightarrow c = 2$

Finding b: $c^2 = a^2 - b^2 \Rightarrow b^2 = a^2 - c^2 = 16 - 4 = 12$

The equation is: $\dfrac{x^2}{12} + \dfrac{y^2}{16} = 1$

33. The vertex and focus is on the line $x = 0$ so the major axis is vertical: $\dfrac{x^2}{b^2} + \dfrac{y^2}{a^2} = 1$

Vertex $(0,6) \Rightarrow a = 6$; Focus $(0,4) \Rightarrow c = 4$

Finding b: $c^2 = a^2 - b^2 \Rightarrow b^2 = a^2 - c^2 = 36 - 16 = 20$

The equation is: $\dfrac{x^2}{20} + \dfrac{y^2}{36} = 1$

34. The vertex and focus is on the line $y=0$ so the major axis is horizontal: $\dfrac{x^2}{a^2}+\dfrac{y^2}{b^2}=1$

Vertex $(5,0)\Rightarrow a=5$; Focus $(3,0)\Rightarrow c=3$

Finding b: $c^2=a^2-b^2\Rightarrow b^2=a^2-c^2=25-9=16$

The equation is: $\dfrac{x^2}{25}+\dfrac{y^2}{16}=1$

35. Major axis length 10: $2a=10\Rightarrow a=5$

The foci are on the line $y=0$ so the major axis is horizontal: $\dfrac{x^2}{a^2}+\dfrac{y^2}{b^2}=1$

Focus $(3,0)\Rightarrow c=3$

Finding b: $c^2=a^2-b^2\Rightarrow b^2=a^2-c^2=25-9=16$

The equation is: $\dfrac{x^2}{25}+\dfrac{y^2}{16}=1$

36. The vertex and focus is on the line $y=0$ so the major axis is horizontal: $\dfrac{x^2}{a^2}+\dfrac{y^2}{b^2}=1$

Vertex $(-6,0)\Rightarrow a=6$; Focus $(1,0)\Rightarrow c=1$

Finding b: $c^2=a^2-b^2\Rightarrow b^2=a^2-c^2=36-1=35$

The equation is: $\dfrac{x^2}{36}+\dfrac{y^2}{35}=1$

37. Major axis length 80 $\Rightarrow 2a=80\Rightarrow a=40$

Distance between foci $\dfrac{1}{4}$ of length of major axis $\Rightarrow 2c=20\Rightarrow c=10$

Finding b: $c^2=a^2-b^2\Rightarrow b^2=a^2-c^2=1600-100=1500$ so $b=\sqrt{1500}=10\sqrt{15}$

Thus the length of the minor axis is $2b=20\sqrt{15}$ AU.

38. Finding the ratio: $\dfrac{2a}{2b}=\dfrac{17}{13}\Rightarrow a=\dfrac{17}{13}b$

Finding a and b: $2a=15\Rightarrow a=\dfrac{15}{2}$; $\dfrac{17}{13}b=\dfrac{15}{2}\Rightarrow b=\dfrac{195}{34}$

Finding c: $c^2=a^2-b^2=\left(\dfrac{15}{2}\right)^2-\left(\dfrac{195}{34}\right)^2=\dfrac{6750}{289}\Rightarrow c=\dfrac{15\sqrt{30}}{17}$ inches

39. The transverse axis is vertical with $a=6$ and $b=5$. Finding c: $c=\sqrt{a^2+b^2}=\sqrt{36+25}=\sqrt{61}$

The center is $(0,0)$, the vertices are $(0,-6)$ and $(0,6)$, the foci are $\left(0,-\sqrt{61}\right)$ and $\left(0,\sqrt{61}\right)$, and the asymptotes

are $y=-\dfrac{6}{5}x$, $y=\dfrac{6}{5}x$. Sketching the graph:

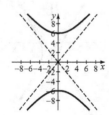

40. The transverse axis is vertical with $a = 5$ and $b = 6$. Finding c: $c = \sqrt{a^2 + b^2} = \sqrt{25 + 36} = \sqrt{61}$

The center is $(0,1)$, the vertices are $(0,1-5) = (0,-4)$ and $(0,1+5) = (0,6)$, the foci are $\left(0,1-\sqrt{61}\right)$ and $\left(0,1+\sqrt{61}\right)$,

and the asymptotes are $y = -\dfrac{5}{6}x + 1$, $y = \dfrac{5}{6}x + 1$. Sketching the graph:

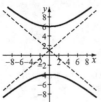

41. The transverse axis is vertical with $a = 2$ and $b = 2$. Finding c: $c = \sqrt{a^2 + b^2} = \sqrt{4 + 4} = \sqrt{8} = 2\sqrt{2}$

The center is $(1,-2)$, the vertices are $(1,-2-2) = (1,-4)$ and $(1,-2+2) = (1,0)$, the foci are

$\left(1,-2-2\sqrt{2}\right)$ and $\left(1,-2+2\sqrt{2}\right)$, and the asymptotes are $y = -\dfrac{2}{2}(x-1) - 2 = -x - 1$, $y = \dfrac{2}{2}(x-1) - 2 = x - 3$.

Sketching the graph:

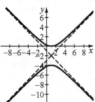

42. The transverse axis is horizontal with $a = 3$ and $b = 3$. Finding c: $c = \sqrt{a^2 + b^2} = \sqrt{9 + 9} = \sqrt{18} = 3\sqrt{2}$

The center is $(0,0)$, the vertices are $(-3,0)$ and $(3,0)$, the foci are $\left(-3\sqrt{2},0\right)$ and $\left(3\sqrt{2},0\right)$, and the asymptotes are

$y = -\dfrac{3}{3}x = -x$, $y = \dfrac{3}{3}x = x$. Sketching the graph:

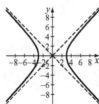

43. The transverse axis is horizontal with $a = 2$ and $b = 3$. Finding c: $c = \sqrt{a^2 + b^2} = \sqrt{4 + 9} = \sqrt{13}$

The center is $(0,-2)$, the vertices are $(-2,-2)$ and $(2,-2)$, the foci are $\left(-\sqrt{13},-2\right)$ and $\left(\sqrt{13},-2\right)$, and the asymptotes

are $y = -\dfrac{3}{2}x - 2$, $y = \dfrac{3}{2}x - 2$. Sketching the graph:

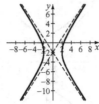

44. The transverse axis is horizontal with $a = 2$ and $b = 1$. Finding c: $c = \sqrt{a^2 + b^2} = \sqrt{4+1} = \sqrt{5}$

The center is $(1,3)$, the vertices are $(1-2,3) = (-1,3)$ and $(1+2,3) = (3,3)$, the foci are $\left(1-\sqrt{5},3\right)$ and $\left(1+\sqrt{5},3\right)$, and

the asymptotes are $y = -\dfrac{1}{2}(x-1) + 3 = -\dfrac{1}{2}x + \dfrac{7}{2}$, $y = \dfrac{1}{2}(x-1) + 3 = \dfrac{1}{2}x + \dfrac{5}{2}$. Sketching the graph:

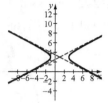

45. First complete the square:
$$16y^2 - x^2 - 4x = 20$$
$$16y^2 - \left(x^2 + 4x + 4\right) = 20 - 4$$
$$16y^2 - (x+2)^2 = 16$$
$$y^2 - \frac{(x+2)^2}{16} = 1$$

The transverse axis is vertical with $a = 1$ and $b = 4$. Finding c: $c = \sqrt{a^2 + b^2} = \sqrt{1+16} = \sqrt{17}$

The center is $(-2,0)$, the vertices are $(-2, 0-1) = (-2,-1)$ and $(-2, 0+1) = (-2,1)$, the foci are

$\left(-2, -\sqrt{17}\right)$ and $\left(-2, \sqrt{17}\right)$, and the asymptotes are $y = -\dfrac{1}{4}(x+2) = -\dfrac{1}{4}x - \dfrac{1}{2}$, $y = \dfrac{1}{4}(x+2) = \dfrac{1}{4}x + \dfrac{1}{2}$.

Sketching the graph:

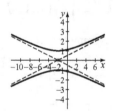

46. First complete the square:
$$y^2 + 10y - 4x^2 - 16x + 5 = 0$$
$$\left(y^2 + 10y + 25\right) - 4\left(x^2 + 4x + 4\right) = -5 + 25 - 16$$
$$(y+5)^2 - 4(x+2)^2 = 4$$
$$\frac{(y+5)^2}{4} - \frac{(x+2)^2}{1} = 1$$

The transverse axis is vertical with $a = 2$ and $b = 1$. Finding c: $c = \sqrt{a^2 + b^2} = \sqrt{4+1} = \sqrt{5}$

The center is $(-2,-5)$, the vertices are $(-2, -5-2) = (-2,-7)$ and $(-2, -5+2) = (-2,-3)$, the foci are

$\left(-2, -5-\sqrt{5}\right)$ and $\left(-2, -5+\sqrt{5}\right)$, and the asymptotes are $y = -\dfrac{2}{1}(x+2) - 5 = -2x - 9$, $y = 2(x+2) - 5 = 2x - 1$.

Sketching the graph:

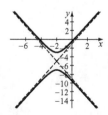

47. Converting the equation to standard form:

$$8x^2 - y^2 = 64$$

$$\frac{x^2}{8} - \frac{y^2}{64} = 1$$

The transverse axis is horizontal with $a = \sqrt{8} = 2\sqrt{2}$ and $b = 8$. Finding c: $c = \sqrt{a^2 + b^2} = \sqrt{8 + 64} = \sqrt{72} = 6\sqrt{2}$

The center is $(0,0)$, the vertices are $\left(-2\sqrt{2},0\right)$ and $\left(2\sqrt{2},0\right)$, the foci are $\left(-6\sqrt{2},0\right)$ and $\left(6\sqrt{2},0\right)$, and the

asymptotes are $y = -2\sqrt{2}x$, $y = 2\sqrt{2}x$. Sketching the graph:

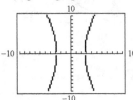

48. First complete the square:

$$7x^2 + 42x - 5y^2 - 50y = 307$$

$$7\left(x^2 + 6x + 9\right) - 5\left(y^2 + 10y + 25\right) = 307 + 63 - 125$$

$$7\left(x+3\right)^2 - 5\left(y+5\right)^2 = 245$$

$$\frac{\left(x+3\right)^2}{35} - \frac{\left(y+5\right)^2}{49} = 1$$

The transverse axis is horizontal with $a = \sqrt{35}$ and $b = 7$. Finding c: $c = \sqrt{a^2 + b^2} = \sqrt{35 + 49} = \sqrt{84} = 2\sqrt{21}$

The center is $(-3,-5)$, the vertices are $\left(-3-\sqrt{35},-5\right)$ and $\left(-3+\sqrt{35},-5\right)$, the foci are

$\left(-3-2\sqrt{21},-5\right)$ and $\left(-3+2\sqrt{21},-5\right)$, and the asymptotes are

$y = -\dfrac{7}{\sqrt{35}}(x+3) - 5 = -\dfrac{\sqrt{35}}{5}x - \dfrac{3\sqrt{35}}{5} - 5$, $y = \dfrac{7}{\sqrt{35}}(x+3) - 5 = \dfrac{\sqrt{35}}{5}x + \dfrac{3\sqrt{35}}{5} - 5$. Sketching the graph:

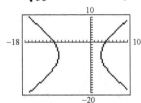

49. The foci are on the line $x = 0$ so the transverse axis is vertical: $\dfrac{\left(y-k\right)^2}{a^2} - \dfrac{\left(x-h\right)^2}{b^2} = 1$

Center = midpoint of foci: $(0,0)$

Focus $(0,6) \Rightarrow c = 6$

Transverse axis of length $4 \Rightarrow a = 2$

Finding b: $c^2 = a^2 + b^2 \Rightarrow 36 = 4 + b^2 \Rightarrow b^2 = 32$

The equation is: $\dfrac{y^2}{4} - \dfrac{x^2}{32} = 1$

50. The vertices are on the line $x = -2$ so the transverse axis is vertical: $\dfrac{(y-k)^2}{a^2} - \dfrac{(x-h)^2}{b^2} = 1$

Center = midpoint of vertices: $(-2, -2)$

Distance between vertices: $2a = 2 - (-6) = 8 \implies a = 4$

Distance between vertex $(-2, -6)$ and focus $(-2, -9)$: $c - a = -6 - (-9) = 3 \implies c = 3 + a = 4$

Finding b: $c^2 = a^2 + b^2 \implies 49 = 16 + b^2 \implies b^2 = 33$

The equation is: $\dfrac{(y+2)^2}{16} - \dfrac{(x+2)^2}{33} = 1$

51. Transverse axis length $6 \implies a = 3$

Distance between center and foci: $c = 1 - (-4) = 5$

Finding b: $c^2 = a^2 + b^2 \implies 25 = 9 + b^2 \implies b^2 = 16$

Center and foci are on the line $x = 3$ so the transverse axis is vertical: $\dfrac{(y-k)^2}{a^2} - \dfrac{(x-h)^2}{b^2} = 1$

The equation is: $\dfrac{(y+4)^2}{9} - \dfrac{(x-3)^2}{16} = 1$

52. The vertices are on the line $y = 0$ so the transverse axis is horizontal: $\dfrac{(x-h)^2}{a^2} - \dfrac{(y-k)^2}{b^2} = 1$

Center = midpoint of vertices: $(0, 0)$

Distance from center to vertices: $a = 3$

Slope of asymptote = -4:

$$\frac{b}{a} = -4$$

$$b = -4a = -12$$

$$b^2 = 144$$

The equation is: $\dfrac{x^2}{9} - \dfrac{y^2}{144} = 1$

53. The center and focus are on the line $y = 2$ so the transverse axis is horizontal: $\dfrac{(x-h)^2}{a^2} - \dfrac{(y-k)^2}{b^2} = 1$

Transverse axis of length $8 \implies a = 4$

Distance from center to focus: $c = 2 - (-4) = 6$

Finding b: $c^2 = a^2 + b^2 \implies 36 = 16 + b^2 \implies b^2 = 20$

The equation is: $\dfrac{(x+4)^2}{16} - \dfrac{(y-2)^2}{20} = 1$

54. Transverse axis length $16 \Rightarrow 2a = 16 \Rightarrow a = 8$

Transverse axis horizontal $\Rightarrow$ slope of asymptotes $= \pm\dfrac{b}{a}$

Slope of asymptote $= \dfrac{7}{8}$:

$$\dfrac{b}{a} = \dfrac{7}{8}$$

$$b = \dfrac{7}{8}a = 7$$

Finding b: $c^2 = a^2 + b^2 = 64 + 49 = 113$; $c = \sqrt{113}$

The rosebushes are $2c = 2\sqrt{113} \approx 21.26$ feet apart.

55. Converting the coordinates:

$$u = x\cos\theta + y\sin\theta = 2\cos\dfrac{\pi}{3} + 0\sin\dfrac{\pi}{3} = 1$$

$$v = -x\sin\theta + y\cos\theta = -2\sin\dfrac{\pi}{3} + 0\cos\dfrac{\pi}{3} = -\sqrt{3}$$

The rotated point is: $(u, v) = \left(1, -\sqrt{3}\right)$

56. Converting the coordinates:

$$u = x\cos\theta + y\sin\theta = 0\cos\dfrac{\pi}{3} + (-3)\sin\dfrac{\pi}{3} = -\dfrac{3\sqrt{3}}{2}$$

$$v = -x\sin\theta + y\cos\theta = -0\sin\dfrac{\pi}{3} + (-3)\cos\dfrac{\pi}{3} = -\dfrac{3}{2}$$

The rotated point is: $(u, v) = \left(-\dfrac{3\sqrt{3}}{2}, -\dfrac{3}{2}\right)$

57. Converting the coordinates:

$$x = u\cos\theta - v\sin\theta = -4\cos\dfrac{\pi}{6} - 0\sin\dfrac{\pi}{6} = -2\sqrt{3}$$

$$y = u\sin\theta + v\cos\theta = -4\sin\dfrac{\pi}{6} + 0\cos\dfrac{\pi}{6} = -2$$

The original point is: $(x, y) = \left(-2\sqrt{3}, -2\right)$

58. Converting the coordinates:

$$x = u\cos\theta - v\sin\theta = 0\cos\dfrac{\pi}{6} - (-2)\sin\dfrac{\pi}{6} = 1$$

$$y = u\sin\theta + v\cos\theta = 0\sin\dfrac{\pi}{6} + (-2)\cos\dfrac{\pi}{6} = -\sqrt{3}$$

The original point is: $(x, y) = \left(1, -\sqrt{3}\right)$

59. **a.** Let $A = 0$, $B = 1$, $C = 0$: $B^2 - 4AC = 1^2 - 4(0)(0) = 1 > 0$

The conic is a hyperbola.

b. Finding the angle of rotation: $\cot 2\theta = \dfrac{A - C}{B} = 0 \Rightarrow 2\theta = \dfrac{\pi}{2} \Rightarrow \theta = \dfrac{\pi}{4}$

Finding the coordinate conversions:

$$x = u\cos\dfrac{\pi}{4} - v\sin\dfrac{\pi}{4} = \dfrac{\sqrt{2}}{2}u - \dfrac{\sqrt{2}}{2}v = \dfrac{\sqrt{2}}{2}(u - v)$$

$$y = u\sin\dfrac{\pi}{4} + v\cos\dfrac{\pi}{4} = \dfrac{\sqrt{2}}{2}u + \dfrac{\sqrt{2}}{2}v = \dfrac{\sqrt{2}}{2}(u + v)$$

Converting the equation:

$$xy - 6 = 0$$

$$\left[\frac{\sqrt{2}}{2}(u-v)\right]\left[\frac{\sqrt{2}}{2}(u+v)\right] - 6 = 0$$

$$\frac{1}{2}(u^2 - v^2) = 6$$

$$\frac{1}{2}u^2 - \frac{1}{2}v^2 = 6$$

$$\frac{u^2}{12} - \frac{v^2}{12} = 1$$

c. Finding a: $a^2 = 12 \Rightarrow a = 2\sqrt{3}$

The vertices are: $(u, v) = \left(-2\sqrt{3}, 0\right), \left(2\sqrt{3}, 0\right)$

Sketching the graph:

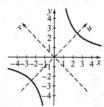

60. **a.** Let $A = -2$, $B = 2\sqrt{3}$, $C = 0$: $B^2 - 4AC = \left(2\sqrt{3}\right)^2 - 4(-2)(0) = 12 > 0$

The conic is a hyperbola.

b. Finding the angle of rotation: $\cot 2\theta = \dfrac{A-C}{B} = \dfrac{-2-0}{2\sqrt{3}} = -\dfrac{1}{\sqrt{3}} \Rightarrow 2\theta = \dfrac{2\pi}{3} \Rightarrow \theta = \dfrac{\pi}{3}$

Finding the coordinate conversions:

$$x = u\cos\frac{\pi}{3} - v\sin\frac{\pi}{3} = \frac{1}{2}u - \frac{\sqrt{3}}{2}v = \frac{1}{2}\left(u - \sqrt{3}v\right)$$

$$y = u\sin\frac{\pi}{3} + v\cos\frac{\pi}{3} = \frac{\sqrt{3}}{2}u + \frac{1}{2}v = \frac{1}{2}\left(\sqrt{3}u + v\right)$$

Simplifying parts of the equation:

$$-2x^2 = -2\left[\frac{1}{2}\left(u - \sqrt{3}v\right)\right]^2 = -2 \cdot \frac{1}{4}\left(u^2 - 2\sqrt{3}uv + 3v^2\right) = -\frac{1}{2}u^2 + \sqrt{3}uv - \frac{3}{2}v^2$$

$$2xy\sqrt{3} = 2\sqrt{3}\left[\frac{1}{2}\left(u - \sqrt{3}v\right)\right]\left[\frac{1}{2}\left(\sqrt{3}u + v\right)\right] = 2\sqrt{3} \cdot \frac{1}{4}\left(\sqrt{3}u^2 + uv - 3uv - \sqrt{3}v^2\right) = \frac{3}{2}u^2 - \sqrt{3}uv - \frac{3}{2}v^2$$

Converting the equation:

$$-2x^2 + 2xy\sqrt{3} - 6 = 0$$

$$-\frac{1}{2}u^2 + \sqrt{3}uv - \frac{3}{2}v^2 + \frac{3}{2}u^2 - \sqrt{3}uv - \frac{3}{2}v^2 - 6 = 0$$

$$u^2 - 3v^2 - 6 = 0$$

$$u^2 - 3v^2 = 6$$

$$\frac{u^2}{6} - \frac{v^2}{2} = 1$$

c.   Finding a: $a^2 = 6 \Rightarrow a = \sqrt{6}$

The vertices are: $(u,v) = \left(-\sqrt{6},0\right), \left(\sqrt{6},0\right)$

Sketching the graph:

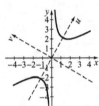

61.   **a.**   Let $A = \dfrac{3}{2}$, $B = -1$, $C = \dfrac{3}{2}$: $B^2 - 4AC = (-1)^2 - 4\left(\dfrac{3}{2}\right)\left(\dfrac{3}{2}\right) = -8 < 0$

The conic is an ellipse.

b.   Finding the angle of rotation: $\cot 2\theta = \dfrac{A-C}{B} = \dfrac{\dfrac{3}{2} - \dfrac{3}{2}}{-1} = 0 \Rightarrow 2\theta = \dfrac{\pi}{2} \Rightarrow \theta = \dfrac{\pi}{4}$

Finding the coordinate conversions:

$$x = u\cos\frac{\pi}{4} - v\sin\frac{\pi}{4} = \frac{\sqrt{2}}{2}u - \frac{\sqrt{2}}{2}v = \frac{\sqrt{2}}{2}(u-v)$$

$$y = u\sin\frac{\pi}{4} + v\cos\frac{\pi}{4} = \frac{\sqrt{2}}{2}u + \frac{\sqrt{2}}{2}v = \frac{\sqrt{2}}{2}(u+v)$$

Simplifying parts of the equation:

$$\frac{3}{2}x^2 = \frac{3}{2}\left[\frac{\sqrt{2}}{2}(u-v)\right]^2 = \frac{3}{2}\cdot\frac{1}{2}\left(u^2 - 2uv + v^2\right) = \frac{3}{4}u^2 - \frac{3}{2}uv + \frac{3}{4}v^2$$

$$-xy = -\left[\frac{\sqrt{2}}{2}(u-v)\right]\left[\frac{\sqrt{2}}{2}(u+v)\right] = -\frac{1}{2}\left(u^2 - v^2\right) = -\frac{1}{2}u^2 + \frac{1}{2}v^2$$

$$\frac{3}{2}y^2 = \frac{3}{2}\left[\frac{\sqrt{2}}{2}(u+v)\right]^2 = \frac{3}{2}\cdot\frac{1}{2}\left(u^2 + 2uv + v^2\right) = \frac{3}{4}u^2 + \frac{3}{2}uv + \frac{3}{4}v^2$$

Converting the equation:

$$\frac{3}{2}x^2 - xy + \frac{3}{2}y^2 - 4 = 0$$

$$\frac{3}{4}u^2 - \frac{3}{2}uv + \frac{3}{4}v^2 - \frac{1}{2}u^2 + \frac{1}{2}v^2 + \frac{3}{4}u^2 + \frac{3}{2}uv + \frac{3}{4}v^2 - 4 = 0$$

$$u^2 + 2v^2 - 4 = 0$$

$$u^2 + 2v^2 = 4$$

$$\frac{u^2}{4} + \frac{v^2}{2} = 1$$

c.   Finding a: $a^2 = 4 \Rightarrow a = 2$

The vertices are: $(u,v) = (-2,0), (2,0)$

Sketching the graph:

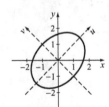

62. **a.** Let $A = \dfrac{1}{2}$, $B = 1$, $C = \dfrac{1}{2}$: $B^2 - 4AC = (1)^2 - 4\left(\dfrac{1}{2}\right)\left(\dfrac{1}{2}\right) = 0$

The conic is a parabola.

b. Finding the angle of rotation: $\cot 2\theta = \dfrac{A-C}{B} = \dfrac{\dfrac{1}{2} - \dfrac{1}{2}}{1} = 0 \;\Rightarrow\; 2\theta = \dfrac{\pi}{2} \Rightarrow \theta = \dfrac{\pi}{4}$

Finding the coordinate conversions:

$$x = u\cos\frac{\pi}{4} - v\sin\frac{\pi}{4} = \frac{\sqrt{2}}{2}u - \frac{\sqrt{2}}{2}v = \frac{\sqrt{2}}{2}(u-v)$$

$$y = u\sin\frac{\pi}{4} + v\cos\frac{\pi}{4} = \frac{\sqrt{2}}{2}u + \frac{\sqrt{2}}{2}v = \frac{\sqrt{2}}{2}(u+v)$$

Simplifying parts of the equation:

$$\frac{1}{2}x^2 = \frac{1}{2}\left[\frac{\sqrt{2}}{2}(u-v)\right]^2 = \frac{1}{2}\cdot\frac{1}{2}\left(u^2 - 2uv + v^2\right) = \frac{1}{4}u^2 - \frac{1}{2}uv + \frac{1}{4}v^2$$

$$xy = \left[\frac{\sqrt{2}}{2}(u-v)\right]\left[\frac{\sqrt{2}}{2}(u+v)\right] = \frac{1}{2}\left(u^2 - v^2\right) = \frac{1}{2}u^2 - \frac{1}{2}v^2$$

$$\frac{1}{2}y^2 = \frac{1}{2}\left[\frac{\sqrt{2}}{2}(u+v)\right]^2 = \frac{1}{2}\cdot\frac{1}{2}\left(u^2 + 2uv + v^2\right) = \frac{1}{4}u^2 + \frac{1}{2}uv + \frac{1}{4}v^2$$

$$-2x\sqrt{2} = -2\sqrt{2}\cdot\frac{\sqrt{2}}{2}(u-v) = -2u + 2v$$

$$2y\sqrt{2} = 2\sqrt{2}\cdot\frac{\sqrt{2}}{2}(u+v) = 2u + 2v$$

Converting the equation:

$$\frac{1}{2}x^2 + xy + \frac{1}{2}y^2 - 2x\sqrt{2} + 2y\sqrt{2} = 0$$

$$\frac{1}{4}u^2 - \frac{1}{2}uv + \frac{1}{4}v^2 + \frac{1}{2}u^2 - \frac{1}{2}v^2 + \frac{1}{4}u^2 + \frac{1}{2}uv + \frac{1}{4}v^2 - 2u + 2v + 2u + 2v = 0$$

$$u^2 + 4v = 0$$

$$u^2 = -4v$$

c. The vertex is: $(u,v) = (0,0)$

Sketching the graph:

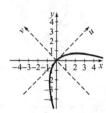

63. Given: $r = \dfrac{4}{1-\sin\theta} \Rightarrow e = 1;$ parabola opening upward

Because the vertex lies on the ray $\theta = \dfrac{3\pi}{2}$, we have $r = \dfrac{4}{1-\sin\dfrac{3\pi}{2}} = 2 \Rightarrow$ vertex $= \left(2, \dfrac{3\pi}{2}\right)$.

Two other points: $(4,0),(4,\pi)$. Sketching the graph:

64. Given: $r = \dfrac{8}{1+3\sin\theta} \Rightarrow e = 3;$ hyperbola with vertical transverse axis

$\theta = \dfrac{\pi}{2}$ gives $r = \dfrac{8}{1+3\sin\dfrac{\pi}{2}} = 2$ and $\theta = \dfrac{3\pi}{2}$ gives $r = \dfrac{8}{1+3\sin\dfrac{3\pi}{2}} = -4$.

Vertices $= \left(2, \dfrac{\pi}{2}\right), \left(-4, \dfrac{3\pi}{2}\right)$. Other points: $(8,0),(8,\pi),\left(\dfrac{16}{5}, \dfrac{\pi}{6}\right),\left(\dfrac{16}{5}, \dfrac{5\pi}{6}\right)$. Sketching the graph:

65. Given: $r = \dfrac{6}{2-2\cos\theta} = \dfrac{3}{1-\cos\theta} \Rightarrow e = 1;$ parabola opening to the right.

Because the vertex lies on the ray $\theta = \pi$, we have $r = \dfrac{6}{2-2\cos\pi} = \dfrac{3}{2} \Rightarrow$ vertex $= \left(\dfrac{3}{2}, \pi\right)$.

Other points: $\left(6, \dfrac{\pi}{3}\right),\left(3, \dfrac{\pi}{2}\right),\left(2, \dfrac{2\pi}{3}\right),\left(3, \dfrac{3\pi}{2}\right)$. Sketching the graph:

66. Given: $r = \dfrac{4}{1-2\cos\theta} \Rightarrow e = 2;$ hyperbola with horizontal transverse axis.

$\theta = 0$ gives $r = \dfrac{4}{1-2\cos 0} = -4$ and $\theta = \pi$ gives $r = \dfrac{4}{1-2\cos\pi} = \dfrac{4}{3}$.

Vertices $= (-4,0), \left(\dfrac{4}{3}, \pi\right)$. Other points: $\left(4, \dfrac{\pi}{2}\right),\left(2, \dfrac{2\pi}{3}\right),\left(2, \dfrac{4\pi}{3}\right),\left(4, \dfrac{3\pi}{2}\right)$. Sketching the graph:

67. Solving for t:

$$x = -t$$

$$t = -x$$

Substituting:

$$y = 2t + 1$$

$$y = -2x + 1, x \le 0$$

Completing the table:

t	0	1	2	3	4
$x = -t$	0	-1	-2	-3	-4
$y = 2t + 1$	1	3	5	7	9

Sketching the graph:

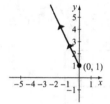

68. Solving for t:

$$x = t - 1$$

$$t = x + 1$$

Substituting:

$$y = -t$$

$$y = -(x + 1)$$

$$y = -x - 1, -4 \le x \le 2$$

Completing the table:

t	-3	-2	-1	0	1	2	3
$x = t - 1$	-4	-3	-2	-1	0	1	2
$y = -t$	3	2	1	0	-1	-2	-3

Sketching the graph:

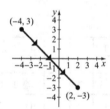

69. Solving for t:

$$x = -t + 2$$

$$t = 2 - x$$

Substituting:

$$y = t^2$$

$$y = (2 - x)^2, 0 \le x \le 4$$

Completing the table:

t	-2	-1	0	1	2
$x = -t + 2$	4	3	2	1	0
$y = t^2$	4	1	0	1	4

Sketching the graph:

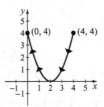

70. Solving for t:
$$y = -t$$
$$t = -y$$

Substituting:
$$x = t^2$$
$$x = (-y)^2 = y^2, 0 \le x \le 4$$

Completing the table:

t	-2	-1	0	1	2
$x = t^2$	4	1	0	1	4
$y = -t$	2	1	0	-1	-2

Sketching the graph:

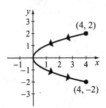

71. Substituting:
$$x^2 + y^2 = (2\sin t)^2 + (2\cos t)^2$$
$$x^2 + y^2 = 4\sin^2 t + 4\cos^2 t$$
$$x^2 + y^2 = 4(\sin^2 t + \cos^2 t)$$
$$x^2 + y^2 = 4, -2 \le x \le 2$$

Completing the table:

t	0	$\dfrac{\pi}{6}$	$\dfrac{\pi}{3}$	$\dfrac{\pi}{2}$	π	$\dfrac{3\pi}{2}$	2π
$x = 2\sin t$	0	1	$\sqrt{3}$	2	0	-2	0
$y = 2\cos t$	2	$\sqrt{3}$	1	0	-2	0	2

Sketching the graph:

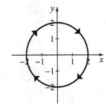

72. Solving for $\cos t$ and $\sin t$:

$$y = 2\cos t \implies \frac{y}{2} = \cos t, x = \sin t$$

Substituting:

$$x^2 + \left(\frac{y}{2}\right)^2 = \sin^2 t + \cos^2 t$$

$$x^2 + \frac{y^2}{4} = 1, 0 \le x \le 1$$

Completing the table:

t	0	$\dfrac{\pi}{6}$	$\dfrac{\pi}{3}$	$\dfrac{\pi}{2}$	π	$\dfrac{3\pi}{2}$	2π
$x = \sin t$	0	$\dfrac{1}{2}$	$\dfrac{\sqrt{3}}{2}$	1	0	-1	0
$y = 2\cos t$	2	$\sqrt{3}$	1	0	-2	0	2

Sketching the graph:

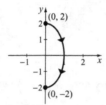

73. **a.** Finding the parametric equations:

$$x = v_0(\cos\theta)t = 120(\cos 30°)t = 120\left(\frac{\sqrt{3}}{2}\right)t = \left(60\sqrt{3}\right)t$$

$$y = -16t^2 + v_0(\sin\theta)t + h = -16t^2 + 120(\sin 30°)t + 4 = -16t^2 + 120\left(\frac{1}{2}\right)t + 4 = -16t^2 + 60t + 4$$

b. Using the vertex formula: $t = \dfrac{-b}{2a} = \dfrac{-60}{2(-16)} \approx 1.875$ seconds

The maximum height is: $y = -16(1.875)^2 + 60(1.875) + 4 \approx 60.25$ feet

Chapter 9 Test

1. Finding p:

$$4p = -12$$

$$p = -3$$

The vertex is $(-1, -3)$, the focus is $(-1-3, -3) = (-4, -3)$, and the directrix is $x = -1+3 = 2$. Sketching the graph:

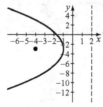

2. First complete the square:

$$y^2 - 4y + 4x = 0$$

$$y^2 - 4y + 4 = -4x + 4$$

$$(y-2)^2 = -4(x-1)$$

Finding p:
$$4p = -4$$
$$p = -1$$

The vertex is $(1,2)$, the focus is $(1-1,2) = (0,2)$, and the directrix is $x = 1+1 = 2$. Sketching the graph:

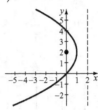

3. Vertical axis $\Rightarrow (x-h)^2 = 4p(y-k)$

Vertex at $(0,-2) \Rightarrow x^2 = 4p(y+2)$

Substituting the point $(4,0)$:
$$4^2 = 4p(0+2)$$
$$16 = 8p$$
$$p = 2$$

The equation is: $x^2 = 8(y+2)$

4. Directrix $x = -3 \Rightarrow$ horizontal axis of symmetry and so $(y-k)^2 = 4p(x-h)$

Focus $(3,0) \Rightarrow$ axis of symmetry: $y = 0 = k$

Center = midpoint of line segment between focus $(3,0)$ the point $(-3,0)$ joining the directrix and axis:
$$\left(\frac{-3+3}{2},0\right) = (0,0)$$

Distance from vertex to center: $p = 3-0 = 3 \Rightarrow 4p = 12$

The equation is: $y^2 = 12x$

5. Using $a = 5$ and $b = 4$, find c: $c = \sqrt{a^2 - b^2} = \sqrt{5^2 - 4^2} = \sqrt{9} = 3$

The center is $(-2,3)$, the vertices are $(-2,3-5) = (-2,-2)$ and $(-2,3+5) = (-2,8)$, and the foci are $(-2,3-3) = (-2,0)$ and $(-2,3+3) = (-2,6)$. Sketching the graph:

6. Using $a = 3$ and $b = 2$, find c: $c = \sqrt{a^2 - b^2} = \sqrt{3^2 - 2^2} = \sqrt{5}$

The center is $(0,-1)$, the vertices are $(0-3,-1) = (-3,-1)$ and $(0+3,-1) = (3,-1)$, and the foci are $\left(-\sqrt{5},-1\right)$ and $\left(\sqrt{5},-1\right)$. Sketching the graph:

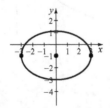

7. Completing the square:

$$4x^2 + 8x + y^2 = 0$$

$$4\left(x^2 + 2x + 1\right) + y^2 = 4$$

$$4\left(x+1\right)^2 + y^2 = 4$$

$$\frac{\left(x+1\right)^2}{1} + \frac{y^2}{4} = 1$$

8. The foci are on the vertical line $x = 0$ so the major axis vertical: $\dfrac{\left(x-h\right)^2}{b^2} + \dfrac{\left(y-k\right)^2}{a^2} = 1$

Center = midpoint of foci: $\left(0,0\right)$

Focus $\left(0,3\right) \Rightarrow c = 3; c^2 = 9$

Vertex $\left(0,-5\right) \Rightarrow a = 5; a^2 = 25$

Finding b: $c^2 = a^2 - b^2 \Rightarrow b^2 = a^2 - c^2 = 25 - 9 = 16$

The equation is: $\dfrac{x^2}{16} + \dfrac{y^2}{25} = 1$

9. The transverse axis is vertical with $a = 2$ and $b = 1$. Finding c: $c = \sqrt{a^2 + b^2} = \sqrt{4+1} = \sqrt{5}$

The center is $\left(0,0\right)$, the vertices are $\left(0,-2\right)$ and $\left(0,2\right)$, the foci are $\left(0,-\sqrt{5}\right)$ and $\left(0,\sqrt{5}\right)$, and

the asymptotes are $y = -\dfrac{2}{1}x = -2x, y = \dfrac{2}{1}x = 2x$. Sketching the graph:

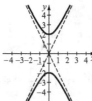

10. The transverse axis is horizontal with $a = 3$ and $b = 4$. Finding c: $c = \sqrt{a^2 + b^2} = \sqrt{9+16} = \sqrt{25} = 5$

The center is $\left(-2,0\right)$, the vertices are $\left(-2-3,0\right) = \left(-5,0\right)$ and $\left(-2+3,0\right) = \left(1,0\right)$, the foci are

$\left(-2-5,0\right) = \left(-7,0\right)$ and $\left(-2+5,0\right) = \left(3,0\right)$, and the asymptotes are $y = -\dfrac{4}{3}\left(x+2\right) = -\dfrac{4}{3}x - \dfrac{8}{3}, y = \dfrac{4}{3}\left(x+2\right) = \dfrac{4}{3}x + \dfrac{8}{3}$.

Sketching the graph:

11. The foci are on the line $y = 0$ so the transverse axis is horizontal: $\dfrac{\left(x-h\right)^2}{a^2} - \dfrac{\left(y-k\right)^2}{b^2} = 1$

Center = midpoint of foci: $\left(0,0\right)$

Transverse axis of length 2: $2a = 2 \Rightarrow a = 1$

Distance between foci: $2c = 3 - \left(-3\right) = 6 \Rightarrow c = 3$

Finding b: $c^2 = a^2 + b^2 \Rightarrow 9 = 1 + b^2 \Rightarrow b^2 = 8$

The equation is: $\dfrac{x^2}{1} - \dfrac{y^2}{8} = 1$

12. The vertices are on the line $x = 0$ so the transverse axis is vertical: $\dfrac{(y-k)^2}{a^2} - \dfrac{(x-h)^2}{b^2} = 1$

Center = midpoint of vertices: $(0,0)$

Vertex $(0,1) \Rightarrow a = 1$

Slope of asymptote = -3: $-\dfrac{a}{b} = -3 \Rightarrow b = \dfrac{a}{3} = \dfrac{1}{3}$

The equation is: $\dfrac{y^2}{1} - \dfrac{x^2}{\left(\dfrac{1}{9}\right)} = 1 \Rightarrow y^2 - 9x^2 = 1$

13. **a.** Let $A = \dfrac{1}{2}$, $B = -1$, $C = \dfrac{1}{2}$: $B^2 - 4AC = (-1)^2 - 4\left(\dfrac{1}{2}\right)\left(\dfrac{1}{2}\right) = 0$

The conic is a parabola.

b. Finding the angle of rotation: $\cot 2\theta = \dfrac{A-C}{B} = \dfrac{\dfrac{1}{2} - \dfrac{1}{2}}{1} = 0 \Rightarrow 2\theta = \dfrac{\pi}{2} \Rightarrow \theta = \dfrac{\pi}{4}$

Finding the coordinate conversions:

$$x = u\cos\dfrac{\pi}{4} - v\sin\dfrac{\pi}{4} = \dfrac{\sqrt{2}}{2}u - \dfrac{\sqrt{2}}{2}v = \dfrac{\sqrt{2}}{2}(u - v)$$

$$y = u\sin\dfrac{\pi}{4} + v\cos\dfrac{\pi}{4} = \dfrac{\sqrt{2}}{2}u + \dfrac{\sqrt{2}}{2}v = \dfrac{\sqrt{2}}{2}(u + v)$$

Simplifying parts of the equation:

$$\dfrac{1}{2}x^2 = \dfrac{1}{2}\left[\dfrac{\sqrt{2}}{2}(u-v)\right]^2 = \dfrac{1}{2}\cdot\dfrac{1}{2}\left(u^2 - 2uv + v^2\right) = \dfrac{1}{4}u^2 - \dfrac{1}{2}uv + \dfrac{1}{4}v^2$$

$$-xy = \left[\dfrac{\sqrt{2}}{2}(u-v)\right]\left[\dfrac{\sqrt{2}}{2}(u+v)\right] = -\dfrac{1}{2}\left(u^2 - v^2\right) = -\dfrac{1}{2}u^2 + \dfrac{1}{2}v^2$$

$$\dfrac{1}{2}y^2 = \dfrac{1}{2}\left[\dfrac{\sqrt{2}}{2}(u+v)\right]^2 = \dfrac{1}{2}\cdot\dfrac{1}{2}\left(u^2 + 2uv + v^2\right) = \dfrac{1}{4}u^2 + \dfrac{1}{2}uv + \dfrac{1}{4}v^2$$

$$-x\sqrt{2} = -\sqrt{2}\cdot\dfrac{\sqrt{2}}{2}(u-v) = -u + v$$

$$-y\sqrt{2} = -\sqrt{2}\cdot\dfrac{\sqrt{2}}{2}(u+v) = -u - v$$

Converting the equation:

$$\dfrac{1}{2}x^2 - xy + \dfrac{1}{2}y^2 - x\sqrt{2} - y\sqrt{2} = 0$$

$$\dfrac{1}{4}u^2 - \dfrac{1}{2}uv + \dfrac{1}{4}v^2 - \dfrac{1}{2}u^2 + \dfrac{1}{2}v^2 + \dfrac{1}{4}u^2 + \dfrac{1}{2}uv + \dfrac{1}{4}v^2 - u + v - u - v = 0$$

$$v^2 - 2u = 0$$

$$v^2 = 2u$$

c. The vertex is: $(u,v) = (0,0)$

Sketching the graph:

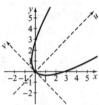

14. a. Let $A = 3$, $B = 4\sqrt{3}$, $C = 7$: $B^2 - 4AC = \left(4\sqrt{3}\right)^2 - 4(3)(7) = -36 < 0$

The conic is an ellipse.

b. Finding the angle of rotation: $\cot 2\theta = \dfrac{A-C}{B} = \dfrac{3-7}{4\sqrt{3}} = -\dfrac{1}{\sqrt{3}} \implies 2\theta = \dfrac{2\pi}{3} \implies \theta = \dfrac{\pi}{3}$

Finding the coordinate conversions:

$$x = u\cos\frac{\pi}{3} - v\sin\frac{\pi}{3} = \frac{1}{2}u - \frac{\sqrt{3}}{2}v = \frac{1}{2}\left(u - \sqrt{3}v\right)$$

$$y = u\sin\frac{\pi}{3} + v\cos\frac{\pi}{3} = \frac{\sqrt{3}}{2}u + \frac{1}{2}v = \frac{1}{2}\left(\sqrt{3}u + v\right)$$

Simplifying parts of the equation:

$$3x^2 = 3\left[\frac{1}{2}\left(u - \sqrt{3}v\right)\right]^2 = 3 \cdot \frac{1}{4}\left(u^2 - 2\sqrt{3}uv + 3v^2\right) = \frac{3}{4}u^2 - \frac{3\sqrt{3}}{2}uv + \frac{9}{4}v^2$$

$$4xy\sqrt{3} = 4\sqrt{3}\left[\frac{1}{2}\left(u - \sqrt{3}v\right)\right]\left[\frac{1}{2}\left(\sqrt{3}u + v\right)\right] = 4\sqrt{3} \cdot \frac{1}{4}\left(\sqrt{3}u^2 + uv - 3uv - \sqrt{3}v^2\right) = 3u^2 - 2\sqrt{3}uv - 3v^2$$

$$7y^2 = 7\left[\frac{1}{2}\left(\sqrt{3}u + v\right)\right]^2 = 7 \cdot \frac{1}{4}\left(3u^2 + 2\sqrt{3}uv + v^2\right) = \frac{21}{4}u^2 + \frac{7\sqrt{3}}{2}uv + \frac{7}{4}v^2$$

Converting the equation:

$$3x^2 + 4xy\sqrt{3} + 7y^2 - 9 = 0$$

$$\frac{3}{4}u^2 - \frac{3\sqrt{3}}{2}uv + \frac{9}{4}v^2 + 3u^2 - 2\sqrt{3}uv - 3v^2 + \frac{21}{4}u^2 + \frac{7\sqrt{3}}{2}uv + \frac{7}{4}v^2 - 9 = 0$$

$$9u^2 + v^2 - 9 = 0$$

$$9u^2 + v^2 = 9$$

$$\frac{u^2}{1} + \frac{v^2}{9} = 1$$

c. Finding a: $a^2 = 9 \implies a = 3$

The vertices are: $(u,v) = (0,-3),(0,3)$

Sketching the graph:

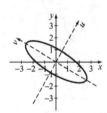

15. Given: $r = \dfrac{6}{3-6\sin\theta} = \dfrac{2}{1-2\sin\theta} \Rightarrow e = 2$; hyperbola

$\theta = \dfrac{\pi}{2}$ gives $r = \dfrac{6}{3-6\sin\dfrac{\pi}{2}} = -2$ and $\theta = \dfrac{3\pi}{2}$ gives $r = \dfrac{6}{3-6\sin\dfrac{3\pi}{2}} = \dfrac{2}{3}$

Vertices $= \left(-2, \dfrac{\pi}{2}\right), \left(\dfrac{2}{3}, \dfrac{3\pi}{2}\right)$. Other points: $(2,0), (2,\pi), \left(1, \dfrac{7\pi}{6}\right), \left(1, \dfrac{11\pi}{6}\right)$. Sketching the graph:

16. Given: $r = \dfrac{4}{4+2\cos\theta} = \dfrac{1}{1+0.5\cos\theta} \Rightarrow e = 0.5$; ellipse

$\theta = 0$ gives $r = \dfrac{4}{4+2\cos 0} = \dfrac{2}{3}$ and $\theta = \pi$ gives $r = \dfrac{4}{4+2\cos\pi} = 2$

Vertices $= \left(\dfrac{2}{3}, 0\right), (2,\pi)$. Other points: $\left(1, \dfrac{\pi}{2}\right), \left(1, \dfrac{3\pi}{2}\right), \left(\dfrac{4}{5}, \dfrac{\pi}{3}\right), \left(\dfrac{4}{3}, \dfrac{2\pi}{3}\right)$. Sketching the graph:

17. Solving for t:

$$x = -t + 2$$
$$t = 2 - x$$

Substituting:

$$y = -t^2 + 1$$
$$y = -(2-x)^2 + 1, \; 0 \le x \le 4$$

Completing the table:

t	−2	−1	0	1	2
$x = -t+2$	4	3	2	1	0
$y = -t^2+1$	−3	0	1	0	−3

Sketching the graph:

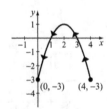

18. Solving for $\cos t$ and $\sin t$:

$$x = -3\cos t \;\Rightarrow\; -\frac{x}{3} = \cos t,\; y = \sin t$$

Substituting:

$$\left(-\frac{x}{3}\right)^2 + y^2 = \cos^2 t + \sin^2 t$$

$$\frac{x^2}{9} + y^2 = 1,\, -3 \le x \le 3$$

Completing the table:

t	0	$\dfrac{\pi}{6}$	$\dfrac{\pi}{3}$	$\dfrac{\pi}{2}$	π	$\dfrac{3\pi}{2}$	2π
$x = -3\cos t$	-3	$-\dfrac{3\sqrt{3}}{2}$	$-\dfrac{3}{2}$	0	3	0	-3
$y = \sin t$	0	$\dfrac{1}{2}$	$\dfrac{\sqrt{3}}{2}$	1	0	-1	0

Sketching the graph:

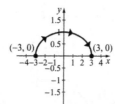

19. Having the center correspond with the origin, we have from the figure $a = 20$ and $b = 12$.
Thus: $c^2 = a^2 - b^2 = 400 - 144 = 256 \;\Rightarrow\; c = 16$
They should stand 16 feet from the center of the gallery.

20. Having the vertex correspond with the origin, the equation of the parabola would be $x^2 = 4py$. By the dimensions of the cross-section, the parabola passes through $(1, 4)$.

Substituting: $1^2 = 4p(4) \;\Rightarrow\; p = \dfrac{1}{16}$.

The receiver should be placed $\dfrac{1}{16}$ inches from the vertex.

21. **a.** Finding the parametric equations:

$$x = v_0 (\cos \theta)t = 100(\cos 30°)t = 100\left(\frac{\sqrt{3}}{2}\right)t = \left(50\sqrt{3}\right)t$$

$$y = -16t^2 + v_0(\sin \theta)t + h = -16t^2 + 100(\sin 30°)t + 3 = -16t^2 + 100\left(\frac{1}{2}\right)t + 3 = -16t^2 + 50t + 3$$

b. Finding when the ball hits the ground:

$$-16t^2 + 50t + 3 = 0$$

$$16t^2 - 50t - 3 = 0$$

$$t = \frac{50 \pm \sqrt{(-50)^2 - 4(16)(-3)}}{2(16)} \approx 3.1839$$

The horizontal distance traveled is: $x = 50\sqrt{3}(3.1839) \approx 276$ feet

Chapter 10
More Topics in Algebra

10.1 Sequences

1. This statement is true.

3. Finding the balance: $A = 100\left(1 + \dfrac{0.04}{2}\right)^{2(2)} \approx \$108.24$

5. Finding the first three terms:
$$a_0 = 4 + 6(0) = 4$$
$$a_1 = 4 + 6(1) = 10$$
$$a_2 = 4 + 6(2) = 16$$

7. Finding the first three terms:
$$a_0 = -5 + 3(0) = -5$$
$$a_1 = -5 + 3(1) = -2$$
$$a_2 = -5 + 3(2) = 1$$

9. Finding the first three terms:
$$a_0 = -4 - 4(0) = -4$$
$$a_1 = -4 - 4(1) = -8$$
$$a_2 = -4 - 4(2) = -12$$

11. Finding the first three terms:
$$a_0 = 8 - 2(0) = 8$$
$$a_1 = 8 - 2(1) = 6$$
$$a_2 = 8 - 2(2) = 4$$

13. Finding the first three terms:
$$a_0 = 7\left(4^0\right) = 7(1) = 7$$
$$a_1 = 7\left(4^1\right) = 7(4) = 28$$
$$a_2 = 7\left(4^2\right) = 7(16) = 112$$

15. Finding the first three terms:
$$a_0 = 5\left(3^0\right) = 5(1) = 5$$
$$a_1 = 5\left(3^1\right) = 5(3) = 15$$
$$a_2 = 5\left(3^2\right) = 5(9) = 45$$

17. Finding the first three terms:
$$a_0 = -2\left(3^0\right) = -2(1) = -2$$
$$a_1 = -2\left(3^1\right) = -2(3) = -6$$
$$a_2 = -2\left(3^2\right) = -2(9) = -18$$

19. Finding the first three terms:
$$a_0 = -3\left(5^0\right) = -3(1) = -3$$
$$a_1 = -3\left(5^1\right) = -3(5) = -15$$
$$a_2 = -3\left(5^2\right) = -3(25) = -75$$

21. Finding d: $d = a_1 - a_0 = 3 - (-3) = 6$

The rule is: $a_n = -3 + 6n$

23. Finding d: $d = g(7) - g(6) = 12 - 8 = 4$

Finding the first term:
$$g(6) = g(0) + 4(6)$$
$$8 = g(0) + 24$$
$$g(0) = -16$$

The rule is: $g(n) = -16 + 4n$

25. Finding d:
$$b_{12} = b_{10} + d(2)$$
$$16 = 10 + 2d$$
$$d = 3$$
The rule is: $b_n = -20 + 3n$

Finding the first term:
$$b_6 = b_0 + 3(12)$$
$$16 = b_0 + 36$$
$$b_0 = -20$$

27. Finding the first term:
$$a_9 = a_0 + 5(9)$$
$$55 = a_0 + 45$$
$$a_0 = 10$$
The rule is: $a_n = 10 + 5n$

29. Finding the first term:
$$a_8 = a_0 - 2(8)$$
$$5 = a_0 - 16$$
$$a_0 = 21$$
The rule is: $a_n = 21 - 2n$

31. Finding the first term:
$$b_6 = b_0 + \frac{1}{2}(6)$$
$$13 = b_0 + 3$$
$$b_0 = 10$$
The rule is: $b_n = 10 + \frac{1}{2}n$

33. Finding r: $r = \dfrac{a_1}{a_0} = \dfrac{6}{3} = 2$

The rule is: $a_n = 3(2)^n$

35. Finding r: $r = \dfrac{h(3)}{h(2)} = \dfrac{128}{32} = 4$

Finding the first term:
$$h(2) = h(0) \cdot (4)^2$$
$$32 = 16 \cdot h(0)$$
$$h(0) = 2$$
The rule is: $h(n) = 2(4)^n$

37. Finding r:
$$b_7 = b_4 (r)^3$$
$$\frac{3}{128} = \frac{3}{16} r^3$$
$$r^3 = \frac{1}{8}$$
$$r = \frac{1}{2}$$
Finding the first term:
$$b_4 = b_0 \left(\frac{1}{2}\right)^4$$
$$\frac{3}{16} = \frac{1}{16} b_0$$
$$b_0 = 3$$

The rule is: $b_n = 3\left(\dfrac{1}{2}\right)^n$

39. Finding the first term:

$$a_5 = a_0 (2)^5$$
$$128 = 32a_0$$
$$a_0 = 4$$

The rule is: $a_n = 4(2)^n$

41. Finding the first term:

$$b_4 = b_0 \left(\frac{3}{2}\right)^4$$
$$\frac{81}{4} = \frac{81}{16} b_0$$
$$b_0 = 4$$

The rule is: $b_n = 4\left(\frac{3}{2}\right)^n$

43. Finding the first term:

$$a_4 = a_0 (5)^4$$
$$2500 = 625a_0$$
$$a_0 = 4$$

The rule is: $a_n = 4(5)^n$

45. Finding d: $d = a_2 - a_1 = 8 - 5 = 3$

Finding the first term:

$$a_1 = a_0 + 3(1)$$
$$5 = a_0 + 3$$
$$a_0 = 2$$

The rule is $a_n = 2 + 3n$, therefore: $a_3 = 2 + 3(3) = 11$

47. Finding d: $d = a_2 - a_1 = 6 - 2 = 4$

Finding the first term:

$$a_1 = a_0 + 4(1)$$
$$2 = a_0 + 4$$
$$a_0 = -2$$

The rule is $a_n = -2 + 4n$, therefore: $a_3 = -2 + 4(3) = 10$

49. Finding d: $d = a_2 - a_1 = 1 - 3 = -2$

Finding the first term:

$$a_1 = a_0 - 2(1)$$
$$3 = a_0 - 2$$
$$a_0 = 5$$

The rule is $a_n = 5 - 2n$, therefore: $a_3 = 5 - 2(3) = -1$

51. Finding r: $r = \dfrac{a_2}{a_1} = \dfrac{9}{3} = 3$

Finding the first term:

$$a_1 = a_0 (3)^1$$
$$3 = 3a_0$$
$$a_0 = 1$$

Therefore: $a_3 = 1(3)^3 = 27$

53. Finding r: $r = \dfrac{a_2}{a_1} = \dfrac{50}{10} = 5$

Finding the first term:

$$a_1 = a_0 (5)^1$$
$$10 = 5a_0$$
$$a_0 = 2$$

Therefore: $a_3 = 2(5)^3 = 250$

55. Finding r: $r = \dfrac{a_2}{a_1} = \dfrac{1/8}{1/4} = \dfrac{1}{2}$

Finding the first term:

$$a_1 = a_0 \left(\frac{1}{2}\right)^1$$
$$\frac{1}{4} = \frac{1}{2} a_0$$
$$a_0 = \frac{1}{2}$$

Therefore: $a_3 = \dfrac{1}{2}\left(\dfrac{1}{2}\right)^3 = \dfrac{1}{16}$

57. The difference between successive terms is 2 so the sequence is arithmetic.
59. The ratio of successive terms is 3 so the sequence is geometric.
61. The difference between successive terms is -4 so the sequence is arithmetic.
63. The ratio of successive terms is $\dfrac{1}{3}$ so the sequence is geometric.
65. The difference between successive terms is $\dfrac{1}{250}$ so the sequence is arithmetic.
67. The ratio of successive terms is 0.2 so the sequence is geometric.
69. **a.** The annual interest is $\$2000(0.06) = \$120$.

Completing the table:

Year	Total Value ($)
1	$2{,}000 + 120 = 2{,}120$
2	$2{,}120 + 120 = 2{,}000 + 120(2) = 2{,}240$
3	$2{,}240 + 120 = 2{,}000 + 120(3) = 2{,}360$
4	$2{,}360 + 120 = 2{,}000 + 120(4) = 2{,}480$

   b. The value is given by: $V = 2000 + 120n$

71. **a.** The sequence is arithmetic, since the number of stitches in successive rows differs by 4.
   b. Computing the rows:
$$\text{row } 1: a_1 = 100$$
$$\text{row } 2: a_2 = 104 = 100 + 4$$
$$\text{row } 3: a_3 = 108 = 100 + 4(2)$$
$$\text{row } 4: a_4 = 112 = 100 + 4(3)$$
$$\vdots$$
$$\text{row } n: a_n = 100 + 4(n - 1)$$

   c. Using the general formula:
$$168 = 100 + 4(n - 1)$$
$$68 = 4n - 4$$
$$72 = 4n$$
$$18 = n$$
There must be 18 rows knitted.

73. **a.** The sequence is geometric, since the ratio of successive frequencies is 2.
   b. Finding the next two terms:
$$220 \times 2 = 440 \text{ Hz}$$
$$440 \times 2 = 220 \times 2(2) = 880 \text{ Hz}$$

   c. Computing the rows:
$$1 \to a_1 = 55$$
$$2 \to a_2 = 110 = 55(2)$$
$$3 \to a_3 = 220 = 110(2) = 55(2)(2) = 55(2)^2$$
$$4 \to a_4 = 440 = 220(2) = 55(2)^2(2) = 55(2)^3$$
$$\vdots$$
$$n \to a_n = 55(2)^{n-1}$$

75. The sequence is geometric, since the ratio of salaries for successive years is 1.04:
$$a_n = 40{,}000(1.04)^n \qquad\qquad a_6 = 40{,}000(1.04)^6 \approx \$50{,}613$$

77. **a.** Finding the amount of cells after 4 hours:

$$0 \text{ hr} \rightarrow a_0 = 10,000$$

$$1 \text{ hr} \rightarrow a_1 = 10,000(2) = 20,000$$

$$2 \text{ hr} \rightarrow a_2 = 20,000(2) = 10,000(2)(2) = 40,000$$

$$3 \text{ hr} \rightarrow a_3 = 40,000(2) = 10,000(2)^2(2) = 80,000$$

$$4 \text{ hr} \rightarrow a_4 = 80,000(2) = 10,000(2)^3(2) = 160,000$$

b. The sequence is geometric, since the ratio of the number of cells for successive hours is 2.

c. Based on the pattern established in part **a**, $a_n = 10,000(2)^n$. Thus;

$$1,280,000 = 10,000(2)^n$$

$$128 = (2)^n$$

$$n\ln 2 = \ln 128$$

$$n = \frac{\ln 128}{\ln 2} = 7 \text{ hours}$$

79. **a.** Looking at the sequence of perimeters:

$$1 \rightarrow P_1 = 4(1) = 4$$

$$2 \rightarrow P_2 = 4(2) = 8$$

$$3 \rightarrow P_3 = 4(3) = 12$$

$$4 \rightarrow P_4 = 4(4) = 16$$

$$\vdots$$

$$n \rightarrow P_n = 4n$$

The perimeters of the boards form an arithmetic sequence, since the difference of successive perimeters is 4.

b. Looking at the sequence of areas:

$$1 \rightarrow A_1 = (1)^2 = 1$$

$$2 \rightarrow A_2 = (2)^2 = 4$$

$$3 \rightarrow A_3 = (3)^2 = 9$$

$$4 \rightarrow A_4 = (4)^2 = 16$$

$$\vdots$$

$$n \rightarrow A_n = n^2$$

The sequence is neither arithmetic nor geometric, it is a sequence of squared terms.

81. **a.** The function is: $f(n) = 550.1 + 28.11n$

b. In 2007, $n = 2007 - 1999 = 8$. Evaluating the function: $f(8) = 550.1 + 28.11(8) = 774.98 \approx \$775$ billion

83. The terms are: $a_0, a_0, a_0, \ldots$

85. **a.** Finding d:

$$a_3 = a_1 + d(2)$$

$$9 = 1 + 2d$$

$$d = 4$$

Finding the first term:

$$a_1 = a_0 + 4(1)$$

$$1 = a_0 + 4$$

$$a_0 = -3$$

The sequence is: $a_n = -3 + 4n$

b. Finding r:

$$a_3 = a_1 r^2$$
$$9 = 1r^2$$
$$9 = r^2$$
$$r = 3$$

Finding the first term:

$$a_1 = a_0 (3)^1$$
$$1 = 3a_0$$
$$a_0 = \frac{1}{3}$$

The sequence is: $a_n = \frac{1}{3}(3)^n$

c. Finding the next five terms assuming an arithmetic sequence:

$$a_4 = -3 + 4(4) = 13 \qquad\qquad a_5 = -3 + 4(5) = 17$$
$$a_6 = -3 + 4(6) = 21 \qquad\qquad a_7 = -3 + 4(7) = 25$$
$$a_8 = -3 + 4(8) = 29$$

d. Finding the next five terms assuming a geometric sequence:

$$a_4 = \frac{1}{3}(3)^4 = 27 \qquad\qquad a_5 = \frac{1}{3}(3)^5 = 81$$
$$a_6 = \frac{1}{3}(3)^6 = 243 \qquad\qquad a_7 = \frac{1}{3}(3)^7 = 729$$
$$a_8 = \frac{1}{3}(3)^8 = 2{,}187$$

e. The sequence in part **b** grows faster because it is geometric.

87. Following the pattern, the next two terms are $(1+x)^4$ and $(1+x)^5$. The common ratio is $r = \dfrac{(1+x)^3}{(1+x)^2} = 1 + x$.

89. This sequence is geometric, since each term can be written in the form $a_n^3 = a_0^3 \left(r^3\right)^n$.

10.2 Sums of Terms of Sequences

1. This statement is false.

3. Finding the balance: $A = 1000\left(1 + \dfrac{0.02}{2}\right)^{2(2)} = \$1{,}040.60$

5. Using $a_0 = 3, d = 3, n = 14$, find the sum: $S_{14} = \dfrac{14}{2}(2(3) + 3(14-1)) = 7(45) = 315$

7. Using $a_0 = 3, d = 3, n = 14$, find the sum: $S_{14} = \dfrac{14}{2}(2(-6) + 5(14-1)) = 7(53) = 371$

9. Using $a_0 = 2, d = 5, n = 14$, find the sum: $S_{14} = \dfrac{14}{2}(2(2) + 5(14-1)) = 7(69) = 483$

11. Using $a_0 = 3, r = \dfrac{6}{3} = 2$, find the sum: $S_8 = 3\left(\dfrac{1-2^8}{1-2}\right) = 3\left(\dfrac{1-256}{-1}\right) = 3(255) = 765$

13. Using $a_0 = 6, r = \dfrac{3}{6} = \dfrac{1}{2}$, find the sum: $S_8 = 6\left(\dfrac{1-\left(\frac{1}{2}\right)^8}{1-\frac{1}{2}}\right) = 6\left(\dfrac{1-\frac{1}{256}}{\frac{1}{2}}\right) = 6\left(\dfrac{255}{128}\right) = \dfrac{765}{64} = 11\dfrac{61}{64}$

15. Using $a_0 = 2, r = \dfrac{3}{2}$, find the sum: $S_8 = 2\left(\dfrac{1-\left(\frac{3}{2}\right)^8}{1-\frac{3}{2}}\right) = 2\left(\dfrac{1-\frac{6561}{256}}{-\frac{1}{2}}\right) = 2\left(\dfrac{6305}{128}\right) = \dfrac{6305}{64} = 98\dfrac{33}{64}$

17. Finding the sum: $3 + 6 + 9 + \cdots + 90 = S_{30} = \dfrac{30}{2}(3 + 90) = 1{,}395$

19. Finding the sum: $10 + 13 + 16 + \cdots + 55 = S_{16} = \dfrac{16}{2}(10 + 55) = 520$

21. Finding the sum: $4 + 9 + 14 + \cdots + (5n + 4) = S_n = \dfrac{n}{2}[4 + (5n + 4)] = \dfrac{n}{2}(5n + 8)$

23. Finding the value of n:

$$a_n = (5)^n$$
$$78{,}125 = 5^n$$
$$n = \dfrac{\ln 78{,}125}{\ln 5} = 7$$

Finding the sum: $1 + 5 + 25 + \cdots + 78{,}125 = \dfrac{1 - 5^8}{1 - 5} = \dfrac{-390{,}624}{-4} = 97{,}656$

25. Finding the value of n:

$$a_n = 2(3)^n$$
$$1458 = 2(3)^n$$
$$729 = 3^n$$
$$n = \dfrac{\ln 729}{\ln 3} = 6$$

Finding the sum: $2 + 6 + 18 + \cdots + 1458 = 2\left(\dfrac{1 - 3^7}{1 - 3}\right) = 2\left(\dfrac{-2186}{-2}\right) = 2{,}186$

27. There are $\dfrac{125 - 5}{2} + 1 = 61$ odd numbers between 5 and 125, inclusive. Therefore:

$$S_{61} = \dfrac{61}{2}(5 + 125) = \dfrac{61}{2}(130) = 3{,}965$$

29. There are $\dfrac{115 - 27}{2} + 1 = 45$ odd numbers between 27 and 115, inclusive. Therefore:

$$S_{45} = \dfrac{45}{2}(27 + 115) = \dfrac{45}{2}(142) = 3{,}195$$

31. There are $\dfrac{130 - 4}{2} + 1 = 64$ even numbers between 4 and 130, inclusive. Therefore:

$$S_{64} = \dfrac{64}{2}(4 + 130) = 32(134) = 4{,}288$$

33. There are $\dfrac{102 - 10}{2} + 1 = 47$ even numbers between 10 and 102, inclusive. Therefore:

$$S_{47} = \dfrac{47}{2}(10 + 102) = \dfrac{47}{2}(112) = 2{,}632$$

35. Finding the sum: $\displaystyle\sum_{i=0}^{6} 2i = \frac{7}{2}(0+12) = 42$

37. Finding the sum: $\displaystyle\sum_{i=0}^{10}(5+2i) = \frac{11}{2}(5+25) = 165$

39. Finding the sum: $\displaystyle\sum_{i=0}^{4}\left(\frac{1}{2}\right)^i = \frac{1-\left(\frac{1}{2}\right)^5}{1-\frac{1}{2}} = \frac{31/32}{1/2} = \frac{31}{16} = 1\frac{15}{16}$

41. Finding the sum: $\displaystyle\sum_{i=0}^{4} 8(3^i) = 8\left(\frac{1-3^5}{1-3}\right) = 8\left(\frac{-242}{-2}\right) = 968$

43. **a.** Here $a_0 = 2$, the common difference is $d = 2$, and there are $\dfrac{40-2}{2}+1 = 20$ terms in the sum: $\displaystyle\sum_{i=0}^{19}(2+2i)$

    b. Finding the sum: $\displaystyle\sum_{i=0}^{19}(2+2i) = \frac{20}{2}(2+40) = 420$

45. **a.** Here $a_1 = a$, the common difference is $d = a$, and there are $\dfrac{60a-a}{a}+1 = 60$ terms in the sum: $\displaystyle\sum_{i=1}^{60}(ai)$

    b. Finding the sum: $\displaystyle\sum_{i=1}^{60} ai = \frac{60}{2}(a+60a) = 30(61a) = 1830a$

47. **a.** The common ratio is $r = 2$ and the general term is $a_n = 2^n$. Thus $1024 = 2^n \Rightarrow n = 10$: $\displaystyle\sum_{i=1}^{10} 2^i$

    b. Finding the sum: $\displaystyle\sum_{i=1}^{10} 2^i = \sum_{i=0}^{9} 2^{i+1} = \sum_{i=0}^{9} 2(2)^i = 2\left(\frac{1-2^{10}}{1-2}\right) = 2{,}046$

49. **a.** The common ratio is $r = a$ and the general term is $a_n = a^n$. Thus $a^{40} = a^n \Rightarrow n = 40$: $\displaystyle\sum_{i=1}^{40} a^i$

    b. Finding the sum: $\displaystyle\sum_{i=1}^{40} a^i = \sum_{i=0}^{39} a^{i+1} = \sum_{i=0}^{39} a(a^i) = a\left(\frac{1-a^{40}}{1-a}\right)$

51. **a.** Writing in summation notation: $\displaystyle\sum_{i=0}^{24}(2.5i)$

    b. Finding the sum: $\displaystyle\sum_{i=0}^{24} 2.5i = \frac{25}{2}\left[0 + 2.5(24)\right] = \frac{25}{2}(60) = 750$

53. **a.** Writing in summation notation: $\displaystyle\sum_{i=0}^{44}(0.5)^i$

    b. Finding the sum: $\displaystyle\sum_{i=0}^{44}(0.5)^i = \frac{1-(0.5)^{45}}{1-0.5} = 2$

55. The sum is arithmetic, with $d = 2$: $\displaystyle\sum_{k=0}^{6}(2k+1) = \frac{7}{2}(1+13) = 49$

57. The sum is arithmetic, with $d = 0.5$: $\displaystyle\sum_{k=0}^{20}(0.5k) = \frac{21}{2}(0+10) = 105$

59. The sum is geometric, with $r = 2$: $\displaystyle\sum_{k=0}^{6} 2^{k-1} = \sum_{k=0}^{6} 2^{k}\left(2^{-1}\right) = \sum_{k=0}^{6} \frac{1}{2}\left(2^{k}\right) = \frac{1}{2}\left(\frac{1-2^{7}}{1-2}\right) = \frac{127}{2}$

61. The sum is geometric, with $r = 0.5$: $\displaystyle\sum_{k=5}^{10} (0.5)^{k-4} = \sum_{k=0}^{5} (0.5)^{(k+5)-4} = \sum_{k=0}^{5} (0.5)^{k+1} = \sum_{k=0}^{5} (0.5)(0.5)^{k} = 0.5\left(\frac{1-(0.5)^{6}}{1-0.5}\right) = \frac{63}{64}$

63. The sum is geometric, with $r = 0.5$: $\displaystyle\sum_{k=1}^{5} 2(0.5)^{k} = \sum_{k=0}^{4} 2(0.5)^{k+1} = \sum_{k=0}^{4} 2(0.5)^{k}(0.5) = \sum_{k=0}^{4} (0.5)^{k} = \left(\frac{1-(0.5)^{5}}{1-0.5}\right) = \frac{31}{16} = 1\frac{15}{16}$

65. The sum is arithmetic, with $d = 6$: $\displaystyle\sum_{k=0}^{5} \left(3(k+2)+3(k-1)\right) = \sum_{k=0}^{5} (6k+3) = \frac{6}{2}(3+33) = 108$

67. Since $r = \dfrac{3}{6} = \dfrac{1}{2}$, $|r| < 1$ so the series has a sum. Using $a_0 = 6$, the sum is: $S = \dfrac{6}{1-\dfrac{1}{2}} = \dfrac{6}{\dfrac{1}{2}} = 12$

69. Since $r = \dfrac{3}{9} = \dfrac{1}{3}$, $|r| < 1$ so the series has a sum. Using $a_0 = 9$, the sum is: $S = \dfrac{9}{1-\dfrac{1}{3}} = \dfrac{9}{\dfrac{2}{3}} = \dfrac{27}{2}$

71. Since $r = \dfrac{8}{4} = 2$, $|r| > 1$ so the series does not have a sum.

73. Since $r = 0.5$, $|r| < 1$ so the series has a sum. Using $a_0 = 2$, the sum is: $S = \dfrac{2}{1-0.5} = \dfrac{2}{0.5} = 4$

75. Since $r = \dfrac{1}{5}$, $|r| < 1$ so the series has a sum. Using $a_0 = 3$, the sum is: $S = \dfrac{3}{1-\dfrac{1}{5}} = \dfrac{3}{\dfrac{4}{5}} = \dfrac{15}{4}$

77. **a.** Finding the number of boxes:
$$1+2+3+\cdots+n = 55$$
$$\frac{n(n+1)}{2} = 55$$
$$n^2 + n = 110$$
$$n^2 + n - 110 = 0$$
$$(n+11)(n-10) = 0$$
$$n = 10 \quad (n \ne -11)$$
There must be 10 boxes placed in the bottom row.

b. The next possible arrangement would require 11 boxes in the bottom row, accounting for 66 boxes, followed by the arrangement requiring 12 boxes on the bottom row, calling for 78 boxes. Therefore it is impossible to have 70 boxes arranged in this manner.

c. From part **b**, using 11 boxes for the bottom row will result in 66 boxes used, leaving 4 boxes left over.

79. Finding the sum:
$$S = 1500(1.06)^{18} + 1500(1.06)^{17} + 1500(1.06)^{16} + \cdots + 1500(1.06) + 1500 = 1500\left(\frac{1-(1.06)^{19}}{1-1.06}\right) = \$50{,}639.99$$

81. When the ball hits the ground on the first bounce, it has traveled 10 ft: $a_1 = 10$.

Bounce 2: $a_2 = 2(10)\left(\dfrac{3}{4}\right)$

Bounce 3: $a_3 = 2\left[10\left(\dfrac{3}{4}\right)\right]\left(\dfrac{3}{4}\right) = 2(10)\left(\dfrac{3}{4}\right)^{2}$

Total distance: $10 + 2(10)\left(\dfrac{3}{4}\right) + 2(10)\left(\dfrac{3}{4}\right)^{2} = 10 + 15 + 11.25 = 36.25$ feet

83. **a.** This is a geometric sequence: $1 + 7 + 7^2 + 7^3 + 7^4 = \sum_{i=0}^{4} 7^i$

b. Finding the sum: $\sum_{i=0}^{4} 7^i = \dfrac{1 - 7^5}{1 - 7} = \dfrac{-16,806}{-6} = 2,801$

85. The following expressions hold:

$a_0 = 4; \quad a_0 + a_1 + a_2 = 24 \implies a_1 + a_2 = 20$

$a_1 = a_0 + d \implies a_1 = 4 + d$

$a_2 = a_0 + 2d \implies a_2 = 4 + 2d$

Substituting:

$$a_1 + a_2 = 20$$
$$(4 + d) + (4 + 2d) = 20$$
$$8 + 3d = 20$$
$$3d = 12$$
$$d = 4$$

Finding the sum: $\sum_{i=0}^{7} (4 + 4i) = \dfrac{8}{2}(4 + 32) = 144$

87. Finding d:

$$a_6 - a_2 = 4d$$
$$2 - 13 = 4d$$
$$-12 = 4d$$
$$d = -3$$

Using $a_0 = 20$, the sum is: $\sum_{k=1}^{8} (20 - 3i) = \dfrac{8}{2}(17 - 4) = 52$

89. Finding a_0:

$$3 = \sum_{j=0}^{4} a_0 \left(\frac{1}{2}\right)^j$$

$$3 = a_0 \left(\dfrac{1 - \left(\frac{1}{2}\right)^5}{1 - \frac{1}{2}} \right)$$

$$3 = \frac{31}{16} a_0$$

$$a_0 = \frac{48}{31}$$

10.3 General Sequences and Series

1. Finding the first five terms:
$$a_0 = -4(0) + 6 = 6 \qquad a_1 = -4(1) + 6 = 2$$
$$a_2 = -4(2) + 6 = -2 \qquad a_3 = -4(3) + 6 = -6$$
$$a_4 = -4(4) + 6 = -10$$

3. Finding the first five terms:
$$a_0 = -4\left(\frac{1}{3}\right)^0 = -4 \qquad a_1 = -4\left(\frac{1}{3}\right)^1 = -\frac{4}{3}$$
$$a_2 = -4\left(\frac{1}{3}\right)^2 = -\frac{4}{9} \qquad a_3 = -4\left(\frac{1}{3}\right)^3 = -\frac{4}{27}$$
$$a_4 = -4\left(\frac{1}{3}\right)^4 = -\frac{4}{81}$$

5. Finding the first five terms:
$$b_0 = (0)^2 + 4 = 4 \qquad b_1 = (1)^2 + 4 = 5$$
$$b_2 = (2)^2 + 4 = 8 \qquad b_3 = (3)^2 + 4 = 13$$
$$b_4 = (4)^2 + 4 = 20$$

7. Finding the first five terms:
$$f(1) = \frac{1}{2(1)^2 + 1} = \frac{1}{3} \qquad f(2) = \frac{2}{2(2)^2 + 1} = \frac{2}{9}$$
$$f(3) = \frac{3}{2(3)^2 + 1} = \frac{3}{19} \qquad f(4) = \frac{4}{2(4)^2 + 1} = \frac{4}{33}$$
$$f(5) = \frac{5}{2(5)^2 + 1} = \frac{5}{51}$$

9. Finding the first five terms:
$$a_0 = (-1)^0 e^{0+1} = e \qquad a_1 = (-1)^1 e^{1+1} = -e^2$$
$$a_2 = (-1)^2 e^{2+1} = e^3 \qquad a_3 = (-1)^3 e^{3+1} = -e^4$$
$$a_4 = (-1)^4 e^{4+1} = e^5$$

11. Finding the first five terms:
$$g(1) = \frac{2^1 + 1}{(1)^2 + 1} = \frac{3}{2} \qquad g(2) = \frac{2^2 + 1}{(2)^2 + 1} = \frac{5}{5} = 1$$
$$g(3) = \frac{2^3 + 1}{(3)^2 + 1} = \frac{9}{10} \qquad g(4) = \frac{2^4 + 1}{(4)^2 + 1} = \frac{17}{17} = 1$$
$$g(5) = \frac{2^5 + 1}{(5)^2 + 1} = \frac{33}{26}$$

13. Finding the first five terms:
$$a_0 = \sqrt{2(0) + 4} = 2 \qquad a_1 = \sqrt{2(1) + 4} = \sqrt{6}$$
$$a_2 = \sqrt{2(2) + 4} = \sqrt{8} = 2\sqrt{2} \qquad a_3 = \sqrt{2(3) + 4} = \sqrt{10}$$
$$a_4 = \sqrt{2(4) + 4} = \sqrt{12} = 2\sqrt{3}$$

15. Finding the first five terms:

$$a_0 = (0)^2 + 2 = 2 \qquad\qquad a_1 = (1)^2 + 2 = 3$$

$$a_2 = (2)^2 + 2 = 6 \qquad\qquad a_3 = (3)^2 + 2 = 11$$

$$a_4 = (4)^2 + 2 = 18$$

17. Finding the first five terms:

$$a_0 = 2(0)^3 = 0 \qquad\qquad a_1 = 2(1)^3 = 2$$

$$a_2 = 2(2)^3 = 16 \qquad\qquad a_3 = 2(3)^3 = 54$$

$$a_4 = 2(4)^3 = 128$$

19. The difference of successive terms is –4 so this is an arithmetic sequence with $a_0 = -2$ and $d = -4$:

$$a_n = -2 - 4n, n = 0, 1, 2, 3, \ldots$$

21. Each term is the reciprocal of a power of 2: $a_n = \dfrac{1}{2^n}, n = 0, 1, 2, 3, \ldots$

23. Each term is the square root of successive whole numbers: $a_n = \sqrt{n}, n = 1, 2, 3, \ldots$

25. Each term is a power of 0.4: $a_n = (0.4)^n, n = 0, 1, 2, \ldots$

27. Each term is the square root of a multiple of 3: $a_n = \sqrt{3n}, n = 1, 2, 3, \ldots$

29. Finding the first four terms:

$$a_0 = 6 \qquad\qquad a_1 = 6 - 2 = 4$$

$$a_2 = 4 - 2 = 2 \qquad\qquad a_3 = 2 - 2 = 0$$

31. Finding the first four terms:

$$b_1 = 4 \qquad\qquad b_2 = \frac{1}{4}(4) = 1$$

$$b_3 = \frac{1}{4}(1) = \frac{1}{4} \qquad\qquad b_4 = \frac{1}{4}\left(\frac{1}{4}\right) = \frac{1}{16}$$

33. Finding the first four terms:

$$a_0 = -1 \qquad\qquad a_1 = -1 + 1 = 0$$

$$a_2 = 0 + 2 = 2 \qquad\qquad a_3 = 2 + 3 = 5$$

35. Finding the first four terms:

$$b_1 = \sqrt{3} \qquad\qquad b_2 = \sqrt{\sqrt{3} + 3}$$

$$b_3 = \sqrt{\sqrt{\sqrt{3} + 3} + 3} \qquad\qquad b_4 = \sqrt{\sqrt{\sqrt{\sqrt{3} + 3} + 3} + 3}$$

37. Finding the first four terms:

$$a_0 = -4 \qquad\qquad a_1 = -4 + 2 = -2$$

$$a_2 = -2 + 2 = 0 \qquad\qquad a_3 = 0 + 2 = 2$$

The rule is: $a_n = -4 + 2n, n = 0, 1, 2, 3, \ldots$

39. Finding the first four terms:

$$b_1 = 6 \qquad\qquad b_2 = \frac{1}{2}(6) = 3$$

$$b_3 = \frac{1}{2}(3) = \frac{3}{2} \qquad\qquad b_4 = \frac{1}{2}\left(\frac{3}{2}\right) = \frac{3}{4}$$

The rule is: $b_n = 6\left(\dfrac{1}{2}\right)^{n-1}, n = 1, 2, 3, 4, \ldots$

41. **a.** The recursive formula is: $p_1 = 200,\ p_n = 1.04\,p_{n-1}$

      b. Writing in terms of n: $p_n = 200(1.04)^n$

      c. Finding the price after 3 years: $p_3 = 200(1.04)^3 \approx \$224.97$

      d. Finding the time:

$$250 = 200(1.04)^n$$
$$1.25 = (1.04)^n$$
$$\ln 1.25 = n \ln 1.04$$
$$n = \frac{\ln 1.25}{\ln 1.04} = 5.69 \approx 6 \text{ years}$$

      e. Finding the time:

$$300 = 200(1.04)^n$$
$$1.5 = (1.04)^n$$
$$\ln 1.5 = n \ln 1.04$$
$$n = \frac{\ln 1.5}{\ln 1.04} = 10.3 \approx 11 \text{ years}$$

43. **a.** The perimeter is given by: $P = 2h + 2w = 2(36) + 2w = 72 + 2w$

         Finding the expression: $P_n = 72 + 2\left(18 + \frac{1}{2}n\right) = 108 + n$

      b. The area is given by: $A = h \cdot w = 36w$

         Finding the expression: $A_n = 36\left(18 + \frac{1}{2}n\right) = 648 + 18n$

      c. The dimensions are: 36×20.5

         The perimeter is $P_5 = 113$ inches and the area is $A_5 = 738$ square inches.

      d. The cost function is: $c_n = 250 + 20(0.5n) = 250 + 10n$

         Finding the cost for each window:

$$19.5 \text{ in.} \Rightarrow n = 3 : c_3 = 250 + 10(3) = \$280$$
$$36 \text{ in.} \Rightarrow n = 36 : c_{36} = 250 + 10(36) = \$610$$

         The total cost is: $280 + 5(610) = \$3,330$

45. **a.** Completing the table:

Day	Matt's Contribution
1	a
2	$a + 0.03$
3	$a + 0.03 + 0.03 = a + 0.03(2)$
4	$a + 0.03(2) + 0.03 = a + 0.03(3)$
$\vdots$	$\vdots$
n	$a + 0.03(n-1)$

Thus for any day n, Matt's contribution is $a_n = a + 0.03(n-1)$ and the Aunt's contribution is therefore $b_n = a + 0.03(n-1) + 0.10$. Finding the value of a:

$$\sum_{i=1}^{21} a_i + \sum_{i=1}^{21} b_i = \$17.22$$

$$\frac{21}{2}\left[a + (a + 0.03(20))\right] + \frac{21}{2}\left[(a + 0.10) + (a + 0.03(20) + 0.10)\right] = 17.22$$

$$\frac{21}{2}(2a + 0.6) + \frac{21}{2}(2a + 0.8) = 17.22$$

$$(21a + 6.3) + (21a + 8.4) = 17.22$$

$$42a + 14.7 = 17.22$$

$$42a = 2.52$$

$$a = 0.06$$

Matt contributed $0.06 on the first day.

b. Finding the sum: $S_{21} = \frac{21}{2}\left[0.06 + (0.06 + 0.03(20))\right] = \frac{21}{2}(0.72) = \$7.56$

c. Matt's aunt donation is: $\$17.22 - \$7.56 = \$9.66$

47. For $n = 5$, the sum is: $\left|\sum_{i=0}^{n-1}(3i^2 - 2)\right| = \left|(-2) + 1 + 10 + 25 + 46 + 73\right| \geq 81$

49. Finding an expression for a_3: $a_3 = 3a_2 + 2 = 3(3a_1 + 2) + 2 = 9a_1 + 8 = 9(3a_0 + 2) + 8 = 27a_0 + 26$

Solving the equation:

$$a_3 = 27a_0 + 26$$
$$134 = 27a_0 + 26$$
$$108 = 27a_0$$
$$4 = a_0$$

51. It is alternating if $a_0 < 0$.

10.4 Counting Methods

1. Evaluating the expression: $4! = 4 \cdot 3 \cdot 2 \cdot 1 = 24$

3. Evaluating the expression: $\dfrac{5!}{2!} = \dfrac{120}{2} = 60$

5. Evaluating the expression: $\dfrac{6!}{4!} = \dfrac{6 \cdot 5 \cdot 4!}{4!} = 30$

7. Evaluating the expression: $P(4,3) = \dfrac{4!}{(4-3)!} = \dfrac{4!}{1!} = 4! = 24$

9. Evaluating the expression: $P(7,5) = \dfrac{7!}{(7-5)!} = \dfrac{7!}{2!} = \dfrac{5040}{2} = 2,520$

11. Evaluating the expression: $P(8,5) = \dfrac{8!}{(8-5)!} = \dfrac{8!}{3!} = 8 \cdot 7 \cdot 6 \cdot 5 \cdot 4 = 6,720$

13. Evaluating the expression: $C(4,3) = \dfrac{(4)(3)(2)}{3!} = \dfrac{24}{6} = 4$

15. Evaluating the expression: $C(8,5) = \dfrac{(8)(7)(6)(5)(4)}{5!} = 56$

17. Evaluating the expression: $\binom{8}{6} = \frac{8!}{(2!)(6!)} = \frac{(8)(7)}{2!} = 28$

19. Evaluating the expression: $\binom{8}{8} = \frac{8!}{(0!)(8!)} = 1$

21. Evaluating the expression: $\binom{100}{99} = \frac{100!}{(1!)(99!)} = \frac{100}{1!} = 100$

23. There are $(3)(2)(1) = 6$ possible arrangements: BCZ, BZC, CBZ, CZB, ZBC, ZCB.

25. There are $C(4,3) = \frac{4!}{(1!)(3!)} = \frac{4}{1!} = 4$ possible subcommittees: John, Maria, Susan; Susan, Angelo, John;

    John, Susan, Angelo; John, Maria, Angelo

27. There are $4! = 24$ different photographs possible.

29. There are $(2!)(3!) = (2)(6) = 12$ different photographs possible.

31. Finding the number of committees: $C(12,3) = \frac{12!}{(9!)(3!)} = \frac{(12)(11)(10)}{(3)(2)(1)} = (2)(11)(10) = 220$

33. The number of ways is: $C(10,2) = \frac{10!}{(8!)(2!)} = \frac{(10)(9)}{(2)(1)} = (5)(9) = 45$

35. The number of ways is: $C(20,4) = \frac{20!}{(16!)(4!)} = \frac{(20)(19)(18)(17)}{(4)(3)(2)(1)} = (5)(19)(3)(17) = 4,845$

37. The number of arrangements is: $(8)(7)(6) = 336$

39. The number of ways is: $C(20,6) = \frac{20!}{(14!)(6!)} = \frac{(20)(19)(18)(17)(16)(15)}{(6)(5)(4)(3)(2)(1)} = (18)(17)(8)(15) = 38,760$

41. The number of ways is: $P(22,4) = \frac{22!}{4!} = (22)(21)(20)(19) = 175,560$

43. The number of ways is: $\binom{10}{2}\binom{5}{2}\binom{3}{1} = \frac{10!}{(8!)(2!)} \cdot \frac{5!}{(3!)(2!)} \cdot \frac{3!}{(2!)(1!)} = \frac{(10)(9)}{2} \cdot \frac{(5)(4)}{2} \cdot 3 = 1,350$

45. The number of orders is: $(15)(14)(13) = 2,730$

47. The number of ways is: $C(7,4) = \frac{7!}{3!4!} = \frac{(7)(6)(5)}{(3)(2)(1)} = (7)(5) = 35$

    The lock uses the multiplication principle rather than combinations.

49. The number of license plates is: $(26)(26)(10)(10)(10)(26) = 17,576,000$

51. The number of combinations is: $\binom{53}{6} \cdot 44 = \frac{53!}{(47!)(6!)} \cdot 44 = \frac{(53)(52)(51)(50)(49)(48)}{(6)(5)(4)(3)(2)(1)} = 1,010,129,120$

53. The number of bridge hands is: $\binom{52}{13} = \frac{52!}{(39!)(13!)} = 635,013,559,600$

55. The number of photographs is: $5(2) \cdot 4! = 240$

57. If the passwords are case sensitive, then that adds 26 more possible characters, making the number of available characters 62. Thus there are $(62)^6 = 56,800,235,584$ possible passwords. There are $(52)^6 = 19,770,609,664$ possible passwords containing just letters. Thus there are $56,800,235,584 - 19,770,609,664 = 37,029,625,920$ passwords containing at least one digit.

59. **a.** The options are: $\begin{pmatrix} 3 \\ 1 \end{pmatrix}\begin{pmatrix} 2 \\ 1 \end{pmatrix} = (3)(2) = 6$

b. The options are: $\begin{pmatrix} 3 \\ 1 \end{pmatrix}\begin{pmatrix} 2 \\ 1 \end{pmatrix}\begin{pmatrix} 4 \\ 4 \end{pmatrix} = (3)(2)(1) = 6$

c. The options are: $\begin{pmatrix} 3 \\ 1 \end{pmatrix}\begin{pmatrix} 2 \\ 1 \end{pmatrix}\begin{pmatrix} 4 \\ 2 \end{pmatrix} = (3)(2)(6) = 36$

d. The options are:

$\begin{pmatrix} 3 \\ 1 \end{pmatrix}\begin{pmatrix} 2 \\ 1 \end{pmatrix}\begin{pmatrix} 4 \\ 2 \end{pmatrix} + \begin{pmatrix} 3 \\ 1 \end{pmatrix}\begin{pmatrix} 2 \\ 1 \end{pmatrix}\begin{pmatrix} 4 \\ 1 \end{pmatrix} + \begin{pmatrix} 3 \\ 1 \end{pmatrix}\begin{pmatrix} 2 \\ 1 \end{pmatrix}\begin{pmatrix} 4 \\ 0 \end{pmatrix} = (3)(2)(6) + (3)(2)(4) + (3)(2)(1) = 66$

61. The number of ways is: $(n-1) + (n-2) + \cdots + 1$

63. For a pentagon there are 5 diagonals, and for an octagon there are 20 diagonals.

The general formula for an n-gon is: $2(n-3) + (n-4) + (n-5) + \cdots + 1$

65. The number of ways of placing each letter are:

M: $\begin{pmatrix} 11 \\ 1 \end{pmatrix} = 11$ I: $\begin{pmatrix} 10 \\ 4 \end{pmatrix} = 210$

S: $\begin{pmatrix} 6 \\ 4 \end{pmatrix} = 15$ P: $\begin{pmatrix} 2 \\ 2 \end{pmatrix} = 1$

The total number of arrangements is therefore: $(11)(210)(15)(1) = 34{,}650$

10.5 Probability

1. Listing the sample space: {HH, HT, TH, TT}

3. Listing the complement: {TT}

5. Listing the event: {1, 3, 5}

7. Finding the probability: $P(\text{greater than or equal to } 5) = \dfrac{2}{6} = \dfrac{1}{3}$

9. Listing the event: {ace of spades, 2 of spades, 3 of spades, 4 of spades, 5 of spades, 6 of spades, 7 of spades, 8 of spades, 9 of spades, 10 of spades, jack of spades, queen of spades, king of spades}

11. Finding the probability: $P(\text{ace of spades}) = \dfrac{1}{52}$

13. Listing the sample space: {quarter, dime, nickel, penny}

15. Finding the probability: $P(\text{nickel}) = \dfrac{1}{4}$

17. This statement if false, since 2 is an even number.

19. This statement is true.

21. This statement is true.

Number of Hearts	Probability
0	$\dfrac{1}{16}$
1	$\dfrac{1}{4}$
2	$\dfrac{3}{8}$
3	$\dfrac{1}{4}$
4	$\dfrac{1}{16}$

23. Completing the table:

If n = number of heads, then $P(n) = P(4-n)$. No, these outcomes are not equally likely.

25. Finding the probability: $P(\text{ace}) = \dfrac{4}{52} = \dfrac{1}{13}$

27. Finding the probability: $P(4 \text{ of clubs}) = \dfrac{1}{52}$

29. Finding the probability: $P(\text{face card}) = \dfrac{12}{52} = \dfrac{3}{13}$

31. The event sum is 7: $\{(6,1),(1,6),(5,2),(2,5),(4,3),(3,4)\}$. Total number of possible outcomes: $(6)(6) = 36$

Finding the probability: $P(\text{sum is } 7) = \dfrac{6}{36} = \dfrac{1}{6}$

33. Finding the probability: $P(\text{both boys}) = \dfrac{C(5,2)}{C(10,2)} = \dfrac{10}{45} = \dfrac{2}{9}$

35. The number of outcomes is: $(10)^4 = 10,000$

37. Finding the probability: $P(\text{all different}) = \dfrac{(10)(9)(8)(7)}{10,000} = \dfrac{63}{125} = 0.504$

39. Finding the probability: $P(\text{Ann selected}) = \dfrac{C(5,1)}{C(10,2)} = \dfrac{5}{45} = \dfrac{1}{9}$

41. Finding the probability: $P(\text{win on next card}) = \dfrac{2}{32} = \dfrac{1}{16}$

43. Finding the probability: $P(\text{hitting shaded inner region}) = \dfrac{\pi(3)^2}{\pi(6)^2} = \dfrac{9}{36} = \dfrac{1}{4}$

45. This answer over counts a card, since there is one spade that is a king; $P(\text{king or spade}) = \dfrac{4+12}{52} = \dfrac{16}{52} = \dfrac{4}{13}$

47. Finding the probability: $P(3 \text{ cherries}) = \dfrac{C(4,3) \times 9}{(10)^4} = \dfrac{(4)(9)}{10,000} = \dfrac{9}{2500}$

49. Neither, the probabilities are the same.

51. **a.** Listing the sample space: {YYYY, YYYN, YYNY, YNYY, NYYY, YYNN, YNYN, NYYN, NYNY, NNYY, YNNY, NNNY, NNYN, NYNN, YNNN, NNNN}

b. Finding the probability: $P(\text{seen exactly } 2) = \dfrac{6}{16} = \dfrac{3}{8}$

c. Finding the probability: $P(\text{seen all } 4) = \dfrac{1}{16}$

53. **a.** The number of ways is: $C(8,2) = \dfrac{8!}{(6!)(2!)} = 28$

b. Finding the probability: $P(2 \text{ coins of equal value}) = \dfrac{\dbinom{3}{2} + \dbinom{2}{2} + \dbinom{2}{2}}{28} = \dfrac{3+1+1}{28} = \dfrac{5}{28}$

10.6 The Binomial Theorem

1. The variable parts are: $a^5, a^4b, a^3b^2, a^2b^3, ab^4, b^5$

3. The variable parts are: $x^7, x^6y, x^5y^2, x^4y^3, x^3y^4, x^2y^5, xy^6, y^7$

5. Evaluating: $4! = (4)(3)(2)(1) = 24$

7. Evaluating: $\dfrac{3!}{2!} = \dfrac{3 \cdot 2 \cdot 1}{2 \cdot 1} = 3$

9. Evaluating: $\dbinom{6}{2} = \dfrac{6!}{(6-2)!2!} = \dfrac{6!}{(4!)(2!)} = \dfrac{6 \cdot 5 \cdot 4 \cdot 3 \cdot 2 \cdot 1}{(4 \cdot 3 \cdot 2 \cdot 1)(2 \cdot 1)} = 15$

11. Evaluating: $\dbinom{7}{5} = \dfrac{7!}{(7-5)!5!} = \dfrac{7!}{(2!)(5!)} = \dfrac{7 \cdot 6 \cdot 5 \cdot 4 \cdot 3 \cdot 2 \cdot 1}{(2 \cdot 1)(5 \cdot 4 \cdot 3 \cdot 2 \cdot 1)} = 21$

13. Evaluating: $\dbinom{10}{10} = \dfrac{10!}{(10-10)!10!} = \dfrac{10!}{(0!)(10!)} = 1$

15. Evaluating: $\dbinom{100}{0} = \dfrac{100!}{(100-0)!0!} = \dfrac{100!}{(100!)(0!)} = 1$

17. Using the binomial theorem:
$$(x+2)^4 = \dbinom{4}{0}x^4 + \dbinom{4}{1}x^3(2) + \dbinom{4}{2}x^2(2)^2 + \dbinom{4}{3}x(2)^3 + \dbinom{4}{4}(2)^4$$
$$= x^4 + 4x^3(2) + 6x^2(4) + 4x(8) + 16$$
$$= x^4 + 8x^3 + 24x^2 + 32x + 16$$

19. Using the binomial theorem:
$$(2x-1)^3 = \dbinom{3}{0}(2x)^3 + \dbinom{3}{1}(2x)^2(-1) + \dbinom{3}{2}(2x)(-1)^2 + \dbinom{3}{3}(-1)^3$$
$$= 8x^3 + (3)(4x^2)(-1) + (3)(2x)(1) + (-1)$$
$$= 8x^3 - 12x^2 + 6x - 1$$

21. Using the binomial theorem:
$$(3+y)^5 = \dbinom{5}{0}(3)^5 + \dbinom{5}{1}(3)^4 y + \dbinom{5}{2}(3)^3 y^2 + \dbinom{5}{3}(3)^2 y^3 + \dbinom{5}{4}(3)y^4 + \dbinom{5}{5}y^5$$
$$= 243 + 5(81)y + 10(27)y^2 + 10(9)y^3 + 5(3)y^4 + y^5$$
$$= 243 + 405y + 270y^2 + 90y^3 + 15y^4 + y^5$$

23. Using the binomial theorem:
$$(x-3z)^4 = \dbinom{4}{0}x^4 + \dbinom{4}{1}x^3(-3z) + \dbinom{4}{2}x^2(-3z)^2 + \dbinom{4}{3}x(-3z)^3 + \dbinom{4}{4}(-3z)^4$$
$$= x^4 + 4x^3(-3z) + 6x^2(9z^2) + 4x(-27z^3) + 81z^4$$
$$= x^4 - 12x^3z + 54x^2z^2 - 108xz^3 + 81z^4$$

25. Using the binomial theorem:

$$\left(x^2+1\right)^3 = \binom{3}{0}\left(x^2\right)^3 + \binom{3}{1}\left(x^2\right)^2(1) + \binom{3}{2}\left(x^2\right)(1)^2 + \binom{3}{3}(1)^3 = x^6 + 3x^4 + 3x^2 + 1$$

27. Using the binomial theorem:

$$\left(y-2x\right)^4 = \binom{4}{0}y^4 + \binom{4}{1}y^3(-2x) + \binom{4}{2}y^2(-2x)^2 + \binom{4}{3}y(-2x)^3 + \binom{4}{4}(-2x)^4$$

$$= y^4 + 4y^3(-2x) + 6y^2\left(4x^2\right) + 4y\left(-8x^3\right) + 16x^4$$

$$= y^4 - 8y^3x + 24y^2x^2 - 32yx^3 + 16x^4$$

29. Finding the term: $\binom{5}{2}x^3(4)^2 = 10x^3(16) = 160x^3$

The coefficient is 160.

31. Finding the term: $\binom{6}{1}(3x)^5(2) = 6\left(243x^5\right)(2) = 2916x^5$

The coefficient is 2,916.

33. Finding the term: $\binom{8}{2}x^6(1)^2 = 28x^6$

The coefficient is 28.

35. Finding the term: $\binom{6}{3-1}x^{6-3+1}(-4)^{3-1} = \binom{6}{2}x^4(-4)^2 = 15x^4(16) = 240x^4$

37. Finding the term: $\binom{5}{6-1}x^{5-6+1}(4y)^{6-1} = \binom{5}{5}x^0(4y)^5 = 1024y^5$

39. Finding the term: $\binom{6}{5-1}(3x)^{6-5+1}(-2)^{5-1} = \binom{6}{4}(3x)^2(-2)^4 = 15\left(9x^2\right)(16) = 2160x^2$

41. Finding the term: $\binom{6}{4-1}(4x)^{6-4+1}(-2)^{4-1} = \binom{6}{3}(4x)^3(-2)^3 = 20\left(64x^3\right)(-8) = -10,240x^3$

43. Working from the left side: $\binom{n}{r} = \dfrac{n!}{(n-r)!r!} = \dfrac{n!}{(n-r)!(n-(n-r))!} = \binom{n}{n-r}$

45. Evaluating: $\binom{4}{0}\left(\dfrac{1}{3}\right)^4 + \binom{4}{1}\left(\dfrac{1}{3}\right)^3\left(\dfrac{2}{3}\right) + \binom{4}{2}\left(\dfrac{1}{3}\right)^2\left(\dfrac{2}{3}\right)^2 + \binom{4}{3}\left(\dfrac{1}{3}\right)\left(\dfrac{2}{3}\right)^3 + \binom{4}{4}\left(\dfrac{2}{3}\right)^4 = \left(\dfrac{1}{3}+\dfrac{2}{3}\right)^4 = (1)^4 = 1$

10.7 Mathematical Induction

1. Substituting $k + 1$: $(k+1)\big(((k+1)+1)+(k+1)+2\big) = (k+1)(k+2)(k+3)$

3. Substituting $k + 1$: $\dfrac{k+1}{(k+1)+1} = \dfrac{k+1}{k+2}$

5. Verifying P_1 is true: $2(1)+1 = 1(1+2)$

Assume P_k is true: $3+5+\cdots+(2k+1) = k(k+2)$

Now proving P_{k+1} is true:

$$3+5+\cdots+(2k+1)+(2(k+1)+1) = 3+5+\cdots+(2k+1)+(2k+3)$$
$$= k(k+2)+(2k+3)$$
$$= k^2+2k+2k+3$$
$$= k^2+4k+3$$
$$= (k+1)(k+3)$$
$$= (k+1)(k+1+2)$$

7. Verifying P_1 is true: $3(1)-2 = \dfrac{1(3(1)-1)}{2}$

Assume P_k is true: $1+4+7+\cdots+(3k-2) = \dfrac{k(3k-1)}{2}$

Now proving P_{k+1} is true:

$$1+4+7+\cdots+(3k-2)+(3(k+1)-2) = \dfrac{k(3k-1)}{2}+(3k+3-2)$$
$$= \dfrac{k(3k-1)}{2}+\dfrac{2(3k+1)}{2}$$
$$= \dfrac{3k^2-k+6k+2}{2}$$
$$= \dfrac{3k^2+5k+2}{2}$$
$$= \dfrac{(3k+2)(k+1)}{2}$$
$$= \dfrac{(k+1)(3k+2)}{2}$$
$$= \dfrac{(k+1)(3(k+1)-1)}{2}$$

9. Verifying P_1 is true: $9-2(1) = -(1)+8(1)$

Assume P_k is true: $7+5+3+\cdots+(9-2k) = -k^2+8k$

Now proving P_{k+1} is true:

$$7+5+3+\cdots+(9-2k)+(9-2(k+1)) = -k^2+8k+(9-2k-2)$$
$$= -k^2+6k+7$$
$$= -(k^2+2k+1)+8k+7+1$$
$$= -(k+1)^2+8k+8$$
$$= -(k+1)^2+8(k+1)$$

11. Verifying P_1 is true: $3(1) - 1 = \frac{1}{2}(1)(3(1)+1)$

Assume P_k is true: $2 + 5 + 8 + \cdots + (3k - 1) = \frac{1}{2}k(3k + 1)$

Now proving P_{k+1} is true:

$$2 + 5 + 8 + \cdots + (3k - 1) + (3(k+1) - 1) = \frac{1}{2}k(3k+1) + (3(k+1) - 1)$$
$$= \frac{3}{2}k^2 + \frac{1}{2}k + 3k + 2$$
$$= \frac{3}{2}k^2 + \frac{7}{2}k + 2$$
$$= \frac{1}{2}(3k^2 + 7k + 4)$$
$$= \frac{1}{2}(3k + 4)(k + 1)$$
$$= \frac{1}{2}(k + 1)(3k + 4)$$
$$= \frac{1}{2}(k + 1)(3(k+1) + 1)$$

13. Verifying P_1 is true: $(1)^3 = \frac{(1)^2(1+1)^2}{4}$

Assume P_k is true: $1^3 + 2^3 + 3^3 + \cdots + k^3 = \frac{k^2(k+1)^2}{4}$

Now proving P_{k+1} is true:

$$1^3 + 2^3 + 3^3 + \cdots + k^3 + (k+1)^3 = \frac{k^2(k+1)^2}{4} + (k+1)^3$$
$$= \frac{k^2(k+1)^2}{4} + \frac{4(k+1)^3}{4}$$
$$= \frac{(k+1)^2(k^2 + 4k + 4)}{4}$$
$$= \frac{(k+1)^2(k+2)^2}{4}$$
$$= \frac{(k+1)^2((k+1)+1)^2}{4}$$

15. Verifying P_1 is true: $(2(1)-1)^2 = \dfrac{(1)(2(1)-1)(2(1)+1)}{3}$

Assume P_k is true: $1^2 + 3^2 + \cdots + (2k-1)^2 = \dfrac{k(2k-1)(2k+1)}{3}$

Now proving P_{k+1} is true:

$$1^2 + 3^2 + \cdots + (2k-1)^2 + (2(k+1)-1)^2 = \dfrac{k(2k-1)(2k+1)}{3} + (2k+1)^2$$

$$= \dfrac{k(2k-1)(2k+1)}{3} + \dfrac{3(2k+1)^2}{3}$$

$$= \dfrac{(2k+1)(2k^2 - k + 6k + 3)}{3}$$

$$= \dfrac{(2k+1)(2k^2 + 5k + 3)}{3}$$

$$= \dfrac{(2k+1)(2k+3)(k+1)}{3}$$

$$= \dfrac{(k+1)(2k+1)(2k+3)}{3}$$

$$= \dfrac{(k+1)(2(k+1)-1)(2(k+1)+1)}{3}$$

17. Verifying P_1 is true: $(1)(1+1) = \dfrac{(1)(1+1)(1+2)}{3}$

Assume P_k is true: $1 \cdot 2 + 2 \cdot 3 + 3 \cdot 4 + \cdots + k(k+1) = \dfrac{k(k+1)(k+2)}{3}$

Now proving P_{k+1} is true:

$$1 \cdot 2 + 2 \cdot 3 + 3 \cdot 4 + \cdots + k(k+1) + (k+1)((k+1)+1) = \dfrac{k(k+1)(k+2)}{3} + (k+1)(k+2)$$

$$= \dfrac{k(k+1)(k+2)}{3} + \dfrac{3(k+1)(k+2)}{3}$$

$$= \dfrac{(k+1)(k+2)(k+3)}{3}$$

$$= \dfrac{(k+1)((k+1)+1)((k+1)+2)}{3}$$

19. Verifying P_1 is true: $5^{1-1} = \dfrac{5^1 - 1}{4}$

Assume P_k is true: $1 + 5 + 5^2 + \cdots + 5^{k-1} = \dfrac{5^k - 1}{4}$

Now proving P_{k+1} is true: $1 + 5 + 5^2 + \cdots + 5^{k-1} + 5^{(k+1)-1} = \dfrac{5^k - 1}{4} + 5^k = \dfrac{5^k - 1}{4} + \dfrac{4(5^k)}{4} = \dfrac{5(5^k) - 1}{4} = \dfrac{5^{k+1} - 1}{4}$

21. Verifying P_1 is true: $3^1 - 1 = 2$ is divisible by 2

Assume P_k is true: $3^k - 1$ is divisible by 2

Now proving P_{k+1} is true: $3^{k+1} - 1 = 3(3^k) - 1 = 3(3^k - 1) - 1 + 3 = 3(3^k - 1) + 2$

Since $3^k - 1$ is divisible by 2, $3(3^k - 1) + 2$ is divisible by 2.

23. Verifying P_1 is true: $(1)^2 + 3(1) = 4$ is divisible by 2

Assume P_k is true: $k^2 + 3k$ is divisible by 2

Now proving P_{k+1} is true: $(k+1)^2 + 3(k+1) = k^2 + 2k + 1 + 3k + 3 = (k^2 + 3k) + 2k + 4 = (k^2 + 3k) + 2(k+2)$

Both $(k^2 + 3k)$ and $2(k+2)$ are divisible by 2, so $(k^2 + 3k) + 2(k+2)$ is divisible by 2.

25. Verifying P_1 is true: $2^1 > 1$

Assume P_k is true: $2^k > k$

Now proving P_{k+1} is true: $2^{k+1} = 2(2^k) > 2(k) = k + k \geq k + 1$

27. Factoring: $a^3 - b^3 = (a-b)(a^2 + ab + b^2)$. Since $a - b$ is a factor of $a^3 - b^3$, it is divisible by $a - b$.

29. The sum $1 + 4 + 4^2 + \cdots + 4^{n-1}$ is a geometric sequence $a_0 = 1$ and $r = 4$. Thus:

$$S_n = a_0 \left(\frac{1 - r^n}{1 - r} \right) = 1 \left(\frac{1 - 4^n}{1 - 4} \right) = \frac{1 - 4^n}{-3} = \frac{4^n - 1}{3}$$

Chapter 10 Review Exercises

1. Finding d: $d = a_1 - a_0 = 9 - 7 = 2$

The rule is: $a_n = 7 + 2n$

2. Finding d: $d = a_1 - a_0 = -1 - 2 = -3$

The rule is: $a_n = 2 - 3n$

3. Finding the first term:
$$a_2 = a_0 + 2(4)$$
$$9 = a_0 + 8$$
$$a_0 = 1$$
The rule is: $a_n = 1 + 4n$

4. Finding the first term:
$$a_6 = a_0 + (-2)(6)$$
$$10 = a_0 - 12$$
$$a_0 = 22$$
The rule is: $a_n = 22 - 2n$

5. Finding r: $r = \dfrac{a_1}{a_0} = \dfrac{10}{5} = 2$

The rule is: $a_n = 5(2)^n$

6. Finding r: $r = \dfrac{a_1}{a_0} = \dfrac{4}{8} = \dfrac{1}{2}$

The rule is: $a_n = 8\left(\dfrac{1}{2}\right)^n$

7. Finding the first term:

$$a_3 = a_0(3)^3$$
$$54 = 27a_0$$
$$a_0 = 2$$

The rule is: $a_n = 2(3)^n$

8. Finding the first term:
$$b_2 = b_0\left(\frac{1}{3}\right)^2$$
$$9 = \frac{1}{9}b_0$$
$$b_0 = 81$$

The rule is: $b_n = 81\left(\dfrac{1}{3}\right)^n$

9. The sequence is: $a_n = 36{,}000 + 1500n, n = 0, 1, 2, 3, \ldots$

Finding the fifth term: $a_5 = 36{,}000 + 1500(5) = \$43{,}500$

10. Finding the sum: $1 + 5 + 9 + \cdots + 61 = S_{16} = \dfrac{16}{2}(1 + 61) = 496$

11. Finding the sum: $2 + 7 + 12 + \cdots + 102 = S_{21} = \dfrac{21}{2}(2 + 102) = 1{,}092$

12. Finding the sum: $S_{20} = \dfrac{20}{2}\left[4 + (4 + 5(19))\right] = 10(103) = 1{,}030$

13. Finding the sum: $S_{15} = \dfrac{15}{2}\left[2 + \left(2 - 3(14)\right)\right] = \dfrac{15}{2}(-38) = -285$

14. Using $a_0 = 4, r = \dfrac{8}{4} = 2$, find the sum: $4 + 8 + 16 + 32 + 64 + 128 + 256 = 4\left(\dfrac{1 - 2^7}{1 - 2}\right) = 4\left(\dfrac{-127}{-1}\right) = 508$

15. Using $a_0 = 0.6, r = \dfrac{1.8}{0.6} = 3$, find the sum: $0.6 + 1.8 + 5.4 + 16.2 = 0.6\left(\dfrac{1 - 3^4}{1 - 3}\right) = 0.6\left(\dfrac{-80}{-2}\right) = 24$

16. Using $a_0 = 1, r = \dfrac{1}{2}$, find the sum: $\displaystyle\sum_{i=0}^{5}\left(\dfrac{1}{2}\right)^i = \dfrac{1 - \left(\dfrac{1}{2}\right)^6}{1 - \dfrac{1}{2}} = \dfrac{\dfrac{63}{64}}{\dfrac{1}{2}} = \dfrac{63}{32}$

17. Using $a_0 = 1, r = 3$, find the sum: $\displaystyle\sum_{i=0}^{7}(3)^i = \dfrac{1 - 3^8}{1 - 3} = \dfrac{-6560}{-2} = 3{,}280$

18. **a.** Here $a_0 = 0$, the common difference is $d = 3$. The sum is: $\displaystyle\sum_{i=0}^{24}(3i)$

    b. Finding the sum: $\displaystyle\sum_{i=0}^{24}(3i) = \dfrac{25}{2}\left[0 + 3(24)\right] = \dfrac{25}{2}(72) = 900$

19. **a.** Here $a_0 = 0$, the common difference is $d = 2.5$. The sum is: $\displaystyle\sum_{i=0}^{9}(2.5i)$

    b. Finding the sum: $\displaystyle\sum_{i=0}^{9}(2.5i) = \dfrac{10}{2}\left[0 + 2.5(9)\right] = 5(22.5) = 112.5$

20. **a.** Here $a_0 = 1$, the common ratio is $r = 2$. The sum is: $\displaystyle\sum_{i=0}^{7}2^i$

    b. Finding the sum: $\displaystyle\sum_{i=0}^{7}2^i = 1\left(\dfrac{1 - 2^8}{1 - 2}\right) = \dfrac{-255}{-1} = 255$

21. **a.** Here $a_0 = a$, the common ratio is $r = a$. The sum is: $\displaystyle\sum_{i=0}^{15}a(a^i) = \sum_{i=0}^{15}a^{i+1} = \sum_{i=1}^{16}a^i$

    b. Finding the sum: $\displaystyle\sum_{i=1}^{16}a^i = a\left(\dfrac{1 - a^{16}}{1 - a}\right) = \dfrac{a\left(1 - a^{16}\right)}{1 - a}$

22. Since $r = \dfrac{\dfrac{1}{3}}{1} = \dfrac{1}{3}$, $|r| < 1$ so the series has a sum. Using $a_0 = 1$, the sum is: $S = \dfrac{1}{1 - \dfrac{1}{3}} = \dfrac{1}{\dfrac{2}{3}} = \dfrac{3}{2}$

23. Since $r = \dfrac{9}{27} = \dfrac{1}{3}$, $|r| < 1$ so the series has a sum. Using $a_0 = 27$, the sum is: $S = \dfrac{27}{1 - \dfrac{1}{3}} = \dfrac{27}{\dfrac{2}{3}} = \dfrac{81}{2}$

24. Since $r = \dfrac{1.1}{1} = 1.1$, $|r| > 1$ so the series does not have a sum.

25. Since $r = \dfrac{2}{3}$, $|r| < 1$ so the series has a sum. Using $a_0 = 3$, the sum is: $S = \dfrac{3}{1 - \dfrac{2}{3}} = \dfrac{3}{\dfrac{1}{3}} = 9$

26. The sequence is: $a_n = 32\left(\dfrac{1}{2}\right)^n$, $n = 0, 1, 2, 3, \ldots$

   Finding n:

   $$a_n = 1$$

   $$1 = 32\left(\dfrac{1}{2}\right)^n$$

   $$\dfrac{1}{32} = \dfrac{1}{2^n}$$

   $$n = 5$$

   There were 5 rounds of games played.

27. Finding the first five terms:

   $$a_0 = -2(0) + 5 = 5 \qquad\qquad a_1 = -2(1) + 5 = 3$$

   $$a_2 = -2(2) + 5 = 1 \qquad\qquad a_3 = -2(3) + 5 = -1$$

   $$a_4 = -2(4) + 5 = -3$$

28. Finding the first five terms:

   $$a_0 = 4(0) + 1 = 1 \qquad\qquad a_1 = 4(1) + 1 = 5$$

   $$a_2 = 4(2) + 1 = 9 \qquad\qquad a_3 = 4(3) + 1 = 13$$

   $$a_4 = 4(4) + 1 = 17$$

29. Finding the first five terms:

   $$a_0 = -3\left(\dfrac{1}{2}\right)^0 = -3 \qquad\qquad a_1 = -3\left(\dfrac{1}{2}\right)^1 = -\dfrac{3}{2}$$

   $$a_2 = -3\left(\dfrac{1}{2}\right)^2 = -\dfrac{3}{4} \qquad\qquad a_3 = -3\left(\dfrac{1}{2}\right)^3 = -\dfrac{3}{8}$$

   $$a_4 = -3\left(\dfrac{1}{2}\right)^4 = -\dfrac{3}{16}$$

30. Finding the first five terms:

   $$a_0 = -\left(\dfrac{2}{3}\right)^0 = -1 \qquad\qquad a_1 = -\left(\dfrac{2}{3}\right)^1 = -\dfrac{2}{3}$$

   $$a_2 = -\left(\dfrac{2}{3}\right)^2 = -\dfrac{4}{9} \qquad\qquad a_3 = -\left(\dfrac{2}{3}\right)^3 = -\dfrac{8}{27}$$

   $$a_4 = -\left(\dfrac{2}{3}\right)^4 = -\dfrac{16}{81}$$

31. Finding the first five terms:

   $$b_0 = -(0)^2 + 1 = 1 \qquad\qquad b_1 = -(1)^2 + 1 = 0$$

   $$b_2 = -(2)^2 + 1 = -3 \qquad\qquad b_3 = -(3)^2 + 1 = -8$$

   $$b_4 = -(4)^2 + 1 = -15$$

32. Finding the first five terms:

   $$b_0 = 3(0)^3 - 1 = -1 \qquad\qquad b_1 = 3(1)^3 - 1 = 2$$

   $$b_2 = 3(2)^3 - 1 = 23 \qquad\qquad b_3 = 3(3)^3 - 1 = 80$$

   $$b_4 = 3(4)^3 - 1 = 191$$

33. Finding the first five terms:

$$f(1) = \frac{1}{(1)^2 + 1} = \frac{1}{2} \qquad\qquad f(2) = \frac{2}{(2)^2 + 1} = \frac{2}{5}$$

$$f(3) = \frac{3}{(3)^2 + 1} = \frac{3}{10} \qquad\qquad f(4) = \frac{4}{(4)^2 + 1} = \frac{4}{17}$$

$$f(5) = \frac{5}{(5)^2 + 1} = \frac{5}{26}$$

34. Finding the first five terms:

$$f(1) = \frac{1}{2(1)^2 - 1} = 1 \qquad\qquad f(2) = \frac{1}{2(2)^2 - 1} = \frac{1}{7}$$

$$f(3) = \frac{1}{2(3)^2 - 1} = \frac{1}{17} \qquad\qquad f(4) = \frac{1}{2(4)^2 - 1} = \frac{1}{31}$$

$$f(5) = \frac{1}{2(5)^2 - 1} = \frac{1}{49}$$

35. Finding the first five terms:

$$a_1 = (-1)^1 \left(\frac{1}{3}\right)^1 = -\frac{1}{3} \qquad\qquad a_2 = (-1)^2 \left(\frac{1}{3}\right)^2 = \frac{1}{9}$$

$$a_3 = (-1)^3 \left(\frac{1}{3}\right)^3 = -\frac{1}{27} \qquad\qquad a_4 = (-1)^4 \left(\frac{1}{3}\right)^4 = \frac{1}{81}$$

$$a_5 = (-1)^5 \left(\frac{1}{3}\right)^5 = -\frac{1}{243}$$

36. Finding the first five terms:

$$a_1 = (-1)^1 \left(2(1) + 3\right) = -5 \qquad\qquad a_2 = (-1)^2 \left(2(2) + 3\right) = 7$$

$$a_3 = (-1)^3 \left(2(3) + 3\right) = -9 \qquad\qquad a_4 = (-1)^4 \left(2(4) + 3\right) = 11$$

$$a_5 = (-1)^5 \left(2(5) + 3\right) = -13$$

37. Finding the first four terms:

$$a_0 = 4 \qquad\qquad a_1 = 4 + 3 = 7$$

$$a_2 = 7 + 3 = 10 \qquad\qquad a_3 = 10 + 3 = 13$$

38. Finding the first four terms:

$$a_0 = -2 \qquad\qquad a_1 = -2 + 0.5 = -1.5$$

$$a_2 = -1.5 + 0.5 = -1 \qquad\qquad a_3 = -1 + 0.5 = -0.5$$

39. Finding the first four terms:

$$a_0 = -1 \qquad\qquad a_1 = -1 + 2(1) = 1$$

$$a_2 = 1 + 2(2) = 5 \qquad\qquad a_3 = 5 + 2(3) = 11$$

40. Finding the first four terms:

$$b_1 = \sqrt{2} \qquad\qquad b_2 = \sqrt{\sqrt{2} + 2}$$

$$b_3 = \sqrt{\sqrt{\sqrt{2} + 2} + 2} \qquad\qquad b_4 = \sqrt{\sqrt{\sqrt{\sqrt{2} + 2} + 2} + 2}$$

41. Finding the sum: $\displaystyle\sum_{i=0}^{3} 2i^2 = 2(0)^2 + 2(1)^2 + 2(2)^2 + 2(3)^2 = 0 + 2 + 8 + 18 = 28$

42. Finding the sum: $\displaystyle\sum_{i=0}^{3} (-1)^i (2i + 1) = (-1)^0 \left(2(0) + 1\right) + (-1)^1 \left(2(1) + 1\right) + (-1)^2 \left(2(2) + 1\right) + (-1)^3 \left(2(3) + 1\right) = 1 - 3 + 5 - 7 = -4$

43. **a.** Evaluating: $\dfrac{4!}{2!} = \dfrac{4 \cdot 3 \cdot 2 \cdot 1}{2 \cdot 1} = 12$

   b. Evaluating: $P(5,4) = \dfrac{5!}{(5-4)!} = \dfrac{5!}{1!} = 5 \cdot 4 \cdot 3 \cdot 2 \cdot 1 = 120$

   c. Evaluating: $P(4,4) = \dfrac{4!}{(4-4)!} = \dfrac{4!}{0!} = 4 \cdot 3 \cdot 2 \cdot 1 = 24$

   d. Evaluating: $P(6,3) = \dfrac{6!}{(6-3)!} = \dfrac{6!}{3!} = \dfrac{6 \cdot 5 \cdot 4 \cdot 3 \cdot 2 \cdot 1}{3 \cdot 2 \cdot 1} = 120$

44. **a.** Evaluating: $\dfrac{5!}{3!} = \dfrac{5 \cdot 4 \cdot 3 \cdot 2 \cdot 1}{3 \cdot 2 \cdot 1} = 20$

   b. Evaluating: $C(5,4) = \dfrac{5!}{(5-4)!4!} = \dfrac{5!}{(1!)(4!)} = 5$

   c. Evaluating: $\begin{pmatrix} 4 \\ 4 \end{pmatrix} = \dfrac{4!}{(4-4)!4!} = \dfrac{4!}{(0!)(4!)} = 1$

   d. Evaluating: $C(6,3) = \dfrac{6!}{(6-3)!3!} = \dfrac{6!}{(3!)(3!)} = 20$

45. Evaluating: $5! = 5 \cdot 4 \cdot 3 \cdot 2 \cdot 1 = 120$
    There are 120 different photographs possible.

46. Evaluating: $P(6,4) = \dfrac{6!}{2!} = 6 \cdot 5 \cdot 4 \cdot 3 = 360$

    There are 360 different photographs possible.

47. Evaluating: $(4!)(3!) = 144$

    There are 144 different photographs possible.

48. Evaluating: $C(10,3) = \dfrac{10!}{(10-3)!3!} = \dfrac{10!}{(7!)(3!)} = \dfrac{10 \cdot 9 \cdot 8}{3 \cdot 2 \cdot 1} = 120$

    There are 120 different three-person committees that can be formed.

49. Evaluating: $5! = 120$
    There are 120 different five-letter words that can be formed.

50. **a.** Evaluating: $8! = 40,320$
        There are 40,320 ways to arrange the books.

   b. Evaluating: $6(3) \cdot 2(2) \cdot 2(3) = 432$

        There are 432 ways to arrange the books.

51. The sequence is: $a_n = a_1 + (n-1), n = 1, 2, 3, \cdots$

    Using $a_6 = 69$ gives:

$$S_6 = \dfrac{6}{2}\left[a_1 + \left(a_1 + (6-1)\right)\right]$$
$$69 = 3(2a_1 + 5)$$
$$69 = 6a_1 + 15$$
$$54 = 6a_1$$
$$a_1 = 9$$

    Finding the sixth term: $a_6 = 9 + (6-1) = 14$

    There are 14 graduates.

52. Evaluating: $C(18,11) = \dfrac{18!}{(18-11)!11!} = \dfrac{18!}{(7!)(11!)} = 31,824$

    There are 31,824 ways a swim team can be formed.

53. Listing the outcomes: {HHH, HHT, HTH, THH, HTT, THT, TTH, TTT}
54. Listing the event: {HHH, HHT, HTH, THH, HTT, THT, TTH}
55. Listing the sample space: {HHH, HHT, HTH, THH, HTT, THT, TTH, TTT}
56. Yes, since they can't occur at the same time.
57. Listing the complement: {TTT}

58. Finding the probability: $P(\text{at least 1 head}) = 1 - P(\text{no heads}) = 1 - P(\text{TTT}) = 1 - \dfrac{1}{8} = \dfrac{7}{8}$

59. There are $3 + 2 + 4 = 9$ marbles, so $P(\text{white marble}) = \dfrac{2}{9}$.

60. There is 1 ace of hearts and 1 ace of spades, therefore: $P(\text{ace of hearts or ace of spades}) = \dfrac{2}{52} = \dfrac{1}{26}$

61. Finding the probability: $P(\text{5 red cards}) = \dfrac{C(26,5)}{C(52,5)} = \dfrac{\dfrac{26!}{(21!)(5!)}}{\dfrac{52!}{(47!)(5!)}} = \dfrac{26 \cdot 25 \cdot 24 \cdot 23 \cdot 22}{52 \cdot 51 \cdot 50 \cdot 49 \cdot 48} = \dfrac{253}{9{,}996}$

62. Finding the probability: $\dfrac{26}{(26)^4} = \dfrac{1}{17{,}576}$

63. Using the binomial theorem:
$$(x+3)^4 = \binom{4}{0}x^4 + \binom{4}{1}x^3(3) + \binom{4}{2}x^2(3)^2 + \binom{4}{3}x(3)^3 + \binom{4}{4}(3)^4$$
$$= x^4 + 4x^3(3) + 6x^2(9) + 4x(27) + 81$$
$$= x^4 + 12x^3 + 54x^2 + 108x + 81$$

64. Using the binomial theorem:
$$(2x+1)^3 = \binom{3}{0}(2x)^3 + \binom{3}{1}(2x)^2(1) + \binom{3}{2}(2x)(1)^2 + \binom{3}{3}(1)^3$$
$$= 8x^3 + (3)(4x^2)(1) + (3)(2x)(1) + (1)$$
$$= 8x^3 + 12x^2 + 6x + 1$$

65. Using the binomial theorem:
$$(3x+y)^3 = \binom{3}{0}(3x)^3 + \binom{3}{1}(3x)^2 y + \binom{3}{2}(3x)y^2 + \binom{3}{3}y^3$$
$$= 27x^3 + 3(9x^2)y + 3(3x)y^2 + y^3$$
$$= 27x^3 + 27x^2y + 9xy^2 + y^3$$

66. Using the binomial theorem:
$$(3z-2w)^4 = \binom{4}{0}(3z)^4 + \binom{4}{1}(3z)^3(-2w) + \binom{4}{2}(3z)^2(-2w)^2 + \binom{4}{3}(3z)(-2w)^3 + \binom{4}{4}(-2w)^4$$
$$= 81z^4 + 4(27z^3)(-2w) + 6(9z^2)(4w^2) + 4(3z)(-8w^3) + 16w^4$$
$$= 81z^4 - 216z^3w + 216z^2w^2 - 96zw^3 + 16w^4$$

67. Finding the term: $\binom{5}{1}x^4(3)^1 = 5x^4(3) = 15x^4$

   The coefficient is 15.

68. Finding the term: $\binom{5}{2}(2y)^3(1)^2 = 10(8y^3) = 80y^3$

   The coefficient is 80.

69. Finding the term: $\begin{pmatrix} 3 \\ 2-1 \end{pmatrix} x^{3-2+1} (2y)^{2-1} = \begin{pmatrix} 3 \\ 1 \end{pmatrix} x^2 (2y) = 3x^2 (2y) = 6x^2 y$

70. Finding the term: $\begin{pmatrix} 4 \\ 3-1 \end{pmatrix} y^{4-3+1} (-z)^{3-1} = \begin{pmatrix} 4 \\ 2 \end{pmatrix} y^2 (-z)^2 = 6y^2 z^2$

71. Verifying P_1 is true: $1 + \dfrac{1}{2^1} = 2 - \dfrac{1}{2^1}$

Assume P_k is true: $1 + \dfrac{1}{2} + \dfrac{1}{4} + \cdots + \dfrac{1}{2^k} = 2 - \dfrac{1}{2^k}$

Now proving P_{k+1} is true: $1 + \dfrac{1}{2} + \dfrac{1}{4} + \cdots + \dfrac{1}{2^k} + \dfrac{1}{2^{k+1}} = 2 - \dfrac{1}{2^k} + \dfrac{1}{2^{k+1}} = 2 - \dfrac{2}{2^{k+1}} + \dfrac{1}{2^{k+1}} = 2 - \dfrac{1}{2^{k+1}}$

72. Verifying P_1 is true: $\dfrac{(1)(1+1)}{2} = \dfrac{(1)(1+1)(1+2)}{6}$

Assume P_k is true: $1 + 3 + 6 + \cdots + \dfrac{k(k+1)}{2} = \dfrac{k(k+1)(k+2)}{6}$

Now proving P_{k+1} is true:

$$1 + 3 + 6 + \cdots + \dfrac{k(k+1)}{2} + \dfrac{(k+1)\big((k+1)+1\big)}{2} = \dfrac{k(k+1)(k+2)}{6} + \dfrac{(k+1)(k+2)}{2}$$

$$= \dfrac{k(k+1)(k+2)}{6} + \dfrac{3(k+1)(k+2)}{6}$$

$$= \dfrac{(k+1)(k+2)(k+3)}{6}$$

$$= \dfrac{(k+1)\big((k+1)+1\big)\big((k+1)+2\big)}{6}$$

73. Verifying P_1 is true: $(1+1)^2 + 1 = 5$ is odd

Assume P_k is true: $(k+1)^2 + k$ is odd

Now proving P_{k+1} is true:

$$\big((k+1)+1\big)^2 + (k+1) = (k+2)^2 + (k+1) = k^2 + 4k + 4 + k + 1 = \big(k^2 + 2k + 1\big) + k + (2k+4) = \Big[(k+1)^2 + k\Big] + 2(k+2)$$

By assumption, $(k+1)^2 + k$ is odd, and $2(k+2)$ is even. Since the sum of an odd number and an even number is odd, the result is odd.

74. Verifying P_1 is true: $(1)^3 + 2(1) = 3$ is divisible by 3

Assume P_k is true: $k^3 + 2k$ is divisible by 3

Now proving P_{k+1} is true:

$$(k+1)^3 + 2(k+1) = k^3 + 3k^2 + 3k + 1 + 2k + 2 = k^3 + 3k^2 + 5k + 3 = \big(k^3 + 2k\big) + \big(3k^2 + 3k + 3\big) = \big(k^3 + 2k\big) + 3\big(k^2 + k + 1\big)$$

Both $\big(k^3 + 2k\big)$ and $3\big(k^2 + k + 1\big)$ are divisible by 3, so $(k+1)^3 + 2(k+1)$ is divisible by 3.

75. Verifying P_1 is true: $3(1) = \dfrac{3}{2}(1)(1+1)$

Assume P_k is true: $3 + 6 + 9 + \cdots + 3k = \dfrac{3}{2}k(k+1)$

Now proving P_{k+1} is true:

$$3 + 6 + 9 + \cdots + 3k + 3(k+1) = \dfrac{3}{2}k(k+1) + 3(k+1) = \dfrac{3}{2}k(k+1) + \dfrac{6}{2}(k+1) = \dfrac{3}{2}(k+1)(k+2) = \dfrac{3}{2}(k+1)\big((k+1)+1\big)$$

76. Verifying P_1 is true: $4(1) - 3 = (1)(2(1) - 1)$

Assume P_k is true: $1 + 5 + 9 + \cdots + (4k - 3) = k(2k - 1)$

Now proving P_{k+1} is true:

$$1 + 5 + 9 + \cdots + (4k - 3) + (4(k+1) - 3) = k(2k - 1) + (4k + 1)$$
$$= 2k^2 - k + 4k + 1$$
$$= 2k^2 + 3k + 1$$
$$= (2k + 1)(k + 1)$$
$$= (k + 1)(2k + 1)$$
$$= (k + 1)(2(k + 1) - 1)$$

Chapter 10 Test

1. Finding d: $d = a_1 - a_0 = 11 - 8 = 3$

The rule is: $a_n = 8 + 3n$

2. Finding the first term:
$$a_4 = a_0 + 5(4)$$
$$27 = a_0 + 20$$
$$a_0 = 7$$

The rule is: $a_n = 7 + 5n$

3. Finding r: $r = \dfrac{a_1}{a_0} = \dfrac{5}{15} = \dfrac{1}{3}$

The rule is: $a_n = 15\left(\dfrac{1}{3}\right)^n$

4. Finding the first term:
$$a_2 = a_0 \left(\dfrac{2}{3}\right)^2$$
$$2 = \dfrac{4}{9} a_0$$
$$a_0 = \dfrac{9}{2}$$

The rule is: $a_n = \dfrac{9}{2}\left(\dfrac{2}{3}\right)^n$

5. This sum is arithmetic with $a_0 = 5$ and $d = 3$. The number of terms is $\dfrac{104 - 5}{3} + 1 = 34$. Finding the sum:

$$S_{34} = \dfrac{34}{2}(5 + 104) = 17(109) = 1{,}853$$

6. Using $a_0 = -2$, we can find: $a_{29} = -2 + 4(29) = 114$

The sum is: $S_{30} = \dfrac{30}{2}(a_0 + a_{29}) = 15(-2 + 114) = 15(112) = 1{,}680$

7. Finding the sum: $\displaystyle\sum_{i=0}^{9} 5i = \dfrac{10}{2}(a_0 + a_9) = 5(0 + 45) = 225$

8.   Finding the first four terms:

$$a_0 = -2(0)^3 + 2 = 2 \qquad\qquad a_1 = -2(1)^3 + 2 = 0$$

$$a_2 = -2(2)^3 + 2 = -14 \qquad\qquad a_3 = -2(3)^3 + 2 = -52$$

9.   Finding the first five terms:

$$a_0 = (-1)^0 \left(\frac{1}{4}\right)^0 = 1 \qquad\qquad a_1 = (-1)^1 \left(\frac{1}{4}\right)^0 = -\frac{1}{4}$$

$$a_2 = (-1)^2 \left(\frac{1}{4}\right)^2 = \frac{1}{16} \qquad\qquad a_3 = (-1)^3 \left(\frac{1}{4}\right)^3 = -\frac{1}{64}$$

$$a_4 = (-1)^4 \left(\frac{1}{4}\right)^4 = \frac{1}{256}$$

10.   Finding the first five terms:

$$a_0 = 4 \qquad\qquad a_1 = 4 - 1 = 3$$

$$a_2 = 3 - 2 = 1 \qquad\qquad a_3 = 1 - 3 = -2$$

$$a_4 = -2 - 4 = -6$$

11.   Evaluating the sum: $\displaystyle\sum_{i=0}^{3}(3i+2) = \frac{4}{2}(a_0 + a_3) = 2(2+11) = 26$

12.   **a.**   Evaluating: $\dfrac{5!}{2!} = \dfrac{5 \cdot 4 \cdot 3 \cdot 2 \cdot 1}{2 \cdot 1} = 60$

      b.   Evaluating: $C(6,4) = \dfrac{6!}{(2!)(4!)} = \dfrac{6 \cdot 5}{2 \cdot 1} = 15$

      c.   Evaluating: $P(7,1) = \dfrac{7!}{6!} = 7$

      d.   Evaluating: $P(6,4) = \dfrac{6!}{2!} = 6 \cdot 5 \cdot 4 \cdot 3 = 360$

13.   Evaluating: $C(12,3) = \dfrac{12!}{(9!)(3!)} = \dfrac{12 \cdot 11 \cdot 10}{3 \cdot 2 \cdot 1} = 220$

There are 220 committees possible.

14.   Evaluating: $7! = 720$

There are 720 six-letter words possible.

15.   Evaluating: $6(4) \cdot 4(2) \cdot 3(3) = 1{,}728$

There are 1,728 ways the books can be arranged.

16.   The possible outcomes are: {red, blue, white}

17.   Finding the probability: $P(\text{white}) = \dfrac{2}{11}$

18.   Finding the probability: $P(\text{blue marble not drawn}) = P(\text{red or white}) = \dfrac{4+2}{11} = \dfrac{6}{11}$

19.   Finding the probability: $P(\text{queen of heart or jack of spades}) = \dfrac{2}{52} = \dfrac{1}{26}$

20.   Using the binomial theorem:

$$(3x+2)^4 = \binom{4}{0}(3x)^4 + \binom{4}{1}(3x)^3(2) + \binom{4}{2}(3x)^2(2)^2 + \binom{4}{3}(3x)(2)^3 + \binom{4}{4}(2)^4$$

$$= 81x^4 + 4(27x^3)(2) + 6(9x^2)(4) + 4(3x)(8) + 16$$

$$= 81x^4 + 216x^3 + 216x^2 + 96x + 16$$

21. Verifying P_1 is true: $4(1) - 2 = 2(1)^2$

Assume P_k is true: $2 + 6 + 10 + \cdots + (4k - 2) = 2k^2$

Now proving P_{k+1} is true:

$$2 + 6 + 10 + \cdots + (4k - 2) + (4(k+1) - 2) = 2k^2 + 4k + 2 = 2(k^2 + 2k + 1) = 2(k+1)^2$$

22. The number of outfits is: $(3)(4)(2) = 24$

23. The number of license plates is: $(26 \cdot 25)(9 \cdot 8 \cdot 7) = 327,600$